OH - IF ONLY I'D WRITTEN IT DOWN

Reflections on a wonderful farming life

Dedication - to all the family who have had to endure the repetition of these stories so many times.

First edition published June 2021 by The Farm Organisation
ISBN: 978-1-5272-9309-0

Printed by:
Alverton Press, Portland Way, Leeming Bar, Northallerton DL7 9UH
01677 427436

"Indispensable Man"
By Saxon White Kessinger

Some time, when you're feeling important,

Some time, when your ego's in bloom,

Some time, when you take it for granted you're the most qualified one in the room –

Some time, when you feel that your going would leave an unfillable hole,

Just follow this simple instruction

And see how it humbles your soul.

Take a bucket and fill it with water

Put your hands in it up to the wrists

Pull them out – and the hole that remains

Is a measure of how you'll be missed.

You may splash all you please when you enter,

You may stir up the water galore,

But stop, and you'll find in a minute

That it looks just the same as before.

The moral of this is quite simple,

Just do the best you can,

Be proud of yourself, but remember

There's no indispensable man!

Contents

Prologue

The irony is in the title, in that most of them have been written down in a day-to-day diary kept for more than 45 years (the first one was the year I got married and only lasted about half a year, after that barely a day has been missed), which not only provides an overview of the variations within different seasons in different years, and the development of our family and a way of life, but has also been very useful over the years in settling arguments over what happened and when, what clothes were worn on various occasions and the varying weather patterns in different years.

The recording of various dates, such as the first daffodil flowering or the swallows arriving show a fascinating variation, as do the start and finish dates of harvest. In many ways also , the diary sometimes gives an insight into the thought processes behind various things which have happened, but above all else it tells the story of the glorious way of life, living in the marvellous countryside of North Yorkshire at the foot of Wensleydale.

As I deliberated over how to style the book I was undecided whether to chapter it by time lines or to feature various combinations of events, but eventually decided to record things as they occurred and then perhaps feature one or two of the central characters again in a dedicated chapter at the end of the book. I also gave great thought as to the characters who will appear in the text - should I give them pseudo-names or use their proper names, and after much deliberation felt that as most of the characters would be known to most of the local readers, there was little point in trying to disguise their identity, and to those more general readers it wouldn't really matter whether or not it is their actual name. Wherever possible I have made contact with the people involved to make sure they are happy with this.

I should also point out that as far as I know (particularly where the early stages of my life are concerned) everything is absolutely true and did actually happen. Many of them are very simple events that spring to mind and probably and hopefully are even more amusing to the person reading of them for the first time.

Whilst there are obviously many serious parts of the story, it is written particularly from the humorous aspects of life and where others are involved there is no intent to embarrass or otherwise, and the humour is as much self inflicted on me as it is aimed at anyone else.

Enjoy this story of a superbly enjoyable life in the wonderful agricultural community of North Yorkshire, the wider friendships and events within the cattle breeding fraternity and the even wider escapades onto the world stage.

Please note - This memoir was written between 2017 and 2019 and since those times certain changes may have occurred with reference to people and happenings.

Chapter One - An Early Life and Family History

I should have been called Sam.

So Mother used to keep reminding me on many occasions.

When I was born, Mother wasn't very well and Father had to register my birth, and not being the most inventive of souls he christened me exactly the same as he was - John Bernard and he was always known as John and I therefore became Bernard for the rest of my life apart from the odd person who would insist on "Bernie" or Mr Werry from "Werrcroft" in Canada who called me "Ber-nard". Strangely enough when we retired to Harkness Close- our neighbour across the way was always called "Bernie" and was quite happy with the shortened name and it was strange for the same and not very popular name to live so close together.

Father was one of six brothers and four sisters, three of his elder brothers Ralph, Harry and Adam were all by then farming on their own, as was father, Louis had no interest and was a policeman and then a private detective in the Middlesbrough area. That only left the youngest son Sam at home, and thus he was the only one called up into the forces for service during the war. He was a private in the 2nd Battalion of the Hampshire Regiment and was sadly killed on the beaches in Italy on 5th December 1944 and lies in the Forli War Cemetery. He was apparently, always Mothers favourite brother-in-law, hence her unrequited wish to remember him by calling me Sam.

When I was born, Father and Mother were farming at Oak Tree Farm, which was at the back of Roseberry Topping, the steading no longer exists and no one seems to be able to tell us when and why it was razed to the ground. Mother as I mentioned was rather poorly after I was born, and spent some time in hospital, and being just a baby I was looked after during those early months by Grandma Hood and Aunt Emily who lived at New Row, the row of cottages set back from the road between Kildale and Commondale.

Being born in 1946, it just so happened that I was with Aunt Emily when the "Winter of 47" started. There are not many people alive now who remember it from an adults perspective, but it was remembered as the worst winter there has ever been, with massive amounts of snow and very cold weather, with sheep buried under drifts etc for many weeks. Many times over the years when it got into February time, people would comment "Winters getting towards the end - it's nearly over for another year", only for some more elderly gentleman who was active at the time to say "remember '47 didn't start until late on - end of February into March". No doubt it was a severe winter that lasted a long time, and so I had to stay at Aunt Emily's longer than I needed to. Ultimately when spring finally began to arrive and things were beginning to improve Father apparently walked across by Kildale to collect me in a bag on his back across the moor via the Donkey Ponds, Captain Cooks monument and so to home for us to be reunited as a family. I don't know and my sister Mary doesn't seem to remember what happened to her at that time but being only 2 $^{3/4}$ years older than me we assume she also stayed at New Row for several weeks.

At that age I have no recollection of the farming system or what was happening, but the next stage of family life occurred sometime in 1948 when father left that farm, which was subsequently farmed by his sister Nellie and her husband Ted Hepworth. We as a family all moved to Nidderdale, where Father took a job as a shepherd/ stockman at Humberstone Bank Farm near Blubberhouses for the Heseltine family. We were always under the impression that they were the farm owners until the farm made the news in Autumn of 2016.

The farm is and was owned by Yorkshire Water and was a 2234 acre farm with 1500 acres of it designated as a Site of Specific Scientific Interest (SSI), a Special Preservation Area and a Special Area of Conservation. We had sought out Humberstone Bank in September 2014 when I was beginning research for the writing of this book, and had met Mrs Heseltine who remembered us being there for a short while and who's daughter in law, whom we also met had originated from Middlesmoor. The reason the farm made the agricultural press in 2016 was that the Heseltine family had given up the farm tenancy, and Yorkshire Water were looking for a new tenant and were specifically looking for a younger person who would buy into its "beyond nature" vision for the future, that encompassed wildlife biodiversity, water quality and carbon storage as well as more traditional farming practice. The tenancy was awarded to Johnathan Grayshon, 28, originally from Dacre, down in the Lower Nidderdale valley.

My very first recollection as a child is from when we lived at Humberstone Bank. I remember walking up to the end of the farm lane to meet Mary off the school bus and then coming back down on the old three wheeler cycle we had at the time and Mother with the hand end of her stick hooked round the rear axle to stop me going too fast.

Father didn't stay there for very long, I think about a year, before he got the tenancy of Ivy House Farm at Middlesmoor, right at the very top of Nidderdale. It was aptly named - it literally was in the middle of nowhere, eight miles up the dale from Pateley Bridge and no other way in or out - the road from Lofthouse to Masham was barely passable with a tractor in those days, let alone with a car as it is now.

Strangely many of Fathers family had moved from the Great Ayton area over into Nidderdale. Uncles Adam and Harry both farmed in the Greenhow area up the hill from Pateley and Uncle Ralph then farmed on more hospitable land near Darley. In addition one of the sisters, Aunt Clarice and her husband Jack Challis farmed High Riggs farm which was another couple of miles further up into the moor - it no longer stands as a steading, the last time we walked across to it, it was and had been for a long time derelict.

Quite remarkably other than Grandfather Adam Liddle, no Liddle's were left farming in the Great Ayton area, though a couple of his daughters and their husbands did so for quite a number of years. Lonsdale was quite a large and well farmed farm in its day, but from what I can gather Adam was not the easiest of men to get on with. David Petch of Aytonian Holstein fame, (whose brother Clifford later farmed Lonsdale) from

Whitegates Farm which looks out onto Roseberry Topping, tells me that he can just remember when he was a small boy Adam Liddle going past on his horse every day to the library to get his reading books for that day. Particularly in later life he was an avid reader and after he died the house was full of magazines, papers etc and they were even under the floor boards. David Petch also gave me a cutting from a very old newspaper in which an ancestor had been fined for burying some family member in the wrong sort of cloth- Adam Liddle seemingly was very proud of this bit of history. I can just remember, not long after we had moved to Middlesmoor, Father and the rest of the family (not Mother) going off to his funeral.

Back to Middlesmoor, and our early life there. For a small community at the head of the dales, it had two shops, one of which was also the post office, Crown Hotel, Church and Chapel and a school. How different from today when many villages much larger have none or very few of such amenities. There is a marvellous small book on Middlesmoor written in 2005 by Dinah Lee, called "Middlesmoor- A Stone's throw from Heaven". Mrs Lee was a part time teacher at our large school at Middlesmoor- 11 pupils the year I left along with four others and it didn't last very long after that, and was subsequently converted into the village hall. In her book Mrs Lee reveals in the early history of the place, that back in the late nineteenth and early twentieth centuries that Middlesmoor was used by wealthy mill owners and the like from Industrial West and South Yorkshire and even Lancastrians as a holiday destination in the summertime.

As an aside and being nowhere more appropriate to place it, there is a story regarding 'Middlesmoor - A stones throw from Heaven'. Back in 2005, as was usual sister Mary brought Birthday presents around mid/end of May to cover Marnies in early May and Sarah's and mine in early June. It was not until later in June I suddenly realised I hadn't had a present that year. Indignantly I said I was going to ring big sister up and tell her she had forgotten, but Marnie said I couldn't do that and dissuaded me. The matter went to sleep for another week or two and then I remembered again, only to be told it would be totally impolite to remind Mary of the omission. Finally all was revealed. Middlesmoor had always held the Bell Festival in early June to commemorate the hanging of the bells in the church and I remember when at school the procession down the village from school to church for the service, followed by tea and sports in the later afternoon. Originally the date was 11th June whatever day of the week, eventually it moved to the Saturday nearest to that date. In 2005 it was actually on the 11th, my birthday and Mrs Lee's book was being launched there on that day. Mary had arranged for her to sign me a copy on my birthday at the Bell Festival, hence the lateness of my birthday present that year, we then reverted in the following year to the usual practice and timing.

Back to the early 1950's, the road up into Middlesmoor had quite a sharp bend at the bottom and a short, but sharp rise. In those days there were still a lot of Austin 7's and such like about, much removed from the cars of today, and a lot of drivers who didn't have much experience and in fact many who had not even taken a driving test.

There was a time back to pre-war and during the war when one didn't have to take a test (Father fell into that category - he never did like driving a vehicle on the road and was a very poor driver - quite frightening to travel with). Many of these inexperienced drivers, often with their first car, came for a ride out up the dale on Saturday or Sunday afternoons, nothing much to see at Middlesmoor so just turned round and went back down to Pateley Bridge. Quite a few of these motorists could not get up the hill and Father was often called into rescuing them by towing them up the hill with his Fergie 20, and probably made as much doing that as he did all week farming as many were generous in their thanks. I well remember one time receiving a letter of thanks addressed to 'The Farmer who lives at the top of the hill opposite the chapel just as you enter the village, Middlesmoor'. It arrived only about a day after it was written - one can't imagine that arriving as quickly if at all in 2017!!

Talking of Fergi 20's, I can remember going with Father soon after we had gone to Middlesmoor to buy his first tractor. I think it was before I started school and we went to Glover's of Ripon. They later became Ripon Farm Services and at that time were situated beside the bridge as you go out on the Harrogate road. Father really pushed the boat out and bought a Fergi 20 plus grass cutter for £247-10 shillings and the salesman gave me the little silver and blue enamel badge of tractor and plough- The Ferguson System. That is still a treasured possession and is probably worth as much as the tractor cost some 65 years ago. Included with the tractor and mower were the instruction books in the heavy waxed envelopes of those days. I don't think Father ever had them out, and they were still in pristine condition when I gave them to John Moffitt for his Ferguson museum up at Hunday, one of which he did not have. The Hunday Ferguson Museum was latterly Mr Moffitt's private collection and I was privileged to visit it twice, once at the open day after Hunday had won the RABDF- Gold Cup and the second time with the Yorkshire Holstein Club who went to see the cattle and the tractors - there were all kinds of implements for the Fergi 20 and all sorts of adaptations of them, including some of the ones used by Sir Vivian Fuchs when he made the first over land crossing of Antarctica via the South Pole in 1958.

Shortly after this acquisition, though I had by then started school, Father got his first milking machine. They fitted it one day whilst I was at school, a pipeline through the byre, with two units - made life much easier and one man able to milk rather more cows than in the hand milking days. Again in 65 years it is amazing how far we have travelled in milking technology to where we are now with cows milked robotically or large numbers milked on large scale rotary platforms, and you can now even get a robotic rotary which costs millions to install, but undoubtedly will become more used as the shortage of labour on dairy farms continues to cause problems.

On the milk front it also happened that in most winters Father, along with the other farmers who had cows, had on quite a lot of days to take the milk on the back of the tractor down to Lofthouse to be loaded onto the milk-churn lorry. That was because of snow and the many large drifts which blocked the single track road between the walls and he and the others spent hours digging through the drifts by hand to be able

4

to get out and deliver the milk. I was relating this story to one of my young employees during a spell of bad weather just before Christmas about 2009/10 and he said, quite innocently, "Well why didn't they just dig it out with the JCB Loadall and tip it over the walls." I said to Stuart, "you don't realise that at that time, the fore-end loader with hydraulics had only just come into being, there was no such thing as specialised loaders with extending booms in those days". Yet again the passage of time hides the memory of what things were like or done in earlier days, and I am sure the Ferguson hydraulic system on a petrol driven tractor was a great advance in its time.

The first day of school dawned and provided quite a shock for a young boy. In those days particularly up in the dales, there were no such things as playschools or pre-school classes, I don't think there was even an induction day the term before starting. Nowadays, by the time a child starts school they have had up to three years of some sort of group teaching and as such proper school is no great change for many of them. While this undoubtedly has made children much more aware at a younger age, it has to a certain extent robbed them of a fuller childhood. There were six of us all started that day at Middlesmoor, five boys and one girl, and included Daniel Docherty who lived even further across the fields and as such had had even less contact with other youngsters - he didn't take kindly to it and I remember that he cried non-stop all that first day and was a fairly infrequent attendee thereafter.

The head teacher was Miss Ridley who lived in the village, and so was fully aware of all that was going on outside school as well as in it. She ruled with a rod of iron, but learn we did, you hardly dared not to, and walking up to the institute for lunch, eating it with us, with no multiple choice as there is today, one learned good manners as well as discipline, apart from the lessons. It was an accepted practice that at Christmas time Miss Ridley was invited to all the pupils homes for tea, and that was a particularly nerve-wracking experience, certainly to start with as you were that frightened you would do something wrong in front of her and you would be made to suffer for it once back at school. I had a slight advantage in this, because with an older sister I had already endured a couple of such experiences before I myself started school.

My great friend before and at junior school was Martin Holmes, who will be well known to all in the Nidderdale area. Martin's Father was the senior partner in Lee and Holmes who were builders, joiners and undertakers based in Middlesmoor but working up and down the dale. Martin eventually took over the business and though he lived at Pateley Bridge, continued to operate the business from the village, later converting the old sawmill house etc into holiday cottages. Only recently I saw in the Farmers Guardian an advert under Otley Auction Markets the dispersal sale of all his building equipment in the yard/field, and he now only practises as an Undertaker in his semi retirement.

Martin and I were great friends at the time and had many adventures over the five or six years at school and three in particular stand out in the memory. The first was one night I had been up at Martin's and it was teatime, he went in first for his and I ran down the village to home for mine. At that time I had a lump on one knee which had been there for a long time (it may have been there since birth for all I can remember) and the slightest bump it used to swell up rather nastily. On the raised bit below the cottage halfway up the village there was a thin piece of stone which stuck out an inch or two. In running full tilt home that night I was so close to the raised stone forecourt that I sliced the lump open on it. It immediately swelled up and bled fairly profusely. Once the bruising from the injury and the gash had gone, the lump was substantially smaller and to this day, some 60-65 years later it has never swollen up again - in effect the boil must have been lanced.

On another occasion the same bit of village featured again in the story. It must have been winter time because my coat was involved. I had been up to Martin's after school and again it was after school and again it was teatime, but too early for mine, so while Martin and his Mother and Father had theirs, I sat on the ledge in front of the range oven, right next to the open fire. Suddenly I realised it was my teatime, said my hurried goodbyes and set off running full bore down the village. The coat tail had obviously been smouldering in the fire and once outside with the breeze and running it burst into flames. I was unaware of this until I realised Mr Holmes and Martin were running after me and shouting. We soon got the coat fire out and I continued on home for my tea and they walked back home to finish theirs.

The third event and to me the most memorable was a bit of naughtiness that boys used to get into bother for. Lee and Holmes had a paddock, about a couple of acres which housed their store yard and a couple of sheds and at the far end there was some rough grassland. Martin and I, and it may even have been before we started school had a flock of imaginary sheep which we gathered in the top bit of the paddock and were ready to move them to some fresh grass when we realised there was no imaginary gate out of this field which was all stone walled. No problem!! We just took down a stretch of dry stonewall and the stones rolled down onto the verge and the roadside. We took down a reasonable length because we had quite a large flock of imaginary sheep and took them through. When our two fathers became aware of what we had done, we both got a good talking to. Father asked me why, so I told him and he still wasn't amused - but I told him that at least we had got the sheep out! For all they were builders, Lee and Holmes didn't do dry stone walling, whereas Father was a good waller and so it fell to him to rebuild the wall which he did with a lot of grumbling at me as he did so and I helped him.

Either just before or just after starting school, Father was still not fully stocked with his own animals, and took in store cattle for wintering. I well remember going with him to put these cattle into the cattle stalling at Tanpit barn for the start of winter. They had not been tied by the neck before and were fairly wild but we eventually got them into the byre and the door shut. "You stand over there son by the wall out of the way while I get some tied up at the other end." So I did as I was told - at that age you did so. I think it was on the second beast it suddenly charged past Father and straight at me, pinning me to the wall between its horns. Nearly all cattle then were still horned, and the length of the horns meant that it couldn't crush a thin little boy, and so I was unharmed if somewhat scared, even more so by the thought of what might have been if the animals direction and aim had been a little off centre and pierced my stomach with a horn. Needless to say we just carried on and got them all fastened up.

Tanpit came into another rather frightening experience soon afterwards, it was at least after I had started school. Mother always kept a few laying hens for eggs which she cleaned and packed regularly and they were collected weekly by the egg man and all eggs in those days went through the Egg Marketing Board and it would be before they were stamped with the little lion and long before Edwina Currie virtually killed the egg industry by associating E-coli with fresh eggs. Mother had one lot near the home on the hillside and another lot across near Tanpit. It was one of my jobs in those early days to go across after school and before dark to fasten them in for the night. One particular late autumn evening I set off to do my job. It was easy going across to them as there was a very strong and cold easterly wind, which behind me propelled me across the two fields very quickly. I checked there was none still out and dropped the hatch, and turned for home. The trouble was the wind was so strong against a small boys frame, that I could make no headway and though paddling hard was getting absolutely nowhere and becoming quite alarmed. Sense prevailed within my worried mind and I allowed the wind to take me back to the shelter of Tanpit barns, where I got out of the wind and took time to gather my thoughts and work out what to do. I realised that if I took a circuitous route back to the village, so that I was behind the stone walls all the way I would be protected from the vile wind, which I was able to do and arrived safely back home.

In those early days, as even now I was a great lover and eater of both cheese and cucumber. There wasn't the great array of cheeses available in those days that there are now, pretty well the only choices were red, white and blue. Only Father liked blue cheese but it was too expensive to eat in a regular way- if Mother had been to Harrogate she might bring him back a small piece of Gorgonzola as a special treat. Cheese in those days was not all shrink wrapped in plastic as much of it is today, but cut straight from the whole cheeses and cucumbers were not available all year round as now, but only when in season. I used to slip into the pantry and get the chunk of cheese in one hand and the cucumber in the other and just eat away at them, until getting tired of this Mother started to hide them so I couldn't devour them and there was some there for tea when we were supposed to have it.

Again at a similar time, when I was barely six, we were at school and it was time for our music lesson. At that time our music lesson came over the radio, and Miss Ridley not being the most technically minded of teachers, was struggling to get tuned into the Light programme. Eventually after several minutes without success she sent one of the older children across to the Post Office to get Mr Eglin to come across to tune us in, which he willingly did. I remember as clearly as if it was yesterday his trying for a minute or two and then saying aloud "You stupid man, the King has died and there is nothing on the radio at all". It is quite an astonishing fact that because of the

7

remarkable reign of our current Queen Elizabeth II that no one under 70 remembers any other Sovereign. There was of course a year later a great deal of activity and celebration around the Coronation, with the scaling of Everest and other such worldwide and national achievements coinciding with the event. It was of course the one event which really got television on its way - at least one house in every village got one so it could be watched by everyone. Without the Coronation television may never have taken off!!

In those days, compared to now, parents had no fear of letting their children go off without supervision and we along with others took full advantage of the wonderful countryside around Middlesmoor, particularly in the summer, and we would often go down across the fields, giving Roger the horse a wide berth as he was a bit on the nasty side if taunted, which sometimes he was. We used to go down to the River Stean and we would gather wild flowers, see kingfishers near the small waterfall, and follow the riverside down to How Stean Gorge. Now a tourist attraction in the area, it was in those days only known to locals, and we spent many hours exploring every nook and cranny, and the caves and potholes which now attract visitors to the mouth of it up towards Middlesmoor were as far as I can remember unknown and unheard of.

Having mentioned Mr Carlin Eglin at the Post Office with reference to the King's death, I should also mention the other shop in the village which was run by Mr and Mrs Gosney. I don't have a lot of recognition of Mrs Gosney, but Mr Gosney was a lovely little man. A keen cricket fan and a member of Yorkshire Cricket Club he used to sometimes take me to Headingley with him to see a match. For a young country boy this was quite an adventure to go to Leeds by bus and train. The one match I really remember was in July 1957, the highlight of those trips to see an England vs. West Indies Test Match when the West Indies were in their first heyday and the three W's were all playing - Worrell, Weekes and Walcott and bowling legends such as Trueman and Statham along with the wicket keeper Godfrey Evans played for England, and the remarkable part of that particular days cricket, right as we were having to leave just before close of play to catch the train home was a hat-trick by the English bowler (Peter Loader).

In those days, virtually all the hay made up in the dales was loose and stored in the barns in each field to be fed to the cattle through winter. Silage had barely become known and the only bales were great big ones often tied with wire rather than string. By the time Father left Middlesmoor much of the hay was by then baled into small bales using a contractor to do so. Many of the crops up in that part of the world were not particularly heavy - very little fertiliser was used and such places were virtually overrun with rabbits before Myxomatosis sorted them out. There was a very large loft above the cowshed at Ivy House, and it was usually filled with beautiful old land soft and smelly hay and once so much had been used, Father used to bring it up from some of the other barns on sledges. The loose hay was cut into blocks with a very sharp hay spade and it was then easily handled on and off the sledges. One particular day, and I think it was when Mother and Father went to Kildale for Grandmother Hood's funeral,

Mary and I had to see to giving the cows their midday feed. For that we had to put the loose hay from the loft down through a bob-hole into the passage in front of the cows. We didn't mess about putting forkfuls down through the hole, but instead first piled it all up in a big heap over the hole and then were struggling when it jammed and wouldn't go through. We then jumped and bounced on this hay with no success at all until suddenly like a cork from a bottle it went along with Mary and I who maybe bumped on the walls of the passageway but otherwise were unhurt and we got the cows fed and Mother and Father were unaware of our bit of excitement, though we knew in future to put the hay through the bob-hole a forkful at a time.

Wintertime at Middlesmoor was always exciting, with very large snowfalls, which, while it made work much harder for Mother and Father, was great fun for we children. Massive drifts, one in particular at the top of the village towards the institute against the high wall was all dug out and became a giant igloo, but we also actually built igloos and we had one tremendous sledge run - just across the road in the little Hill paddock. Very steep so you got plenty of speed up, there was a bump in the middle to jump over and the wall at the bottom stopped you finishing up on the road.

In the summer months well into the summer holidays it was the grouse-shooting season. Middlesmoor had a very well respected grouse moor, and there was always a great deal of excitement around the 'Glorious Twelfth'. All the 'gentlemen' guns stayed at the Crown Hotel and many of them brought their own loaders with them, so there was quite an influx of people into the village, along with the gathering each shooting morning of more local men and lads who were going to be beaters. As youngsters and too young to be actually involved, the great excitement for us came at the end of the shooting day. The road/track up onto the High Moor had six or eight gates on the way to it, some of it through Father's land and it was custom for the local children to go to the gates to open them as the vehicles returned for the evening. The very young children went to the first or second gates, while the older ones who could walk a lot further made their way to the farthest gates nearer to the moor. At the end of the day, it was often the guns who came down first and the custom was they threw out money to the children in return for opening the gates. The guns being the wealthy ones threw out half-crowns and florins (2s/6d or 2s in those days, equivalent to $12^1/_2$p or 10p in today's terminology). The next ones down would be the loaders in the older Landrovers, and they threw out shillings or sixpences (5p or $2^1/_2$p), followed by the beaters, ordinary working men, with less money who would get rid of their loose change, three penny bits, pennies, half pennies and even farthings ($1^1/_4$p down to $^1/_8$p). All were raced after and gathered by the children. As was only fair, more was thrown out at the higher gates than the ones nearer the village, but at that time children's' pocket money at seven or eight years old might be as high as sixpence ($2^1/_2$p), so it was most welcome. We were very fortunate in that if we were busy helping in the hay field, we could see the vehicles start to leave the moors to wind slowly down and could just stop doing whatever it was and go to the gates and then just go back and carry on. This tradition no longer happens since the installation of cattle grids on the moors.

The same scenario could be seen and watched at various times of the year when the sheep were gathered on the moor, where the various tenants had differing numbers of 'gaits' according to the size of the holding. On gathering days all the farmers who shared the moor headed up there and had their respective areas to gather, bringing all the sheep to a central point where there was a massive holding pen, with, round the outside, smaller pens for the individual farmers to shed their sheep into. At that point they would probably have their bit of packed lunch to let the sheep settle down and then sort them all out in the afternoon. All the sheep would have a 'rudd' marking in different colours on various parts of the fleece so they were easily distinguishable and being Dalesbred sheep if there was any dispute each farmer had a distinctive horn burn which was inarguable. Fathers' was an L in a circle, like this **L** . Once they were all sorted each farmer brought his flock home and they set off at 10-15 minute intervals with their own dogs and it was a great sight to see them weaving their way home. It was a long, hard day and Father was usually 'knackered' by night despite his lean frame and long legs. That was in the days before three or four wheeled ATV's, so it was all a case of walking and having a good dog or two. When I was a bit older I did go a few times to help Father, particularly with the shedding and the bringing home, but never had a sheep dog or such to control or use.

The final 'event' of the summer season was Pateley Show or to give it its proper title 'Nidderdale Show'. There was anticipation in the week or two building up to it, the Fair came into the corner of Bewerley Park for the weekend before and during the show which was held on the Monday nearest to the 21st September. As children the great thing was that all the schools closed for the day and I believe still do to this day. If they hadn't done I suspect most of the children would have been poorly anyway on that day. It was a great day for people to meet up with friends and relations and do some bragging or leg-pulling of each other depending on their success or otherwise in stock, handicraft, cookery or children's classes.

In more recent years it has been an honour to return to Pateley Bridge to judge the Holstein, Local Cattle Classes and for three years in a row to judge the Supreme Dairy Championships. I have also judged the Black and Whites and the Championships at Stokesley Show, on one occasion Stokesley on the Saturday and Nidderdale on the Monday, the last two shows of the Northern Show Season. So it has been great to judge at the two shows associated with my early years.

Chapter Two – Senior School

A new life opened in 1957 when I started senior school, and it was quite a shock for a young dales boy from a school with 11 pupils to go as a boarder to a much larger grammar school. Although not that far to Ripon, it was too far to travel every day, and so I had no option but to be a boarder at Ripon Grammar School and make a host of new friends. Martin, Cynthia and the twins Michael and Peter all continued their education elsewhere and so it was a whole new world to me. After the initial shock and change to a more regimented schooling, I thoroughly enjoyed my time as a boarder, and experienced sport and other activities which I would otherwise never have got involved with.

At the same time as I started at Ripon a new headmaster also took over and Mr Atkinson rapidly regained the Schools reputation which had begun to get run down in the previous few years. He also lived in the house on the job which adjoined the boarding house, and so there was no escaping him when not actually at school. He could have a savage temper and he like so many other masters of the time did things which would not only be frowned upon today, but would no doubt get them drummed out of the educational system, such as the throwing of chalk or even the board duster at you if you weren't paying attention, the clip round the ear, and in those days, the use of the cane, still in common usage, and I don't think it did any of us any harm.

I remember on one occasion there was a lot of noise and games going on in the top corridor of the Boarding House off which the three dormitories led. The headmasters study backed onto the corridor and this particular time he burst through the door to see what the commotion was about. When he saw that it was just high jinks he decided he needed to boss the problem, and getting no admittance of any responsibility from anyone he made the whole boarding house, I think there were 64 of us line up outside his study, and one by one from the youngest to the eldest, including the prefects, we all got three strokes of the cane from him. Apart from anything else he was remarkably fit to be able to dole out that amount of energy in such a short period.

On another occasion, our maths teacher of the time 'Killer' Kelsey finished up in one lesson giving the answer to a problem in feet and inches. The bell went and it was to be continued in the next lesson, when he correctly got the sum demonstrated in minutes and seconds. He wasn't overly impressed when I asked him how long he had stayed up at night working it out and I had to go and see him after lessons. That at least did give me the chance to rush up to the dormitory and put a couple of extra pairs of underpants on, so I hardly felt the three strokes for insubordination. Mr Kelsey who had a superb, grey handlebar moustache and played the cello, also had a fairly imaginative and colourful vocabulary. At the start of a new term, the room had been redecorated during the holidays a particularly awful colour which when he walked in immediately christened it as "scour yellow".

In the junior dormitory the new starter on my left was Pogson, who cried non-stop all night for the first night. He like quite a few of the boarders came from over Halifax, Hebden Bridge, Todmorden way – I don't know why, along with quite a few whose parents were abroad with the forces. On the right hand side my adjacent pupil was Smith who ultimately became an airline pilot and was also a relief organist at Ripon Cathedral – he was a very good pianist in those days.

It was a rather depressing start to life at Ripon- as we came out of the Dining Hall on the first day of school, having checked in the night before, I was very sick and immediately whisked off to the sickbay – I was the first of virtually the whole school who gradually went down with the flu, and that was the great Asian Flu epidemic of 1957. Odd ones within the boarding house seemed to be immune despite in some cases doing their very best to contract the flu by clambering into affected patients beds – all to no avail. After being the first one back to normality, classes were very hit and miss at the time, being not only short of pupils but also a shortage of teachers, but I did eventually a week or two later catch a second dose, though nowhere near as badly. One often over the years hear people talking about having flu, when in most cases all they have had is a very heavy cold. If you have ever had proper flu there isn't much you can do about it, certainly not try to go to work, your legs go and you are literally almost as helpless with no bodily strength to do anything. Apparently, there were 80,000 deaths from Asian Flu putting into perspective the 50 thousand plus in mid-November 2020 from the Coronavirus pandemic.

The school had its own Cadet Force for both army and air force - they had their own glider which they used to launch with a giant elastic band from the sports field, but I didn't really fancy marching up and down every Tuesday afternoon. With my agricultural background I was allowed to work in the school gardens instead, along with one or two other abstainers - the strange thing was that one of those went on afterschool to join and have a long and successful career in the Army. With Mr Hall the head gardener being of more senior years he was almost a grandfather to us, but was a wise old chap who kept us on the straight and narrow and got us to do some of the heavier jobs for him.

The great thing for me about boarding at Ripon was the chance to be involved in team sports, something that had been impossible in a small village with so few young boys and girls to make up a team of anything. The school had its own outdoor swimming pool (though later converted to indoor and heated) and whilst never much of a swimmer we did have the odd lesson and were allowed to use it at weekends in summer. There were two or three tennis courts just outside the boarding house, and again they filled in weekend afternoons in summer and there is still a very Englishness playing on well maintained grass courts and one really learns how to spin the ball on them. In addition there were large playing fields with a lovely cricket pitch and two rugby pitches, plus the athletics track with jumping pits etc. Having always been interested in sports I was happy to get engaged, and took to rugby from that first day, and was involved in every age group through school. In those days there was a games afternoon on a Wednesday and much of the time matches both that day and Saturdays either at school or away matches to most of the rugby playing schools all over North Yorkshire. Masters at that time were not only expected, but were quite happy to coach and take practices after school and on those afternoons to be involved with the games - rather different today when many schools struggle to get teachers to give up their time to assist or escort teams to matches. There was never any chance of not all being dressed in school uniform to go to away matches so that as you descended from the coach, you at least looked like a team, and even on the field all had the same colour boots (black) rather than the multitude of rainbow colours one sees being worn today.

One particular event sticks in my mind while playing for one of the U/13 or U/14 teams at home. I had the ball and was thrown/manhandled into touch, unfortunately on top of the ball with my private parts squashed about it by players on top of me. As if not in enough pain from that I became aware of being kicked on the arm several times and when I eventually was able to look upwards, who should it be but the headmaster who's only comment was -"get up boy and get on with it". In my last year at school, which would be the 1961-62 year, we never played rugby the whole spring term of 1962. It was a very hard, frosty winter, though, certainly at Ripon no vast amounts of snow. The frosts lasted for weeks, and a lot of it was a really 'rime' frost which built up on the trees almost like snow, and was fantastic to see, particularly if it was sunlight. The frost had really got into the ground and it was not playable before the Easter holidays. During this period I was back to my study after breakfast to make my bed before lessons when my back suddenly went and all I could do was roll over onto the bed and wait for someone to come and find me. I had physio on my back five days a week for about six weeks and it eventually mended - the doctors said I had injured it playing rugby the previous term and it had taken until then to make its presence felt. Fortunately it was never any problem to me again either playing rugby or in work over the following decades. The other injury I remember were torn stomach muscles which matron strapped up with a long sticky crepe bandage - it did the job and all was well until the bandage had to come off - matron pulled it off ok, but it was so sticky it pulled the muscles again in removing it and I had to have a non-sticky bandage for a further couple of weeks.

One of the day boys at school was nicknamed "Bungalow", which stuck right through school, and rather cruelly it was because he had nothing up top. The lack of brainpower was quite noticeable - how on earth he managed to pass his Eleven Plus was an absolute mystery to most of us. It made a change for somebody with the surname Clarke not to be called "Nobby"- we shall come across another one later in the book.

It just so happened one Sunday afternoon that I had nothing particular planned or anyone to play tennis with, and before I was old enough to be allowed out cycling. For want of anything better, I was persuaded by one of my boarding pals by the name of Gavin Wrigley to go fishing with him. That is the only time I have ever been fishing in my life or am ever likely to be encouraged to do so again. Gavin just had the one rod and complained all afternoon because I kept talking. In those days the time curfews out of school were very strict and one daren't be late getting signed back in. Just as we were about to pack up to go back, Gavin got his first bite of the afternoon and rather slowly got the fish ashore - it was only a tiddler, he promptly took the hook out and threw it back into the stream. I thought then "what a pointless exercise and a total waste of time". Far too slow an occupation for me, though I have many friends and contacts who enjoy their fishing and find it very therapeutic, but I'm afraid it's not for me. Having said that I am an enthusiastic eater of all sorts of fish, so should be glad that some are happy to catch them and on occasions generous enough to give us fresh caught trout or salmon!

At the end of one particular summer term, when the cadets always had a week away to camp, Mr Petchey took a group of we 'abstainers' away on a history trip to Whitby where we stayed at an YHA hostel and didn't do a lot of history but had a great time. One other year at the same time Gavin and I were allowed to go camping instead and walked two or three miles out of Ripon before we pitched tent. Despite a camp fire, half cooked and warmed up beans at night and not much of a breakfast after a terrible nights cold sleep, camping didn't suit either of us and we were soon back to school. Like the fishing that's the one and only time I have been camping and it put me off for life - I prefer a more comfortable bed!

One of the subjects done at Ripon in the first two years was Latin - and then if you wanted to, you could take it forward as a GCE subject, only a few did so. The first year we were taught by Rev. Buck, who was a clergyman at Ripon Cathedral, who was only filling in the vacant teaching position until a replacement was appointed. He was a smashing chap, always wore a cloak which he used to swing round his arms, always smiling and very soft natured. If we had a lot of homework in other subjects we just used to tell him, and he would let us off Latin for that night. His replacement duly arrived for the start of the second year and what a contrast he was. Mr Rowland wasn't just strict, he was a real authoritarian and couldn't stand anyone who didn't understand or didn't want to understand Latin and just as Rev Buck would let us off homework, he piled extra on. The only bit of hilarity I ever remember was Mr Rowland teaching us the imaginary Latin verb "to pee" - po, pis, pit, penis, pistis, pants. At the end of year 1 under Rev Buck in the Latin exam I scored 79% and was placed 26th in a class of 30. At the end of the first term under Mr Rowland I scored 13% and was third out of the same number. Make of that what you will. Needless to say I dropped Latin after the second year, but it is amazing how right until the present day, little bits of it come back to be useful in some way or other, even if it is in doing a crossword!

Whilst I was at Ripon, the decision was taken to experiment with the top class of the year taking their GCE exams at the end of their fourth year instead of after five years. Being in that top group, albeit at the lower end, I came into that category and did reasonably well, getting sufficient subjects to be able to carry on and do 'A' Levels. Knowing already that I wanted to go on and study agriculture, I thought Geography, History and English Literature were the best subjects to help in that field. No I didn't, but I wasn't very good at Sciences! Whilst always good at mental arithmetic due to Miss Ridley's influence at Middlesmoor, I could just about manage basic algebra and geometry, but things like trigonometry left me totally cold and never did understand it or for that matter see its significance or practical use. Physics I just about scraped through at GCE level, so not good enough to do "A's" and I had failed Chemistry so was unable to that, so couldn't do Biology which wasn't available as an 'O' level and which I would have quite liked to do. So you see, there wasn't a lot of choice on the subjects available. Having said that those three subjects did teach me how to write essays and reason both sides of an argument and then draw a conclusion, things which you didn't really do in pure Chemistry or Physics. Jumping forward a few years to life at Cirencester I was dreading doing the sciences against all the students who had done A levels in those subjects including Biology, but I often outdid them because I was coming to the subject purely from a taught agricultural viewpoint rather than the scientific view, added to which I could write essays and reason within the writing on agricultural sciences from that practical angle. Back to school, I had to have Chemistry to qualify for the Royal Agricultural College, and finally just got it passed on the third attempt. Whilst doing the three main subjects we also did general studies including a course on statistics which, liking simple maths I found quite fascinating - a fascination that has stayed with me to this day. We also did an odd lesson on woodwork which had never before been done at Ripon, being taught by a new, young teacher Mr Chambers. He didn't have a lot to work on with me, DIY etc not really being my forte. I never did, while at school, finish the wooden table light I started in fact it is still somewhere up in the attic awaiting completion at some time into the future. Mr Chambers along with one or two of the other teachers were still there when Sarah (my daughter) went to the same school, and were still teaching when she left, and occasionally I would see Mr Chambers in Ripon or Northallerton and he always knew me and my name - quite remarkable given the thousands of students who went through his tutelage over all those years. Some of those teachers seemed old when I was at school never mind when Sarah was there. I suppose they weren't that much older than me - it was just in those days everyone dressed much older - all slacks and cords along with sports jackets, and always a collar and tie.

English Literature which I enjoyed involved studying the works of Dickens, DH Lawrence, As You Like It and King Lear, along with the poets, like John Donne and Gerard Manley Hopkins (both who I struggled to understand), Alexander Pope and John Milton. In the lower sixth it was taught by Mr Temple, who was a real flowery poet type - he and I weren't really on the same wavelength - and at the end of that first year we did two 3 hour written papers and I scored about 23-27% on each of them and written in large red writing was Disgraceful on one and Disgusting on the other. In the second year we had a lady teacher (the Grammar School and Girls High School had amalgamated during the summer holidays) and I found her much more accommodating to more normal students such as I, and I managed to get enough improvement to get my A level.

History was split into two sections - British and European, the one taken by Mr Petchey who was a very good teacher and the other in the first year by a Mr Thomas who was nearly retiring age and was rather hard work, but I always enjoyed History and did quite well in it, as I did with Geography. This was and still is my favourite subject, travelling, but also watching many of the superb television documentaries from all over the world which still fascinate me. Our Geography master was Mr Crawford, who I remember always cycled to school, whatever the weather, I don't even know if he had a car. He was a very enthusiastic teacher and progressed to the very top of the tree, finishing up as Headmaster of Manchester Royal Grammar School. I was able to keep up to date with him at later dates, as the vicar who officiated at our wedding some ten years later was his father Canon Crawford. There is a story with regard to Mr Crawford, but I will leave that until later when we go on a trip to Iceland.

That was about it for school, and with taking 'O' levels a year early, I was only just 17 when I left school, in fact I was still only 16 when we started the A level exams. They never repeated the experiment to do them early again, so I assume they were not too enamoured of its success, from a personal point of view it didn't do me any harm, but always meant I was quite young to be doing various things for the rest of my life.

The year I left school was also the year that my sister Mary got married, more of that later, and also the year Father gave up the tenancy of Ivy House Farm at Middlesmoor, being succeeded in the tenancy by Alan Firth from just outside Pateley Bridge who at that time ran a contracting business and had done Fathers baling and muck spreading work for several years. Father had not had the best of health for quite a long time, since before I was born, Mother said it was from when he used to smoke. He apparently could smoke up to 40 un-tipped cigarettes in addition to a pipe until he had bronchitis and pneumonia at the same time. He stopped then and as far as I know never smoked again, but was left with a very weak chest. Long after Father had died, but Uncle Ralph, his eldest brother was still alive though in a retirement home, I used to try and visit him two or three times a year. By this stage he was getting a bit "Waffly", and used to go on about Father always being a "Weakly" lad who really shouldn't have survived childhood. After telling me that two or three times in a few minutes I used to stop him by telling him that if Father hadn't lived I wouldn't have been there to come and visit him, which he seemed to accept. At a similar time we were trying to identify people on some of the old photographs that had come to us after Mother had passed on. We thought we were doing quite well until we suddenly realised on getting home and going through them again, that we had the same name for two or three different people or the other way round.

Mother and Father had been looking for somewhere throughout the previous year or two and that early summer managed to buy Missies Farm at Galphay, which was sold by a business man who had fancied farming but really hadn't much of a clue, and they had seen it advertised for sale in the Yorkshire Post as a going concern, and they managed to get it for about £9500 I think. It was only a small holding of about 28 acres with a dozen milk cows, but was large enough for them as a semi-retirement project, so not only had they a move to make, they had a farm sale to plan, and a daughter's wedding to organise, though I don't think Father would get too involved with that. With milking cows at both places, it was fortunate that it all coincided with me leaving school, and after a few days back at home, I was back down to Galphay to look after that farm. I lodged with a Mr and Mrs King at Galphay and cycled backwards and forwards to Missies Farm which would be about one and half miles each way, and I was a young, fit lad who was used to quite a bit of cycling. Things went ok and I enjoyed the freedom and responsibility and returned up the dale a few times, I remember one time taking a Fergi 20 tractor back from Missies Farm. I went the shortest way to Pateley Bridge over Dallowgill and the steep hill straight down into the top of Pateley Bridge. I knocked it out of gear at the top of the hill and just about managed to keep control and pull up by we got there - fortunately there wasn't the amount of traffic then as there is now, or I suspect the ending would have been much more spectacular.

One or two final memories of Middlesmoor and Father in particular. Mother was a very keen Wesleyan and a regular attender at the Chapel across the road, and up and down the dale at other villages on special occasions such as Harvest Festivals, we went with her when we were younger. Whoever was the local preacher at Middlesmoor (including Uncle Ralph who was a local Methodist preacher - and one of the driest when it came to his sermons) they often finished up at Ivy House for tea before they went on to take an evening service. By then I or Mary were old enough to have enough interest in the world around us to read a newspaper, but if a preacher was coming for tea, the Sunday paper had to be hidden under the chair seat or somewhere. I used to wind Mother up by telling her it was really Monday's paper that should be hidden as it was printed on a Sunday, whereas Sunday's paper was usually printed on a Saturday evening. At that time most Methodists, Father included only did what was necessary on a Sunday, and would never, for instance hay time on a Sunday, and, if truth be told, they didn't make bad hay as a result, timing the cutting of the grass to fit around a Sunday. A few years later, I remember talking with Alan who was the yard manager at Lancaster Auction Mart, who in a previous job had been a milk churn lorry driver in that part of the world. One particular farm he collected from always left him out a cup of tea and either a scone or a teacake, except on a Sunday when there was nothing - not even any milk to collect, and what's more there wasn't any extra either the day before or the day after, so Alan surmised that they must have poured away Sunday's milk! I digress from the Chapel stories - back to Father. He would go to Chapel - and wasn't averse to having a sleep through the sermon - one particular day there was a motorbike came up the hill into the village and backfired loudly. This woke Father up suddenly, and he stood bolt upright in the pew in the middle of the sermon much to our and everyone else's amusement apart from Mother who was mortified by the embarrassment. When Father went to Chapel he enjoyed the hymns, but didn't sing, he just opened and shut his mouth in time to the music! They say genetics will out, and Adam (my son) who never knew his grandfather is exactly the same.

During our childhood, there was never really either the money or the availability of a lot of holiday places, and other than the seaside, there weren't many places to go, and package holidays abroad had at that time not got going. The most usual holidays for country people who tended to be more spread out than people in more industrial areas who all tended to live fairly close together, was to go away to stay with Aunts and Uncles, the converse of which is that cousins often came to Middlesmoor and stayed with us. The holidays we went away to all tended to be with Mother's family and with three of her brothers not having children, and Uncle Ralph Hoods being much older than we were, our choice was between Auntie Gladys and Aunt Emily. Auntie Gladys and Uncle David were a family combination in that Auntie Gladys and Mother were sisters and Uncle David was Fathers cousin. They lived at Strensall near York on a small holding, but they also had the vast acreage of Strensall Common on a long term lease from the Army, on which Uncle David ran a lot of sheep. They had four children, Jane who was quite a bit older than us and so we didn't see as much of her, David who was about Mary's age and was into anything mechanical and all sorts of trouble, Eleanor who was a tomboy and as daft as a brush, which she still is (though sadly she died very suddenly while we were in Australia in Spring 2019), and the baby, younger than me was Jimmy who was quiet and thoughtful, epitomised by his later interest in mending watches and clocks and an interest in old cars and pretty much anything antique.

David in later life has had a great interest in motor bikes and racing, and competed to a high level in various different types of two wheeled racing and was at one time British Grass Track Racing Champion. The great attraction of going to stay at Strensall was the common and all that went with it as a training and recreation area for the Army, and although we were hardly big enough to manage many of the obstacles, it was great fun to go round the assault course. Of course you could only go on it at the times when the Army were not out on the common and I'm sure nowadays you wouldn't be able to go anywhere near it at any time - in use or not. The other thing that sticks in the mind about holidays with Auntie Gladys was the fact that the only milk was from a couple of goats. They were to milk once a day and goats milk after being used to cows' milk was horrible - it was very strong in both taste and smell.

When we went to stay with Aunt Emily, she had two daughters, Maureen and Edna, and they lived in Kildale and we used to roam all over around the village and down by the railway and station, which for a small village still has an operational station going today on the Whitby line, and trains stop a few times a day. Later Aunt Emily took the job of Housekeeper to Sir Thomas Dugdale, later to become Lord Crathorne. He had been the member of Parliament for the Richmond constituency and the Minister of Agriculture when it was a much more important post than it is now. Aunt Emily had a flat up in the top of the house, and it was a whole new world to us, with a chauffeur and many fine rooms and grounds. I remember staying there in 1960 when the Rome Olympics were being held - we were allowed to watch them on the big colour television - the first time I had ever seen a colour television and the name of Mennea winning the 100m for Italy in his home Olympics has stuck in my mind ever since. Again, there was a large extensive country estate to explore. Crathorne Hall ceased to be a family home years ago now, and became a Country House Hotel, and we have visited it since at various functions, including a wedding on one of the wettest nights I can remember. Later in my working life I had quite a lot of contact with one of Lord Crathorne's sons, David, on various dairy/milk matters and in fact when we bought our first milk quota in the 1980's we shared a large amount with Crathorne Farms at what we were told at the time was absolute madness at about 11 pence per litre and we would never get our money back. It didn't look too much of a gamble a few years later when it was worth 70 pence plus per litre.

Back at home in Middlesmoor during the holidays we had the return visits from our cousins and all the other children had the same kind of visits from their relations and we all mixed in together and made new friends if only for a few days. Summer holiday time was the right time of year to go cutting peat and it was often a great adventure to set off with Father and a trailer load of kids both local and otherwise up onto the moor, where the different farmers had their own peat 'pit'. Father had all the gear for cutting the peat, into pieces of wet, grungy stuff from a face a few feet deep. We children had to get these pieces moved and laid out on all the surrounding bits of land to dry out naturally, and in between times, gather up the slices from a previous trip and make them up into a small stack, to stop it getting too wet if it rained and to get the wind flowing through it to finish drying it out, and usually from those to load up the trailer to bring back home as we returned. It was stored loose up in the loft above Father's 'workshop' and used throughout the winter. Burning peat makes a tremendously warm fire on bitterly cold nights and is fairly slow burning. It is easy to understand why the moorland fires in summer can sometimes take so long to put out, as it can smoulder away to quite a depth for weeks.

Towards the end of our stay at Middlesmoor, it was Mary's wedding. She had trained as a nursery nurse and was working at one of the Dr Banardo's homes in Ripon where she had met Eric. They often came up to Middlesmoor and Eric and I spent many hours playing snooker on the full sized table up at the Village Institute and we were fairly evenly matched and played to a remarkable standard. Eric asked me to be his Best Man which was quite a daunting prospect for a young man of 17 just out of school. This entailed having a new suit for the job, and that suit brings about another tale. The weekend after they returned from their honeymoon they were up at Middlesmoor, which also happened to be the Chapel Harvest Festival, which entailed both an afternoon and an evening service, with the preacher having tea at Ivy House. The service at Harvest Festivals are usually some of the better ones in the church year and we all went to the afternoon service - myself bedecked in my new suit for its second wearing. After the service and not wanting to keep the preacher entertained all afternoon, Eric and I went for a walk up the back lane from the village to come back down across the fields. It was my own fault and I should have got changed before setting off, but didn't, and you've guessed it, climbing back over a fence that had a strand of barbed wire across its top, I caught a trouser leg and tore it. Calamity, Mother would 'blow her top', so we concocted a plan as we went home, immediately involving Mary in the scheme. Father took an awful lot of persuading that out of the goodness of our hearts, Eric and I would do the milking so that he could go to the evening service as well (he reckoned once a day was plenty even at Harvest Festival time) but eventually we prevailed and Mary convinced Mother to leave the washing up and she would do it while they were at Chapel. All was set and while Eric and I milked and Mother and Father said their prayers, Mary got the offending torn trouser leg neatly sewn up, and all packed up with my other clothes to go back to Ladybridge ready for work the next day. Some considerable time later, Mother was doing something and saw the damaged trouser leg and immediately wanted to know how it had occurred. Little white lies never do any harm if done to protect people but some quick thinking was necessary as I hadn't thought of the damage being detected. "Oh we were going to Chapel one Sunday morning from Ladybridge and as we pulled out of the farmyard, saw some pigs were out on the other side of the road. I jumped out of the car to run round the back of them, having to jump a barbed wire fence to do so, and caught the trousers on the top, which Mrs Almack later mended for me." "Oh well", Mother said, "if you were on your way to Chapel and you got the pigs back in without them causing any damage, it can't be helped". We managed to keep the secret and Mother died without ever knowing the real truth.

Final remembrances of other things that happened whilst at Middlesmoor:

As a young boy going fencing with Father and he would ask me to pass him nails - he would ask me for three or four, I gave him the benefit of the doubt and took four to be told "When I say three or four I mean at least half a dozen". I soon learned the lesson and took the half dozen only to be reminded that he didn't want that many!

Similarly if we were doing something with water or feed he would ask for three parts of a bucket - and I always got it wrong. I asked him many times what he meant by three parts to be told "well - three parts" and I used to ask him what that was - did he mean three quarters or some other amount but the answer was always the same "- three parts"!

One of the earliest models of a Snowblower was tested at the foot of the hill up into Middlesmoor and the Nidderdale Times had a photo of it with we school children all crowded round it in the background.

Father and ceremonial cleaning of a gripe shaft. He couldn't abide a dirty shaft and if I got his gripe, I inevitably got muck on it. When he took it back he had to make a big scene out of getting a handful of hay or straw to wipe it down, along with a lot of knowing faces.

During the summer holidays from senior school we were busy with something across the fields and we saw a sheep not looking too happy and so set off to investigate, Father driving the tractor and as we approached the gate, Ron Petch (no relation as far as I know to Aytonian) who worked for Father for quite a few years, jumped off the trailer to run to the gate to open it. I jumped onto Ron's back for a piggy back ride and pulled him over on top of me breaking my leg. We had to go to the nearest hospital at Harrogate to get it set in plaster and then back again a week later to be checked - they hadn't got it set quite straight, so had to break again and re-set - not a massive job - just meant it was an extra week before I was mobile again and playing rugby.

The crossbred Jersey x Holstein that many of the 'New Zealand' type dairy farmers of today think is something new, is only new second time around. Back in the late 1950's and the early 1960's, BOCM as they were then, before later amalgamations and name changes through BOCM-Silcock, BOCM-Pauls to ForFarmers, had a mill at Selby and a testing/experimental farm at Barlby. They pioneered and ran a test on "Jersians" and Father had a couple of these at Middlesmoor - very nice cattle, good to work with, and all the benefits of hybrid vigour but the fault then as now is where do you go for the next cross. The idea of the "Jersian" never took hold and after a short time was never heard of again for the next 40 years or so.

Weatherheads the butchers of Pateley Bridge who are still present and well known, had a touring butchers van that used to come once a week up to Middlesmoor and do a tremendous trade. Their pork pies, still renowned today, and thought by many to be some of the best available were only 6d ($2^1/_2$p) in those early days, a massive difference to today's £1.35 or so. Talking of Weatherheads, they had established the caravan site as you entered Pateley from up the dale while we were still there - that's 50 plus years ago - so they were a long way ahead of their time in appreciating the leisure requirements of future generations.

Mother did quite a lot of looking after people in the village if they were poorly or had various other problems, over many years she helped on an almost daily basis with a lady who had a very bad stroke but lived for many years from the late 1950's which in those days was a long time to survive while she had brought up a young boy called Nicholas. Nicholas' real mother had died and there was no father, only an elder brother. However, I do remember Nicholas' real mother having some large poodles and was a real "doggy" lady, and she showed them right up to Crufts' standards.

Mother did a lot of looking after a little spinster called Kate, who quite often ran out of milk and used to come with a jug to get some from Father who used to joke after the book title "What Katy Did Next" - come for a pint of milk?! After her death at the sale of the furniture from the house, Father bought her Davenport desk for 10 shillings (50p). Both Adam and Sarah over the years have argued over who will ultimately have it, agreed it will be Sarah's choice as the eldest, to which Adam's retort was - ok then I'll have what's inside it, knowing that it housed most of the important papers of the family.

The dentist Mr Gray lived between Lofthouse and Ramsgill behind the big beech hedge that is still there. I remember going with Father an odd time and it was painful to watch never mind feel the drill which was still pedal operated. Father had a shocking set of teeth and one was to come out, with the dentist trying every bit of equipment and was still unable to get it out, but left the broken off piece in.

The final act at Middlesmoor was the farm sale, and I have the summary of the sale conducted by Oswald Lister & Son from Clint Banks, Ripley on 26th September 1963. It makes fascinating reading and includes intriguing things - a peat spade failed to raise a bid, a spade at three shillings, a Fergi 20 fan belt at 2/- and two buckets at 1/-, 10 cow chains at 1/6d each, five gallons of Winter Sheep Dip £3. Moving on to the machinery a, by then almost obsolete, pike bogey at 10/-, a set of chain harrows £5, side delivery rake at £1-10/-, a petrol Fergi 20 at £50 and a TVO Model Fergi 20 at £56. 25 hens made 6/- apiece and 20 old ones 2/6d each, while the hen house made 10/-. (Note a shilling is the equivalent of todays 5p).

Moving on to the sheep, the top priced pen of two shear ewes Dalesbred at £7, the same for three shears, a Dalesbred tup at £3-15s, and a Wensleydale two shear tup topped the sheep section at £8-10s.

I think though I can't remember that Father took a few of the better milk cows to Missies farm, because the two top priced cows in full milk were an Ayrshire at £53 and a Black and White at £52, in calf heifers up to £42, a Friesian heifer calf at £2-10s, an Aberdeen Angus bull calf at £5-5s and a red bullock at £20-10s.

His sheepdog only made £2, which probably tells you it wasn't very good, though in the past he had some good ones.

Moving onto the surplus furniture, it was a total disaster only totalling £5-7s-6d including a chest of draws at half a crown, an extending dining table with four chairs totalled £2, and two bed stands made five bob each.

In all the total proceeds of the sale £2,860 -2s which doesn't seem to have been the greatest of sales, but if you put it in to today's prices from 56 years ago it would have been equivalent to approximately £50,000.

Within the sale book for the Middlesmoor dispersal, I found the sale notice card for Fathers sale at Oak Tree Farm, Lonsdale on 22nd April 1947 before he moved to Nidderdale. Interestingly by this date I was less than a year old when Mother and Father moved to Humberstone Bank, rather than the two plus years I always thought I was. The auction was run by H.A. Richardson and in those days details were circulated round the local farming community on photo postcards - a copy of which is shown among the photographs. Unusually for that time in that part of the world was a second calf Gurnsey cow - note the spelling (was that a misspelling by the auctioneer or how they spelt Guernsey in those days?), two horses, 23 head of cattle, 42 ewes and hoggs, 30 hens, various implements, dairy utensils, and various horse harnesses came to a grand total of £610-18s-3d less expenses of £11-4s.

Also within that sale book was an interesting letter from Fathers accountants dated March 1960 pointing out that the improvements in Father's bank balance over the previous six years was rather high at £1636, an average of approx £273 a year. Difficult now to think these figures are true.

Chapter Three – Pre-College Experience

Having got the necessary qualifications and been accepted for the National Diploma in Agriculture course at The Royal Agricultural College, Cirencester, one of the prerequisites for that was that you had to do a minimum 18 months of practical training pre-entry, and this did not include helping on the home farm throughout ones childhood. In effect the 18 month requirement meant that you had two years of practical to fit in between leaving school and the beginning of a college year. Having been raised on an upland dales farm, the experience needed to be widened into other fields, and so for the first year it was to get some experience of arable farming, together with other stock, pigs.

In this gap between school and starting at the first farm I had looked after Missies Farm and helped get ready for the farm sale and had actually started work before the sale itself and Mary's wedding which was all in September 1963.

I don't know/ can't recollect how I came to find a years experience with Mr Dick Almack at Ladybridge Farm. Well, although it was nearer to Thornborough and Carthorpe than it was to Well. In recent years, there has been much quarrying in the area and the discovery of the Thornborough Henges has made both local and national news, but in those days there was never any mention of such things. At that time the large area between West Tanfield and North Stainley was being quarried for gravel by Agglethorpe Quarries, and in those days they did not have the same environmental rules to reinstate the land – that was done at a later date, and it is now a very well farmed area of land. Similarly, Nosterfield Quarries were just starting work and that has now extended to a massive area, right out from the edge of Tanfield to Nosterfield, over the main Masham - Thirsk road round behind Ladybridge and over that road towards Upsall farm. The earlier parts worked have now long been reclaimed and are now a very well established and extensive nature reserve.

Mr and Mrs Almack were very good to me as I lived with them for a year. My starting salary was £4/week for about a 50 hour week, and again compared to today you wonder how you survived on that, paying £1.50 Board and Lodging and ultimately could still afford to run a car and even save some money and didn't live the life of a hermit!

The Almacks had five children, most of which and some of their children will be known to many of you, their only son, Ambrose continued with the farm after his father retired but also established a cattle haulage business - the farm is now run by one of Ambrose and Joyce's daughters. The eldest daughter Christine was married to Fred Donaldson the well known beef farmer and when I was there, their five young children could cause absolute mayhem in a very short time - two of them will be well known locally, Rachel Greensit, who set up and runs a very successful catering business - Haregill Lodge Outside Catering, and Chris who has his own mobile mechanic business and will do work on a lot of local farms in the Northallerton area, and a further generation down his niece Katrina will be known to many on the local show circuit with her beef cattle. Another daughter was married to Alan Duffield - they farmed out York way and he was at one time one of the leading lights and showmen with the Wensleydale sheep breed. Youngest daughter was Jennifer who subsequently married John Swales from Thirsk who again farmed and bred pedigree Limousins. Last time I saw them was having breakfast in the Holstein pavilion at the Great Yorkshire Show, while I was stood behind the door holding the electric trip switch in place because Sarah and her team were producing so many breakfasts in a very short time.

Mrs Almack always used to go to Ripon for the market on a Thursday and so it was always fresh fish for tea that day, and I also remember we always had egg and chips on a Friday. Breakfast was usually some fresh bacon sliced off a home killed pig, which in those days was still more fat than lean meat - not really my cup of tea but in those days a hungry young lad ate pretty well everything.

Just after I had started at Ladybridge we were waiting for the start of harvest and one day we were all sent across to the old farm house at Upsall to pick the Victoria plums that grew right along the front of the house, and we picked basket full's, leaving the ones that weren't ready for further time to ripen. Once harvest started a lot of barley was bagged up into anything from 4 to 16st bags and stored in the old house, and as you came back for the next one, a lovely ripe Victoria plum was very refreshing! A few days later, one damp morning I was dispatched with a big wicker basket to gather the remaining plums. With eating the odd one as I searched for others I finished up with only one in the basket and when I returned to the house got a somewhat frosty reception from Mrs Almack and the comment "you might as well have eaten that one as well".

Outside on the farm, it was my first introduction to working with other people, and the start of meeting some marvellous characters over the years. Two brothers Fred and Harry had worked there for many years and were the main staff. Fred's main work was the pigs and milling while Harry was the main tractor man. The other full time man was Ken Bradshaw who hadn't been there very long. He had no previous experience of farming and had come from the Teeside area. The fascination of Ken was that he still had a racing greyhound and introduced us to the murky world of that sport - you 'pulled' your dog by giving it a feed not long before it was due to run and other such things happened. We all went to the races one night when Ken's dog was running and naturally all had a small wager on our dog, only for it to run very badly and finish tailed off last. I think the only one without a bet on it would be Ken - but we had a great night out.

The other person on the farm who then only worked part time was Jack Woof. Anyone who went to Bedale Ag Centre in its earlier days may remember Mrs Woof - Jacks wife who looked after the kitchen there for many years. Jack had been a full time man before going to work in the NAAFI at RAF Leeming and he could always tell a good tale - on his first day there he was instructed to fill up the "urns" and Jack said he wandered about not knowing what he was looking for before eventually returning to his supervisor to say to him "urns, urns, the only urns I know are the Lucernes the master used to grow".

At that time the Ladybridge herd of Essex Saddleback pigs was quite well thought of and gave me the first real insight and future interest in pedigree stock breeding. At that time the Essex and Wessex were two different breeds, but are now known as British Saddlebacks. Some of the sows were bred pure, and about half were bred to Large White and subsequently Landrace boars to produce the commercial fattening pigs. Just before I finished my year there, we held one of the regular (every three or four years) production sales of both pedigree and commercial breeding stock - again a whole new world to me. The sale was promoted and run by Basil Johnston the auctioneers who at that time ran Boroughbridge Auction Mart which has not operated for many years and is now a housing estate. Incidentally many of you will have been fed by Mr Johnston's grand daughter who ran the cafe/restaurant at Thirsk Auction Mart after it moved to its current site on the York road.

During that first autumn at Ladybridge there were four acres of mangolds to be snagged and Mr Almack let the snagging on a piecework basis to each of us - one acre each. They were in the big long field directly across the road and you can tell how long it was by the fact there were only 16 rows to the acre. We all started at the same time after doing the daily chores and I wondered as I worked away, why the other three men, did a double row just so far and back down again to the hedge. Being young and daft I carried on the full length of the field and at the far end saw why - they were sat behind the hedge having their 'bait'. I set off back and did a double row all the way down again - had my bait and went into the house for lunch - but I had done $\frac{1}{4}$ acre! The next day I followed the other men's example and did short lengths backwards and forwards. When they were all done they were all to cart into an outside 'pie' made with bales and loose straw, loaded by hand with a gripe, and then sheep were "folded" to eat the tops.

Sugar beet tops were also eaten by the sheep in the same way, but by then sugar beet harvesting had just moved to machine work and a contractor Brian Dresser was used to lift the beet and we just drove the trailers alongside. Brian was a real character, his machine wasn't terribly reliable and once a broken chain at the top of the machine needed attention - Brian skinned his hand as he undid a bolt and with a lot of cursing he threw the spanner as far as he could into the standing crop! I can remember him saying "Thou silly bugger Brian, thou'll have to go and find it now". Clambering down off the machine and we all had a fair job to find it among the crop but we did eventually and he carried on.

Potatoes were at that time grown on most arable farms as a break crop within the rotation and Ladybridge was no exception. Mostly they were still picked by hand and local gangs made good money for six or eight weeks in the autumn. The gang at Ladybridge was run by Gordon "Gos" Buckton, who later farmed on one of the

North Yorkshire County Council farms at Catterick Tunstall. Most of the pickers were ladies that he gathered up and mostly from the Bedale area, and it was somewhat intimidating for a young shy lad of 17 to be working in among this host of mostly middle aged ladies as we emptied the baskets into the trailers while they picked - hard work but great fun.

Whilst at Ladybridge I had to find a dairy farm for my second years' practical experience, and Mr Almack enquired of the NFU, and it was Alan Johnston the Bedale area secretary who put me in touch with Mr Ropner and his manager George Heeley. I eventually got fixed up for that 12 months with a job that was to change and shape my entire future life. Before that however I had very serious second thoughts about my future and decided I wasn't going to bother going to college and would carry on just as a worker for Mr Almack and went home to tell my parents. Mother was up the back lane picking brambles when I told her, and fortunately she managed to persuade me to think again and go on as planned to Newton-le-Willows and then Cirencester - who knows what would have been otherwise.

While at Ladybridge I started to learn to drive and had lessons at BSM in Harrogate where I went for my first test on Christmas Eve - not the ideal day in such a busy town. I set off by failing to read the number plate but the examiner accepted that I was looking into the sun and had to squint to be able to see it. Needless to say as most young lads of the time did so, I failed for not using my mirrors sufficiently. Most lads failed I think to steady them up whilst most young ladies passed first time as they were much more cautious drivers then. I realise that writing this in 2017 they will be deemed very sexist remarks, but this was 1963/64 and was generally accepted. Eventually I passed in the spring of 1964 and was soon able to buy my first car - an A30 in a horrible fawn colour for about £50 from George Wallace who had his own little garage in Nosterfield, and it did me very well for a couple of years. I seem to remember insurance was £37-10s and I told Father he was a miserable 'B' because he wouldn't do it under his name - but he said it would have to go under my own name sometime so I might as well start clocking up the no claims discounts straight away, with hind sight he was quite right, I never did a vast mileage in those days, but it was much easier for popping home, or out to see friends, and it saved Father occasionally having to drive to take me somewhere - he hated driving. That was the end of my year at Ladybridge and it had been a great experience, which the Almack family continued, taking a student each year to help them start in farming. I was followed as a student by Martin Ibbotson from over Pickering area, and he was subsequently followed by another person well known to many in the area, Ernie Sherwin - auctioneer, valuer and top breeder of Wensleydale sheep.

So on to the next chapter of my life at Newton Grange. When I had gone for the interview I had got all dressed up in best suit and tie and arrived nervously in the farm yard, I was aware of two men in the field in front of the house which turned out to be George and Mr Jonathan Ropner, who leapt over the fence in his colourful Caribbean shorts, flip-flops and very little else, and I have to say I did wonder what I was letting myself in for - a strange beginning to a long and wonderful association, but one which I have never regretted along with the wonderful people I have met along the way.

I was to live with George and Doris Heeley at Newton Grange, and when I arrived on the Sunday ready for work the next day, the first people I met were Chris Nattrass and his future wife Susan Gaines, who quite often baby sat for George and Doris. Chris of course was involved in the family business in Bedale - Gents outfitters and Ladies clothes plus carpet and flooring, at that time Chris' father and uncle were the main principals, subsequently carried on by Chris, and after he closed down the business, it has been for some time now a bespoke ladies dress shop and cafe under the name of Institution.

My main work at the farm was actually down at Dalesend itself, Patrick Brompton, where Mr and Mrs Ropner lived, which acted as the young stock rearing farm for the then three dairy units which operated at Newton Grange, Home Farm at Hornby, and Arbour Hill at Patrick Brompton, under the guidance of Head Herdsman Gregor McGregor. At that time there were virtually no buildings for young stock down there. The baby calves were reared in the old stables, calves on the bucket wore collars and were fastened round the walls at feeding time to stop cross-sucking etc, and as they got older moved to some boxes across the main Bedale/Leyburn road to which we carried food or gruel for rearing bulls. Those loose boxes are now two cottages, one being called Rebel Cottage - the last animal to live there was a giant Herdwise bull Ebydale Rosamond Rebel. There was up at the top of the drive just the old 24 stall byre with pump and storeroom on the end and one small stone building up at the top which would take about a dozen stirks, plus the two small open hay sheds. All the rest of the heifers were wintered outside mostly in the Park at the front of Dalesend which was all old pasture land which could stand the poaching. It meant handling a lot of food, sometimes not in the nicest of conditions, but saved an awful lot of cost in buildings. Reflecting on the changes over 55 years of farming, one can't help but feel that at times, we have all put a lot of extra cost into the system and whether it has always been to the benefit of either man or beast.

On that first day down at Dalesend, George said the main job was that we were going to clean out the ha-ha - which I laughed at ha-ha, thinking it was some kind of ritual leg-pulling job for a new starter. George was insistent and finally got out the dictionary to show me it was a proper word - a sunken ditch in front of a house to give the impression the land runs straight across - exactly what there is across the front of the lawn at Dalesend and into the Park - I well remember years later being called down there to retrieve a lawnmower that a new user had lost control of and it hadn't quite made the ditch, if it had you could visualise it going all the way down to the Low Wood across 25 acres of Parkland.

Later that week another job was to help with the painting on Greg's house - Oak View in Patrick Brompton. In those days many farmers decorated their own and their staff houses themselves. I didn't really think it was what I came into farming to do, so pointedly made a bad job of painting the window frames - getting far too much onto the window panes - needless to say Greg or rather Mrs Greg didn't want me painting anymore and it was the last painting I did at Dalesend for many years.

At that time the pedigree Dalesend herd and many others still used mostly natural service bulls as still in the early days of AI, there wasn't a wide choice of high end AI bulls, with only the Milk Marketing Board, later to become Genus, who operated such a heavily controlled industry. With three herds at that time, the bulls were all kept at Newton Grange, and semen was collected daily as necessary and fresh semen used for AI on all three farms, using speculum and pipette for the actual insemination. The herdsmen had to ring Greg in by 9am when he was home for breakfast and then he went and did the collection and inseminating as necessary. Usually a young bull was used to run with bunches of heifers at Dalesend. When I was first there, the three bulls standing at the Grange were Terling Brumas, Hunday Brenadema 10 and Morrell Prince Adema 19. Brumas daughters were already milking and not very well at that, so he was replaced by Hunthill Romany 2, a son of Brenadema 10. As an aside, the Romany bull came from the well known Guy Southwell family over in the East Riding and it was a pleasant surprise some 40 years later when we changed insurance companies and the agent who looked after us and still does was a great-nephew, Edwin Southwell.

When talking of cattle not being milky enough as with Terling Brumas, bear in mind that we are talking before Holsteins were in this country and the Dalesend herd average was about 1000gallons/cow - in modern parlance 4500 litres whereas today a herd not averaging close to double that would be thought to not be doing too good a job - many changes since that time which will be built upon as we move through the years. At that time cows grazed as long a summer as possible with no buffer feeding, strip grazed kale until about Christmas whatever the weather and self-fed silage through winter - that at the time was a fairly standard system and could even have been ahead of its time for many holdings - all on loose housing.

Then and throughout the following years there were many, great characters with which to work, and whilst many came and went, they were great fun to work alongside and get to know in rather more detail. The herdsman at Newton Grange when I first went was Brian Chapman - who was there for about another two and a half years before he was replaced by the legendary "Mr Bill" Faulds whom you will read much about as the story unfolds. Again like Edwin Southwell it was fascinating that some thirty or so years later I was supporting Adam at a schools rugby match at Richmond and realised it was Brian along the touchline - he was supporting his grandson, who played scrum-half to Adams' tight-head prop in the school age group teams which were coached by Mr Clark - whose son was a year younger but generally played a year ahead of his age group - Calum Clark, who was a back row forward at Northampton before moving to Saracens and featuring in several England squads.

The cowman up at Home Farm, Hornby went by the name of Bill, but I can't remember his surname and I didn't have a lot to do with him. He wasn't there very long, being replaced by Alan Gregg during my student year. Alan was a member of the well know Gregg family from Bellerby, son of the renowned 'Tot' Gregg who always wore a buttonhole wherever you saw him. Alan was probably the most naturally gifted stockman I ever came across, but tidiness was not his forte - in fact he was the most untidiest man I have ever worked with. He came to Home Farm, back to the family area, previously being a cowman for Mr Bellerby near Harrogate (father of Chris, Graham and Neil). Alan was a master of flower growing and even then caused mayhem among the other men by often not being there to lead straw at harvest time which all the other stockmen did in the middle of the day. He would be away at some local show or other with his flowers and when I jokingly referred the matter to him years later he first laughed and said -"well I used to take Mrs J a great bunch of Dahlias or Chrysanthemums every week after a show, so kept the guvnor on side". Much later when the five herds were dispersed in 1974, Alan rented Home Farm buildings and some unploughable pasture land, bought the unsalable cows and many others at the sale and continued there for a couple of years before he got the tenancy of a Church Commissioners farm at East Boldon, near Sunderland, where he farmed very successfully with his own "Wensleydale" herd. He still farms there, though not with cows, we see him now and again, still showing his flowers very successfully and still with the same very distinctive laugh that he used to start nearly every question put to him.

Whilst talking about Home Farm and Alan, there is another connection to the family which I should perhaps mention. As the name implies it was the Home Farm of the nearby Hornby Castle which had been the pivotal part of the Duke of Leeds, incidentally the last Dukedom in England to die out through lack of heirs. It was a house with a marvellous front facade facing towards Hornby Castle but also had in the far corner of the stack yard a stone built stallion pen. This I later discovered had been designed and built by Marnie's grandfather who was a master builder. They had earlier lived and run the Greyhound Inn at Hackforth which was subsequently run by Marnie's Aunt Lillian and Uncle Jack Darling. It has had many owners and managers since and was closed for a while, including being managed by Mike Miles, who again may well crop up later in the book as he worked for me later as a relief herdsman.

Another character of the time was Hubert Byrom who was the gardener/handyman at Dalesend - the only help farming wise was if we were cleaning out the stable boxes at Dalesend where we reared the calves - all to do by hand, and at least a two movement job to get the muck out into either midden, spreader or trailer. Many youngsters have laughed at me since when I have told them when mucking out a calf box you need to read the bed and take it off in layers rather than just dig in and "rive" at it. It was Hubert who taught me that and he was a master at it. The other thing he did when mucking out was tie paper 4st bags round his legs with string so that he didn't get muck or the smell of it onto his clothes - took him a few minutes to get prepared but for a little man he was remarkably good when he got going. When we were mucking out it was usually Hubert and I, Greg was very good at timing his return to just before lunch and working away when JGR (Mr Ropner) came home for lunch. Hubert was a regular almost nightly supporter of The Green Tree at Patrick Brompton, who got even more polite when he had a drink or two though you never saw him drunk, but he always maintained to remain sober, you had to keep the liquid moving rather than let it settle and always went to the gents after every pint before he started the next one.

Bob Husband took over from David Gaines as head tractor man during that year and will crop up later in various stories that occurred over time. He was another wonderful character who again could tell many a tale about almost anything. He was already there when I arrived, and had previously worked on a farm up Nidderdale somewhere overlooking Gouthwaite reservoir and told the story of standing in the middle of the road one wet Monday telling Walt Rayner, who was a noted Methodist of that era, that he wasn't worried about his hay being wet as he had got it in the previous nice sunny day when Walt wouldn't contemplate hay making on the Sabbath, which was common thinking back then.

The final character to write of in this first year at Newton Grange was Dick Winship and family who lived at and managed the herd at Arbour Hill. This farm had again been a part of the Hornby Castle Estate and had been bought not many years previously, having been farmed previously for a long time by Mr Johnston who was known to everyone as "EBD" which were his initials. He had run the Arbourhill herd of Friesians, and one or two of them were bought at his dispersal sale. The Dalesend cows had only been there for about two years, the nucleus of the herd being the ones which had been run in the byre at Dalesend and augmented by good cows bought from Lancashire Club sales at Lancaster - good high country cows which always did well for us - from the Townley's of 'Knowsley' and 'Mearsbeck', the Rainfords of 'Brock' and the Parkers of 'Bailrigg'. Many years later the dominant family at Dalesend was the 'Pansys' which originated from Bailrigg and I can remember milking Bailrigg Pansy 6th who was a very 'blue-grey' cow - milky but not the tidiest of udders - which ultimately became one of their best features. Probably two of the best cows at that time were Knowsley Jean 2 who went on to breed a very good family that were eventually decimated by the lorry returning them from the first ever "Spectacle of Breeding" overturning as it came over the tops - there was a feature of the event promoting cow families and I think we took nine Jeans. None of them were injured, barely marked even in the overturning, but none of them ever bred again!! The remaining member of the family - a youngster at the time had been a contract mating for the MMB by Finchingfield Envy which had come as a heifer rather than the contract bull. It was an absolute "pillock", classified H5, but we kept breeding her to try and keep the family alive, After five bull calves in a row and no improvement in her conformation, I finally gave up and the family was lost. The other tremendous cow of the time was Elsargh Ad Lorna who had been offered by Mr Townley of 'Knowsley' at a Lancaster sale. As it had to be in those days, it was announced that she had been hand cleansed, which killed the trade, she failed to make the reserve, but Mr J managed to buy her privately afterwards. She went on to develop a good family over the years and Dalesend Caprice Lorna was one of the herds first 100 tonne cows.

Back to Dick - the reason I had more to do with him was twofold - we used to go to Arbour Hill every morning for the house milk for Dalesend and all the staff, which used to sit in a small churn on the mounting block in front of the stables, and everyone brought their cans for a fill up, and the other reason being not many weeks after I started Dick was rushed into hospital with a burst appendix and I did the milking there for many weeks. Just about my first meeting with Dick who spoke very slowly and profoundly and waved his arms all over the place as he did so, was when I went with Greg to get the house milk one morning and Dick told Greg that Arbourhill Mayblem Acorn 3 had calved during the night down in East Park North. Greg asked what it was as it had been a contract mating for a bull for MMB at which Dick threw his hands up in the air and set off to run at full pace to the field - about half a mile. We followed in the van and could barely keep pace - everything was ok and it was the required bull calf.

Whilst I was milking up there, the hunt were out one Monday afternoon and a lady appeared with her horse which had gone lame. "May I use your telephone" she demanded to which I replied we would have to go and ask Mildred, Dicks wife if that was ok - which it was. "Will you hold my horse then" commanded the woman, as she went in to call for her horsebox. When she returned "Thank you my man" and put a sixpence into my hand. I looked at it and looked at her and replied "I'll hold it gladly for nothing, but I'm dammed if I'll hold it for sixpence" and what's more she took the sixpence back!

At a later time when Dick was better again, I was up there one day and aware of some shouting across behind the hedge of the Stackyard Field in Renforth Oak and what I couldn't make out moving along above the hedge. When they came back into view heading back to the farm, it was young Billy being chased by his father with a broom up in the air - fortunately Billy just managed to keep far enough ahead of Dick until they got back by which time they were both so out of breath he hadn't any anger left.

The three sons of Dick and Mildred all made great careers for themselves subsequently but as youngsters they were real rascals and up to all sorts of things. George went into the house for a cup of tea, with them one afternoon and when he came out to put his wellingtons on, on the step, one had 'peed' into one of them and another had done a 'turd' into the other (Dennis was the eldest although which of the lads was guilty never became clear).

On another occasion when I was milking there in what was an abreast parlour - six stalls, I opened the door to let a cow in from the outside collecting yard to be greeted by the youngest Karl with not a stitch of clothes on and covered in cow muck. He had crawled under the gate and through all the cows, fortunately coming to no harm. Dick eventually moved on and for many years ran one of the herds of Mr Ramsden's just outside Ripon, and is now a very old man, but Mildred sadly passed away a couple of year ago. Bill and I went to her funeral at Sawley, and both Dick and Mildred had enjoyed all the reminiscing at the "End of an Era" party we had in Crakehall Village Hall in January 2012.

Another highlight of that first year at Dalesend, or more correctly if that is the terminology - "lowlight" was while I was working in the stables doing something and my beloved little A30 was parked outside, I was aware of a noise of someone banging something. On going to investigate, I found a young Charles Ropner, then about three or four was hitting my car with a stick. Of course I shouted at him to stop in some very choice language and off he ran crying. A few minutes later the nanny Marjorie came to see what the fuss was about and for a translation as she didn't understand some of the words I had used on Charles. I have never forgotten that incident, as I know Charles hasn't, and he would have been most upset if I hadn't included it.

In the spring of 1965, early May and I know because it was FA Cup Final day and neither George nor I were into football (George liked golf and me rugby), so I gave him a hand to plant daffodil bulbs along the fence on the lawn edge in front of the office. Those daffodils will crop up later in the stories, but that is when the seed was sown as it were.

Potatoes were grown at the time but they had become more modernised and had a machine that lifted them onto a turntable to be sorted and into the trailer. Most of them were stored in the Dutch barn at Fox Park and we spent a lot of time that winter riddling and bagging up potatoes - at that time into 1 cwt hessian bags, which all had to be weighed and tied up, though much of the time my job was at the other end of the riddle - sippetting potatoes out of the pie - many youngsters will not know what a sippet is, but it is like a shovel with tines rather than being solid and a round blob of steel on the end of each tine so that it couldn't go into the potatoes. Being young and daft it was great fun to put the potatoes on so fast that you either blocked up the riddle or the bagger often couldn't cope and called a halt. Similarly at harvest time when we were leading straw to put on top of the silage at each of the dairies, Mr J used to help lead nearly all the straw and used to say "faster, faster" and so I put them onto the elevator exactly as told, sometimes two deep which would sometimes stall it and then got told off for being too fit.

That was about it for my years practical experience at Newton Grange and it was time to move on to the next adventure.

Chapter Four – And so to College

September 1965 saw the end of my pre-college training and the start of the last of my formal education, having finally passed 'O' level Chemistry to allow me to go to the Royal Agricultural College at Cirencester, Gloucestershire. At that time it was a private college which meant it was fee paying, but fortunately North Riding of Yorkshire Agricultural College provided me with a bursary for both education and accommodation costs having convinced them I should go there rather than attend their own Askham Bryan College. A variety of courses were run at the college, a one year general introductory course, mostly used by ex-servicemen, sons of country land owners and the like, the two year NDA (National Diploma in Agriculture) course which I was doing and an Estate Management/Land Agent three year course. Whilst I was there they introduced a new one year Advanced Farm Management course which one could either carry on straight into from NDA or come back later to do.

That is where I first met Tom Phillips who came onto that course - we were later both to be heavily involved with Holstein UK, Tom was Chairman at the time I was President. Other notable students at the time who will be known to many readers, all of them on the Estate Management course were Bill Walton, the eldest of three brothers from Middleham and John Tennant the eldest of two brothers who developed the hugely successful auction house at Leyburn. I still see both of them occasionally, John up at Leyburn and Bill sometimes up at Kingston Park seeing Newcastle Falcons playing - he is a practising Land Agent up in Northumberland. While at college they were the unofficial college bookies and would run a book on virtually everything and anything. I well remember the Miss World beauty competition one of those years being won by a complete outsider -Miss India and they didn't have a single bet on her, so they made a killing. The third was Charlie Wyvill of Constable Burton Hall.

I had never been on a visit to Cirencester or any other place of learning as many students do now, taking a tour of several establishments before they chose which one they want to grace with their presence, so it was a trip into the complete unknown when I set off for college. I don't think at that point I had ever been south of the bottom of Yorkshire. We decided it wouldn't be sensible to take my car down to start with, so arrangements were made for me to go by train from Harrogate to Gloucester and then on to Cirencester and then I presume a taxi up to college which was about a mile out of the small country town.

The first occurrence of this new chapter was actually on the train. Sat opposite me in the carriage was a rather dubious looking gentleman, you know the sort I mean. He had a buttoned up raincoat, glasses and wore a beret and was rather shifty, or so I thought, reading a newspaper and casting his eyes around all the time. On my first time trip out into this big, wide world and with my rather furtive imagination working overtime, I thought he was probably a French spy. In those days, train journeys were not the fastest and it was a fairly tortuous sort of a trip down to the southwest. En route we were called to the dining car for lunch, but being rather suspicious of the 'spy', I let him go before me. When I had allowed a minute or two for him to get settled I ventured there for my lunch, only to find that the one spare seat was directly opposite him - imagine my surprise when a few minutes later before he started his meal, he undid his raincoat to reveal he was wearing a "dog-collar", a vicar, not that it necessarily meant he wasn't also a spy!

On arriving at college and checking in to register, I was accommodated at Trent Lodge, a couple of hundred yards from college, which we had to walk back and forwards to for all our meals. Trent Lodge was only a small place with only about 15 two or three bedded rooms, but it was to be my home for the next two years. The first year I shared a three bedded room with Mike Helliwell and I can't remember who else, with the adjoining room a twin shared by Dave Hampson and Bill Higson who were to become lifelong friends and will no doubt crop up later in the stories. In the second year Dave and I shared a twin room on the second floor, while Bill moved up to the main college and shared a room in the Bathurst Wing. Many people have come across the name Trent Lodge in later years, it was at one time the head quarters of AHDB, the Agriculture and Horticultural Development Board which survives on the levies it derives from the various different sectors of agriculture. As it became a much larger organisation with apparently endless members of staff doing very little it moved to new head quarters at the RASE showground at Kenilworth. Just in passing and mentioning RASE, it was just about that time when it became the permanent home of the Royal Show, which hitherto had been a wandering occasion touring all areas of the country on an annual basis. The Great Yorkshire Show had been well ahead of the game and been on its permanent site at Harrogate some 15 years or so, since 1951.

The principal at Cirencester at the time was Frank Garner, a big, bluff East Anglian who had spent most of his career in the Ministry of Agriculture and one of the main men in running the War-Ag nationally during the war. No doubt he was a good administrator, but didn't have the charisma to lead such an establishment after people like the redoubtable Bobby Boutflour or Ken Russell who had by then gone to be head of Shuttleworth College. Those two names are well written in agricultural folklore history. Mr Garner only took us for one lecture a week on general studies and used to say things like "Gentlemen, the days of the horse are numbered, the tractor is here to stay" and spend half the time telling us about recovering bog-oaks when they were ploughing in Norfolk or Suffolk. A bit out of date, even for the mid 1960's. Not that I was involved but I remember two stunts with the principals' car, the first when it was manually carried into the main entrance and up onto the mid-section where the stairs split either way to go up onto the top corridor. The other time his car was hi-jacked, driven to London and abandoned with a litter of young pigs in it. These kind of stunts usually coincided with rag week or other such money raising events.

We were very well looked after at college, the meals were superb, and we were waited on in the dining hall by mostly Polish waiters, who were not the early EU immigrants, but ones who had come over during the war, or as prisoners of war and remained. We had proper breakfast, lunch, afternoon tea at the end of lectures and then dinner at night. In addition we had coffee making facilities down at Trent Lodge, and at weekends would often frequent "The Mad Hatter" cafe in town for a toasted teacake and coffee morning or afternoon. Remember we were all young men getting a fair amount of various kinds of exercise, just as well or we would never have eaten all that food without putting on a lot of weight. The one exception to this excellent food was that occasionally either after dinner or at afternoon tea we were served Edam cheese, which nobody seemed to care for too much and so it got left and Edam cheese gets drier and harder as time goes on making it less and less appetising - eventually I think it was either smuggled out of the dining room to empty the plates or the kitchen eventually gave up. It put me off Edam virtually for life, though I occasionally eat some if it is very fresh.

Having mentioned the Principal lacking much status within the eyes of the students, I must say many of the other lecturers were right out of the top drawer and could deliver interesting lectures on all kinds of diverse subjects with very practical slants. At that time Vic Hughes was the Farms Director and was a fairly intimidating figure, a big, strong Welshman with at times a very bad temper, he lectured us in year 2 on Farm Management and subsequently quite a few years later became College Principal. College did at that time have quite a few students who were there for the social life and 'kudos' of attending the Royal Agricultural College, and were not really bothered about a lot of learning. Fortunately most of them were on the one year course, but there were odd ones doing our NDA course. First lecture under Mr Hughes and two such members rolled in ten minutes late and continued to talk and disrupt things generally. It didn't take long for Vic to get annoyed and he told them in no uncertain terms "I don't care whether you come to lectures or not - you have paid your fees so college will not lose out, so either shut up and pay attention or 'bugger off' and don't come back". What's more they never did appear again at a Farm Management lecture.

Dai Barling was then a relatively young but very good grassland specialist, Jim Lockhart a tremendous crop lecturer, matched by Geoff Craghill on Animal Husbandry. Harry Catlin was a young dynamic farm machinery specialist, and were well supported by more specialist lecturers in subjects like zoology, botany and science. There were two science lecturers, Mr Kershaw who had a marvellous handlebar moustache and a new first job lecturer Pete Biglin, who struggled to keep any control and was easily embarrassed by failing to do so. At the time there was a pop record in the Hit Parade "Peak -a boo I love you", and one of his lectures was on vitamins, elemental requirements for crop and animal health, featuring a condition called "Pica" - an anaemia caused by a shortage of Iron in the diet. Every time he mentioned the word the whole class would strike up "Pica-boo we love you"! We had lectures on farm buildings from Mr Bennett who had his own estate agents and management consultancy in the county, and were taken for veterinary science by a local vet whose name I cannot recall, he was very good and it was my favourite and best subject. Being a vet he was often out on a call and was nearly always late for lectures, one morning particularly so, and with the speed camera set to catch all the students coming out of town up to college, the tip off soon went out to watch it, but not to the late-running vet who was the only one to get caught.

As I said previously there were a fair number of students who just went for the good life, but if you wanted to study and learn properly then they were a tremendous group of lecturers who could really engage the students in their subjects. Added to that we had a lot of outside visits, whether it was onto the college's own farms or to the experimental plots where we pranced about with "fishing nets" to catch various bugs and identify them, or to other outstanding farms in the area to look and see how these people were pushing back the boundaries of agricultural practice and were quite happy to share that knowledge with the next generation. One such visit which lives in the memory was just the other side of Swindon to visit the late, great Ben Cooper of "Normead" fame. He had developed a superb herd of cows and was a leading member within the Black and White breed and as a very progressive dairy farmer of the time - a fascinating day out, and he later came as a guest speaker at college to the Cattle Society and he was at that time talking about wanting cattle with flat lactation curves leading to better quality milk in the early part of the lactation and fewer health and breeding problems. This he was analysing and extrapolating from the individual milk records by hand, remember we are talking over fifty years ago before the advent of computers to be able to do such things at the touch of a button. A man ahead of his time, who sadly passed away at quite a young age to be followed at Winterbourne Monkton by his son Robert, whom I got to know quite well in later years. He had not been involved with the dairy side prior to his father's early demise, having his own sheep and arable farm, but with the help and guidance of first Denis Gilbert and then Jeff Daw, he developed the Noremead herd to a pre-eminent position, being the Holstein UK Premier Pedigree Herd in 2010. Sadly, like many other leading herds, the Noremead herd is no more, having been dispersed in 2016 after Roberts' retirement, though the farming continues under one of his daughters management.

Another herd we visited at the time was the Ayrshire herd of Mr Timbrell, a leading breeder at that time, based not far from college. Many of you will know and see his son Alan officiating in judging rings at various shows, judging all breeds of dairy cows.

We had a longer trip to Richard Ecroyd up near Hereford, who at that time was one of the leading advocates of "New Zealand type" herd management, you see its nothing new and had several herds of cattle in the area run on paddock grazing systems - low yields and low costs. I remember one student asking him how he controlled the nettles and docks which were quite prevalent in the grassland and his response was that if you grazed them hard enough they would eat them!

Socially there was plenty going on whilst at college. Although we worked quite hard from a scholastic point of view compared to today when lectures now seem few and far between, we had solid lectures all day except Wednesday which was sports afternoon, and even had lectures until 11.30 or so on Saturdays. Occasionally I missed an odd lecture on Wednesday or Saturday mornings if we had a rugby match some distance away which required more travelling time. We certainly didn't live life as hermits and we would often go out for a drink later in the evening. As northerners, our regular group were rather used to a good pint of bitter at about 1s10d or 1s11d (9p) and were somewhat put out when a pint of rather watery Courage beer down there was 2s1d or 2s2d. Remember that was in the days before the breathalyser and one wonders just how sometimes we got back to college after a good night. There were also a lot of teacher training colleges at Gloucester, Cheltenham, Bath, Bristol and Hereford, they used to come by coach load to our dances at the Boutflour Hall about once a month on a Saturday night and we would often go to one or other of their regular dances nearly every Friday or Saturday, usually in Bills little red Triumph Herald with the folding roof, in summer we thought we were the business. There were a lot of pubs around at that time in the area, and food wise they were just a bit ahead of what we were used to up in Yorkshire. Unless you were going out for a proper meal at a hotel, there wasn't all the pub-grub that is available today, or takeaway food places other than fish and chips, but one or two of them were just starting to serve chicken or scampi and chips in the basket and that was about it. When it moved north a few months later, the two places I remember which were the first to offer basket meals were the Greyhound at Hackforth and the Revellers Arms at Yafforth, it was a regular Young Farmers haunt at the time, but has been built on as a housing estate now for many years.

Not having played any rugby during my pre-college work, one of the pleasures at Cirencester was picking up the game again and at a much higher level than at school. The college prided itself on its rugby prowess, and over the years had produced quite a few England Internationalists, notably John Pullin the hooker who farmed not far from Gloucester and Rutherford, a full back. They used to bring invitation teams to play against us once or twice a season, quite often with other internationals and county players included, and we could usually give them a good game and occasionally beat them, we were a team whereas they were a collection of better players not used to playing together. I think it would be much more difficult to do that now with the level of preparation, fitness and size of professional rugby players, fifty years ago, they were still all amateurs. Right from the start of that first term, training began in earnest and we used to train up to three nights a week and sometimes on a Sunday morning. Much of the time we would play two games a week Wednesday and Saturday. The Wednesday games were usually against other colleges, Seale Hayne, Harper Adams, Shuttleworth, Wye College (at the time just an agricultural college rather than a part of London University and the home of the much sought after John Nix booklets of costings - almost the bible of agricultural farm management students - I still have my college edition somewhere, I think they cost half a crown (12$^1/_2$p)) and took great delight in showing those upstart colleges who were the bosses. Royal Vet College was one of the longest trips and we also on Wednesdays used to play Army or RAF colleges or stations. Saturdays were against local club teams of all sorts, it was in the days before all the local leagues were set up, so they were of various qualities. We played Bath and Bristol and Gloucester 2nd XV's and usually beat them and travelled up to Hereford, but also played quite a few of the local teams around Gloucester. Remember at that time the southwest was very much the hot-bed and leading region for rugby in the country. There were teams that were feeder teams to Gloucester and if they developed well enough they graduated into the cherry and whites set up. Coney Hill I remember as one of them and they and some of those other local teams were real dirty "bastards", particularly in the scrum, where pretty well anything went - playing in the front row you had to get your kick in first and watch your private parts in the first scrum or two of a match, nor have a shave for a few days prior to a match, otherwise your young tender face would get pretty well roughed up by some of the old dogs who wanted to give the young whippersnappers a lesson or two.

We had one or two outstanding players in the team, Alistair Benson at scrum half and Charles Stuart at stand-off, Geof Gage in the second row who was already a Wiltshire county player, and Peter Clarke in the second or back row who eventually had to stop playing. He had a shoulder which dislocated quite easily, and when it did so he first lay out on the pitch, someone put their feet under his armpit and pulled it back in and he got up and carried on. Eventually it became so slack that it just popped in and out at will. One of the other props whom I competed with for a first team place was Robin Cowling and after a while he gave up the fight and played as a hooker. Later Robin worked on the college farm and Vic Hughes who was a passionate Welsh rugby zealot allowed him to train and play for Gloucester and eventually England as a loose head prop. One of my few regrets in life is that I didn't continue playing after college and see how far I could have progressed. Two or three years ago Robin along with Vic Hughes and Dai Barling were guests at one of our 65-67 course reunions at college. Robin is one of the key figures, I don't know exactly his title, at Exeter rugby the 2016/17 Premiership Champions.

I played little sport as I said in my two years pre-college other than the odd game of tennis and cricket on a regular basis for Galphay in what was then the Wath league, and enjoyed playing as an opening batsman and bowling the odd over spin, never with too much success but I enjoyed it.

Back at college I didn't play any cricket but did play some tennis and played in the college second VI a few times. The other sport, if you can call it a sport, which I played was snooker, and in the second year I was secretary of the college snooker society - not a particularly onerous job, though the snooker table was always in use, particularly through the winter months. I had from Middlesmoor days and through school played table tennis and continued to do so at college, more as recreation than competitively. The one remarkable memory of that was a game I played one evening before dinner with a student who was of middle eastern origin who was very good and an easy winner. He was on a different course and I didn't notice he was missing the next day, and none of us were aware until about two weeks later when police suddenly arrived and arrested him in the middle of dinner for murdering his wife. He lived somewhere in the London area, had suspected and gone home to find his wife in bed with another man, dragged her out into the street and cut her throat with his penknife. I let it be known that I had let him win our table tennis match!!

All the time I was at college I didn't take the sensible approach and work on other different farms to gain wider experience, but returned each time back to Newton-le-Willows, and just settled in with whatever was going on or needed doing, getting more and more interested in the pedigree side of the business and showing. I had a great mentor in Greg who was a master showman, having originally worked with the Strathallan Ayrshire herd up in Scotland before moving down to England some years earlier. You learnt by watching and doing, and I spent many hours holding cattle while he clipped, if your attention wandered or slackened he wasn't averse to jabbing the clippers (still running) into your hand to bring you back to the job. Many hours were spent in breaking and teaching cattle to walk on a halter and at that time we would sell up to 12 or 15 young bulls a year, and they were to exercise regularly. During one of those college holidays - Easter 1966 I was back at Dalesend, it had been a particularly early spring and all the stock were out with plenty of grass but I remember Easter Monday 11th April there was a heavy covering of snow and we went out into the fields with an old snow plough to clear grass for the heifers to be able to graze, - why do I remember that date - it was the day my niece and god-daughter Samantha was born.

While in my final year at college, George Heeley had won a scholarship with the Churchill Foundation for a study tour for six months to study low-cost milk production in New Zealand, and so I was able to help fill in some of the gaps while he was away, but also enjoyed his letters with details of his travels and experiences, particularly in a country which at that time was still very much developing its dairy industry to become one of the world's leading exponents of dairy management. It was while he was away on this trip that George was first ill and ultimately turned it out to be the beginnings of his health problems. He was back home before the Easter holidays that year and I remember helping to get the granary at the Grange all cleaned out and decorated, bar created for his 40th birthday party and the day of the party was a particularly momentous day for this whole book. Brian had given in his notice as the herdsman at Newton Grange, and earlier that birthday morning one of the men interviewed for the job, in fact I think the only one because he came on a personal recommendation was a certain Bill Faulds - later to become known as Mr Bill. Another Scotsman who had originated from the Newton Stewart area but had been a long distance lorry driver, driven for Yorkshire Henebece in his purple trousers in the early days of ready mixed concrete, before returning to his farming roots and being an under-herdsman at David Ackroyd's Nun Monkton Farms with firstly Shorthorns and later Friesians under the guidance of Joe Horner who later moved to Whitsbury Farm and Stud down in Hampshire as the Herds Manager. Ultimately Bill, Lys and their young family moved into the Bungalow at Newton Grange, before eventually moving to the Fox Park farm house when Robert was on the way and also the herdsman at that new unit was unmarried.

Robert was born after we started milking at Fox Park and I was down there one Sunday afternoon when it was to be his Christening. Frankie Suggitt was to be a godfather but rang to say he had got held up at his wife/ girlfriends and wouldn't be back in time. I had to quickly go home, get changed to be a proxy godfather.

During the spring of that final college year, plans were going ahead and building work going on in the conversion of Fox Park into a dairy unit, for another 80 cows or so. Dairy units then were nowhere near as sophisticated as they are now, the old buildings were converted into cubicle sheds (a new idea for keeping cows on self-feed silage with what was then the only design - the Newton Rigg cubicle) and a new building was made to hold the U-shaped walk round tandem parlour, four milking points and an adjoining milk house with a bulk milk tank which again was something very new in the industry at that time. I was asked if I would like to start this unit off from scratch as its herdsman which gave me the opportunity to gain further experience before moving on to more responsible management jobs after a few years - that never actually came to pass as the unfolding story will tell. Much of the initial building work had been done by the time I had finished at college and come back to work fulltime, but I was involved in the final bits and the purchasing of cattle etc.

So to the final term at college, rugby was finished with, I had in that final season led the forwards in what was described in the annual college journal "with typical Yorkshire raucous language" and been awarded full colours for rugby, it seemed to me a little unfair that the presentation was only of a signed certificate to enable you to buy one at the college outfitters in town, you had to pay for it yourself - but I was honoured to do so. Most of that final term was taken up with revision and study for the exams, and the time I really started to smoke quite heavily, something I did for another almost twenty years. One exception to the concentrated swotting was the occasion of my 21st birthday which we celebrated in great style at one of the local hostelries, and one of the few occasions I remember having far too much to drink - on that night mostly whisky- I've never been a great lover of it since!

Back to the studying and the exams and I was very happy and honoured to gain an MRAC First Class and be awarded the Haygarth Gold Medal for the best prospective farmer. The NDA exams were a national rather than a college award, and the exams for those were at Leeds University in July, I remember helping Greg with cattle at the Great Yorkshire Show and then having to leave on the first afternoon to go back home, get things and then head to Leeds for the two days of exams. Fortunately I did well enough, even in my weakest section - machinery to gain a reasonable result and my NDA. That was it - education finished and out into the outside world to earn a living.

Chapter Five – The Start of Adult Life

August 1967 signalled the start of my proper working life and I returned to Newton Grange, still lodging with George, Doris and family, and seeing to the finalisation of the buildings for the new herd at Fox Park next door. The old Dutch barn had had another one erected behind it and with sleeper walls all the way round had become the silage pit, and by then the first cut was already in and the second cut was being made. The little lean to at the end was storage for sawdust/shavings for bedding up the cubicles on a regular basis. The actual cubicle beds were filled with box manure, paddled down and then sawdust on top. This muck was to replace about twice or three times a year as the beds wore down, and it was all to manhandle into the beds and paddle down - "green" bedding which is used now in 2017 on quite a few large dairy units is acknowledged as one of the best cubicle beddings and also the re-cycling of the slurry those cows produce. Was the re-cycling of box muck in 1967 the original "green" bedding?

The milking parlours in those days were fairly basic affairs, once into the dairy the milk went into a kind of vacuum tipper before going into the tank - they were the bane of everybody's life -failing to tip and hence backing milk up the vacuum line and similarly starting to work again for no apparent reason. This unit as with all the other three farms were Vaccar installations fitted by Derek Heath, whose business at the time was just being taken over and was further developed by Tom Archibald from East Harlsey. Tom went on and developed it into quite a large and thriving business with a depot in Quaker Lane, Northallerton. At the time the Vaccar business was run by a Mr Berry who was something of a mechanical development inventor type of person who was quite happy to pump liquids all over the place by all sorts of means, but hadn't a great deal of business sense about him. The one great asset that Vaccar possessed was the quality of their milking teat-cup liners, which were recognised as some of the best in the business - a time consuming job to change them as they came in two parts and a nylon ring, but they did the job very well. Vaccar are still on the go today, no doubt owned by some other conglomerate within the dairy manufacturing industry.

With the buildings all ready for action, enough grass for a bit of autumn grazing, the next stage was to get the cows and as had become the usual source when a new herd was being started, we travelled mostly over to Lancaster to acquire more of those genuine cows. Lancaster at that time had a monthly sale for the Lancashire Friesian Breeders Club and could have up to 150 head on a regular basis. They still have regular club sales, with nowhere near those numbers and are now held at J36 Auction Mart a little further north. I had been to sales over there a couple of times with Greg when we were selling bulls, but that was at the old market, down very near the centre of town, opposite what is as far as I know still the Farmer's Arms, but just as we were buying cows for Fox Park, the new market at Golgotha had been opened - an auction mart way ahead of its times for then, with a super sales ring and tiered seating, super modern penning and general facilities and a lot of lorry and car parking facilities. The wheel goes round and interestingly Sarah has for around three years been producing the Lancaster sale catalogues.

The first cow we bought for Fox Park I remember was Andred Laura from Mr Wrathall, who proudly wore the number 1 collar at Fox Park for several years. Other early purchases were a Unice from Tarnbrook, two really good heifers from Mr Melling at Ribble, a Hyacinth was one of them. Whilst at one of those early sales we were told of a Mr Bolland who farmed not far away, and though quite a young man, was in ill health and had to disperse his Yatehouse and Yateholm herd and we bought about eight good young cows from him, one of which was Yateholm Dale Moll. At that time milk recording was done by NMR, but was a much more laborious process, which in our case was done by either Fred or Mollie Smith who were both full time recorders. Recording was monthly and as opposed to now when it is usually six weekly and then that is more or less the end of it and the details come back by computer within a few hours, in those days, each herd had a file register which contained individual cow sheets and the recorder took these away and manually calculated the additional milk over the previous month to update the records to their current status plus anything else like AI services etc and return them when completed. Fred and Mollie weren't too good at getting them back to you and were often to chase up. I first met Mollie when milking at Arbour Hill when Dick was in hospital - there were three quite steep steps out of the dairy down into the abreast parlour, Mollie didn't like them so when recording you had to take the sample for her and take it to the top of the steps and tell her how much the cow had given and which cow it was - very accurate! Fred and Mollie had no children, but Mollie in particular was a very well travelled lady and had holidayed all over the world in fairly remote places and did quite a few talks on her travels for the Women's Institutes and the like. The first time she came to record after we had bought the Yateholm cattle I said we had bought a cow specially with her in mind, to which she took great offence that a "Moll" was a loose living woman, something she had never been.

We bought cattle from other places, notably from the Ranby, Rockley and Salvin herds down on the Yorkshire / Nottinghamshire border. They were three herds close together by the A1 road, and had a regular annual or biannual draft sale, which were quite regular events in those days, and I think we bought 11 or 12 in total from milking cows down to in calf heifers. I don't think any of the three herds are still in existence, but they did us very well without ever really developing into recognised families with us. One in particular stands out for all the wrong reasons. Although the silage pit was full of silage the shed itself was incomplete and all the side cladding etc was being done in house before it got into winter. While welding some of the metal bars in place to carry the sheeting, sparks had dropped down the edge of the silage and while everyone was away at lunch it eventually got hold in the silage and was smouldering away, when I went back after lunch it had got a reasonable hold and that together with the creosoted sleepers around the wall were burning nicely producing a lot of smoke. The fire brigade were called and the water poured onto the silage didn't do it a lot of good but soon put it out and no real damage done. After ringing the fire brigade, I let all the cows out into the back field and Newton Pasture to get them out of the smoke and away from the firemen, but all was ok by milking time and the cows were gathered in and things returned to normal. It wasn't until the next day I realised I was one short and after an extensive search of Newton Pasture we found Ranby Mavis 52nd on the other side of the big ditch which ran down one side, on a very narrow strip between the gutter and the fence/hedge. She had been keen enough to cross the gutter, but took a lot of coaxing to get her down into and back out of the ditch.

The following summer was the first grazing season at Fox Park and all the paddocks were to set up ready for it. Bill and I worked together if they were two men jobs, and we helped each other putting up the electric fences, which in Bill's case at Newton Grange were already marked out from previous years, but at Fox Park were all to layout from scratch. By the time we got to putting them up in the 18 acre, the cows were already out and grazing and we were connecting up each electrified line as we completed another paddock. Bill disliked the kick of an electric fencer, and as he was rolling out wire at the far end of the field, metal reel holder in both hands, I accidently on purpose touched it across onto an already live wire. Bill suddenly shot up in the air cursing loudly much to my amusement.

The other part of grassland management at the time was a legacy of George's Churchill Scholarship to New Zealand - the taranaki gate. We had them everywhere that cows were grazing, for anyone who can't visualise them, three or four strands of barbed wire with a couple of strips of wood down them, fastened to a post at one end, and a light post on the other end fitted into a loop of wire on the bottom of the clashing post and a longer piece at the top hooked over to hold it in place and relatively tight. They were ok when fastened shut, but when open were turned back along the hedge or fence and were there for everything or body to get tangled up in - a proper gate might be more expensive but much easier to work with. I'm sure some are in use on the grazing dairy herds in this country and I know they are still in use in New Zealand - we have seen them over there - they are even more dangerous to a man when he is wearing shorts.

At a very similar time Bill had a cow calve twins, one of which was dead. Cliftonmill Ella 5th was the cow and when we went back up to the Grange one day for lunch we went to gather up said calf from the Shed field. I was driving the Fergie 20 with scraper on and Bill rode on the back, jumped off to put the calf on to bring it home, and one leg came off in his hand. Never liking anything dead or a bit ripe as this dead calf was. Bill turned tail and set off to run home at full bore, stopping to puke in the hedge back as he went, leaving me to gather up the calf and take back on my own. The knackerman of the time was Mr Varley from over Ripon way, who was a real character and I think had been used as the prototype for that character in James Herriot's "All Creatures Great and Small". In those days compared to now, it was much easier to get rid of fallen stock or animals at death's door, Mr Varley was known to call in at farms if he saw an animal near its end and offer to remove it. He was also known on occasions having been refused such a request, to sit at the end of the farm drive until the said animal did pass away. There was no such thing as passports, movement records, BCMS or requirements for ear tags in both ears as there is now, it was much easier to move animals around without all the red tape that goes with it.

Water supply in those days at the farms was not very great, a joint mains supply came from Newton-le-Willows and we were right on the end of the line, meaning pressure at certain times of the day was very poor. It wasn't too bad at Fox Park down in the hollow a bit, but up at the Grange it was bad enough in the kitchen, but often there was insufficient pressure to lift the water up to the bathroom, and very often I would have a wash and freshen up down there after milking before I went back for tea or if going out.

Back into full time life by now, the choices of recreation were more limited than they are now, and within a rural environment, the Young Farmers Movement was one of the major social activities. I had been, when at Ladybridge and Dalesend previously, been a member of Ripon Young Farmers along with Stephen Webster who was Chairman, Oriella Broadwith was Secretary and Richard Alton, David Webster and I often used to travel there together for meetings in the NFU offices next to what used to be Burton's on the corner of the market place. Although not a large club, Ripon used to have interclub nights, play cricket etc against clubs such as Bedale, and one of the highlights was preparing a float for the annual St. Wilfred's procession through Ripon which took two or three hours. It was very well supported in those days, the streets were lined with people and a lot of money was raised for charity. I remember one year being bent double for much of that time as the back half of a horse, with a young Pat English from Wath riding on my back.

Now permanently back to Newton-le-Willows, it seemed much more sensible to get involved with Bedale Young Farmers who at that time were a much larger and probably more progressive club under the leadership of Mr Wes Johnson, father of Alan of NFU fame and his brother who ran the family farm at Hackforth. We held meetings fortnightly and had about a three month break through the very busy summer season farming wise and had visiting speakers from all over locally and had visits and stock judging nights in early summer culminating in the Yorkshire rally at Harrogate. I was involved at a time with such members as Fred and Sid Craggs, Arthur Barker, Colin Thompson and within competing clubs in the area members such as Brian Phillips, Gordon Sanderson and Peter Tweddle at Northallerton. We had huge amounts of fun, learnt a lot and made lifetime friends. Apart from the regular meetings, quite a lot of time was spent through the winter preparing for Entertainments competitions or Public Speaking, Northallerton being very good at the former and one year winning the National Final, Bedale and Amotherby were good in the talking department and a joint team representing the North Riding twice made the National Finals.

One or two incidents during that time spring to mind. At a mock auction one year at Websters at Mowbray Hill, Well, Peter Robinson who was a member and a junior member of the auctioneering family who ran Pannal Auction Mart at that time, acted as the auctioneer. A pair of bullocks came into the ring to be "sold" and as if they had timed it, they both coughed at the same time and the shit from both of them hit Peter directly on the left and right breast – hilarious, as was Peter's singing of "Little Arrows" in one of the entertainment productions. Incidentally for those whose memories don't go back so far, the Robinson family lived at Leeming Bar in Leeming Garth which has for many years now been a care home for old people, and where we had to go to vote as the polling station when we first moved to Leeming Bar on our retirement.

Another incident involved a farmers son from out towards Kirklington, who was notorious for not getting his hands in his pocket when we went for a drink afterwards, which was usually to the Green Dragon at Exelby. This went on for some time, and at one meeting we all got set up to teach him a lesson. He was very good at appearing late and getting his drink when everyone had got theirs. This particular night we all got ours and when he walked in at the back, we just parted the way for him to go to the bar and told him it was his round. At least he did stand the round, but he never came to a meeting again.

We had a cricket match against Bedale, when I was still at Ripon one nice summers evening and I was having a whale of a time, being one of the few members who had ever played cricket properly and surprisingly for me had scored my first and only ever century when in desperation Kath Snaith who later married John Wilkinson was put on to bowl and did so underarm. Imagine my embarrassment when about on the third ball, it bobbled along, I had given a gigantic swing at it and missed and it had just enough energy in it to hit the wickets to bowl me!

In the late 60's, barbecues through summer were pretty well a weekly event, usually on a Friday night and run as fundraisers by all sorts of organisations including Young Conservatives who held one at Leeming Bar, the home of Sir Timothy Kitson, the local MP at that time and many of the local Young Farmers Clubs held one. So they were well attended by both young and old, and usually consisted as the name would suggest of some cooked meat, salads and a bread bun, the music was usually provided by steel bands playing on the cut to various sizes 40 gallon drums or dustbins. Great fun and a crowd of people everyone knew and mixed and drank with.

At that time, nearly all the Young Farmer's Clubs, used to have a Christmas party, to which all the other local clubs were invited, so there was a fairly hectic spell from mid-December to mid-January. Bedale usually held theirs at Hackforth Village Hall and at the Christmas party of 1967 there were two noteworthy occurrences, one of them much more important and momentous than the other. The least important of the two was when someone jumped up and pulled a streamer which was attached to the clock above the door. Village Hall clocks in those days were fairly large and cumbersome affairs, but this one came down and standing right underneath it was Granville Fairburn of Marriforth, who had a sore head but was otherwise ok. No doubt today it would have led to a long drawn out enquiry and all sorts of risk assessments needing to be done before the place could even be used for such an event.

The other much more memorable occasion, and a date I will always remember - 17th December, was the date I first met my future wife Marnie Thompson of Clapham Lodge, Londonderry. Whilst we were both active in YFC at that time and knew each other, it was the first time we had really talked or danced, and we got on well and I took her home that night - the start of up to now fifty years of happiness and a marvellous life together. We went to the big YFC dance at the Royal Hall at Harrogate that next Saturday night, and were very soon going out regularly. The very first time I took Marnie out for a meal, we went to the Chequers at Bishop Thornton which had a good name then and is still well spoken of today, though I haven't eaten there for many years. That was a night neither of us will ever forget, and often laugh about it still, particularly if we go into somewhere when it is not too busy. This particular night we were the only people in for a meal and were greeted by the head waiter, who continually changed his jacket for whichever job he was doing, wine waiter to take our order, put the chefs jacket on to cook our meal and then back into waiters attire to serve the meal. It was really hilarious and to be fair he made a good job of serving us a good meal.

Talking of eating out, and don't get the idea we did it every week or anything, we went out one night to the White Swan at Ampleforth and it is also remembered for two reasons, firstly they had the radio on because there was a big boxing match taking place - it was the night Henry Cooper sat Cassius Clay (Muhammad Ali) on his backside, though he did get back up to stop "our Enry". That night we had just started our meal when I suddenly realised I had forgotten to put money into my pocket before coming out. We were on our starters and already ordered our main courses, Marnie got her handbag out and we just had enough cash to pay for those two courses, so we told the waiter we were too full for a sweet, nor had time for coffee, and made a hasty retreat, and yes I did pay her back - in those days if you took a girl out you did the treating and no discussion about who was paying.

Another place we sometimes went to eat at for a special occasion was the Fauconberg Arms at Coxwold where many people will remember the flamboyant front of house who made everyone feel they were the most important people in the world. His brother was the head chef and his duck with black cherry sauce was fantastic, how he got the skin so crisp is a still unanswered culinary mystery. Later the two brothers started their own business at the Old Schoolroom at Birdforth on the side of the A19 between Thirsk and York, it was equally as good, sadly the front of house died suddenly at a young age, and it was never the same again.

Marnie's family welcomed me into their midst with open arms, and we had many nights there, just talking, having supper and playing rummy, something which the family still does today. Clapham Lodge had by then lost much of its land which had been taken by the Ministry of Defence and had become RAF Leeming just at the start of the second World War. Marnie was the youngest of the four children, Mollie was by then married to Len Thwaites and lived up at Barnard Castle, some will remember TT Leathers which they founded, Colin and Kathryn were twins, Colin farming with his father and doing other work off farm, and Kathryn a teacher at Miss Peel's Greenwell House private junior school at Bedale. Marnie was training at the Ag Centre at Bedale and doing Advanced Cookery and Catering Management, already doing dinner parties for people and the rest of the time helping at home. The cooking skills she had inherited from her mother who had been a regular exhibitor and winner at the many local shows of the area, - we still use the Richmond Cleaners tea pot which was a trophy at one of them even now, so as a young, single man, the good suppers were an added attraction over and above their lovely daughter.

Marnie's Dad, always said it as he saw it and I remember once his brother Fred who farmed at Ellerton, the home now of a farm shop/cafe etc, called for supper and he said to his brother "I thought I would have seen you earlier today Sid" "Where was that Fred?". At so and so's funeral replied Uncle Fred. Marnie's Dad didn't miss a beat and came straight back "I didn't rate the beggar when he was alive and I'm not going to change my mind because he's died".

Back to Young Farmers and as we continued our courtship - by this time I had become our club Chairman and Marnie the Secretary. Timing had got a bit lax under the previous Chairman and I told Marnie before my first meeting that I would pick her up in good time, she didn't drive at that time, and we would start the meeting on time. We did, smack on 7.30pm and there weren't many there and they drifted in over the next quarter of an hour, but they were all there for the start of the next one, a fortnight later. The adherence to time had already rubbed off onto me from Mr J who was a stickler for timeliness.

Another Young Farmers meeting at that time involved Bill Foggitt as the speaker, Mr Foggitt was a noted amateur weather forecaster based on observance and various things like seaweed going damp and such like, but he was every bit as accurate as official forecasts in those days or generally as they are now for all the hundreds of millions spent on computers etc by the MET Office. Mr Foggitt didn't drive and lived at Thirsk, was a well known and read regular contributor to the Darlington and Stockton Times, so he was to go and collect and bring to the meeting. When he was speaking to the meeting he picked up his glass of water, as it happened at the time talking about rainfall, and quite unintentionally missed his mouth and poured it all down his front. After a very interesting talk and supper he was to take home and whilst he kept pointing out pubs on the way, which as a staunch Methodist I was surprised about, I was more interested in getting him back to Thirsk and then taking Marnie home. As we went back he told me the story of the Rev. Newton, whom I knew of, as he had been the Methodist minister at Masham before moving to Thirsk, and his son Chris, who later became a director of I 'Anson's at Masham, was in the same class as me at Ripon. Rev. Newton at the time had an Austin 7 and wasn't the greatest of drivers. Mr Foggitt was out with Rev. and Mrs Newton for a ride one day and on a reprimand from Mrs

Newton in the rear because of his driving, came the reply from the Reverend "Woman where's your faith, you're in the hands of the Lord".

Still North Riding as a regional Young Farmers area at the time, Marnie represented them in various cookery competitions, one year she won the Cledale group domestic section single-handedly, and I competed in dairy cattle judging which brings forward another couple of stories. In those days the National Competition was a pair of competitors per club, judging two breeds of cattle one Friesian and the other one of the various other breeds. One year it was Cledale area to host the North Riding and whilst Ayrshire's were judged up the road at Messrs Potts at Craggs Lane, the black and whites were at Newton Grange. I wasn't competing that year as the hosts, the master judge was George Leggott senior of the "Cockleton" herd at Dalton-on-Tees. One of the cows in the class was Ribal Jean 3rd, a cow we had bought at Lancaster who had a terrific udder but could have had better legs. While we were having tea and cakes before the results Mr Leggott said to me he was a little bothered as nearly all the competitors had put first the cow he had put last. He himself said afterwards he was mightily relieved when we returned to the cattle for his reasons and the results when Ribal Jean 3rd was the only cow of the six which had laid down to take the weight off its feet, and Mr Leggott could not do with a cow which didn't have good legs and feet.

One other year Arthur Barker and I won for Bedale but the top ten or so competitors went all over the North Riding to practice nights or afternoons on various breeds. At a Jersey practice the trainer judge told us you must have a tea-cup handle on them - in otherwords the type of tail-head setting you really wouldn't want but was a prominent feature in the Jersey breed at that time. We both qualified to go to the Dairy Show in what I think would be its last time at Olympia, myself to do Black and Whites and Arthur the Jerseys. After his reasons, the master judge asked Arthur what this "tea-cup handle" business was - was it a North Country thing, as no one else had apparently mentioned it.

The following year we qualified again, this time Arthur, who had never milked a cow in his life, was to judge the Friesians while I was to compete in the Guernsey ring, a breed of which I knew nothing. When training up in the north, our master judge told us, you must look in the tail for a good dark pigmentation to the skin as this was indicative of high milk quality - one of the main attributes of the breed. This I put into practice down at the National Finals, only to notice none of the other competitors were bothered about the cows tails, but still mentioned it a time or two in my reasons - that must be why I finished up "highly commended" which I think was 4th.

Another bit of fun we had through YFC was competing in the "It's My Opinion" speaking competition, and Arthur and I were in the National Finals that year, the finals were held at the Welsh Agricultural College at Golden Grove near Carmarthen. On the Sunday after the event, we were coming home across country and chanced upon Lake Vyrnwy in mid-Wales, and stopped at the Lake Vyrnwy Hotel for lunch. Marnie and Anne, Arthur's future wife and we two can still remember the smell of stewed cabbage which was typical of a very old fashioned oak panelled hotel, though now is a very high-end luxury hotel and spa. After eating Arthur and I would play a trick on the girls and disappear so we jumped over the wall of the dam across the reservoir - it was only when we looked round we discovered we were on a very narrow ledge and nearly had disappeared altogether. Further home towards Shrewsbury we were having fun with the "Royal wave" as we came into the town and it was amazing the response we got from many people, thinking we were really important people. At a set of traffic lights we stopped for red and a motor bike with a "boy racer" type pulled alongside. I kept touching the accelerator and inching forward which he kept matching, and as the lights changed he wasn't going to be beaten off the mark, so really gave her some revs and the motor bike reared up and very nearly threw him off, but he was away and we never saw him again. I don't know who was the daftest, us or him.

One other factor that was developed during our active time with Bedale YFC was the beginning of the Beat Barn Dance, not that we would claim any credit for its establishment. It was conceived as the clubs main fundraiser as the days of the barbecue summer evenings began to wane. The first home for it which we found was at Malcolm Trewhitt's at Carthorpe. The first year in particular but each year after that there was quite a lot of time and effort involved for all the members to get it cleaned out after all the cattle and sheep were out after winter and to get it tidied up and decorated for the actual event towards the end of May, coinciding as it did with silage making and the end of spring outside work. The event was held on May Bank Holiday Monday at the end of the month (the early May Bank Holiday - Labour Day hadn't been thought of then) and right from the first one it was very well supported by all the other clubs and the general junior population at large. Following that success other organisations avoided that date and the event grew and grew. From the first event we also served burgers, sausages, cakes etc and ran a bar, which all contributed to the money raised on an annual event. The other main reason for its success were the live bands that were sourced to play. This culminated in a band being booked a year in advance before they had been heard of, and they just happened to hit number 1 in the Hit Parade the week before the Beat Barn Dance - the group was the Bay City Rollers. The place was inundated with fans, from all over the north, we realised what was going to happen and had organised extra security assistance over and above our own club members, and they were certainly needed as the place was almost overrun. Credit for finding that group so early must go to John Weighell, at the time one of the club's leaders, and fair do's to the Bay City Rollers, they stuck to their original contract when they could have easily broken it and demanded much higher fees. The event continued at Carthorpe after we were no longer involved with YFC before subsequently moving to Mark Sampson's farm at Well. Not many years after, Bedale YFC as a whole ran out of active members having rather chased "the green welly brigade", and went out of existence - such a pity for what had been such a hugely successful club over many years.

Enough of all this social life, we had better get back to the main job and do some farming. Back at Dalesend there had been quite a few changes - Dick had left Arbour Hill to be replaced by Roy Smith who could get large volumes of milk from his cows and was very meticulous in his herd management, but it was now a very high cost system chasing those high yields rather than the low cost system so well managed by George.

Old Park House on the side of the tank road had been recently purchased, and it wasn't long before a fifth dairy unit was planned for there. It was to be the first herringbone parlour on the farm and at that time still not a widely recognised style of parlour - how that was to change over the next 30 or 40 years until we had the advent of rotary and robot milking systems. What was even more revolutionary about Old Park House was that it was going to have the usual 70 or 80 cows on only 35 acres of grassland, with the cows being fed throughout the winter on BOCM-Silcock's Foddermatch. It really was a remarkable concept - the cows got I think it was 2kg Foddermatch in one feed per day with straw available as forage at all times and normal cake fed with milking twice a day. I inherited the system from day one and had visions of cows being ravenously hungry, but it was quite amazing. The cows had to be fed at a very regular time and we aimed at 12 noon - you could walk among the cows with a bag on your back at quarter to and they wouldn't bother you, but odd times it was unavoidable to be a bit late, and at quarter past they would nearly eat you and the bag if you went among them. A very efficient system based on the assumption that it was a very level base ration that varied barely at all - straw had little or no feed value so there could be very little variation. Whilst it didn't produce masses of yield per cow, it was highly economic on 2 cows per acre, and at that time we had plenty of straw and it wasn't worth a lot. The idea never really took off, and ultimately Foddermatch went off the market, but the concept was very attractive at the time. The herdsman who came to Old Park House to work the system was John Birkbeck, many of you will remember him later as herdsman for a lot of years for Willis Tuer at Birkby.

It was during the second year of my spell at Fox Park that George Heeley became really ill with cancer. I helped him out as best I could and acted as his understudy whilst carrying on as the herdsman at Fox Park. Ultimately the disease caught up with George and he died in September of 1969, his funeral being held on the day of the Society Heifer Show and Sale at Lancaster which at the time was a high profile event which we had always consigned to and by then was permanently at Lancaster having previously alternated between Reading and Crewe. We withdrew our entries as a mark of respect and after a short time without a manager Mr Ropner invited me to take up the position - never even bothering to advertise it or seek anyone else. At the young age of 23 it was a daunting prospect but one which I was happy to accept. In all honesty if George hadn't passed away so young, I would probably only have stayed there another year or two before moving on to another under manager or such role to gain further experience, but that is just how things happen. Right from day one I had huge support from all the staff the majority of which were considerably older than me, except one who was somewhat aggrieved at a youngster doing the job and tried for a week or two to undermine me and cause trouble until the other senior men took him aside one day and gave him a real good talking to and he accepted the inevitable.

Soon after taking over we had to go to see the accountants before the year end, as at that time Mr J was paying 95p in the pound tax. Dennis Courtney of Thomson McLintock, before it became part of KPMG opened by saying we needed to buy two new tractors before the year end to which I told him it was a funny way of going on when we were losing money. I don't think as a senior figure he had ever been spoken to like that, and we became firm friends and used to meet up a couple of times a year, once at Lilac time when I took him some right up until his death in April 2020.

With being appointed to manage the farms, my days of being a full time herdsman were over, so one of the first jobs was to find a replacement for Fox Park. Eventually after several interviews Mr J and I travelled up to Northumberland to Eshott to see Archie McDonald and his family. Archie had started life as a jockey cum stable lad and a fall had ended that career and left him with a limp, but that did not deter us from taking him on and he moved down to live in the bungalow at Newton Grange as Bill was well established in Fox Park farm house. The one abiding memory I have of Archie was his love of Fox's Glacier Mints - he didn't just suck them and make them last, he could, despite his false teeth "crunch" them at an alarming rate, and if you went to find him at Fox Park all you had to do was follow the trail of their blue and white wrappers and you soon found him.

So that was the full complement of five herdsmen, and they all stayed with us until the major reduction sale five years later when we went down to one herd. With five herds with the addition of Old Park House, and even before that, the farm had employed Frankie Suggitt as a full time relief milker. Each of the herdsmen had one day off a week, moving forward one day each week until it got to the weekend when they had both Saturday and Sunday off. It worked very well and everyone fitted into the system and there was flexibility if they needed a different specific day off they could swap with another as long as they let Frankie know. At that time the shortening of working hours and the increase in holiday entitlements, meant that we almost needed a second relief man to cover five plus Frankie and include holidays and any sickness - Mike Miles filled that role and also did some work at Dalesend as well - it by that time had more buildings for the increasing numbers of young stock. Calves were now reared in the old stone buildings which had been altered inside, together with the open-fronted Solari boxes along the top which took six or eight older calves and weanlings and a large Crendon loose housed barn had been erected, and soon afterwards we put up the large AtCost building which housed two silage pits and two double rows of cubicles for heifers, with a handling race down one side and outside feeding area on both sides together with a muck holding area across the end, and two isolation boxes as were then required on all farms to be brucellosis accredited. Mike's father Eric was the licensee of The Wheatsheaf in Newton-le-Willows, which is still there, but not been a pub for fifteen years or so and in a desperate state of repair - a real eyesore in the centre of the village, but at that time became the farm's regular watering hole if we had a meeting or such like, and later when Mr Bush was the landlord we always had our farm Christmas lunch there, and some of the best steak I have eaten anywhere in the world. Mike lived in one of the little cottages at Akebar, right on the roadside at the back of what is now the very popular Friars Head pub and restaurant. Mike later was fixed up with a job by Mr J to fulfil his wish to go to Canada and was first with Mr Fred Stewart at the Stewarthaven herd near Niagara and then for several years was herdsman for Gordie Atkinson at Meadolake Farms. Ultimately he returned to England and must have inherited the trait from his father becoming manager or tenant of The White Rose at Leeming Bar, then a spell at the Old Royal George at Morton-on-Swale and for some years ran The Greyhound at Hackforth.

Frankie was a trained and qualified joiner, but he decided he preferred working with cattle rather than wood. His parents lived at Newton-le-Willows at what was popularly known as Suggitts Corner where they had a couple of petrol pumps one of which was hand cranked, and from where Mr Suggitt operated as an electrician. Apart from the fuel, they also sold cigarettes and I, plus the farm and many others ran an account there. Mr Suggitt wasn't very good at sending out his bills and every so often we had to insist on paying for a couple of months fuel and I paid regularly for my cigarettes, but many didn't and when Mr Suggitt died, they said some people were on their third cooker and hadn't paid for the first two. The other son John who was also an electrician with NEEB tried to work out the backlog of bills both for fuel and electrical work done by his father, we paid our bill knowing it would be well on the right side, but many didn't. If Mr Suggitt did some electrical work you just needed to tell him what you wanted doing and get out of the way for he loved to draw complicated diagrams on the back of any old bit of paper and go into long explanations of exactly what he was going to do. The other thing I remember which for an electrician I found highly amusing was that the catch was broken on Mrs Suggitts cooker door and it was propped shut with an especially sawn length of wood, which had been in use for so long that it was polished smooth. Frankie was very good at moving round the farms on a regular basis, and if one of the cowmen was on holiday he would milk there for the full length of the holiday and became very protective of his herd. I remember one time he was doing a holiday spell at Arbour Hill when we were doing silage up there and unfortunately the cows were shut out one day and couldn't get any water which, together with the trailers rattling, and in Frankies view disturbing the cows, I caught him attacking a trailer with a big hammer hoping it might take note! When he had spare time, Frankie did some joinery work on the side, he made us a great set of fitted cupboards in the spare room at Newton Grange, and also fitted out two mini-vans with insulation and plywood to be the first delivery vehicles for a fledgling company the Guv'nor had just started from its first small factory in Aiskew, Dalepak Foods, which has just been sold and I suspect will be replaced by houses.

Frankie had initially no cattle knowledge and he came running to the kitchen window one day, "George, George, so and so has just calved and the calf has no top teeth". "Oh" said George, "I'll ring the vet after lunch and order a set then", and carried on with his lunch and Frankie went away quite happily.

Now in charge of the whole farm, I had to get more involved with the arable, cropping side of the business, which Bob Husband had kept going admirably during George's illness. Staffing was much greater in those days, smaller machines and still a lot of physical work involved. Bob was assisted on the tractor side by two fairly young lads, both called Ian. Fortunately one was blond and the other black haired, and so they were referred to as "Black Ian" and "White Ian" which no doubt today would be totally politically incorrect. While George was still in charge he caught them one day when mucking out the fold yards at Arbour Hill, when both a fore end and rear muck loader were in use to fill the spreaders stood outside. White Ian hid outside until Black Ian came out and with his loader down got him amid-ships and lifted the tractor off the ground. Not the best of things to do when the manager was about and both got a severe bollocking and a final warning as to their future behaviour. Sometime later after George's passing, we were picking stones the following spring. Stone picking in those days was a major job that everyone did in spring usually before the field was rolled, either spring barley or winter wheat, - in those times no one thought of rolling winter corn in the autumn, you left a rough finish to give the plants some protection against the weather. The land at Arbour Hill, Old Park House and Home Farm was very stony and it was a slow and tedious job, not too bad when there were quite a few of you and fairish of banter going on. Back then, many times the tractor would be set going in the lowest possible gear and the driver got off as well to pick stones too - you wouldn't want to risk that nowadays, but help is at hand as we move into the age of driverless vehicles which are now being tested on public roads. Bob was a master at not picking the big ones - we always carried a sack on top of the tractor to roll a large stone onto and then two could lift it onto the trailer, but Bob would say to the young Ian's when a big one was nearby "now don't you lads lift that on your own, you'll strain something and finish up with a hernia, wait while I get the sack " by which time one or other of the ultra competitive lads had already done so on his own. The next time a large stone was to do, the other Ian wouldn't be out done and so repeated the job while Bob got his sack from the front. The two Ian's didn't last very long after that and we had one or two other young men to help on the tractor side, both of whom were really good men - two in particular spring to mind - again people whom many of you in the area will either know or recognise the names - John Thislethwaite and Dick Towler. John was a farmers son from near Leyburn and was a particularly good mechanic and engineer but also did a lot of tractor work; his particular forte being buck raking at silage time - not as it is now pushing it up with a great big extending boom on a JCB, but with a rear mounted buck rake on the tractor hydraulics and a handle to pull to tip it. John could keep any amount of trailers going all day, without any problem and was inarguably the best man I have ever seen operating on a silage pit. Dick on the other hand was probably the worst - he was a very good worker and tractor man but liked to do things at his own pace, and if he was stopped at any time by such as a bent tine, he made sure the trailers stopped tipping while he changed it, and didn't step up a gear when he got it mended to clear the backlog. They were both good engineers and at that time as the cow housing moved from straw yards to cubicles made all the cubicles and gates and pretty well anything else that needed making. After a few years John left to set up his own business and ultimately Dick went to work with him and they did much of the local repair work in the area on agricultural machinery, made stock equipment and at the time ran three or four combines at harvest time. Ultimately John will perhaps be best remembered for his development of one of the first roll-over JT cattle crushes, both a mobile version such as the ones engineered for the well known foot trimmer Norman Walker and the more widely used static model which are in operation on many larger dairy units not only in the area but around the country. John also developed one of the early bale squeezers for handling and stacking big round bales of either straw, hay or silage in particular which had by then become very widely used rather than hay making with small bales.

Just about at that time 1971 or 1972, or perhaps even before then, we had the opportunity to buy Thornton Grange up the hill a bit towards Finghall. Some of the land was grassland unsuitable for cropping which made ideal summering land for the ever increasing numbers of heifers we had about and the rest was reasonable arable land - there was a good continuous drier there which we moved down to Newton Grange to replace the old tray system that had originally come from an old ICI grass-drying plant when it was de-commissioned. We bought Thornton Grange knowing full well it was scheduled to have a reservoir constructed on it by Yorkshire Water. When it came to the deal with them we had George Darwin representing us. Many of you will remember Mr Darwin from the estate agency they operated from and alongside the Dales Furniture Salesroom on the Bridge at Bedale, a big, bluff man who could "bluster" when he needed to. The meeting was in the farm office, Mr J, George Darwin, myself and two little men from Yorkshire Water. After a few opening gambits before we got to business, Mr Darwin very soon cut to the chase and asked for some indication of the sort of price they were prepared to pay. When the two men suggested a lowish figure, Mr Darwin just slammed shut his folder, put it in his briefcase, stood up and told them he was too busy a man to have his time wasted and shot out of the office towards his car, with the two little men running after him imploring him to return to the table. He put on a good act and they eventually persuaded him to return, but by then he had them just where he wanted them and a good deal was done. We continued to farm the land until they required it, plus take the surrounding parts for another year or two. The land which we retained on the other side of the road we sold to Mr Carlisle who had recently moved over from the Craven area to farm Thornton Lodge, and he subsequently acquired the excess land after Yorkshire Water had got the reservoir completed and some of the outlying fields were surplus to requirements. The reservoir was to service Northallerton and we had further benefits from the scheme some years later as will no doubt come up in later chapters.

One other story at that time features two particular cows Uphall Jessie 8th and Uphall Marigold 17. Mr J was great friends with Jim Alston of Diss in Norfolk and his

Uphall herd. When he was having one of his early draft sales he went to support him and bought two in calf heifers. Uphall Jessie 8 went to Home Farm and under Alan's management developed into a very good cow and ultimately was contract mated by John Mattley for the MMB for a bull calf. He hadn't noticed, and for a long time neither had we, until after the contract was signed that she had an almost black tail. At that time, strange as it may seem today, cows had to have four white socks on their legs so far above the hoof and required a certain length of white skin on the bone before the switch in the tail. I remember organising to get some "dry-ice" which was used in freeze branding from ICI at Billingham and we spent an endless amount of time trying to turn the black skin on her tail white, all to no avail, and in the fullness of time it didn't matter as she had a heifer calf and she wasn't re-contracted. She was the start of our very successful Jessie family which was one of the larger families when we dispersed, as were the Marigolds that all descended from Uphall Marigold 17. When she calved as a heifer and for every year afterwards, she was a real handful, could kick like a mule and wasn't good to milk. Eventually we got her calmed down, but only Bill or I could or would milk her, and even then it was a bit hairy on any occasion when she was slightly upset or someone made any noise. If it was Bill's weekend off, whoever was milking for him had to come and get me, and if I was away or at one of the other farms, harvesting or the like, she simply didn't get milked. She bred an outstanding Linmack daughter D. Mac Marigold who really developed the family, though she was a character in her own right - the parlour at the Grange was a tandem and she always had to be the last cow in . and only into the back stall on one side, even if the other five were empty. That was obviously a bit longer stall though not obviously so, because as soon as we went into the new herringbone in 1986, when a fairly old cow, she immediately would come into either side in any position, and after that as far as I can remember the Marigolds were no further problem from a temperament point of view.

Marnie and I had got engaged just before Christmas 1970 and were moving toward getting married in the summer of 1972, but this chapter finishes at the end of 1971.

Chapter Six – From Memory to Reality

Up until this point the book has all been written from memory of those first $25^1/_2$ years of my life, as far as I know I have remembered accurately and honestly without any poetic licence, but all that changes from now on, and it is factually correct, virtually all drawn from the page a day diary I have kept since 1972 right up to the present day, and so it was written down at the time it occurred. That is not quite true, because the first year I only managed to keep up the routine for the first five months or so, running out of time and the discipline it takes just before we got married and the rest of the year obviously flashed past in newly wedded bliss.

Throughout the years, the diary at times got a little behind at such as harvest time, holidays or other odd times, but generally I used to try and write it just before we ate in an evening, and since retirement I usually write it before breakfast for the previous day, with a comment on the weather at the beginning of that day. As I wrote in the foreword the diaries have recorded many events and occurrences, both public and private to do with farming and our personal lives, and over the years has resolved numerous family arguments over all manner of things even though sometimes the facts are not always accepted. The best example of this came in the early 90's, when one Mother's Day we went in the afternoon to visit Marnie's Mother (Muv). She immediately asked where we had been out for lunch to which we replied nowhere, we never go out on Mother's Day, we may go the weekend before or after, but not on the actual day when it might be half as much again for a limited menu. Muv wouldn't accept this as she believed we always went out for lunch on Mother's Day, so when we got back home I got out the old diaries and went back through 17 years, to find that it was either two or three occasions we had been out for lunch, but every time it had been for a reason other than because it was Mother's day. Next time I saw Muv I told her the facts which she still refused to accept and I retorted that I had obviously been falsifying my diaries for the previous 17 years just so it was ready for her asking the question. She never did accept the facts.

Doris and family had remained at the Grange after George's death with me not wanting the house at that time, and I continued to lodge there with them, and Mr and Mrs Gaines, who were retired lived in the bungalow. They had originally had the second shop in Newton-le-Willows, up the main street and which had just closed before I first came to Dalesend. At that time it also had a post office further up the village - a sign of the times and how shopping habits and rural lives have changed over the years, it no longer has any shop or post office, pub or school, though it does still have an active village hall, but both its Chapels are also now houses. Mrs Gaines was a marvellous cook and produced all kinds of great cakes and the like, but one particular time, for some unknown reason they were as solid as a rock having barely risen. She often went with Doris to visit Andrew who was in a special needs home at Easingwold. One of his great loves was to go and feed the ducks and Mrs Gaines disposed of the cake - rumour has it some of them were never seen again and the term "duck sinker" was coined and passed into more common usage! The Gaines' had to move out of the bungalow when Archie took my job as herdsman at Fox Park and they went to live in one of the Houses at Home Farm.

With me getting married in the summer of 1972, Doris, Michael and Anne moved in April to Northallerton, where they lived in South Parade. Michael eventually moving South having a high powered job with Marley the tile people and Anne subsequently living in South Yorkshire. She was always mad about horses and no doubt will still have some involvement with them.

That left about two months in which to get the house re-decorated before our wedding at a time which also coincided with Marnie's parents moving from Clapham Lodge to Field House, Londonderry, and her brother Colin going to Norway for at least a year to work on an Agricultural Research Farm near Bryne. There had been YFC exchange visits between a group from that area of Norway to Cledale area Young Farmers, with the members staying with families, two having stayed at Clapham Lodge, and Colin went off to Norway in mid-April, on condition from Marnie that he came back to be a groomsman at our wedding.

It was during this period of getting the house ready that I set out one day to cut the farm lawns. You may remember me earlier telling you about planting daffodils with George. He loved daffodils, but wasn't interested in them once the flowers had gone, and couldn't do with all the untidiness of the dead flowers and leaves and so cut them all off straight away. I had done most of the lawn mowing the previous couple of years when George was unwell and after his death, so carried on as he had taught me. As soon as I started to chop them off there was a lot of shouting to tell me to stop as that would rid the yard of daffodils in a few years - it was something I didn't know anything about, but took the word of Marnie, and her Mother who was a very good gardener. This was the start of a long running saga about the daffodils which carried on for the next 40 years or so. The following year when they flowered, I counted the blooms and there were about 300 or so. I counted them every year after that, moved some bulbs about when they got very thick in bunches, but no more bulbs were bought or planted so it was a true multiplication exercise, - they peaked in 2004 with 6769 blooms, and the final year before the farm sale had the second highest total with 6622. I used to count them over a few days, so many days after the first flower came into bloom, and did it in sections, usually at night, though occasionally it might be during the day. All the men on the farm used to take the "mickey" out of me, and once or twice I was caught doing it by unexpected visitors who wondered what was going on. I was doing so on one occasion when a sales rep came unannounced into the yard and as I didn't particularly want to see him kept my head down and carried on. He wasn't going to be deterred and returned a day or two later and told me he had called earlier and the only person he had seen was someone in the lawn who appeared to be counting flowers. I replied by telling him I knew who that would be and to take no notice, he just had a screw loose. It just went to show that allowing them to die back fully really does preserve them, and we had them down part of the drive side, out on the roadside at the drive end and at their best they were a terrific sight. I usually try and have a ride up into the yard when passing at that time of year, they have got back to being chopped off rather earlier, and the numbers have declined quite markedly in just four or five years.

In looking back in the diary for early 1972 it is interesting to note that I sold some feed wheat at £23.75 per ton, we bought some hay from Peter Knox at £11 per ton, and we bought a new 6 tonne Salop corn trailer with silage side extensions for £490. I also note that spring that we had to get one or two jobs finished and the claims submitted, particularly the completed dairy unit at Old Park House by 18th March before the grant rate dropped from 40% to 30%. We also got all our years fertiliser for the following year, which in those days was still in 1 cwt bags to handle manually, before 31st May because the subsidy on it fell on 1st June, but I don't have a note, nor can I remember how much it was at that time, though I believe it would be paid to the manufacturer rather than the farmer.

Believe it or not in this day and age, but back then there was, under FHDS schemes, a grant on new machinery and tractors, and I remember claiming the 25% grant on a MF65 which cost just under £1000. Oh, how you wish you could buy a bit of a tractor for that sort of money today!!

Spring of 1972 was also a very interesting spell as it was the time we had regular power cuts to save usage. There had been a lot of trades union action at that time, coal stocks were low and the supply of electricity was in danger of being insufficient nationally and we went through a spell where areas would have cuts for three hours at various times of day and from a dairy point of view it meant we had to move milking times about a bit to make sure we got done either side of these cuts which could be morning, afternoon or evening. It was a good job you were informed a week or so in advance of the timings so you could plan and we got through it without too much problem. I remember us going to Newcastle with Arthur and Anne to see the Russian Red Army Singers and Dancers at the theatre and seeing sections of the city in total darkness and others with lights, all in straight lines up the streets, it was quite an amazing sight and really brought home to you the problems it could potentially cause, and fortunately we have moved on a long way in labour relations since that day - though you never know, they could return.

During 1971 we had founded Herdwise, the AI company. Mr J had always had a dream to start such a company and had been dissuaded by George from doing so, but sensing that I was a little more pedigree orientated compared to George's more commercial aspect, he felt he might be able to convince me of its viability. I did initial budgets and cash flows for him which clearly showed it would take considerable capital and a fair length of time to do so. That wasn't enough to dampen his entrepreneurial spirit and the firm was established with David Ropner and Frank Carr as the other directors. David Ropner lived in London and was at that time Chairman of Ropner Holdings which was a quoted company and Frank Carr had been very high up in the management of Taylor Woodrow Northern, the building company. Most of the meetings were held up here and unless David Ropner was up here, I acted on his behalf before I became a director in my own right. Ultimately when the company became larger I chaired the bull selection committee and travelled extensively in this country, Europe and Canada. At this stage as a fledgling company it had one employee, Malcolm Peasnall and in early 1972 appointed a second one in Trevor Warren. At that time the private AI sector was dominated by CBS and SFS, who both had several of the leading breeders involved with them. On forming Herdwise, Mr J was asked by one of them why he thought "a piddling little AI company with one breeder of a second rate herd could succeed", I don't know what the answer was, but 24 years later when Herdwise was sold as a going concern it was the leading private AI company in the UK, and those other two no longer existed!

During the spring of 72 Marnie and I had to get organised for the wedding which meant seeing about getting Banns read etc. We had decided to get married at Hornby Church because that was where Marnie's parents were married, rather than her parish of Leeming. In those days you should need a residency in the parish in which you married, when we went to meet Cannon Crawford, referred to earlier when his son taught me geography, I remember him saying to Marnie - oh just throw a suitcase into your Grandmothers at Hackforth and pretend you are living there and that'll be ok. The other bit of advice was with regard to the actual church service - don't choose any airy-fairy hymns that no one has ever heard before - choose ones everyone knows and can have a good sing to.

We also had to see the vicar at Leeming - Rev. Davis, who insisted both with that first visit about the Banns and when we went to collect them that we went to the morning service and would see him afterwards. He was a strange vicar, with some Caribbean connections, but hadn't much of a following at Leeming and by insisting that he would see us immediately after morning prayer his congregation was increased from three to five. The other bit of church business was me being confirmed at Ripon Cathedral in mid-May.

That spring in 1972 was rather a sad time among all the happiness as we headed towards our wedding. Marnie's two Aunts and Grandmother were badly injured in a road accident and sadly Nanny didn't survive and died the day after, Colin sailed for Norway, Nobby the young lad who worked for me, of whom more later, lost his father suddenly, and at the same time Robert's wife also passed away suddenly. Just a few weeks before that, Robert was telling me one day that he and Mrs Husband were having a bit of trouble with their daughter Anne who had just finished school and was kicking over the traces a bit and beginning to be late coming in at night. Mrs Husband told Bob he would have to talk to her and put his foot down as she had not come in until 11 o'clock the night before. I asked Bob the next day how he had come on and he said it was no problem - when Mrs Husband asked him what he had said and if he had put his foot down he said that when he spoke to her he was sat cross-legged in the chair so he uncrossed them and put his foot down onto the floor. I can just imagine the response that explanation drew from Mrs Husband who could be a bit sharp at the best of times! While Robert was off work for a week or two, the young lad stepped up to the plate and finished drilling all the spring barley, fortunately Robert had shown him the ropes around the corn drill just a few days before - Adrian Clarke.

Adrian like nearly all Clarkes was called 'Nobby' I don't really know why, but he was no exception. The only exception I know of was the one in the same class at senior school who was nicknamed 'Bungalow' because he had nothing up top. Nobby came to work for me straight from school, coming to work on his little motorbike from Bellerby where his parents had the shop and Post Office. He was a very good worker and had a very quick wit and an answer for almost anything. Three particular humorous memories remain of Nobby. The first was one spring day when he had been helping me to do something in the pouring rain and we had got absolutely soaked. Taking pity on him I asked him in to have his lunch by the old Rayburn so that he could dry out. I was going to a grassland society meeting in the afternoon, gulped a very quick lunch and shot upstairs to get changed and was back down in a very short time. As I entered the kitchen Nobby just looked up at me and said "Have you seen Bernard anywhere, I think he's looking for you." Another time we were silaging at Arbour Hill down in East Park North when we had a breakdown right over the far side beside the stream, over which stands Hornby Castle. As Bob, Nobby and I were mending, I think a chain of the Kidd double chop forager (we used to do our own in those days) there was quite a bit of banter going on and Nobby said if I wasn't careful he would throw me in the stream. He was only a little, slight lad and I was a fairly big strong young man, he thought I had ignored his threat until with one movement I just scooped him up and threw him into the stream where he just sat and shook his head, it was a good hot, sunny day and so he soon dried out.

The best bit of fun was one day we were silaging at Fox Park and I had gone down to check how they were getting on just before lunch. Nobby was driving one of the trailers and the pit was getting fairly full with still a few acres to go in and he asked me how we were going to get it all in. Fortunately I had a big spanner in my hand at the time and said that's what I was doing, I had been undoing the big bolts at the top of the posts and the helicopter was booked for that afternoon to lift the roof off by the big ring in the centre of it, had he never noticed it. Nobby set off back down to the 18 acre for the last load before lunch, as soon as he got alongside the forager, Bob got off and I saw them looking back up at the buildings and a lot of arms being waved about. They got the load picked up and came back up for lunch. Bob riding on the trailer drawbar as you used to in those days and Nobby tipped the load and came back round to close the back door, Bob said what's this lad on about with bolts and helicopters? I winked at him and explained about it coming in the afternoon to lift the roof off, Bob immediately picked up the leg-pull and said "oh I thought he wasn't coming until tomorrow morning". Nothing more was said and then about two or three weeks later, it suddenly dawned on Nobby that nothing had ever happened and he said "That helicopter never did come, you B*******, you were just winding me up," and we had a real good laugh about it.

Nobby stayed for quite a few years, and left suddenly after we had an assistant manager for a short while and we were away on holiday. I never did find out why and Nobby would never tell me, so I don't know what happened. He went to work up at the Wensleydale Creamery at Hawes where his brother already worked and who is still there as head cheese maker. Sadly, Nobby soon after was diagnosed with multiple sclerosis and didn't survive for very long after that, such a tragic loss of a very bright young life. A similar fate awaited Kevin Smith, Roy from Arbour Hill's son who was still at school at that time, helped with some tractor work in holidays and weekends. Arbour Hill lane was nearly a mile long and Kevin had an old banger of a black car that he used to drive to the lane end to get the school bus, which he could handle at quite a speed and I had one or two near meetings with him up that lane.

There were two other events on that lane which are worth mentioning. The first one was with an AI man, at the time this was before DIY AI was allowed, and they always travelled at a good speed as they had a lot of visits to make in those days. I met him one day on the narrow lane where there was no side to get onto - we saw each other in time, but under braking on a gravel/stone road we just slid into each other in slow motion and had a slight bump which dented both cars but no great damage to man or vehicle was done. Another time Roy rang to ask for some help with a calving - it was a Monday afternoon and the hunt were out up in the area and in those days had a large following with vehicles as well as up to 80 or 100 on horseback. As I got to the cattle grid into the final field up to the yard, my way was blocked by vehicles, most of which had been abandoned and there was just an odd person stood looking across to Cuckoo Hills. I asked him to move two vehicles and he said he couldn't - didn't I realise it was the hunt and was of great importance that the followers were out. I told him it was of great importance they moved off our roadway as I had to go to a calving emergency and if he didn't do so I would just barge them out of the way with the Landrover which we ran at the time. Needless to say people left keys in vehicles in those days and he soon got them moved and a live calf resulted. Up the side of the lane up to Arbour Hill was one of the larger fields we had, Park Hills, again the hunt were out one very wet day amid a wet spell, when they really shouldn't have been, and 80 plus horses came round the edge of Park Hills making quite a mess on the autumn sown winter wheat. I complained to the hunt and the secretary at the time. Mr Henderson came out a few days later to inspect the mess and admitted it wasn't good. We agreed that if it showed up at harvest time and yield was affected they would pay some compensation, but I had to admit that by then you couldn't see where they had been.

So back to personal matters and it was wedding time. In those days people didn't have all the stag nights/weekends that they tend to do now, and in a lot of cases the ladies didn't have anything. We had a bit of a drink one night at The Buck Inn at Thornton Watlass and that was it. Wedding day was 17th June 1972, with Arthur as my best man, Colin and Michael Heeley as Groomsmen, Kathryn was Marnie's bridesmaid with Emma and Samantha as little ones. After the wedding at Hornby, the reception was at Motel Leeming and a great time was had by all before we went off on honeymoon, at that time it was unusual to also have an evening 'do'. Not because I want to detail the costs, readers will find it fascinating to know what sort of costs were incurred in those days at a wedding. All the flowers which included the buttonholes, two posies, bridesmaid and brides bouquets were from Braithwaites at Leeming Bar and came to £10.64 and the hire of two wedding cars from T Smirthwaite Ltd of Northallerton cost the astronomical sum of £12.14. We went to Scotland for our honeymoon, spending the first two nights at the Trust House Hotels - The Tontine at Peebles, dinner, bed and breakfast for two nights totalled £24.51 including a 10% service charge. I still have those accounts in the bureau, so those prices are inarguable, along with many others I have kept over the years, and which make fascinating reading.

We were planning to travel round Scotland - I had at the time a farm car provided, a Marina which was supposedly the British car to really save BMC from all their industrial problems, it was alright when we were away but I have to say was the worst car we have ever had, and no wonder the British motor industry went into meltdown from which it has never recovered. We said we would keep travelling until the weather took up when we would stay for a few days, it never really did and we got right round and back to Edinburgh for the last couple of nights. We went from Peebles across to Dundee, around Edinburgh on what was then the first day of the Royal Highland Show and all the traffic it had even 45 years ago, a couple of nights in Dundee and then up the East coast, staying at Macduff one night, Aberdeen, Inverness and then to Thursoe. We went the next day to John O' Groats when we were up so near to it, must have been about 26th June or so, and it snowed while we were there. Across the top of Scotland we stayed at Gairloch one night and ate at the famous "Baillie Nicole Garvie" restaurant where we were amazed to see an American on the next table eating his steak. He cut it into pieces, put each into his mouth gave it one quick chew and took it out onto the side of his plate, when he had got that done he proceeded to go round it all again for a second chew! We stayed in Oban over a weekend when the weather was a bit better but then came across and into the Trossachs and stayed in Callander, famous at the time for the television series Dr Finlay's Casebook. It was thick fog and heavy rain in the Trossachs so we only stayed one night and finished up for the last two or three days in Edinburgh, and walked miles, including The Royal Mile. As we made our way back home, we stopped for a meal in the Fir Tree Arms at Crook which was well known at the time, we really pushed the boat out for our last meal while away, Sunday lunch - two starters, two roast main courses, two sweets and two coffees all for £2.84.

And so back to home and reality.

Marnie didn't drive at the time and so was rather stuck at the Grange, two and a half miles from Bedale or a mile from either Newton or Crakehall shops, so she set about learning, and it was good practice to go into a silage field rowed up ready for collection to be able to use the rows as roads, with junctions at the end, but it wasn't until July 1974 that she drove on the road for the first time, down to Fieldhouse and back and after six lessons passed her test first time at the end of September that year.

I don't remember anything much happening during the latter part of 1972, other than in the autumn, Mr J's good friend Jim Alston was going to Canada to buy two or three bulls and asked if Dalesend would like to be involved. With the recent beginnings of Herdwise, the chance to prove them properly was irresistible and he bought one bull just for himself and two to be owned jointly. In those days, a young bull had to be brought into the country and re-named and tested and isolated for a considerable time before the semen could be collected. One bull was very expensive from a very good line and so took the Uphall prefix and the other was the make weight to cheapen the whole deal but from a family with oceans of milk, so he took the Dalesend prefix. That young bull arrived on the 23rd January 1973 by the name of Hyways Star and became Dalesend Cascade. By the way, the night before had been the Yorkshire Milk Records awards dinner at York, Mr and Mrs J went separately as he was going to be away very early the next morning to Prestwick to collect the bull, and as he was leaving asked if I could lend him some money as he had no cash and in case he needed fuel. I gladly lent him some, probably £20 or so and come to think of it, I don't think I ever got it back, not that I'm too worried about that.

Talking of cash and petrol, it was about the same time that Mr J came up to the office one late afternoon and said he had had a very close shave earlier. Thinking he meant he had almost had a bad accident I asked what had happened. At the time the car he used was provided for him by Raisby Quarries up in Durham of which he was Chairman and when he went up for a Board Meeting he would get it serviced. This particular day they gave him an old mini to go from the garage the couple of miles to his meeting and when he set off the fuel indicator was banging on zero. Fearing he may run out, he shot into a garage as he passed, pulled up at the pump and realised he hadn't a lot of cash on him. A quick scratch about in his pockets rendered a few pence and he had a quick calculation, remember back then fuel was only about 15 pence a gallon. When the young man came out to fill him up, he was rather taken aback when Mr J said "can I have a pint of petrol please", but he did oblige. I said he was lucky as if it had been an ordinary person, the young man would have told him to "F-off". But he was quite chuffed with his bargain purchase and it got him there and back without any trouble.

Talking of Raisby, another little cameo comes to mind regarding Mr David Ropner who was also a director there and used to come up and stay overnight at Dalesend before the meeting. One day he came with Mr J up to the office so he could check the mail before heading north. At that time in the days when everyone used to be paid weekly in cash, they used to do our wages for us and send them down by registered post on a Friday. If there was any overtime I used to ring it through to Libby, the wages clerk, and send a confirmatory note by post. This particular morning while Mr J was looking through his post, I was talking with Mr David when he spied an envelope addressed to Libby waiting to go to the post, and without saying a word, got out his little silver pocket knife, slit it open and took out the note, telling me he would hand it over when he got to Raisby, and a little bit of sellotape would mean the stamp could be used again. I realised that was why he had a silver penknife and mine was a Sam Turner's best - at that time they used to give good customers one every so often.

Back to Dalesend Cascade - he came into one of the bullpens at the Grange for Bill to look after, he was a big, lean, black bull and quickly became leaner as he wouldn't eat. The first few days we just thought that was a change of diet, but soon realised it was more than that and a vet visit confirmed a twisted gut - displaced abomasum, no doubt brought on by his travel from Canada. In those days, operations for a displacement weren't done and it was down to rolling them which we had to do two or three times before it eventually stayed where it was supposed to be and he went on from there to be ok. Eventually when these two bulls came back with their first proofs it was Dalesend Cascade who came out with the good figures for both type and production, while the expensive Uphall Reflection Perseus fell well short of expectations on both milk and type. Cascade was one of the early proven Canadian Holstein bulls when the first cross onto the traditional British Friesian became very popular, so you got the instant lift in milk yield and almost "hybrid vigour" from the two entirely different types of animal. Cascade went on to be one of the leading bulls of his generation and was the bull which probably set Herdwise on its way to a pre-eminent position within the AI industry. It is amazing even now some 40 plus years later that people still remember him and ask after him, and it was only in 2010 or 11 when I was in Northern Ireland as Society President that someone had just had a heifer calf by him, and a son was sold at quite a good price.

At another milk records dinner a year or two after, Greg and Bett went with us to the event and while we were having a drink before the meal, another local breeder came in and came to join us. He was a rather strait-laced Methodist and Greg asked him if he would like a drink - no thank you we don't drink. In those days people still smoked quite openly inside at such events. Would he like a cigarette asked Greg - "no we don't smoke" came the reply. Greg's immediate response with a twinkle and a wink in his eye "how many children did you say you have?" to which he got a frosty "two".

Although I kept a diary through 1973, there was not that many things of note happening and it was a very busy year of fairly mundane jobs. Many younger pedigree breeders of today who simply ring in or e-mail the parents and date of birth to register a calf, probably don't realise that in the 1970's, we still had to sketch the markings on the calves, and what's more actually fill in the black bits before sending them off to Rickmansworth. At that time I used to sketch calves on a Friday morning when I went round with the wages, and then quite often do the inking in and all the pedigree details on a night at home and it could be quite a time consuming job, with calves from some 400 cows plus the calving heifers to see to, there might be ten or a dozen in any one week, and you had to keep on top of them.

In the summer of that year I was up to Leyburn Mart and as it was a Friday market day, Marnie went with me. After doing the mart business we walked into town to get some things on the market and we saw Jack Charlton (The 1966 World Cup winner) who had a home up in the dales, coming away from Carricks fruit stall eating the biggest, juiciest peach I have ever seen – and I don't suppose he even had to pay for it!!

Harvest time back then was still fairly basic, we had the continuous flow drier that we had moved from Thornton Grange, which was ok, but rather slow and needed nearly full time attention and as seems to me, on most farms it becomes the job of the farmer or farm manager. At times I used to keep it going right through the night to get on top of the grain. After a few nights with very little sleep Mr J said he would do a night shift so I could get some sleep. He arrived about 10 o'clock at night and I gave him a full run down of how to make sure it was coming out properly dried at one end and the corn was running in ok at the inlet to keep it full all the time. I wouldn't say I slept terribly well, wondering if he was managing ok, and the fact he was moving about in the office immediately below our bedroom, and eventually gave up trying to sleep and got up about 6.30am. Going straight away to check things were ok, imagine my consternation when I saw the drier was going full bore but had been allowed to run completely empty, so had to start all over again by stopping the continuous flow while I got it filled up and a couple of hours of heat before it could be set going again.

The reservoir at Thornton Grange had been completed in the previous couple of years, and the pipeline which fed the water down to Northallerton had been laid, coming onto our land in Newton Pasture and going up the back of Newton Grange and out through the 20 acre into Mudfields land of Neville Dyson. We had continued to farm the remaining land up there, with both corn and heifers, but it was time consuming and always "sods law" that a couple of heifers would get out on a Sunday afternoon, and always seemed to head towards Mr Wilson's at Hutton Hang where there would be cattle grazing, and needless to say he was never too enamoured by being disturbed from his Sunday tea. At that time mid 1973, Hill Top East came onto the market. Tommy Walker farmed it with his son Albert, but Tommy was planning to retire, but wouldn't hand it on to Albert, hence the sale. I can remember Mr J and I meeting Albert the day after and him saying he was glad we had bought it as he knew we would look after it, to which Mr J replied that he would far rather he hadn't bought it and Albert could have carried on. At that time Mr J was always wary of going to an auction fearing that he may get "run-up" and on this occasion, Mr Lawson who was company secretary of Ropner Holdings went to buy the farm, which he successfully did at £69,000 for 95 acres or £726.32/acre. When he came up to the office to report on his success he told Mr J and I that it was far too much, but Mr J told him it had fantastic views as far as Teesside - he wasn't impressed - he said a view was worth nothing, a thought few of us would agree with. With being able to farm Hill Top East right opposite our drive end, and one field on the side of the drive, it was an opportunity which couldn't be missed and we also sold the land up at Thornton

Grange and so saving a lot of time running backwards and forwards to either check stock or with machinery.

As we moved into 1974, Herdwise was beginning to expand quite quickly and for every bull which was launched into the sales mix, daughters were to prepare and photograph and much of this work was done for them by the farm, usually Greg went off to do it, but on one occasion two bulls were to do at the same time, and so Marnie and I went over into Lancashire to prepare Noremead Jason and some of his daughters. In that part of the world, straw was at something of a premium, and Jason lived on a railway sleeper bed, and while comfortable was never the cleanest of bedding, and he had got quite a lot of muck tackles on his flanks and underbelly and I eventually I decided to just clip the one side of him to be photographed plus any bits that might show through on the other side. After a slow job which fully tested the clippers, we gave him a great deal of hand scrubbing to get him cleaned up ready for photographing the next day. As a concession to his new found cleanliness, Mr Townley said he could be bedded up on some straw, when Peter asked how many he was told two or three. Coming from an area where straw was plentiful I assumed he meant bales and was somewhat bemused when Peter returned with two or three wedges of a small bale, but I was even less amused when next morning we had to start and scrub him clean again all over. The first afternoon after getting Jason clipped and washed we were asked in for tea, which we were pleased to do, but Mr Townley was held up with another job for a few minutes. We were all hands washed and tidied up and sat waiting to start, Marnie couldn't wait any longer and had a sip of tea and immediately attracted severe dragon's looks, we realised why when eventually we started as grace had to be said in what was a strong Methodist household.

By early that year, Father's health was beginning to get the better of him and he decided it was time to retire and they got Missies Farm sold in June for what was then the princely sum of £20,000 and shortly after standing crops of grass for hay were sold for £24/acre. Earlier that spring with Father unable to do a lot other than the basics, such things as mucking out the young stock pens got rather neglected. Marnie and I used to go across when we were able, and one night decided to tackle one pen about three foot deep as the calves could just walk over the top of the pen, or bang their heads on the roof, as we did until it got down a bit. It was all to do by hand and get out into the spreader, and eventually we found ground level.

It was in that same spring, mid-April when Bob was doing something and found a cow down and laid on the electric fence. He claimed he eventually got her moved off it, but as he did so every time he touched her he got an electric shock through her and it left him with a stiff leg!

Tragedy struck very soon after that on 17th July that year, when we were doing second cut silage at Fox Park. It was getting well on into the evening, the dew was beginning to fall, Bob was going on holiday the next day and when he went to change the five gallon drum of additive on the forager, he didn't stop the drive, and when he climbed onto the body of the Claas full chop, his foot slipped over the front and his leg was pulled into the machine. I wasn't there at the time, I was delivering a bull calf up to Mr Sledge at Constable Burton for use in his Craglea herd, and as I headed home heard the siren's going not realising why, and I was down at the machine by the time the fire brigade and ambulance arrived. To get Bob out of the machine we had to take part of it to pieces and I well remember as the ambulance men lifted him clear, bearing in mind he had remained conscious throughout, he lifted the blanket covering his lower body so he could see the damage, took his cap off and threw it on the floor saying "well that's my dancing days over". Well they weren't in actual fact because he used to go off on holiday with Willie Atkinson all over the place and still danced with a false leg. A few days after the accident I went to see him in hospital which I was dreading, but Bob was happy to see me and wanted to talk about the events of that night. He told me that as they went down to the Friarage at Northallerton the men in the ambulance were asking him what he had eaten in the previous few hours, so they could inform the medics ready for his operation. Bob always had teacake in his tea or lunch box, and when he told them that, one of the ambulance men cursed and said "currants" so Bob said "so I told them I had an Eccles cake as well". Just imagine that as you go to hospital, having lost a leg which was to be tidied up and Bob had a false leg from below the knee. Although that was the end of Bob's working life we will catch up with him once or twice further on in the book.

Needless to say the place was crawling with Health and Safety Inspectors the next day, but they could find nothing wrong with either tractor or machine and put it down to accident by negligence on the part of the operator. By late afternoon the next day they concluded all their enquiries and allowed us back to the machine. Nobody else was prepared to go and clear the remains of Bob's leg out of the spout, so I had it to do. I still smoked at the time and so with a cigarette going full bore, I did what had to be done and we got the machine back together and were able to carry on. I could take you to the exact spot where it happened even now, alongside the Low Wood at the bottom of the Wood Field.

Straight after that event, quite a bit of my time was spent across at Galphay helping to get ready for Fathers dispersal sale. Mother's youngest brother, Uncle Joe who was a bachelor was coming to stay to help around the sale and as Father by then wasn't driving I went to take her to Ripon to get some shopping and pick up Uncle Joe from the station. She went into whatever supermarket was in those days, bearing in mind this was in the very early days of such places and long before the development of such as Tesco, Morrison's or Sainsbury's and I have vivid memories of a lady who pushed her trolley under a shelf and put her arm round the back of a big stack of baked beans, not Heinz, and scooped them straight into the basket. I didn't dare ask her what that number were required for, but just assumed it must be for scout camp or such like.

Father had stopped milking a year or two earlier, suckling calves onto the cows and using all beef bulls so that by the time of his sale on 27th July, he had suckler cows and calves to sell. Trade was reasonably good, peaking at £145.50 for a cow with a heifer calf at foot, and Mother's hens making 70p a piece, and some point-of-lay pullets making double that. He had a good 1955 Fergi 20-MAJ 900 which I knew to be in good order and we wanted one back at Dalesend as with five scraper tractors you always needed a fresh one. Bill came over that day and bought it for us at £166 - today you can't touch them for scraper tractors as the amateur tractor restorers will pay much more for them. A few pieces of surplus furniture totalled £2.65, Mother's old sewing machine £9.50, and Bill bought an old 12 bore which Father had never used for £6. Over the years, particularly when up at Middlesmoor, Father had had some good sheep dogs, but the last one at Missies Farm was, to put it bluntly "bloody useless" and I had seen him a few times set it off to bring the cows in for milking, only after a lot of shouting he would whistle it in, fasten it up and say "I might as well go myself" , which he did. Billed in the notice of sale as a "good sheep and cattle dog" I don't think it had ever done anything with sheep and the Mr Hudson who bought it for £36 would I think be bitterly disappointed unless he was a miraculous sheepdog trainer. The whole sale grossed £2138 and with adverts etc at £118 and Commission at 2.5% totalling £53.47 Fathers net proceeds were £1962. Mother and Father eventually moved to Aiskew in their retirement and were very happy there, though Father didn't last many more years.

Just a quick note so you can keep abreast of prices at the time, the Monday after I took 13 bull calves to Darlington Mart, which at the time had a big calf trade, trade that day for Black and Whites beginning to show a bit more dairyness wasn't great. The cheque for the 13 was £76 - it was a struggle not to spend it all at once!

A few years earlier Marnie had spent some time down in London looking after the children of David and Joanna Thomas. Joanna's parents lived at Burneston and Marnie had been doing their dinner parties for them for some time, hence the connection. She had walked the children all around the Sloane Square area of London, Joanna had taken her to see "Fiddler on the Roof" and they had obviously got on very well. In August of 1974 they were up here on holiday and came to visit, never having been on a farm before, the children loved it and David and Joanna were fascinated and we got a cow out onto the lawn and Bill did a bit of hand milking while they filmed it.

Whilst talking of Marnie and her dinner party cooking which she continued with up until Sarah being born, she did the cooking at various country houses in the area, for various numbers of people to a very high standard. It was long before the days of "Masterchef" on the television which she would have walked through with ease. She did a dinner one night for Edward Heath when he was Prime Minister plus most of his Cabinet, regularly cooked for the Sangster's of flat racing fame when they were up here for York races, and for Lee Trevino the famous golfer. She also cooked for a twenty first birthday party attended by Prince Andrew, and very nearly got thrown into the tower for squaring him up and telling him the coffee wasn't for him, it was ladies before gentlemen! One of the highlights of her time was doing the wedding reception for Carey, Mr & Mrs J's daughter on her marriage to Jonny Dickinson which was a wedding breakfast for 150 and an evening reception for 300, all done to the highest level with galantines, decorated whole salmons, crab mousse and such things - all top of the range things and a marvellous day, which was only two days after the official opening of the Dalepak factory at Leeming Bar by Sir Ken Morrison, using the same marquee on the lawn at Dalesend. She was asked to do that event as well, but declined as they were too close together and she wanted to direct all her efforts into getting the wedding spot on. After Sarah was born, Marnie was unable to commit to doing dinner parties, but as a sideline she and Margaret O'Grady did the occasional normal wedding breakfast in the area. Is there any wonder I always carried a little bit of extra weight?!

Back to 1974, and it was becoming increasingly obvious that the farm was at a cross-roads, some of the longer established dairy units had got to the point where they were in need of considerable amounts of money spending to upgrade them, milk quotas were on the horizon, holidays etc were beginning to get longer, wages were rising at a fairly fast rate and it was needing one full time relief man and virtually another to keep the whole thing on the road. It was also thought that one rather better herd was more in keeping with having the AI company than were having five rag, tag and bobtail herds and so the decision was made to just keep the one herd at Newton Grange with Bill as the herdsman. In the October of that year we bought the Unique family from Ullswater and the Babs family from Boustead at the regular bi-annual sale at Ullswater in an effort to step up the quality in the one remaining herd. The other family we bought, the Genga's never got going, the Bab's developed a little but then faded out, but the Unique's developed into one of our better families and was still going strongly when we dispersed.

Just in passing, because it happened on the same day as the Ullswater sale and is noted alongside, what used to be the Post Office in the centre of Patrick Brompton was sold for the princely sum of £9250. It is quite staggering how property prices have moved on over time, even in our area, although not as they have done in the London area.

So the dispersal of the other four herds was planned for the 3rd and 4th November to be held at Old Park House which provided the best facilities for staging such an event. All the other herdsmen who were going to lose their jobs as soon as the sale was over were fantastic and all saw their jobs through to the end and you have to pay tribute to them for that. We moved some of the best cows from each herd to the Grange and sold some of the bottom end from that herd along with the others. Alan up at Home Farm was renting those buildings and buying the silage and also bought the unsaleable cows privately before hand and was also a good buyer at the sale. We got all the dry cows moved to Old Park House a day or two earlier to get them ready, the cows were clipped by Greg and Frankie at their own farm and washed once, then the evening before after milking they were led by lorry to Old Park House where everyone else did the washing and preparing. Bear in mind that the other herdsman still had the other half of the cows to see to before things were repeated the night before the second day. The sale was conducted by Hobsons, and the young man sent up on the Sunday to do the numbering up etc was just starting his career, Chris Norton who subsequently went on to be the leading auctioneer of his generation, and maybe not the first but certainly one of the first sales he ever sold at publicly the next day when he had his turn with the gavel.

Cattle prices were quite depressed at the time, and I well remember that a few minutes before the start time of the first day there were only a couple of cars in the field, but numbers eventually grew and we got things sold.

On the morning of the second day, some of us had not been to bed, never mind got up early, but I do remember it was one of the most fantastic sunrises I have ever seen and lasted for a long time. The other thing I remember of that morning was going home for breakfast and a freshen up, is Marnie waking me up at the breakfast table with the knife halfway through the boiled egg as I took the top off. She also at night had to take the telephone away from me when someone rung up and she said I was talking absolute gibberish - some would say I always have done. Talking of falling asleep there was another sale, and I can't remember which, when at night when it was all over, we would have Chinese takeaway, and I think I can claim to be the only man to fall asleep in the Bedale Chinese while my order was being prepared and having to be woken up to pay for it. We subsequently had a sale later that month to sell the calving and in calf heifers and the following year had two sales to sell more of the young stock as they matured to bring our numbers down to what was required for just the one herd.

Once that excitement was over, things became rather easier to manage and in that first year after the sale, my car mileage dropped by about 15,000 miles, it was nearly a 20 mile round trip to all the farms, including the very long drives of Old Park House and Arbour Hill, and you were round them nearly every day, possibly a second time if there was anything needed urgently as if for instance you were silaging up at Home Farm I might be up there six or seven times in the day. It is often not until you stop doing something that you realise how much time is taken up by doing it, something we also discovered some twenty five years later after we put the big new building up at Newton Grange for young stock rather than housing them at Dalesend.

Chapter Seven– A New Era - Less Cows plus Sarah

Following the sale of most of the cows there was over the winter of 74/75 a period of re-adjustment and settling down, with all the herdsmen leaving and parts of parlours to sell, and a larger amount of arable land to look after. Plans were made to convert Old Park House into the centre of the arable enterprise by installing a large drier, dressing machine and storage facilities in what had been all the cubicle houses plus straw storage and feeding area, so as to be ready for the harvest of 1975.

In the early part of 1975 I have a note that Bill Greetham was inducted at Patrick Brompton Church to replace Canon Crawford. Bill had been the vicar attached to Aysgarth School at Newton-le-Willows and so was well known to most of the parishes which now also covered Crakehall and Hornby parishes.

In March of that year, we installed a new water supply to Hill Top East - the old metal pipe was time expired, had the odd burst and was badly furred up, so that the pressure up there as the name suggests wasn't very good. It had to be taken from the supply line down at Lynas Terrace through land belonging to Blackburns and Hudson's before entering our own. The trench was dug for us, but then Marnie and I put in the new length of alkathene and connected back up to the existing line near the entrance to the farm house and also installed more alkathene round to the troughs in the other grazing fields to cut out most of the old metal work. When all was connected up we subsequently back filled it all with tractor and loader or scraper tractor and it is still ok today.

Good Friday that year was on the 28th March, I don't know why I have that particular date in my diary or the note saying that overtime was the princely price of £1 per hour, and no doubt some of the men were working sowing spring corn. We weren't there over the Easter time, as we were over in Norway for Colin and Liv's wedding. Obviously by this time, Colin had been over there for three years or so, and was still at the research station and living in the "Hybel Hus", a collective house where four or five singles lived, but after marriage they moved into one of the houses on site. While we were over there, we ate mostly Norwegian style, and on Easter Saturday we were supposed to be having "fiske pudding" for lunch, we had eaten and not been very impressed with "fiske balls" on previous visits and fiske pudding was the left over's made into a kind of loaf. Marnie's dad and I decided we didn't fancy it, so we had fish fingers instead. In the early days of visiting Norway, we used to take the car and go by ferry from Newcastle to Stavanger - it no longer runs and we now have to fly, usually via Schipol which makes it a long journey for a short distance.

Back from Norway, and we had to get ready for the surplus machinery sale which we held in the Bungalow field at the end of April. A lot of equipment more associated with dairy farming like scrapers, Fergi 20's, electric fencing and the like, and the day after that I sew the lawn on the other half of the front garden which had originally been a vegetable garden but we had worked on it for three years to clear it of "wickens" and created a flower bed right down one side, and subsequently over the years developed into a very attractive feature of the garden.

In to May and Alan Gregg moved from Home Farm up at Hornby to the farm he had got the tenancy for from the Church Commissioners up near Sunderland, and then just a few days later, not that there was any connection between the two events, I was having a tidy up bonfire out the back when the smoke drifted back across the garden. A very heavily pregnant Marnie was to put it mildly, not too enamoured as she had the quilt off the bed out to dry ready to put away for the summer, and she didn't think smoked quilt was quite the required thing. Just a few days later, we were silaging at the Grange and my jacket was laid on the wall of the nearby bull pen. It was a hot, sunny day and it had been there for a couple of hours when it suddenly burst into flames - to this day I don't know why - I can only assume it was magnified through some glass nearby and was a spontaneous combustion, fortunately it was an old jacket.

Then we came to one of the momentous days in our lives - 3rd June 1975 and daughter Sarah was born. She was born as a breech and Mr Hart the obstetrician wasn't too impressed when he came to tell me and explain what a 'breech' was, when I told him I had delivered many a one - then he realised I meant calves not humans. That particular day was very cold, and there was in fact snow about, I have a newspaper somewhere of that day showing Derbyshire playing cricket and the pitch was white over with snow. That was the last cold day, and it took up then into a very hot, dry summer, we had two in a row and people talk about 1976 because it lasted for so long, but I think 75 was hotter but for a shorter period. The same day as she was born we were due to go to the wedding of Marnie's cousin Anne Thompson to Robert Sanderson - Marnie obviously couldn't go, Mr J said I may as well go as I wouldn't be much use for anything else. Whilst Marnie and Sarah were in the Mount at Northallerton, we had the EU referendum which had a 67% yes vote, a much larger majority than there was last year (2016) when we had the referendum to leave the EU, and then a few days later on my birthday Marnie and Sarah came home, and all of a sudden we were three, and Sarah was christened in the early August, I remember us having the biggest arrangement of sweet peas on the food table I think we have ever had, and they were from our own garden and I suppose was indicative of the good weather there had been.

Just a short time afterwards we went for a ride out one evening and called to see Mr (Tot) Gregg, Alan's father's begonias at Bellerby. He had always pestered us to go and see them and he had a fantastic display of all the colours you could imagine. There was no doubt where Alan got his flower breeding and showing from.

Alan having left Home Farm, and with quite a bit of that land not really suitable for arable farming, it was decided to put it on the market and it was sold in mid-September for £75,500 to the Ramsay family and interestingly enough they have just sold it in the last six months of 2017, when the asking price I believe was £1.5 million, just a fair appreciation plus a realisation of how land prices have risen over 42 years. The harvest of that year, we had a lot of surplus straw to sell and one of my most successful sales ever, of anything, was up at Home Farm. It was just about when that gloriously hot summer broke, I had advertised straw to bale in the Darlington and Stockton Times and had a lot of enquiries that Saturday morning. The Dent brothers who all farmed up the dale were desperate to come and see it and they bought the 45 acres in the pouring rain at £10 an acre - a good price back then - it did eventually fair up and they got it quite well. One of those brothers, Francis at a later date bought Cote House across the road from Newton Grange and was a very good neighbour for many years. He would buy Cote House from John Gatenby who I had a brush with very soon after we bought Hill Top East which adjoined it. Picking stones in the Road End field, and it was fairly stoney, we tipped them out of the loader bucket over the wall onto the roadside - or so I thought until a phone call at lunchtime from an irate Mr Gatenby - that was where the spring fed water trough was with a pump in it that fed all the house and buildings. We did go back to stone picking that afternoon, but out of the water hole rather than from the field. Mr Gatneby's son, also John will be known to many as the owner and managing director of the Vale of Mowbray pork pie factory at Leeming Bar, which has just undergone another large expansion and which we can sometimes smell from our now front door if they are cooking and the wind is in the right direction.

At a similar time I was down to John Henry Gills one morning for some spares in good time, and popped in to see Mother and Father in Aiskew on the way back home. Father was looking particularly glum waiting for his breakfast and upon enquiring what the matter was, he said Mother had told him no more fried eggs as she had heard on the radio the previous day that they were bad for you, so I had to give Mother a severe talking to, telling her he had had two for his breakfast every day except Christmas day, when he had pork pie, and they hadn't done him any harm up to now. Fortunately she relented and I left them with Father a smile back on his face.

In the December of 1975 Mr J and I were going down to Smithfield to meet Alvan Blanch about one or two problems we had with the new dryer in its first season at Old Park House, and at the same time we were going to collect a young bull from Lord Rathcreedan's (Chris Norton's father), Bellehatch Royalty for testing with Herdwise, and so went down in the Dalesend van. Fortunately Mr J knew just where he was going and as we arrived at Earls Court spotted a space between two Rolls Royces and shot straight into it, by which time a super-efficient parking attendant arrived and told us we couldn't park there as it was meant for special people. Mr J explained that he had left his "roller" at home as he had a young bull to collect on the way home from Lord Rathcreedon, so that "Ok, alright Sir." The guvnor pulled a similar stunt many years later when we were guests of BOCM-Pauls at Twickenham for England v's France. I had travelled down with Dick Brown and George and we were already at their hospitality stand when we saw Mr J arrive in his car (he was already down in London) and drive to the VIP gate. Dick said "they'll never let him in there", which two seconds later was proved totally wrong as in he went. When he eventually arrived with us, we enquired as to how he had managed it. Mr J said "well I just told them I was a guest of Mr Brown and they just waved me in". He did however get a bigger shock that same lunchtime when he wandered over to a group of Frenchmen having a picnic and enquired what they were having to eat. One of the Frenchmen took exception and stood up to reveal himself as a 6'6" ex second row forward and Mr J was soon back at our stand.

At that time in late December, Sarah had to go into hospital and was put in plaster from her waist to her ankles with legs out wide so that her hip could grow to the correct shape and size. The only way we could take her anywhere for the next six months was in the bottom draw from a chest of drawers, which sat nicely on the back seat of the car and was never a problem. The first day or so of January we had been to Ripon to Mary's for our Christmas visit and it was a really wild night with gale force winds. As we came back from Well towards Mile House we came over the brow of the hill near the arboretum to find a massive tree blocking our way. A quick reverse took us out of danger and back to the Snape turning and we eventually made it home via Carthorpe and Bedale. Being such a wild night I pulled up at the office door to take the drawer in that way and just as we lifted Sarah out, the big oak tree across the front lawn came crashing down, and snapped the telegraph pole and wires. We had two or three peaceful days without any telephone - the mobile phone still hadn't been invented.

Early spring and someone wanted to buy about 15 cows, so we sorted 20 out and put them separately in the Front Field. He quickly had a look round and said he would take them all. Before I could say anything Mr J jumped in and said we would like £120, he would likely offer £80, so lets say £100 and not mess around, to which the buyer readily agreed. When he had gone I said to Mr J that was a funny way of selling cows and he asked what I would have done. So I said I would have asked £180 and he would have offered £120 and we would have settled at £150, "In that case you had better sell the 'f'ing' things yourself in future" was his reply, and in all honesty he never did any selling himself again.

A week or two later he came back from a regional MMB meeting which they both sat on and said I had cost him £20. On enquiring why he said the buyer had asked for £1/head "luck money" which I had never given. I had told him that the luck was in the price as he had got them so cheap, off went a letter telling him that and requesting the return of his £20. A letter soon came back without the money and saying I was a right 'b*****'. Back went another letter from JGR "I know that's why I employ him".

A notable local event in early May 76 was the official opening of the new pavilion for Bedale Athletic and Sports Association, which had been organised and financed without any grants or other handouts and brought together, cricket, football, squash and tennis and was very well supported by local groups and people and is still going strongly today.

1976 was the very hot, dry year which seemed to go on forever, with hot, balmy evenings, and we had all sorts of fun at barbecues and garden parties. It was during that summer, harvest came early and we were unloading straw into the shed in the yard when a salesman appeared and began to try and sell me and others life insurance or assurance. He didn't help his cause by saying that if I were to book it before a certain time that day, he could ring into his office and he would get a free turkey for Christmas. Needless to say I wasn't impressed and sent him on his way with a few carefully chosen choice words!!

In August of that year a young man by the name of Paul Turner came to work for us for a year before going to college, which he did, but then came back to work for us full time for a few years afterwards. He was keen on rallying and had a rally car which he spent hours tinkering with. One day he had been down at Newton Grange during the morning, but took a tractor back up to Old Park House for his lunch and I would bring his car up afterwards. Easier said than done. Having explained to me how to get it started, it still needed a couple of phone calls to get the fuel on and a couple of switches on before I squeezed my large frame into the bucket seat. I hadn't realised how bare a rally car was inside and the vibration in the car was unbelievable, so much so, that without a word of a lie, a button came off the front of my shirt on the three and a half mile journey and it took me about half an hour to recover from the experience. Paul's great friend Horace used to quite often come to visit and I remember his girlfriend with fuzzy hair was rather unkindly nicknamed 'bog brush' by Paul.

During that very hot year of 1976, I well remember at harvest time when the loads of corn were tipped for the dryer, they were absolutely teaming with ladybirds. Not that the corn needed drying that year, but it did need to go through on cold air to cool it down before going into storage after the dresser. I have never seen as many ladybirds in my life.

Another amusing incident occurred in September of that year when we had some heifers entered in the Society sale at Lancaster. Greg, who would normally have taken them was off work after a heart attack and so Marnie and I took them and Greg and Bett just came over the night before the sale to spectate. We were staying at the Farmer's Arms and went out into town for a meal at night. With Greg being on medication and not drinking, Bett had a sherry, Marnie a white wine and I had half a lager with our meal. Next morning at 4.30am Marnie and I set off for the auction mart and as we went through the town we were behind a police car. In Lancashire at that time they didn't have a blue light on the top but a sign in the back window flashing on and off and telling you to stop, which I didn't spot immediately. The policemans opening words as he came to the car was that it smelt of alcohol and he was going to breathalyse me and where was I going. I suppose with hindsight pulling out from behind a pub at that time and saying you were going to wash cows was a bit of a "cock and bull" story, but I explained that he was wasting his time, but he wouldn't be dissuaded. So I had to get out and give a good blow and into the car lights to see

75

it change colour. After about 10 seconds he cursed and said that it was never going to change, I said I had told him that before ever he started. He gave me a talking to and off we went. Up at the auction mart we were washing the second heifer when the young policewoman who had never got out of the car came wandering round to obviously check the story. I asked her where her mate was to which she replied he was back at the station writing his report and having a coffee so I told her to tell him from me that he was a rotten "B" for sending a young lass out on her own at that time of the morning. The fortunate thing was that it was me they picked on in those particular circumstances, if I or Greg had been on our own, we would probably have gone up to check the heifers with three or four other herdsmen, and on getting back to the pub would have probably had two, three or four drinks before going to bed, and whilst still fit enough to drive the next morning, would certainly have failed the breathalyser.

Shortly after that we sold a bull calf to the Bell's from Low Row which we had to deliver. It wasn't the first one we had sold them and I knew the format would include staying for tea, so I left enough time for that. A look round the garden with Miss Bell and I saw a climbing rose on the front of the house, her "rose without thorns". Admiring the rose Miss Bell took a cutting for me, and it was still going strong when we left Newton Grange 36 years later and had some fantastic shows of roses over that time. It is interesting that for the last couple of years I have done some consultancy work for Sarah up at Jamie Close's Low Row, more or less next door to the Bells.

October 1976 saw the World Conference Show and we had cattle there that did very well in some massive classes standing as high as seventh in classes of 40 plus in a marvellous show of wonderful cattle where the Champion was the legendary Shopland Edleet Ruth 6th. It was a big show for Herdwise as well, with live cattle on their stand. The hot bull of the time was launched that day, Ridgwardine Broker from Valeoskene up near Aberdeen, they stayed overnight with us on their way south and there were also some Grove Jesters on display.

Moving through into 1977, I had another brush with the police at the beginning of May. Herdwise at the time ran several caravans that were used as their stand at many of the shows. We were showing cattle up at Ayr show in early May and were also going to Newark and Notts later that week. A caravan was to go from Ayr to Newark so I brought it back home for a couple of days. The cattle having gone down to the show the day before, I left home very early the next morning with the caravan and as I went down the A1 I was aware of a police car in front of me, then he went off at a slip road and came straight back on behind me and did this once or twice. I pulled off at the service station south of Doncaster for breakfast, and saw the police car drift into the car park, as did other police cars for their breakfasts. When I went out I saw them parked right next to me and as I nonchalantly unlocked the car I heard the window come down and as soon as the policeman spoke I asked him what the problem was as they had been following me for miles, to which he replied that in actual fact I had been following them much of the time, but could I explain why the number on the car was registered to J.G. Ropner Co while the Caravan was in the name of Herdwise Ltd.

When I explained that to them and said I was but a simple dales farmer and wasn't it like a tractor and trailer where you could have any number on the trailer as long as the tractor pulling it was registered to the farm. "Oh no sir, this is the Queen's highway and the numbers must correspond" "Do you have pen or chalk that you can put the vehicle number onto the caravan." Which I did and they were quite happy and left with the parting shot "You can please yourself after the next junction as we are turning round there as this is the end of our beat, but just so if another police car stops you for the number they won't also book you for doing 60mph, when you should only be doing 50." I got the caravan ultimately delivered without any problem.

A great day was the last day of June in 77 when Sarah went to see Mr Ashworth and she ran down the corridor to him and he said if she could run like that he didn't want to see her anymore and gave her leg the total all clear. It was followed closely by Patrick Brompton Church holding its first Flower Festival and we were selling raffle tickets at the entrance to the village hall as people went in for tea as Bjorn Borg beat John McEnroe in the Wimbledon Singles Final. Later that month I entered for I think the one and only time the Newton-le-Willows show and won first prize with my peas and second with a tray of vegetables - I was very chuffed.

As harvest time that year, Bill was combining at lunch time while Howard had his break, it was quite windy and the combine fired and by the time the fire brigade got down to Cuckoo Hills North at Arbour Hill it was severely damaged. The same day all the cows got out at home while Bill wasn't there and a big branch came down blocking Newton road, which we had to clear. A day or two later when we were leading straw up in the same field we saw that the combine was beginning to smoulder again. I rang the fire brigade and explained there was no emergency and no need for flashing blue lights and they duly obliged. Not so the police who arrived unnecessarily later as we set off down Arbour Hill road with two loads of straw. Mr J who was driving the front tractor gave him a real talking to - the policeman jumped into his van and reversed the full length of the drive, nearly a mile, JGR in hot pursuit, load of straw not roped on and finally caught the policeman up and apologised, having realised that the old four wheel straw trailers had no brakes nor number plates for which we might get into trouble. We didn't and miraculously the straw all made it down to Dalesend. The burnt out combine caused further problems into the autumn when the NFU assessors would only allow us £1000 on the insurance which was totally unacceptable, and they wouldn't move at all. I eventually persuaded Mr J that we should offer £1001 for it because I thought we could break it up and raise more than that in parts. That was accepted and I advertised it in Farmer's Weekly the weekend of the Smithfield Show and had several phone calls about it, people wanting to come and see it the following week. On the Saturday afternoon we had been out and Mr J rang at night to say he had come back from shooting to find a gentleman in his yard who had wanted to buy it and had given him £500 in cash as a deposit and would return on the Monday. He duly arrived - I still have his visiting card as a memento - he went under the magnificent name of Lazarus Moissiedis, and he wanted to take it back to Greece. We agreed a price of £3000 which he paid in pound notes and gave me two £50 notes for seeing to loading it when it was collected. They came on a pouring wet Christmas Eve and it took Howard and I hours to help get it winched onto a wagon really too narrow, we helped them to get the wheels off etc - was £50 ever as well earned? There was definitely a fiddle on somewhere by the people who tried to take it for the NFU, going by one or two phone calls I subsequently received.

In the autumn of 1977, we had a week's holiday up in Northumberland staying at Cornhill on Tweed at the Collingwood Arms, a smashing hotel. One of the other guests at the time whom we got talking to in the lounge one evening was the Captain of the QE2, who was embarrassed as such a high ranking naval man to have been stranded on Lindisfarne by the rising tide that stopped him getting back to the mainland. On that same trip we went to see the Chillingham Wild White Cattle. After a long walk up to the hills, we finally found them, a real "flea-bitten" collection of very poor cattle - the man in charge wasn't very impressed when I told him they wanted a good worming, he told us not to get anywhere near as they were wild and dangerous, I think a good gallop would have finished them off for good, but really - not having the first calf until five years old and then only three calves in the next ten years or so was so far removed from commercial reality that I couldn't see a lot of point in them. Interestingly enough and purely to show how things have changed over 40 years, our bill for the eight nights dinner, bed and breakfast for the three of us was £157.55.

That autumn there was a terrific crop of pears on the old tree which used to grow alongside the wall opposite the back door and apart from what we ate and gave away, I sold 373lbs of them at 9p/lb to Garner's fruit shop in Bedale. We didn't bottle any that year, Marnie having tried previously only to find them "fizzing" when the top was removed and they would have certainly exploded had they been left.

Another strange occurrence happened in November that year as I set off to go up to Paisley where we had three bulls entered at their major sale of the year. I was stopped three times by the police before I got to Catterick Camp. It was at the time of very high tension with all the troubles in Northern Ireland and so perhaps was understandable. The police had been sat at Patrick Brompton crossroads and seen my car lights come along the back road and intercepted me at Newton-le-Willows, and accepting that it was 4.30am wondered who was moving about. They were easily satisfied and set off ahead of me, when just before the crossroads their blue light went on again -one of the bulbs had gone in my lights as I followed them and they accepted I couldn't do much about it at that time of the morning but promised I would get a replacement before I came back at night which of course I didn't bother to do. Then just as I went into Catterick Camp I was stopped by a police road block checking everyone's movements because of the troubles. The rest of the journey was uneventful both there and back and I think we had decent bull trade.

In the spring of 1978 , I was helping Bill to calve Dalesend Grey Hazel, the cow who had won some trophies a year or two previously when the Dairy Show was held at

Harrogate, she squirted fluid and muck all over him, then when she had gone down and we were down as well, the calf suddenly popped out right on top of him. He wasn't too impressed with me, because I couldn't do anything for laughing at him - it's happened to most of us at one time or another.

A few days later we had a long weekend away and stayed at Spalding, the weekend when the flower procession was held, and all the floats were covered in thousands of flower heads, mostly daffodils and tulips, as were all the fields in the area with the flowers in full bloom. In case any of you think it was a big waste of flowers, let me put your minds to rest, it wasn't, as all these fields were being used to produce bulbs and the heads were soon removed so that all the goodness returned to the bulbs before they were lifted later for sale. On Sunday of that weekend we paid a visit to Sandringham which was open to the public, as we went round, Sarah who was barely three at the time asked if we were staying for tea, but I told her no because the Lady of the House hadn't invited us!

As we were silaging in early June, It had been a good grass growing spring and the grass had got too strong for grazing in a couple of paddocks in the Front Field, and we cut them to ensile. At that time there was quite a big pond in front of the house and just as I stopped to open the gate to go in to pick up the grass, about 40 Canadian Geese landed on the pond. I ran into the house to get my camera, and went down the drive to get behind them and got someone to move the tractor and trailer, hopefully to walk them up into the yard to get a photo of them in the yard. Unfortunately they almost got there but then took off again, but I had quite a few photographs of them. Never seen them again, either before or since.

At the beginning of August that year we had a short term exchange student come to stay with us - I don't know how or why but Sepp Wagner arrived from Austria, and was very useful about the place for a busy time of year, fortunately he spoke good English as our Austrian wasn't too clever. One day he arrived in the house with a great big "puff ball" mushroom which hadn't got to the "puff" stage and wanted Marnie to cook it. Loving proper mushrooms but rather sceptical of this, she cooked a slice off it for Sepp which he enjoyed but we didn't partake. As he was still alive the next day showing no obvious side effects he got me persuaded to try some the next tea time which I did, I can't say it was much different, but at least I'm still alive to tell the tale.

A year or two later we had another interesting student for several weeks. I don't remember how the initial contact came about, though perhaps it was through Askham Bryan college, but Dick Agass was the student. He had trained as a teacher and was from the East End of London, but had decided to retrain as a social worker. As part of his course he had to do two months of completely unrelated work. When he first came he was totally useless, never having been in the countryside never mind working on a farm, and for the first week more or less just followed or rode about with me. He was staggered by how people knew and acknowledged each other's existence. As we went past Lynas Terrace and I gave "Wacker" Williams a wave, or through the village one to old Fred Bond, he asked if I knew them and when I said I saw them regularly, he just couldn't comprehend how people would be so friendly to others, as he didn't even know the name of his next door neighbours or what they looked like. For the first week he stayed with us until we found him digs with Mrs Harrison in Patrick Brompton. At the end of the week he asked Marnie how much he owed her for the bed and the meals and was utterly disbelieving when she said nothing – how could anyone do anything for anybody for nothing??

Sometimes on a morning when he came to work, you could see him when he got out of his car, literally breath in the country air and look up the dale in wonderment at the beauty of the countryside.

It was amazing what we did teach him in a short time, and before he left he milked the herd totally on his own with no help at all. Sadly we never kept in touch and so are totally unaware of what became of him, but we learnt as much from him as he did from us, as to how the other half lived and the insight into inner city life of which we were totally unaware.

By this time Dalesend Cascade had come back with his superb first proof and was the hot bull of the moment and we had a lot of visitors being brought by Herdwise to look at the daughters, one or two of which we had bought back as they had been sold as in calf heifers when we had reduced the herd previously. One particular day in August Bob Ede the part time Herdwise man from the South brought several potential customers, including Malcolm Watson, who was at the time the assistant Farm Manager to Malcolm Stansfield at Reading University. As we went across the Front Field to the cattle which had been clipped and washed and separated out for our visitors, Sarah wanted to come with me but I wouldn't let her. Undeterred she was coming anyway and set off running after us, only being small she didn't see the electric fence wire of the paddocks and ran into one "necking" herself which pulled her up and caused a lot of crying. Malcolm took pity on her, went back, consoled her and brought her with him, this started a great friendship between them that has now lasted almost forty years and he became forever afterwards "My Malcolm". Over the years we became friends with he and Eunice, and have swopped visits many times over the years. She seemed quite accident prone at that time, not long afterwards it was Kathryn and Peters wedding at Patrick Brompton at which she was a flower girl, and eating a sweet to pass the time and keep her quiet during the ceremony, she swallowed it and had to be taken outside to get it coughed up.

In September of that year, JGR went to the draft sale of the Weeton herd and bought Weeton Carmen 151 jointly with Keith Bromley to do embryo work on, she produced us one or two decent daughters and a son by Cascade, Dalesend Hi-Noon who was tested through Herdwise. He nearly didn't make it, he was born from a Hereford cross heifer who stood on him at birth and damaged his neck, so that he could barely stand up. Mr J got Mr Ashby the Richmond Physio to come and look at him - it was quite amazing the ability he had which he had previously used on horses. He felt all along the spine of the calf, said he wanted as many men as I could gather up and when six of us were there, two of us held him under the head while the other four took all the weight. When he said go, the four had to let go immediately, and the two of us keep his weight, we let him down into his pen, stood straight up and walked away and was never any more trouble, quite remarkable.

When Weeton Carmen 151 came home we were surprised how small she was compared to our own cows, and we were due to classify soon afterwards. She was already classified Excellent so wasn't really to do, but Bill would have his bit of fun and put her in to be classified and not recognising the cow he said she was too small for EX - at that time there was a minimum height requirement. Bill then explained who she was to Jim Mival, who in fact had made her EX at Weeton, and on measuring her, she just scraped in to his relief, though he did say it had never occurred to him among a herd of at that time British Friesians that she was anything but big enough. Bill had a further bit of fun with Mr Mival who had previously scored a plain heifer by Okery Mark which Bill rather liked very poorly and told him she would never make a cow. Imagine Bill's glee rather later when the same man scored her Excellent and in fact Dalesend Ok Belle went on to give 100 tonnes of milk. Around that time there was a bit of fun with her daughter, one of the very first daughters of Dalesend Cascade. We hosted a North Eastern Club judging night and put out a class of six milk heifers. It was at the time of the big swing over to Holstein blood and we just put Cascade Belle in to confuse the issue. The master judge that night was a diehard Friesian man and so without exception all the competitors put her last. When the judge came to give his placings and reasons he had put her first. "I knew you would all put her last because I was the judge, so I've put her first" was his reason, not the fact that she was a good heifer. The moral to the story of course is not to judge the judge, but judge the cattle.

That autumn we took two cows down to the North West Dairy Show with the car and trailer, by that time I had a Saab, but she was not going so well, and when JGR came down on the day of the show I asked him if he would take my car back home and leave me his car to pull the trailer home, which he readily agreed to. We had a good show with Valeoskene Rosary 14, who I had bought as a bulling heifer when we were promoting Ridgwardine Broker, coming second in a class of 40 plus, and perhaps should have won. As the class was parading round, the judge was putting back out of the ring the one's he didn't consider his top ones and pointed the heifer in front of me to go out, but John Moffitt of Dalton had other ideas and carried on round the ring to eventually win the class, much to my annoyance.

Mr J left in good time and when I saw him the next day, asked about the car. Yes it was fine he said, he took it steady for a mile or two to make sure it was ok, and then he went faster and faster on the basis that the faster he went the nearer home he would be should he break down. Stewart and I had an eventful journey back home. As we came out of Leeds back towards the A1 I saw smoke coming from the trailer, so we stopped immediately to find that one of the side stays on the trailer had sprung and was rubbing on the inside of one of the tyres. We took the two cows out and tied them to the fence at the side of the petrol station, but couldn't manage to get it bent back. Fortunately Walter Bumett, a well known member of the Yorkshire Club, managed a farm just up the road, and he was good enough to loan us his trailer to get the cattle home, and we swopped them back the following day, with no cattle in it the trailer was ok. The two cows tied to the fence caused a lot of comment from passers-by, I don't suppose a lot of people from Leeds had seen many cows at close hand and certainly not tied to a fence in a petrol station!

Sadness was to follow in November of 1978 when Father died. He had not been too well for a while, but his chest was finally giving him a lot of trouble and he was in hospital at Harrogate for two or three weeks and it became obvious that he was unlikely to come home again. It is amazing how he seemed to know that the end was nigh - the last time I went to see him and took Mother, as we were leaving he just said "look after your Mother for me". That was the end of an era, a man of very simple needs, who I don't think would ever do anybody any harm, and would help anybody with anything. What do I most remember about him - what a slow eater he was - I was nearly back in for tea when he finished his lunch, how he rocked back on his chair sideways to the table, something Adam does and he never knew his Grandfather. He couldn't do with a mucky fork or gripe shaft and when I was younger I accidentally got hold of his and got some muck on it, we had to have a ceremonial wiping of it with a bit of hay or straw before he could continue. The other thing among many others that I remember, was the way he looked at Marnie over his glasses if she was picking the chicken bones for the last morsel of meat on them, or the way if you did something wrong he just smacked his lips and peered at you over those glasses. The other thing I can remember is that I never saw him run – walk very quickly yes, but never run. He was a big tall man and with his arms outstretched with a stick in one hand he could block a gateway to turn sheep. He never played cricket with us, it was always Mother who did so, and as far as I know none of the Liddles were sporty so that must have passed down the Hood line.

Chapter Eight– Bill becomes a Mister

By now Sarah was about three and a half years old and was used to going to see Bill with me and generally seeing him about in the yard. Still in those days in the late 1970's, children showed some respect for their elders and called them Mr Faulds, but that didn't seem right for this situation, but she obviously couldn't call him Bill, so we came to the compromise and she called him Mr Bill. That stuck with him and grew over the next forty years or so. He became known generally as Mr Bill, even the guvnor started to call him Mr Bill, and just three or four years ago when Bill was to become President of the North Eastern Holstein Club, quite a few people asked me what his proper surname was as they only knew him as Mr Bill.

In the spring of 1979, we were busy transplanting Weeton Carmen 151 and were using Harry Coulthard at Saul's down in Lincolnshire. We had one hairy trip down there, when a large lorry with cladding on the sides overtook us at great speed and sort of sucked us in and blew us out as he went past - starting the trailer swinging and we were fortunate to get onto a lay by and the edging knocked a tyre off its rim to help slow us up and fortunately a SAAB was a big strong car to hold it. On another trip down there, I had booked a room in Sleaford for overnight, I don't know if you have ever been there, but its name suits it well. After taking the cows to the centre we went back to book in, thankfully it was all locked up and we couldn't raise anyone, just as well as it looked a real dive. That night we booked into another one near Heckington - The Petwood Moathouse - was superb, and had been the home base of the Dambusters during the Second World War, and it must have been about May because all the rhododendrons were fully out, and they were a fantastic sight with massive flowers on them.

That spring, I had become Chairman of the North Eastern Club, in somewhat of a hurry. The previous vice chairman suddenly resigned a few weeks before the AGM, his Father had died and no one had attended the funeral, he hadn't let anyone know so no one was aware of it. So I was vice chairman for only a few weeks and at that time the chairman used to do two years and the president only one year, but under the circumstances the then President George Leggott senior said he would do a further year to help me out and from then on, until the present day, Presidents also do two year terms but change alternately so one helps the other out in their first year all the time. Very soon afterwards it was the clubs annual tour, which in those days nearly all breeders clubs did for a week or so to look at herds in other parts of the country, and for many of the older breeders it was their only holiday of the year. Just a day or two before we went we had the first ever Mayday Bank Holiday brought in by the Labour Party to commemorate Labour day. That year we were going down to Norfolk, I was on my own as with Sarah just being young, Marnie couldn't go as well. As we travelled down to Norfolk Mrs Leggott was explaining to me what happened on such a tour and said the ladies often only got a couple of days shopping while the men went looking at cows, and if they didn't get some such activity, everybody got a bit growly.

We stopped for lunch en-route at Kings Lynn, I had a word with our coach driver to make sure we had plenty of time and before we set off again said that we were only four or five miles from Sandringham - would they like us to stop for an hour, the ladies had never had anything like that done for them before, let alone before the men had been anywhere near a cow, - from then on the ladies were eating out of my hand and I learnt a valuable lesson, to keep the ladies happy and smiling and you are more than half way there!

One of the highlights of our showing up to that point was taking the Championship at the Great Yorkshire Show with Valeoskene Rosary 14th under Jack Brewster of Boclair as the judge. They say breeding will out and it did in that case, she was bred from nothing and she never did breed anything, only ever having one heifer and it was a pillock. Some of you may see the Valeoskene prefix crop up now and again in results in the Canadian Holstein Journal. Bill Throup's son emigrated to Canada many years ago and has developed a successful business over there.

In August of that year we were investigating some kind of automated feeding in the milking parlour. When someone from MAFF came to see about whether we would be eligible for any grant, they enquired as to what the current method of feeding was. When told it was a big shovel - the answer was definitely yes, so we put in a computer controlled feeding box to feed from the hoppers from the granary above rather than the old wheeled feed trolleys that came underneath from the meal house, a big improvement and much easier on the back! Also in August of that year, Francis Dent, mentioned previously buying straw in pouring rain, moved with his family from Walden into Cote House opposite and were the best of neighbours for the next almost forty years.

We had another holiday to Norway that autumn, and the first day there demonstrated to me the difference in culture between the two countries with regard to labour relations, hours of work and such like. We were having lunch on the Friday after arriving and I noticed there was just half a row of unpicked potatoes in the field next door, which was only about three acres, and asked Colin if they had had a breakdown. Oh no he said it was lunchtime and we all stop at lunchtime on a Friday! We always struggled to understand how these very small Norwegian farms seemed to make a good living with fairly new tractors and vehicles in evidence, but eventually one night we got Yarle, (who was one of the original group of Norwegian Young Farmers who stayed at Clapham Lodge on the exchange visit) with just enough drink to loosen his tongue and he explained that written in the Norwegian constitution was that farmers had to have no worse a standard of living than the national average. All farmers received an acreage payment, which meant on the better land they were doing very well, the reasoning being that if they didn't, large parts of the country would be totally wild and de-populated. If the dairy farmers didn't want to milk more than six days a week, if six of them joined together to employ someone for the seventh day, then the government picked up something like 75% of the bill. If they only wanted a five day week and employed a second man, about half his salary was paid by the state.

A little later we had a couple of bulls down at Reading for the Society Bull Show and Sale which was one of the social occasions of the year as well as an important bull market. That particular year we had Dalesend Hustler who was a Grove Jester from the Dalesend OK Belle cow entered. A good looking, well grown black bull and he was sold at 1700gns to go to Munster Cattle Breeders in the Irish Republic and so had to come back home for health tests. We were very low on petrol as we headed home, got him unloaded at Dalesend, but finally ran out of fuel at the entrance to Marwood's on the Newton road and had to walk the rest of the way home, bad enough, but it was a beautiful clear, starlight night. Imagine our disappointment the next morning when we learnt that a cow we had brought in from Canada - Judy had failed an EBL health test and fastened us up for a while meaning the bull couldn't go and the sale was cancelled. He eventually went at the same price to George Corner's, Cinnamire herd at East Harlsey.

Mr J had been struggling for a while to fully convince me of the merits of Holstein cattle. Having himself earlier spent some time at Pabst Farms in America he was already convinced and marched into the office one day and announced that he had booked my ticket to go to Canada as it was the only way I would be convinced. We changed the dates as I wasn't prepared to go on the "Winter Fair Tour" and just go round all the top herds - I wanted to see all sorts and get a balanced view. So off I went in late November, sleeper train down to Kings Cross and then out to Heathrow for the flight. I was met in Toronto by Orton Eby, our man in Canada and he and his wife Dolores looked after me for the time I was there. We went to the Eleeta herd of Murray Eliot who had this great theory that if cows were facing south when they were inseminated they had heifer calves, I did later discover there had been some research work done on this which was inconclusive but certainly there seemed to be heifers everywhere at Eleeta. Orton took me to Agro Acres, they were of Italian descent and were some of the wealthier people in Ontario, originally having been fruit importers and distributors who had turned their attention to cattle breeding and bought in its entirety what had been one of the top herds - Sheffield and with it the Pansy and Patsy families. There were two brothers and the unmarried one lived with the sister in a little bungalow. Angelo who showed us round that day had a bad leg which was bandaged, but as we went round it came undone and gradually unwound until we were walking in the tie-stall barn with about 40 foot of bandage trailing behind which didn't seem to concern him in the slightest. When we went into the office I remember there was a bank of television screens, all on with different channels on each. They had also that morning just calved their first daughter of Paclamar Astronaut and it was not very good. They were large scale dealers in semen at the time and had bought up a lot as reports of them being very good began to come through, but as soon as this bad one calved, they just ditched the lot of it.

We called at the farm of Eldon J Cubitt and his Hyways herd, this was where Jim Alston bought Dalesend Cascade - the one remembrance I have of that farm was the number of flies on the walls in the cattle shed - it was black over with them.

We visited Roybrook and were shown round by the great Roy Ormiston - remember Orton was great friends with all these top breeders having been one himself and at that time was the only man to have judged the Royal Winter Fair twice. The Roybrook herd at that time had been very much in-bred and lost quite a bit of front end strength, but Mr Ormiston was realising he had gone too far and had bought in a cow from one of his families that had been elsewhere and so had outcrosses - Melissa was nearly big enough to eat one of the others for lunch.

Werrcroft of Mr Ron Werry at Oshawa had been one of the joint owners of Roybrook Telstar when he hit the real headlines as a sire of sires and had a good herd of cows run more commercially than some of the leading herds. It was my first meeting with the people who were to give Sarah such a good grounding for six months some fifteen years later.

Oakridges was one of the top show herds of the time with a magnificent trophy room with them all on display. Owned by a businessman but managed by George Darrah, he wore a big stetson and was a most imposing figure. His son who also worked on the farm arrived back from being somewhere up country and he looked just like "Hoss" from Ponderosa a popular television programme we had in England at that time.

One of our last visits on the Saturday was to the Sunny Maple herd of Gerry Livingstone who at that time was housing the "Quality" cows for Paul Eckstein, before he got his own farm. There were some terrific cows there but we didn't meet Mr Eckstein that trip - he was away that day at his son Ari's bar mitzvah.

I was coming home on the Sunday, and as very few Canadians wanted visitors on that day and my flight wasn't until into the evening, Orton and Dolores took me back to Toronto, via Niagara Falls. There had been about eight inches of snow over night, but that day it was bright, clear sunshine and everywhere there was almost magical - the trees were draped in snow and the falls were magnificent and at that time had not become overrun with Japanese tourists. I had some fantastic slides of that day which everyone admired, the first time after that when I took Marnie with me, we went to see them and to be honest, you wouldn't have crossed the road, it was dull, miserable and drizzling rain, and they weren't at all impressive - we have seen them again since when they looked rather better.

Arriving back into King's Cross from Heathrow, the Monday morning was the first day of Smithfield and it was quite enlightening to meet all the farmers arriving for the next day or two's show coming down the platform to meet you, you could pick them out a mile away!

Into 1980 and back to N.E. Club business, our annual dinner and prizegiving was in February and Jim Burrow from Stardale had been our herds competition judge, and he and Mrs Burrow stayed with us overnight, I remember they brought Sarah an Easter egg and she charmed them and another lifelong association was forged. It is quite remarkable how now three generations of the family have each forged tremendous herds at Stardale at different times in cattle breeding, Robert who was on the Holstein

UK Board as I was and then subsequently handed over to James who has continued that great work and the herd was just as good the last time we were there in 2016 and seeing Mr Burrow still fit and active in his upper 90's.

The weekend after that we had a short break down to London and went to see the "Mousetrap" which was then in its 28th year. Quite amazing that it is still going strong to this day - marking its 65th year, the longest running production ever, anywhere in the world.

In May of that year it was another NE Club trip, this time to the Isle of Man - we had a good trip though didn't see many good cows, it was rather good to come home and see better ones, whereas if you went for instance to South Wales and visited Grove, Deri and Brynhyfryd among others, you were somewhat disillusioned with your own efforts. While we were over on the Isle of Man there was a ferryman's strike so we had to either come home a day early or stay an extra day, everyone wanted to stay for the extra day except Mr J who was club President at the time, so he came home, it was too small and steady for him.

Again, Marnie didn't go on the trip as Sarah had just started school about two weeks earlier and it didn't seem fair to leave her parentless so soon. We knew at the time that the school at Newton-le-Willows was due to close the following year and so Sarah went straight to Crakehall right from the start rather than having to have a change after four terms. One of the teachers at Newton-le-Willows was Miss Allbut who I knew through Church meetings and she was acutely embarrassed a year or two later at Richmond Swimming baths. I had taken Sarah up one Saturday morning for a lesson and went for a swim myself while she was having it. Miss Allbut was also swimming but didn't show any recognition. Up in the foyer afterwards she suddenly realised who it was and said out loud in front of a lot of people "Oh I didn't recognise you with no clothes on" and suddenly realised what she had said and scurried away very red faced.

In July of that year we were invited to represent the N.E. Club at the lunch at Durham County Show on the first day. It was at that time quite a large, well attended show, held on the red soil of Lord Lambton's estate. It was a horrible wet day, following a wet week, but going for such an event, we had to get dressed up in all our finery. As we headed for the lunch tent where it was to take place, a vehicle came along the roadway, hit a big puddle and covered us in red water and mud. There was on the television at the time for a firm called "Harton Clean" and the advert was exactly that same scenario, and if we ever get splashed or see someone else get splashed we always have a laugh about the day we were "Harton cleaned".

I had a bit of fun one night later that summer. I was awoken during the night by a lot of noise from the calving yard across past the parlour - knowing that Dalesend Marigold 7 a good Broker daughter was on the point of calving, I got up to see if she was ok. Being a warm September night I didn't bother getting dressed, just went out in my pyjama bottoms and wellies, to find that she had already calved but the calf was outside, the wrong side of the gate. I put the calf back under the gate and immediately saw the error of my ways as she set about the calf as very occasionally cows do, but this time she started butting and pushing it away from the gate and I couldn't reach it over the gate. Thinking I was hardly dressed for an encounter with a mad heifer, I had to go back into the house and get properly dressed before I rescued the calf. I imagined Marigold 7 would be a real pain when we got her into milk, but she was never any trouble and developed into a very good multiple Excellent mature cow.

Through the previous few years, we had some good young men work for us, some of them as one year pre-college students from Askham Bryan, and some just to work full time. John Coles was a big useful lad for a year who Bill kept in touch with and Phillip Bottomley was another. He came from Sowerby Bridge and was very good with stock, after college we were looking for someone to look after the young stock at Dalesend and Phillip fitted the bill and so came back to us full time but must have been nearly the shortest employee we ever had. He had barely been back a week when his uncle who had a farm had a heart attack and Phillip was offered the chance to go back and take it over, he obviously was not going to pass up that chance and so he went back to South Yorkshire. A similar thing happened when I gave up milking at Fox Park, we had appointed Chris Brown to be the herdsman and again he had only been there a week or two when he had the chance to take over the farm of his future Father-in-law when he was taken very ill. Chris later became quite well known in the area as a mountaineer and did a lot of speaking and charity work over the years.

Howard Jackson came to us straight from school. He lived just outside Masham and initially travelled to work on his motorbike. His father I had known for quite a while, he having been a rep for Chapman and Frearson. He came just as a young lad with a good work ethic and very quickly developed into an outstanding arable man - as far as I know and at least as far as I am concerned he coined the word "growler" for a pork pie and he always said if he couldn't eat all his lunch he threw it away or fed it to a dog and would never take any back home or there would be one piece less in his bait box the following day. Howard stayed with us for a considerable time before eventually going to work at l'Ansons at Masham where he worked his way up through the business and for some years now has been their chief materials buyer, and I believe is a director in the company. Howard will therefore be very well known to many of the local farmers, and if I ever go into l'Ansons to get some feed and he comes for a talk, the office girls are not used to someone talking to him as I do!

Another lad who gave us great service over a few years was David Daniels. David came to help Bill at nights, weekends and in the holidays while still at school. He was a very slightly built lad, but as hard as nails, and even then had a motorbike which he used to come across the fields from Patrick Brompton where they lived (his father worked for Sammy Hudson at Manor Farm). I remember one time he was stood on the back of his motorbike as Bill drove it down to Fox Park and he fell off and on the stone track badly skinned all of his back, a real mess, but he just took it all in his stride. When he started full time after school he was mostly based at Dalesend with the young stock and did some weekend milking. As we were preparing for one of our draft sales, he did a lot of the work with me in halter breaking them and got very excited one day when one of them knocked me over as I led it down the race and jumped or walked all over me. He thought I was badly hurt and couldn't believe it when I asked him what was the matter - the heifer had not put a foot on me, simply placing them down either side. In preparing for that same sale, we used to walk them down the drive to the bridge and back, and if they did ok we called them led. One particular heifer had been a bit of a problem and I set off with her, she immediately shot past me and pulled me over as she galloped away, but I clung to the halter and she pulled me on my belly all the way to the bridge, stopped and looked round as if to say - are you still there, I got to my feet and walked all the way back up to the byre with never any more problem. Again at that sale we had a very milky second calver entered who was by Dalesend Cascade, but had rather too much udder. On the morning of the sale Chris Norton wanted me to withdraw her but I refused and David was the leadsman when her turn came in the ring. Tom was selling at the time and started off very low down but her large heifer yield made her a target for a few people. It was the first time in the ring for David and when she got to 1000 his legs began to buckle a bit, at 1500 he was struggling to keep a straight face as was I when I looked at Chris Norton in the box and he was the same. Eventually the hammer dropped at 1900gns and speaking to the buyer afterwards he couldn't believe how lucky he was to have bought her so cheaply. Just goes to show how different people have different ideas on what constitutes a desirable animal.

David and some of his friends used to often have a game of football on the big lawn across the yard. Sarah was only five or six at the time and mad keen on Liverpool as a football club, she had the kit, and it was her football they used. She always wanted to play with these great big lads, but David always looked after her, made sure they didn't bundle her over and gave her chance to have a few kicks.

Although it came somewhat later and will be mentioned somewhere later, David was still with us when we did all the building work in the new cow building in 1986. He was the chief pointer after Peter and Malcolm had laid the blocks and very good he was at it. I have a photo of him sat up on a block up on the big trailer alongside a wall one day and he had fallen asleep mid-point.

Not that much later than that, he began to mix with one or two lads he would have been better avoiding and got rather too much drink too many times and eventually got breathalysed and lost his licence. By then apart from Dalesend he also milked every other weekend at Newton Grange and I told him he could keep his job as long as he got to milk as usual. This he did and used to run across the fields, though I was rather taken aback one morning on going into the parlour to find him like a drowned rat. It was winter time and on his way to milk in the dark that morning he had fallen off the bridge across Crakehall beck and into the water which was quite full at the time.

Unfortunately David didn't get back on track and one or two weekends I had to start milking as he was late and after several warnings and a final warning I was half way through milking when he arrived and knew that we had got to the end of the road. He worked locally on one or two farms for a while after that, but sadly he was killed in a motorcycle accident not long after, a terrible waste of such a young life and I always remember with great affection.

In the autumn of 1980 there was a lot of activity around the area and in the parish preparing for the 800th Anniversary of St Patricks Church at Patrick Brompton, we had all kinds of displays, choirs etc, teas and the celebrant on the Sunday was the Archbishop of York. At about the same time, Mr J went on his own to the Stardale sale, got drawn into something of a contest with a member of one of the other private AI companies and finished up paying 8000gns for Stardale Regal Vaakje 3 who was only a few weeks away from calving. Ten days later she calved a bit early with a dead deformed calf, and being aware that he was going away on his weeks salmon fishing on the Tweed that Sunday afternoon, I rung him to come and see for himself rather than think there had been any negligence on either mine or Bill's part. He summed it up marvellously as soon as he got out of his car, "We are cattle farmers and where there's life, there's death". The Vaakje family are a wonderful family at Stardale, but apart from one really good daughter we never got them going.

By then we had Black Welsh Mountain sheep for decoration in the park in the front of Dalesend. Lovely lamb to eat but they were wild as hawks. The tup got out onto the road one day and it went at full tilt along the road with Stewart in pursuit. He eventually caught up with it just outside Crakehall when it ran into the front of a Land Rover - the tup was ok, but he bent the bumper on the Land Rover – reminds me of years later when we sold a Black Welsh tup for breeding over Pickering way. We delivered him one afternoon and the man was highly delighted but then rung the next morning to see if we had another one, the first one had charged into a tree during the night and broken his neck, unfortunately we hadn't another one to sell him and he had to get fit up elsewhere.

It was a sad end to the year and the start of the next. Hubert, the gardener, handyman at Dalesend, though semi-retired, collapsed and died while they were having the annual family shoot on the last day of the year, and just three days later after a short spell in hospital Marnie's father passed away. The end of a marvellous man who would talk with anyone and help anybody if he could.

Not long after that at the end of January, the North East Club had Henry Willison from Tullithwaite and Bill Towers from Aldingham to do a question and answer interview, and they both stayed over night with us. The next day we had a look round the cows and the young stock at Dalesend. They both picked out a striking black in calf heifer by Judo out of Cascade Belle, the at the time heifer used to confuse the judging competition already referred to. They weren't far wrong in their assessment of her. She went on to win the milk heifer class at the Great Yorkshire Show, before being sold shortly afterwards for big money at our draft sale.

In early May of that year, we had a weekend away down into Staffordshire, on the Saturday afternoon we were walking through Burton-on-Trent when there was a big shout out "What are you doing here", it was Bill Higson from college with an old tractor and trailer. He got off and came to talk, not at all concerned that he had completely blocked the traffic flow, but eventually got back on and released the blockage. He and Roberta came and had dinner with us that night. Just before that, at the end of April we had an unusually heavy fall of snow for that time of year, eight and a half inches in the day. Fortunately at that time of year it didn't hang around for too long, but it was a hell of a mess when it thawed!

In the summer holidays of that year we had a day off to go to the seaside – Runswick Bay, but the only thing I remember is having sand sandwiches for lunch.

Sarah had not long started school and one morning went to her bedroom after breakfast to tidy up before going to school, when she suddenly shouted down excitedly "Dad, Dad, there is a wagon coming up the drive with some giant cups on it." – They were some big circular concrete/composition water troughs being delivered.

In the early 1980's, you were still allowed to burn straw in the field, and we did so with a fair acreage at that time, always observing the safety aspects of doing so – or we did if I or any of the men were doing so, but Mr J was always impatient and couldn't wait for any safety ploughing round the hedgebacks or such like. He was a real pyro-maniac, loved to be having a fire and I got a visit from him late one afternoon up at the drier at Old Park House to tell me he had had a fire in the Plantation field at Hill Top East and it had got away on him and he had to call the fire brigade as it got into a hedge bottom. I think that finally taught him a lesson, and it wasn't long before legislation changed and you were no longer allowed to do such things.

At the end of autumn of that year, Mr J decided he needed to sell the two farms the other side of the Leyburn road in order to finance the expansion of Dalepak Foods as it headed towards becoming a PLC. Arbour Hill and Old Park House went on the market and were auctioned on the 17th November, when again to illustrate how values have increased so markedly since then, Old Park House was sold for £249,000, but Arbour Hill was unsold for £334,000, though later sold below that figure. In that time equated to about £1500 per acre, whereas now it would probably be about £9000 - £10,000.

About the same time, we popped up to Finghall one Saturday night to see the ploughing at the Chapman's farm which was setting a new world record endurance ploughing record, not being very exciting in itself but you must never miss the chance to witness some of those kind of things.

With the sale of the top two farms, it brought about quite a change on the rest of the farm, it was both a bit unsettling for some of the men, and we needed to reduce the work force anyway. Paul Turner, mentioned earlier who lived at Old Park House obviously had to move out of the house, and his job disappeared, Stewart who lived in Arbour Hill and was the main man at Dalesend also left to go and work with brother in law Stephen Knox at Mill Close, leaving just David at Dalesend which was ok, and then in late January of the following year, Howard as also mentioned earlier went as a trainee to I'Ansons, after a good seven and a half years. At that time we took a short term student for a few months – Mark Hinton, son of David Hinton, one of the two brothers who had the very successful chain of Hinton's supermarkets in the North East, before it was later Safeway, which ultimately became part of Morrisons. Mark wanted to become a farmer, he had already had a spell of arable work with Martin Webster at Roundhill, worked with us on stock for about five months before Mr J arranged for him to go to Canada for six months and work with Orton Eby who with his son had by then started his "Heritage" herd. Later Mark and his Father bought part of the Kirby Fleetham Estate where Mark still farms very successfully to this day and are about to install a massive solar panel 'farm'. They became keen supporters and users within the Patrick Brompton Buying Group until it finally became outdated and was closed down about six or seven years ago.

Mother always had her family Christmas party on the Sunday before Christmas, so that it didn't get in the way of all the younger grandchildren and the other side of families relations. That particular year (1981) we got up on the Sunday morning to a lot of snow, still snowing and fairly windy, so that it had drifted quite badly. The first thing to do with the Kramer was to clear the drive and so far down the back road so that the milk tanker could get in. We decided to go to Mother's for her Christmas lunch on the tractor, so we were sure of getting there and more importantly could get back if it kept on drifting. We were fortunate it was only three miles or so to Aiskew, we met Howard en-route who had got stuck in a snowdrift in coming to see if we needed digging out, and got him pulled out. Fortunately we hadn't got overly dressed up as the day was or would have been a real mess. While we were at Mothers I suddenly discovered the keys for the tractor had gone missing, they were eventually found somewhere on the tractor floor where they had dropped as we got out and so we were able to get back home. Mary, Eric and family didn't come from Ripon because of the weather, so there was plenty to eat, as always. Subsequently we were very glad we had made the effort to go despite the weather, as it was the last time Mother ever had her Christmas lunch. When that snow melted after the frost of the time had also gone, there were floods everywhere with all the local rivers having burst their banks, Boroughbridge, West Tanfield and Morton-on-Swale were all cut off.

It was into the spring of 1982 that we had our first brush with officialdom over child welfare. No I tell a lie, the first one was when Sarah was a new born baby and the health visitor came to see her, Marnie got told off because she wouldn't wake Sarah up for her to have a look – so she had to have a cup of tea and wait. On this occasion which was a Sunday afternoon and we were doing a bit of gardening and tidying up in the yard and Sarah was riding about on her bike and went off down the drive. All of a sudden there was such a wailing noise as she came walking back up the hill into the yard. She had come off down the drive and bumped her face causing a heavy nose bleed which she was catching in her upturned toy helmet so she didn't get it on her clothes. She was soon calmed down but the blood was slow to stop and we thought we had better take her to hospital to be sure no further damage had been done. Once there we were asked repeatedly what had happened, and it wasn't until they wanted to speak to Sarah on her own at six and a half years old without us that it dawned on us that they were thinking we had badly abused her. Fortunately we all told the same tale all the time, and after spending the night in hospital to check for concussion she was back home none the worse the next day. What a pity that then as even now, many of the real cases of child abuse never get picked up by the authorities. Talking of nose bleeds, one of the very few I have ever had was when I was a young boy up at Middlesmoor. I very proudly had a little flag on the handlebars of my three wheeler as I raced about the yard, when going over a bump my head went forward and the pennant went right up my nostril causing a fair amount of bleeding – but I was never any the worse for it.

Later that spring, Marnie got involved with a lot of sewing for the Church at Patrick Brompton as they made all new altar clothes, orferies and all the other decorations for the various vestments. They were all done in gold thread. It took many of them many hours of toil to produce this magnificent work. It wasn't until later they were informed that sewing with gold and silver kid should never be done in electric light to protect their eyes. Marnie's eyesight had always been fantastic until then, and it was very soon after that that she had to start and wear glasses.

For anyone who is interested in or remembers Bedale at that time, that spring saw the development of a small shopping arcade in what had been years before the old cinema and The Land of Green Ginger was opened on the 2nd of April. I don't know where the name came from, but its unusualness didn't help too much, and it didn't last too long as a shopping arcade.

Later that month we had a bit more excitement when Valeoskene Lustrous 60 (the poorest of the three Ridgwardine Broker heifers that came from Aberdeen, but ultimately proved the best breeder of them and started a nice line of females) somehow got into the dairy and got wedged between the tank and the wall. She always was a bit headstrong and wouldn't be knocked backwards and eventually we had to jack the tank across to get her out. No harm was done and a fortnight later she produced a good pair of healthy twin heifer calves.

It was a fairly eventful summer that year, we had a new vicar Raymond Pearson inducted for the local parishes and he did a lot of good work for quite a few years. During the summer we had a visit to inspect a young Herdwise bull from the Ministry, - a new young vet called Andrew Cherkowski, whom Bill could never get his tongue around and always called him Mr Tchaikovsky. We saw quite a bit of him, and his wife, who was also a Ministry vet over the years, but had not seen them for a long time until just last year, when they were in the same queue in a café in Ripon waiting to order lunch. We were having one or two drainage problems away from the parlour and dairy and which went way across the Hen field and down behind Fox Park before making its way to Low Wood, and we decided to see if we could get it going the other way to a settling tank and towards the railway. A big trench was open across the yard with string and fertiliser bags tied to it to stop anything coming into the yard the normal way. The milk tanker driver, at that time still MMB, was either asleep and not paying attention or thought it didn't apply to him and came at full speed through the blockade and was embedded in the ditch with the front wheels right down till he was bellied – and took a lot of getting out as all the milk came to the front of the tanker.

Bill's son Robert started to work for us that summer – a useful lad on a tractor, but hated some of the other jobs that a lad gets to do – particularly cutting the lawns in the farmyard to fill in the last hour or so on a Friday afternoon, you could see how he disliked the job as he did it badly and never got any better. By then we were housing quite a lot of bulls in isolation at Fox Park for Herdwise – they were bedded on shavings on a sleeper bed and I taught Robert how to cut round a bale and then just duck your knees into it to snap the piece off, but try as he might he could never master the knack of doing it.

We did quite a bit of showing in the 1982 season, and three particular things stand out, one bad, one good and one actually nothing to do with showing. We showed that year at the Royal Show and as was our usual practice, stayed overnight at the end of the show, everything packed up and loaded onto the lorry so that the cattle were just to milk the next morning and load them – there was just one problem – someone had stolen the milking machine apart from the lid – they had taken the bucket and all the rubbers and the milking claw and liners, what was really upsetting was that it had to be a fellow dairy exhibitor to be able to know where all the things were left in the dairy. Soon after that we did two local shows Ryedale and Driffield, which were two days in a row. I had arranged to stay overnight at a Mr Stonehouse's where we could get the cows milked and plenty of room to rest. Mr Stonehouse kept geese as well and I remember that night as darkness fell, the geese all settled down in a small paddock in a circle all facing out over – whether that was their usual routine or because strangers were there we know not. The next morning we were up and away early over the Wolds to Driffield, and as we went over one hill end in the half light we saw four pea viners coming across the field with all their lights ablaze, they were like alien machines from another world. The good bit took place a little later when Dalesend Star Rosette was Champion Black and White and Reserve overall in the Spillers 3 day Economic Milking Trials. It was the second time she had been Reserve Champion and it was a wonderful feat of stockmanship by Bill to take a 10th calf cow just 10 days calved that distance and do that.

In early August I remember Eric and Gladys Comeley from the Summercourt herd staying overnight at Dalesend and showing them round. When we were in the small fold yard at Dalesend looking at the show team I was smoking a cigarette, (I didn't stop for about another four years after that) and Mrs Comeley gave me a real bollocking for smoking inside. When she had finished she got an even bigger one from Eric for being so rude when they were our guests.

At that time, as mentioned earlier, we used to house and get tested and take the test semen from many of the young progeny test bulls for Herdwise. One such bull was Farleton Roulette from George Robinsons and he was just about a year old when he was to have his first lot of tests and he had never been a problem, but that day as we put him into the short race into the crush, he suddenly turned and came straight at me with his head down and hit me full on with his head right on the knee, knocking me down and leaving me with a very sore twisted knee. I was barely able to walk or drive and went to see Mr Stowe the chiropractor who operated from a room in Haxby, he couldn't do much for the knee except tell me to massage into it the lather from

Sunlight soap. It eased the pain and was gradually getting better until Roulette was due his second set of tests 30 days later. I was well prepared for any eventuality after the first experience, but, damn me if he didn't do exactly the same thing, hit the same knee and put me down again – but he did a good job – I got up and walked away and could tell something had popped back into place and it was never any more bother. Roulette never made it back into service.

The day after he knocked me down the first time, I was due to go on a Herdwise stock committee trip over into Lancashire to look at various potential contract matings or bulls coming back with proofs. As I was unable to drive, Marnie had to drive me and the highlight of the day was lunch, we shall never forget. We had a full days schedule and John Williams who was at that time Herdwise Livestock Officer, treated us to lunch – a bag of crisps each and we stood by the roadside at Burton in Lonsdale - we still have a laugh about it every time we go past the spot.

At the same time, while my knee was well enough for me to drive, but still delicate if I was on it for a long while, we had some bulls entered at Paisley and Marnie went with me to do the water, feed carrying etc. We had for quite a few years when we sold up there two or three times a year stayed with a Mr and Mrs Martin just a short walk from the auction mart. Mrs Martin, though now retired had worked in the café in the mart, Mr Martin had been a factory worker but had a very bad chest from years of cigarettes among other things and didn't do much except sit about and read the newspaper. It was the first time Marnie had been up there with me or met the Martin's, which was something of an experience – the abiding memory was of the orange for breakfast – it wasn't orange juice, it was fairly weak orange squash – that as a breakfast experience ranks alongside one time down at the Reading Bull Sale when Bob Ede of Herdwise had booked a bed and breakfast room for us, two single beds separated by a wardrobe that we could peep at each other behind, but the speciality was half a slice of fried luncheon meat for breakfast – we have lived at times!!

Back to shows again, and whilst at the Royal Show that year, we had arranged a meeting with Malcolm Peasnall, Mr J and myself with an Iranian. He had developed a way of sexing semen (many years before Cogent hit the market with a true version), but he had run out of money to just finalise the research, believing that such a product would give us a major lead in the AI industry, we paid him £1000 to complete his work, needless to say we never saw him, his research or the sexed semen ever again.

Later that same year we were showing at Stokesley Show which is usually about the 20th September, that year it turned out to be one of the hottest days I can ever remember, not only that Marnie was doing the wedding reception for one of Dennis Lamb's daughters at Carnaby, and their biggest problem was keeping all the sweets, butter etc.. from melting and running off the plates.

That same autumn we had cattle at the Society heifer sale at Lancaster – it was at the time when Dalesend Cascade was right at the height of his popularity, and I well remember one very prominent Lancashire breeder who at that time was totally defensive of the British Friesians – invited Mr J and I round the back of the auction mart to order 50 straws of Cascade as he didn't want to be seen or overheard ordering it.

The sadness of 1982 was the sudden death of Mother at the end of October. She had not been ill, though she had had shingles earlier in the year. This particular Sunday she had been along to Aiskew Chapel for the service with her friend. When they walked back Mother made coffee or rather put the kettle on, but before it had boiled she had a massive brain haemorrhage, the other lady rang me at home and by the time I got there she had gone. A wonderful lady who again helped anyone do anything, it was always she when we were young, rather than father who played cricket or got stuck in goal when it was football. It was just as well we had gone for that Christmas lunch on the tractor in the snow the previous year – it was her last one. Whilst it left a large sudden hole when she went so quickly, there was always the consolation that she had never suffered even for a couple of minutes.

Not that long before that, probably earlier that summer I met her in Bedale one market day. She asked if I would look after her shopping trolley/basket while she went to the toilet, (at that time they were just outside the post office), I said no I wouldn't be seen doing that, I knew too many people who would laugh at me if they saw me. I told her to leave it stood over by the shop front on the pavement and I would hover at a distance and keep my eyes on it until she returned. Mother had a very good Christmas rose at Hideaway and it was written into the deeds that when it was sold the plant was to be removed. It transplanted well up to our garden but then gradually over the years got smaller and smaller until it eventually disappeared – I guess they only have a certain life. We keep trying to keep one growing now at Harkness Close in her memory, but have tried about three so far, though the current one is I think the most likely to succeed.

I don't think the temperature had anything to do with the survival or otherwise of the Christmas rose, but there were two occasions when temperature is remembered about that time. One was just before the Christmas of 1982, when we went to Solberge Hall for a meal. It wasn't very busy, I think there was only one other couple in the dining room, but it was bitterly cold, there was no heating on for some reason and we shivered our way through a good meal but couldn't get home quick enough to get warmed up. The other extreme was in the following summer when we went down for the Royal Show when it must have had the best weather it ever had. It was boiling hot from a clear blue sky the whole time and right up to bedtime was such a balmy atmosphere, we well remember staying overnight at Bidford-on-Avon and going for a walk just as dusk fell.

Weather was quite a feature round about then for a variety of reasons, that stick in the memory. One was in June and David and I were worming the in calf heifers up at Hill Top East. We had just got them into the holding pen when the heavens opened and it absolutely poured down. Having got the cattle in we were going to do the job, which we did, not before the water was pretty well running out of the top of our wellingtons. David was so wet and dirty I wouldn't let him ride home in the car. Fortunately the trailer was on the back and he came home in that! A little later into the summer of 1983, we were virtually overrun with mushrooms. At that time we were still growing some kale for the cows and that particular year it was at the far end of the 20 acre. Where the grass had been sprayed off after first cut silage, as the Kale began to get some cover, there grew the most amazing crop of mushrooms I have ever seen, before or since. We picked and ate them for about three weeks, put 100lbs of them into the freezer in various forms and invited all and sundry to pick some, but still many went to waste. Fortunately, the kale survived all the trampling and produced a good crop.

At the time of the fantastic mushroom crop, we went down to West Wales for the dispersal of what was undoubtedly at the time the leading herd of dairy cattle in the country – the Grove herd of Dyfrig Williams, the timing of the sale could not have been better planned, it was just at the time of the swing over to Holstein blood, and those pure British Friesian families would not have been in such high demand only a few months later. We went down the day before the sale and went to view the cattle. Jim Alston of Uphall had been using Holstein blood for may years and liked a big, rangy cow, (even though he was a small man) for the wide open spaces of East Anglia where there was plenty of arable by products to feed. Mr Alston always used the expression "It won't do" if something wasn't to his liking, when we met him as he came out of the field as we went in we exchanged pleasantries and I asked him what the cattle were like. His response "They won't do – even I can see over them." On sale morning there was perhaps the largest collection of people for a cattle sale there had ever been or likely to be in the future. Many people got there very early to be sure of a seat, ourselves included and I well remember Chris Norton testing all the microphones in readiness and with darts having just become very popular on the television calling out "180" to tumultuous applause. The trade was electric throughout with some fantastic prices. The true measure of Mr Williams breeding came just over a year later at the 75th Anniversary Show at Stoneleigh, where he was the judge of the milking classes. Mr Archer who was judging the dry cows had to act as a referee for much of the day, as so many animals from the Grove sale where shown, and the Grove herd of Mr Williams finished up being Premier Breeder.

In early 1983 Peter Sproates came to work for us in charge of the tractor, arable side and was a very good lad for several years, and he will crop up a few times in the coming pages, particularly around the time we were doing the new cow building in 1986. He was unmarried at the time but moved into the bungalow and got married later that year to Dianne. Subsequently they had a son Sean, who was much the same age as Adam and they played together a lot in the yard in the fullness of time.

During that summer David Jones, who many will remember as the chief man at NMR offices in Harrogate and for many years acted as the secretary for the Yorkshire Herds Competition, asked if he could bring a coach load from the offices to look round the farms, many of them had never been on a farm before. We looked after them very well, showed them all round the dairy herd and buildings before a cream tea. To round off the day we took them down to Fox Park to see the Herdwise bulls which were housed there. Many of them had never seen a bull before and were unaware of the sheer size and scale of a mature Holstein, and one or two of the women were quite excited by the size of a mature bulls testicles and sheath.

During the late 70's and early 80's we sold a lot of young bulls at the Reading, Crewe, Lancaster and Paisley sales, and these were usually in October and November and much of the time in October was spent walking all these bulls in readiness for the sale. I mostly did this myself and never had any bother with them until 1983, when one particular bull, a decent bull Dalesend Prejudice out of Dalesend Adema Pansy the matriarch of the family, was entered for the Wexham Cup, but he had a nasty turn to him and I didn't get him much exercise until I persuaded the vet to leave me some "Rumpon" a sedative injection which he warned me was very severe and the dose required was very small. Little did I realise how small until after about ¾ of a cc he collapsed on me on the drive at Dalesend and I had to stand and wait until he recovered to get him back into his pen. The day after an even smaller dose just got him back in before he collapsed across the front of his bed. He eventually went to Crewe but was unfortunately unsold. His mother and sister were there for the Wexham Cup and I could only bring two back in the trailer. Tony Bell (from Holmland) took the bull home for me to pick up from over there the following day. The only thing was I forgot to tell Tony he had a bit of a temperament problem, but all ended well as he was well behaved and came home no problem and he was by then quietened down as the "Rumpon" obviously had a cumulative effect.

That same autumn we had a bull calf due to be born as a contract mating for Genus and two others contracted for MAFF who still then ran the AI Centre at Reading. Guess what – all three had heifer calves – the amazing one was Dalesend Lettice 2 who was a Holmland Adema daughter. We had a run of 16 bull calves in a row apart from one in the middle which was a heifer – that's right Lettice 2's with eight bull calves either side of her.

Later that autumn we had a weekend away and stayed at the Peacock Hotel in Rowsley, Derbyshire. A lovely hotel, still very resident friendly and you were expected to dress for dinner. We did so, but not to the extent that some residents did in putting on dinner jackets and long dresses. The one abiding memory we still have of that trip was the fish course at dinner. If you had been really hungry it wouldn't have made a full mouth full, and we nearly always laugh about it whenever we are eating fish – at least it was fish – better than the lunch at Tennants in the last 12 months or so, that was virtually all batter - I don't know how the fish had been able to get so much batter onto it, but I struggled to find any meat – everyone else round about us who were eating the same, didn't seem to have any such problem.

Right at the end of 1983 I had my first conviction for speeding. At the time our farm wages were done for us by the office department of Dalepak Foods at Amen House in Bedale. Wages were still paid weekly in cash at that time and I was, as usual on my way to collect them just before lunch on Friday. When I pulled out of the Newton road there was nothing coming from Leyburn so far back as Crakehall railway bridge, but the policeman had caught me up by I was going into the town, so he hadn't been going exactly slowly. He followed me into Bedale, turned up at the Post Office and followed me into the car park at Amen House, and I still had no realisation it was me he was after. He followed me into the office, I even held the door open for him and asked in reception if he was looking for someone I could help him with, so you can appreciate I was somewhat surprised when he said it was actually me he wanted to speak to, and that I had been speeding. I did think of pleading not guilty but after consultation with a former JP I decided to accept my fate. What really bugged me when it went to court (there were no fixed penalty notices in those days), on the same day, there was someone who had come straight across the road from Hall's fish and chip shop corner, lost control and embedded the car in the front of the Halifax Building Society. He got fined £10 less than me and one less penalty point. Didn't seem quite right or fair to me!!

In the following late winter I went to a Herdwise Board meeting at Bedale, and after lunch found I could not get straight back home – the road was closed just beyond the Church, and I had to go back and out on the Thornton Watlass road to get onto the Newton road. The reason was the massive collapse of a drain under the Leyburn road just at the end of the Golf Club. It was closed for several days and all the heavy lorries had to use the side roads – making a real mess of them, mud everywhere and many of the roadside verges very badly damaged.

At half term that spring we had a weekend away to Bestwood Lodge, outside Nottingham, a very nice place with good food and a very ornate minstrels gallery around the reception area. We hadn't quite appreciated the architecture of this, until we came out of the dining room to find a little girl in a nightie on the minstrels' gallery – not causing any fuss, just watching what was going on – that's right it was Sarah! That weekend we came back by Harrogate and took her to see the live "Crackerjack" Show at the Royal Hall starring Ed Stewart.

Chapter Nine – A sudden change - Milk Quotas

The spring of 1984 was quite an eventful one, with all kinds of things happening. From a farming point of view, the 1st April saw the introduction of Milk Quotas. We had been aware for sometime that they were due to be introduced, and for several months before producers had been notified of what their quota was going to be and also the various categories under which you could appeal for more quota if you felt that the previous years production figures punished your business unfairly.

We had had a production sale in the year being used for the calculation and so our production had been a long way below normal until we got numbers built up again. Unfortunately this didn't fit in any of the categories under which you could appeal. Several other pedigree herds were similarly caught under the same basis, but appeals and enquiries at all levels were totally fruitless, and so we started the milk quota year with only about half the capacity which we really needed, and it wasn't long before we had to buy quota at what seemed an exorbitant price, but which in the fullness of time was very cheap. In those first few years of quotas the renting of quota for just the one years production became very expensive, towards the tail end of the quota year, and we were fortunate to not get involved in that, though many did, and at time took away nearly half of the price you were getting for your milk, though if you didn't have the quota, the levy did likewise.

The effect that milk quotas had initially was to make everyone look at their costs of production of the marginal litres. Milk price had been good and everyone had been chasing those extra litres with a view to getting a higher quota. Almost overnight, people cut back on concentrate feeding, and looked for far more production from forage and grazing and grassland utilisation improved for a few years, before everyone gradually slipped back to feeding more purchased feed. Eventually of course, several years later as the economics of milk production rather that the actual quota cut production in this country and for a long time there was no levy to pay as national production was well under quota, and then finally a few years ago, they were dismantled by the EU, so that we are back in a free market. For anyone who only had their initial quota, there was no capital loss to be able to use it as it had no starting value or finishing value. Anyone who had bought quota, particularly at the top end when it got up to 75p or so, there was a huge capital loss if you crystallised it and had some capital gain to set it against. The other annoying thing about quotas was that the UK as a nation, and as we always do, played everything by the book, while a lot of the other countries only paid lip-service to it - Italy for example totally ignored quotas - not one of their farmers was ever charged a levy, despite massive over production every year, and I believe their government made payments so far up to about 1992 which they never passed back to the producers. Good luck to the Italian farmers, its back to us doing everything correctly and ultimately one of the reasons so many have turned against the EU and voted to leave. Having said that, to be fair, the French and German governments in particular, who have a much larger rural vote within the general populace, have actually done a fairly good job for UK farmers in ensuring that the CAP payments have remained at high levels over the years. It only remains to be seen what happens beyond transition periods after we are no longer members of the EU.

1984 was quite an eventful year both farming wise and family life. In early spring Uncle Joe, Mother's youngest brother who had always remained a bachelor died suddenly in his sleep, and I had the unenviable task of having to go to identify him. He always used to come for a week to stay with Mother and Father, he always played dominoes at the pub from a lot younger age and you could only sit and marvel at how he knew how the dominoes would fall into place. He would sometimes on picking up his hand before any had been played, put a domino face up on the table and tell you that it would be the winning domino played, and what's more, he was usually right.

That spring, Bill's eldest daughter Jayne got married and we have a lovely photo the next day of Sarah with Mr Bill in his kilt - knobbly knees and all, and that was just a day or two after Sarah had come second at the Leyburn Tournament of Song reciting "Miss Tibbles".

1st May was Mr J's birthday and that particular year he had a memorable evening - we had a Herdwise Staff Meeting during the day, and that continued into the evening when we had a supper but also a private brain's trust which Mr J chaired, and the participants were Orton Eby and Colin George of Brynhyfryd who had been persuaded to make one of his rare excursions away from his beloved cattle in West Wales. What an amazing discussion night with two of the leading cattle men from either side of the Atlantic sharing their thoughts on cattle breeding. Mr J was supposed to be going for a birthday treat to the opera or ballet that night but Orton's wife Dolores went with Mrs J instead and they too had had a marvellous night, but Mr J said he was glad he had cattle breeding discussions instead.

In late June, the North Eastern Holstein Breeders Club had an evening herd visit up into Durham to Northsea Holsteins. It was a relatively new herd established by a businessman and managed by Harold Nicholson, a cattle man of national repute who had worked with leading herds over the years. They had bought some high priced animals and had success round the national show scene for a couple of years. It was a cold raw summers evening on an exposed farm on the edge of the North Sea (hence the prefix) but we were only shown eight cows led out on halters for us and then about 400 cows in a 40 acre field with no herd brochure to be able to identify any of them. By this time everyone was getting very disgruntled and cold and not learning anything of the breeding of the cattle, but what really capped the night, and it is the only thing people remember of that night, some 30 plus years later, is that all we were offered at the end in the garage was a cup of tea in plastic cups and a "Nice" biscuit!!

Shortly after that we had a night out at Uncle Ralph and Aunt Florrie's Golden Wedding party at Skelton. Uncle Ralph was one of Mothers older brothers - they just had one son, Ken, and he was the only Hood boy of that generation. Sadly Ken only had two daughters and so in effect the Hood name, or at least that branch of it died out.

For a year or two after we had sold Old Park House, and with it the corn drier and storage facilities, we had put all out corn through what at that time was David Hoults commercial facility at Leeming Bar. That was convenient, but you were hit quite hard by deductions, particularly if it was a dampish season, because there was both a drying charge and a weight loss charge which could add up to quite a considerable deduction together with the storage time. By now Peter Sproates was working for us, and he and his family had some connection/friendship with the Raine family who farm just past Floodbridge. As such Peter knew John Raine and Brian Donaldson and he suggested we sell corn direct to Stan Donaldson at Floodbridge for his beef enterprise and on 23rd July 1984 we took the first load of barley down there, the beginning of a long and mutually agreeable and beneficial arrangement which is still going on today with Brian at the helm. Over the years we built up the amount we took and for most of the time they took and processed all our barley and wheat to feed through their extensive beef finishing enterprise. We have never over the 33 years had a discussion on price before or during harvest but left it until settling up the bill, when we have always come to a mutually agreeable price in a short time, quite remarkable really and a tribute to the honesty and integrity of the two businesses. At the height of our tonnage it was quite usual for me to take the last load of corn down myself, weigh it off as we always did ourselves, have a cup of tea and cake and settle up for the whole lot and I would call in Bedale on the way back at the bank to pay in a cheque for up to £40,000. All in one go, as simple as that, little or no cost involved and no hassle factor - classical co-operation.

It turned very wet at the end of July and into August and brought harvest to a standstill when we still had quite a lot of winter barley ready to combine. One day as I worked in the office just before lunch Mr J came in and said he was worried about the weather and had lain awake the night before worrying about the £1000's worth of corn being wasted- was I? No I replied, I had slept as sound as a top - to which he said I shouldn't have done, I should have been awake worrying. By this time the sun was out and a light breeze was drying things up, so I said, "well I think we'll be able to get on later this afternoon and I'm fit to go, while you'll be worn out and not fit to go with being awake all night". He got up and walked out on me!!

Marnie and Sarah had gone for a few days with Lynne and the boys to stay in their caravan the previous year at Tanfield beside the River Ure and had a great time. Repeating the exercise this year, they would go to Akebar. The heavens opened on them and a day later I got a plaintiff phone call at lunchtime, "can you come and get us". Holiday over, but a hot bath and dryness soon restored things.

A month later in another spell of moderate weather, I got a somewhat unpleasant shock first thing one morning. As was my usual habit I went into the parlour to see Bill and make sure things were OK. He was milking in his underpants, wellies and apron, not a pretty sight to behold!! He had got soaked getting the cows into milk and thought this the best option. Later that month, Bill was filmed for the Tyne-Tees farming programme in a feature about vets and routine vet visits, which were just beginning to become accepted practise then, rather than a totally shotgun, problem approach. The feature was titled "While you're here" or "Before you go".

After schools went back, Crakehall juniors were doing some work on food in general, and asked if they could bring a class onto the farm to study "milk", to which we readily agreed. In those days we weren't hampered by Health and Safety considerations to the same degree as we are today, when we would have to have assessments and all sorts of things before they even set foot on the place, let alone give them unpasteurised milk and a home-made biscuit. I knew there were a couple of real rascals in that class, and it was at the time that the "A Team" was a runaway television success, so I got a cow chain draped round Bill's neck and told them before we started that this man made "BA Baracas" look like a pussy cat and any nonsense and he would sort them out. We had a marvellous afternoon and it is such a pity it is much more difficult to do such things nowadays.

In November of that year, Marnie and I went on the Herdwise trip to the Royal Winter Fair in Toronto, which included tours to most of the leading herds in that part of Ontario, where everything was presented to you as if in a shop window, which of course you were - large numbers of cattle were being imported into the UK then, and people were actively looking for good cattle. The tours for Herdwise then, were organised by Angus Mcsporran and his son Neil who was a school teacher and Angus a feed adviser in the North West of England. They made a great job of the tour and they later evolved into what is now the highly successful, specialist company Bay Farm Tours, with whom we have enjoyed four fantastic trips in recent years to South America, China, Sri Lanka and Australia. One night while on that trip a group of us went up to eat in the restaurant on the top of the CN Tower, with fantastic views out over the city of Toronto, but what I remember was when we came down to go somewhere else, there were too many of us for one cab. As we jumped into the second one, a young Robert Butterfield of "Ingleview" fame told the driver "Follow that cab", and then confided in us that he had always wanted to say that - I think he must have watched too many American gangster films when even younger. At the Winter Fair a 'fantastic' show of cattle, totally dominated by one cow - A Brookview Tony Charity from Pete Hefferings Hanoverhill show string. At that same show the Royal Classic Sale was held, our first experience of a top Canadian cattle sale, totally different to our very sedate and well ordered English ones - with shouting and going on, arms waving about, pedigree readers and the like. We were amazed to watch the larger than life character Dave "Butch" Crack operating down among the crowd. A little man had the temerity to signal a bid, at which point the massive "Butch" in full Stetson hat descended on him and continually encouraged him to continue the bidding. I think the little man was so frightened that he eventually finished up paying $18,000; I'm sure far more than he intended. A day later we attended the Rowntree Centennial Sale, where every attendee was encouraged to buy a charity ticket, the prize for which was a one ounce gold bar. I missed it by only one number - it was won by Angus Mcsporran, and he still had it in his wallet many years later. Whilst there we went one day in passing to view Niagara Falls, it was wet, cloudy, misty and miserable - you honestly wouldn't have crossed the road to see them! One night, just the two of us walked out into Toronto and ate in a Polynesian restaurant, had a very good meal, and when we paid the bill the young waiter had written on the top - have a good weekend!!. I think he thought we were a young couple on a weekend away - which we were. We flew back from that trip into Amsterdam and stayed there for the weekend - a fascinating city in all kinds of ways from the half or less dressed ladies in their windows, to the wonderful cafes and creole cake we ate for tea one day, and the Van Gogh museum, where you could follow round in his work the mental decline of the artist. A fantastic trip.

Back to reality after that and the normal work through the winter with all the stock work that goes with it, and we were beginning to have thoughts about our future in dairy farming. The buildings were not really fit for purpose anymore, and it was getting to the point where we had to put up a new set of buildings to hold more cows, or get out of the job all together. Thinking was brought to a head one wet winters day when Bill, Mr J and I were in the cubicle house talking and water was dripping in everywhere through the cracked old asbestos roof about which Bill was complaining. He wasn't impressed or amused, and I can't say I blamed him, when I told him it wasn't a problem in good weather. A year of planning from there and we will return to that in the next chapter.

In the spring of 1985 we had a short trip in the Easter holidays to Dorset to visit "My Malcolm" the saviour from the electric fence wire of years earlier. By then Malcolm was managing a large estate down there for a gentleman who was also chairman of a PLC brewing company. Lovely countryside with all the valleys among the chalk downs and we had a good couple of days, looking round the farms and the area, and getting sheep back in when they escaped – you never get far away from such things even when on holiday! On the way back home we called in at Alton Towers in Staffordshire, still on the go today but relatively new in those days. A fascinating place to visit and we had a great day – I still have the badge saying "I rode the 'Corkscrew' and survived". I never have been a lover of such things and was aware of ducking as we came to every supporting pillar or girder – stupid me, if it was beheading people it would soon have been out of business.

Soon after I was playing football with Sarah in our very large bedroom when I twisted my ankle quite badly and hobbled about for a while. I damaged ankle ligaments when playing rugby at College and thereafter always had to be careful on a rough surface or anything. One time I did it as we were going to Beamish for the day. As we went round the outside of the kitchen to the car, I got off the edge of the path and tweaked it, and as I had by then learnt to do, fell to the floor immediately to take the weight off it. Marnie, Sarah and Muv just stood and howled with laughter at my downfall, not giving a thought to the agony I was in, but I did manage to hobble round Beamish all day – that was one of the earliest visits we made there and having just been twice in the summer and autumn of 2017, it is quite amazing how it has been developed over the those years, and is now a massive tourist attraction in the North East, and if you haven't been, I would thoroughly recommend you do so.

Soon after that, we finally put up the flag poles on the lawn at the front of Newton Grange. Anyone who had ever visited Hanoverhill in Canada, would remember the flagpoles there which greeted you whenever you entered their farmyard, and Mr J had wanted to do the same for a long time, ever since that massive tree came down at New Year 1976. We had had the piping for a long time, and I had always poo-hoo'ed the idea and kept finding a reason for not doing them. Eventually Mr J wore me down and I finally submitted and Peter who was very good at making things made the three poles and also the framework to hold them when erect and finally I got them concreted and set along the lawn side of the fence and the flags first flew on 2nd May. The idea was that we would fly a Union Jack, a Canadian flag and our own Dalesend flag on the slightly higher centre one, which is what we did. Herdwise by then was a thriving semen business with quite a strong export arm under Johnny Cooke-Hurle, and we had quite a lot of visits from potential foreign buyers. Mr J suggested we should fly that country's flag when they visited. I pointed out that we would need a lot of different ones, which would be quite costly and time consuming to be forever changing them and finally convinced him that it was not really feasible. He won the war on the flag poles but lost the battle over the flags!!

Spring of that year was quite busy as we had visits from South Wales Club on their annual tour, the Ballymoney Dairy Discussion Group from Ireland and several others, then it was Uncle Bill and Aunt Lena's Golden Wedding Anniversary. Some of you will remember Bill Hood – another of mother's brothers who for many years was the head man in running the estate of Jeremy Graham at Wath near Ripon, before they ultimately retired back to Great Ayton. They quite often visited mother at Aiskew and Uncle Bill never forgot the telling off he got one day when there. Mother was a great tennis fan and everything stopped for Wimbledon fortnight and when they called one day he switched it off while mother was making a cup of tea and he got a real "bollocking" for touching her television. Talking of mother and Wimbledon, one of the few regrets I have in life is that with her dying so suddenly I never got her taken on a surprise birthday trip to actually go there to watch some tennis.

Very shortly after that it was with sadness I went to the funeral of Colin Horner who had been our cattle chauffeur for many years. He had driven our cattle to all the major shows all over the country, to such as the Royal or Royal Highland, he only worked the day there and the day back and took the days in between as holiday, helping me to look after the cattle and sometimes his wife Majorie would come along as well. Far too young an age to leave us, but he was a marvellous handler of cattle on a lorry.

Up at the Royal Highland Show in 1982, there were a few of us from the regular show circuit who were getting tired of a young lad who was with one breeder who kept kicking soil about down the lines and making it dusty. One day as he did so, I whispered to Colin to fetch me a bucket of water and put it nearby. As the young lad continued, I got him by the scruff of the neck and seat of his pants and dunked him head first into the water and stood him back down – his mother said she hoped that would teach him. I wouldn't want to try it now – it was Kenny Logan the Scottish International rugby player!

On midsummers day that year, the North East Club held its first Club Show for 18 years. It was a good do, with some great cattle, held on a Friday evening. Club members supported it greatly for a number of years, as it moved around the club area to be held on farm and many members brought a couple of animals. That first year it was staged at Robin Dickson's at Upsall where Messrs Petch of Aytonian had both Champion and Reserve. There were some good years as the calf show section began to develop under YMA which eventually became HYB (Holstein Young Breeders) and they grew in number until eventually the calves took the space in the trailers and we regrettably had to discontinue the show part. That wasn't before one year we marvelled at the late John Wilkin when he hosted the show at Danby Wiske. Determined to show a couple when he was the host, John hadn't much success in breaking them, even with a "Big Jim" halter, but led them around the ring tied to the back of a tractor and trailer. Great days and great fun when winning wasn't everything.

At the same time the council were altering the bend at the entrance to Newton Grange. The road used to go through a fairly savage Z- bend and over the years there had been quite a few accidents of various levels of seriousness, and despite many discussions with the County Council, they had always refused to do anything about it, until now, when they finally said if the land required at either side of the road was gifted to them they would do the work. Mike Heugh was only too ready as we were to agree to this – both little bits in the greater scheme of things, but it certainly opened out the corner and gave greatly improved vision – the only downside was that it created quite a bit more grass to be cut regularly to keep our entrance attractive.

Just a few days after that, there was one of those days when there was nobody about, Bill was on holiday, as was Peter, Robert was off sick with a broken collarbone and David was going to see Bruce Springsteen in concert, so I both milked and did the youngstock at Dalesend myself.

That reminds me of one Christmas morning several years previously when we still had the five herds, and there was a lot of flu about and we were just about keeping things ticking over with cowmen and relief men falling like ninepins and one almost waiting to be poorly as soon as someone was back. I was milking at the Grange with Bill poorly and needed help to calve a heifer. There was no one else I could get, so rang Mr J, who soon appeared to help and we got a live calf, but as we were delivering it, he thought it highly amusing that the owner and the manager were the only two left standing.

My car was due for a change and at that time and having been very patriotic and had a Morris Marina which had been very poor, I got the first of several Saab's, which were heavy enough to pull the cattle trailer quite easily and also with front wheel drive was much better for farming, and it also meant we could do away with the old Landrover and not replace it as it was barely roadworthy. Whilst not being a car enthusiast – I only ever want them to start when I get in, take me wherever I want to go and get me back again, we have over the years had some interesting times with various cars. First up was the A30 already referred to with Charles and the stick, followed by a green A35 van which got me to and from college for a couple of years. Then really modern when I started work full time and got a white Cortina, which did very well until both front shock absorbers pushed up through the rusting front panels. I replaced that with a more modern silver grey Cortina, which was probably my favourite car of all time, even though it got a couple of dints. Parked well away at Dalesend, when we were teaching heifers to lead, one took off and head down careered straight into the rear door. Vowing that it wouldn't happen again, it wasn't long before I left it even further away and damn me if the same thing didn't happen again, only this time on the opposite side – at least they matched.

The next car was the one I inherited from George Heeley – a big maroon Zephyr 6 – terrible in wet weather when water got up under the bonnet and ran round the big air cleaner and onto the engine. I had trouble with it one time coming back from some YFC event with Marnie, Fred and Vera and it wouldn't start after we stopped at a service station on the A1 and we had to push start it in pouring rain so we could get home. The great thing and probably only thing in its favour was that it had a big bench seat and gears on the steering column which meant Marnie could sit close – as the policeman reminded us on the A1 one night, there was close and too close!! That was followed by the dreadful Marina, plus an odd night I borrowed Bill's Vauxhall Viva which was nearly as bad and of all nights it chose that night for the alternator to fail and I had to manage to get home with little or no lights. A succession of Saab's followed before we moved onto having a contract hire car which made more economic sense for the business, and I had three very good Peugeot cars up until the farm being sold. Subsequent to retirement, we bought a 1 series BMW, the only brand new car I have ever actually owned.

Back to 1985, and while we were clipping the Black Welsh Mountain Sheep outside the byre, two old ladies appeared in a car and asked if they could buy some wool. Turned out they were from Driffield and members of a spinning group (wool spinners that is – the idea of cycling machines in gyms called "spinning" had not surfaced back then), and would love some black wool to give them some contrast. I explained to them that really that shouldn't be done as all wool was supposed to go through the British Wool Marketing Board. Their insistence on wanting to buy some and the chance of a good price weakened my resolve and I agreed to let them have some when we finished clipping. When I judged Driffield Show a month or so later I was only too happy to take them four fleeces for their hobby – it has to be said that Pick your Own Black Wool at £25 was a far better paying proposition than the BWMB, coming to far more than the rest put together. Talking of Pick your own, I did try once "Pick your own stones" but got no takers.

We had a long weekend break the week after that and stayed at Barton Grange Hotel over near Preston, where they also had a very good garden centre and the food was superb. A proper "Hors d'Oeuvres" was served among other starters and their desserts were made for them by a local lady and were very good – particularly the large choux bun which became a feature of Sunday night puddings at home – but not too often as they have too much cream in them.

Tragedy struck in late August when Bill's son Robert had a bad accident on his motorbike just outside BASA on the road from Bedale. Everything stopped for Bill and Lys and the girls for ten days while Robert clung to life, but ultimately lost the battle – such a waste of a young life, and Bill was to nurse through work for quite a while, and you had to walk on eggshells round the anniversary of his death for many years – quite understandably.

Later that year, Sarah took part in the 75th Anniversary of Guiding at the Great Yorkshire Showground, we had Emma's 18th birthday party to go to, Sarah moved bedrooms so that Marnie could decorate the old room which was to become Adam's when he was born later that year.

It is remarkable how sometimes animals have a sixth sense and eventually you come to think that they sometimes know exactly what you are saying or thinking. Just such an occurrence happened in the Autumn of that year. A very good uddered heifer Dalesend Lustrous 8 had had a very difficult calving resulting in a dead bull calf. She had been down for quite a while, and we had been lifting her daily, but she was showing no sign of standing unaided. Bill and I were stood outside the dry cow yard discussing her and had decided that she would have to go in the next day or two. An hour or two later I was round there again and she was stood up and looking over the wall at me. Although always too straight in the leg because of pelvic damage, she never looked back and was no problem over three lactations and had a marvellous nature.

Just before Christmas that year we went out for dinner for what was likely to be the last time for sometime and had booked the Wensleydale Heifer at West Witton. Everywhere was flooded after a lot of rain, and we had to turn up Wensley and go round by the top road and come back down the dale to get our supper.

Marnie had decided that Adam would be born in 1985, as both she and Sarah all had five in their birth dates – but he only just made it – 2.20pm on 31st December Adam John Thompson Liddle came into the world – a blessing we had given up hope of some years previously, but ten years after Sarah it was fantastic.

Chapter Ten – All change again – A new son and a new building

Marnie and Adam came home from the maternity hospital on a very cold and raw day, and it stayed bitterly cold over several days. Our bedroom at the Grange was very large and outside wall on three sides, all above the office, so it was open to the elements and despite having a heater alongside the cot and the central heating on, it was struggling to hold the temperature. On top of that there had been a blow out on the boiler the night before. The central heating which hadn't been in very long was heated by anthracite which at that time was cheaper to run than oil. The hopper for it was unfortunately inside so it was a bit messy filling it up anyway, but if it blew back it put soot particles all over the kitchen – I had spent much of the night washing down and cleaning up the kitchen before they arrived back home. Adam soon got settled into a routine and I note from diaries that it only took until the twelfth of February for him to sleep through the night – he has been a good sleeper ever since.

The day after they came home was also quite a noticeable date – the first time Dick Brown visited as the new local man for BOCM Silcock. He was introduced by Alan Isbister who had been filling in for Stan Dixon for quite a while as Stan had been off sick for a long period, and eventually then took early retirement. Stan was always meticulous in everything he did – if a potato came up crooked in a row, he would pull it out, and when planting his dahlias, they had to be in rows both ways and cross over into the bargain. Dick looked after us for many years as he began to climb the company ladder and he eventually finished up as main board director of BOCM Pauls and then For Farmers before he retired – a remarkable achievement for an ordinary working lad – and we remain great friends to this day – he will crop up once or twice later as we went to various rugby internationals. He once brought a young trainee with him and after a short while I asked the young man if he was any good at his job – to which he replied he didn't really know. That really filled me with confidence in him, and what really amused me was that after he had gone out Dick said he wouldn't care but he had warned him as they came up the drive to watch out for the trick question which he had fallen straight into – needless to say he wasn't with the firm very long.

It is difficult now in 2018 when we have had a virtually static low interest rate/ bank rate for ten years now, down at 0.25 and 0.5% to remember how high they were back in the 1980's, and the day of Dick's visit I have a note that the Bank base rate was put up to 12.5% and inflation was running at 5%.

A couple of days after that I had a meeting with Malcolm Percival about coming to work for us, to replace Robert who had so tragically died some months previously. Malcolm had been made redundant at Anderson's at Ainderby Myers- his brother Dennis already did a lot of our contracting work, and his mother Maisie had lived in several of our houses and worked at Dalesend for quite a while, so I knew a fair bit about him. The added bonus was that he could stay in the cottage at Ainderby Myers for as long as he wanted, which was great as we didn't have a spare house for him at that time. He and Chris did eventually move to the bungalow after Peter left, but that was a year or two away. Malcolm started work for us on 3rd March and will keep cropping up as we progress for the next sixteen years until his untimely death in mid-2002. After I had met Malcolm that first time I had written in my diary "shan't bother seeing anybody else – he'll do for me."

It was late the previous year that we had finally made the decision that we were going to put a new dairy unit up and increase the herd up to 120 cows, so the early part of 1986 took a lot of my time in working on plans and meeting people, visiting other set ups and the like. One of the first decisions we made was the sort of milking parlour we were going to install between Alfa-Laval, Fullwood or the American made Surge. Surge were to our mind ahead of the game with large bore vacuum lines and the like, and we soon decided that despite them being quite a lot more expensive than the others we were going to go down that road with the parlour and their out of parlour feeders. It was interesting that as other companies showed us round set ups, they were very aware of the Surge technology and kept whispering in our ears that they didn't think it was necessary and just a sales gimmick. Needless to say, within two to three years they had all adopted it and it became standard fare.

Eric Bryne who was the Surge representative (Surge were later taken over by Westfalia who then became GEA) took us to see several units to show us their technology and one day at the end of January Bill and I had a memorable trip to see such a unit, over the tops to Cantsfield between Burton-In-Lonsdale and Lancaster. Bill was in a daft mood and as we waited at the traffic lights at the bridge over the railway before Leyburn – there was an old codger in the car in front and he encouraged and dared me to overtake him before the bridge, which we did without much bother and he still remembers if ever we are at a set of traffic lights even now. The farm we were visiting that day was Nelson Quests. He was quite an elderly gentleman, and as he showed us around, I showed him the courtesy of calling him Mr Quest, to which the only response I got was "Ah's Nelson". This happened several times before Eric realised the trouble I was in and came across from talking with Bill and the owners nephew to explain that this was in fact Mr Nelson and he and Mr Quest farmed as a partnership, hence my embarrassment at his continuing reply to all my points – "Ah's Nelson".

Nothing to do with the planned building work but Mr J had suddenly decided, as the forestry man, that the five oaks in the front field were past their best and suddenly they were all felled and led away – totalling £983.50 which was a fair amount back then and just tells you how big and sound they were. The brush was all to clear up and provided us with firewood for quite a while.

In early March we started digging out for the enlarged silage pit we were going to require with more cattle and they needed doing to get concrete etc laid and well set before silaging in two and a half months' time, that included knocking down and clearing the old bull pens, and while they were there they also dug out all the area for the new slurry pit. Liz Hesketh who was a MAFF dairy advisor helped us with the building planning and took us to look at various set ups – one day to Barry Tweddle's, and then Denis Raper's and Peter Gill's up in Durham. Some of them had out of parlour feeders and we decided that was the way to go but JGR took a lot of convincing that it was worthwhile or cost effective. After many discussions I finally found a way to convince him. If we were away anytime on various outings over the years it was always feast or famine – either eating all the time or just a square of chocolate to keep you going – on one Herdwise trip we had breakfast in South Wales, crossed over the bridge and down into Devon to look at a young bulls family, right along the south coast to Mike Carr's Springbird herd at Brighton to then travel home – we stopped on the M1 just through London and the only thing they had left was one bar of Kit Kat so we shared that – it was the only thing we'd had from South Wales. I said to Mr J, which was he most comfortable with- and he said just having a snack as he was always bloated and full of wind when he had big meals – so I explained that's what happened with out of parlour feeders as cattle had cake little and often through the day and night. Problem solved and ordered the next day.

In designing the layout of the new building, it was all drawn out on a foolscap sheet of paper, not using any professional architect, only advice from MAFF. We were restricted a little by the silage pit on one side, and the house on the other which meant that the passageways were narrower than we would have ideally liked. With hindsight we should have perhaps gone for a green field site which would have allowed us to do more of what we wanted, but it would have cost a lot more money, and remember it was costing 15-18% to borrow money at that time. We had also decided that we would do much of the building and fitting work ourselves, so we were in for a very busy year- and in fact over that Summer, the five of us lost about 12 stone in weight- the equivalent to an average person!!

A short interlude before the work really got started was selling some Black Sheep to "good-lifers" for prices well above what they were worth, making a raspberry cage in the back garden, and Adam's christening at Patrick Brompton- they wouldn't let us have it at Hornby where Sarah had been christened and we were married – because we didn't live in the parish- even though all under the same vicar- the sort of inflexibility that has not helped the church to keep its appeal with younger people. Whilst waiting until we got the cows turned out, I went to the HFS judge's school down in the Midlands, where we judged three classes of six cows by majority placings. This was before computers were readily available to do such things and was done manually, so it can be done on the day and is probably a better way than having master judges who will never agree completely anyway. It was at the time when there was a big swing in the showring to the more Holstein type of cow. I remember John Moffitt "Dalton" was chairman of show and sale at the time and on bringing the first class back in after lunch he told us that anyone who hadn't a certain cow at the top shouldn't be on the judges panel, whereas the consensus opinion had it last. This created a long discussion and was ended when young (similar age to me) John Williams of the Grove pointed out that in fact it was Mr Moffitt who was in the wrong as everyone had demonstrated that that was not the sort of cow people wanted, moving into the future.

As the new building was to cut across our back lawn – the old pear tree which had always cropped well had to be felled and removed, we had a wedding on the Saturday and then on the Sunday we went to the opening of the new tennis courts at Bedale.

On 6th May we began to demolish the old buildings and two days later Waddington's cast the bases for the stanchions of the new building and after a week of knocking things down we began constructing again, as we started to concrete the silage pit expansion. Soon after, the frame of the shed was put up by a group of Jehovah's Witnesses who ran up and down and along the girders with no safety nets as you would see today, and I am sure much of that even then contravened health and safety regulations. In demolishing the old building there were some old cast iron roof supports, both free standing and bolted through the walls – nobody could tell me anything about the history of the building which was a pity and it wasn't until later when we fitted some of them to the outside of the new building alongside the house when I was cleaning them of paint that we discovered they had been cast at Mattisons foundry at Leeming Bar, which eventually became John Henry Gill's Massey Ferguson headquarters, and where the rest of the cast had been sold back to as they were still at that time making roller rings etc. For those who don't know our area well, it is worth noting that what was Gill's yard has been converted and just opened in the autumn of 2017 as the local Coop in Leeming Bar.

Some of the design features in the new buildings were at the time quite new and revolutionary, although they would be seen as very old hat nowadays. The cubicles for instance were the first in the area to be put in without the rear legs as in the widely used up until then "Newton Rigg" type , had a bit of a do with a massive man from Tuf Brand from where they came, who couldn't have been more helpful until we had trouble keeping them tight at the front when he didn't want to know – we had to rely on our local "Mr Fixit" Norman Iveson to sort them out. We didn't go down the complete feeder route but put a central feed passage down the middle which we could fill with a materials handler from one end rather than tie tractors up on an expensive machine. The commonest form of parlour wall covering in those days was either the plain walls painted or covered in sheets of plastic. When opening the post one day, there was a pack of advertising cards of products and services and I went through them rather than tossing them in the bin as I would normally have done. The very last card was for a product called "Marbaline" which I made further enquiries about and we decided to use it on the parlour walls and it was mixed and put on by the plasterer as the last coat of plaster and then was painted with an epoxy resin coating the day after. The product and resin cost £420 and were still as good and durable when we left the farm 26 years later – it was good to steam clean and wash down – and purely by fluke of luck had I come across it. The part of the building which housed the milking parlour was built professionally, but that was the only piece of the building we didn't do ourselves. The builders for this job were Donaldson builders from Snape whom we had never worked with before but did an outstanding job. I well remember the first morning when they started digging foundations Mr J came up to mark the occasion and when he was going said to Neil that he hoped he would do a good job and make a little bit for themselves. After he had gone Neil remarked that it was the first time anyone had ever wanted him to make any money – farmers always want everything done for nothing.

We had a great deal of fun amongst all the hard work that summer. We were by then concreting the bottom of the slurry pit and had ready mix lorries coming at regular intervals through the day, when an uninvited fertiliser salesman made his way down to us and he wasn't even from a firm we dealt with. I explained to him that I was busy and to ring in future, but he took no notice and carried on trying to sell, after a short while I asked if he could see that we were rather busy, but he still didn't get the message as the rest of the gang started to laugh as they realised he was getting onto shaky ground. A little while after I told him that I always respected visiting salesman who realised I was busy and went away hoping to catch me at a better time in the future. Still he didn't get the message until finally my temper got the better of me and I told him that if he didn't "f**k off" immediately he would be under the concrete and never heard of again. Later that day after we had got a big lump laid, Bill wanted the rake from the other side and without thinking walked right through the newly laid concrete, got stuck in it and was to manhandle back out of it – much to everyone's great mirth which overtook the annoyance. Another time as we were building the collecting yard wall, David was the pointer and he was sat on a block on the trailer being used as the scaffolding and we caught him asleep with trowel placing mortar between the joints. Malcolm who along with Peter did all the block laying, was always losing or misplacing his trowel, so one day I crept out early after lunch and fastened a chain to the trowel and stapled it to the board that I had put a mixing of concrete on ready for them, when he grabbed the trowel and got it full of concrete he couldn't get it to the wall before he realised what had been done. Great hilarity and there were many such things which we needed as we were working virtually all hours of daylight. The cows managed working amongst tied up gates to form a collecting yard which kept changing shape as things went on – they stood it better than Bill at times – one particular time when they wouldn't come in to be milked and we were actually sheeting up 2nd cut silage and he got really wound up – he shouted and bawled at us, it was all our fault for upsetting the cows. He came out of the parlour and asked the cows in no uncertain or polite terms whether they wanted to be milked or not, they obviously didn't though as none of them replied. It wasn't helped by us all laughing at him, but he finished what was in the parlour, shut down and went home to his tea with only about ten left to milk!!

Earlier in the Spring Sarah had taken the entrance exam for Ripon Grammar School, subsequently passed and we took her one night for a briefing evening prior to starting in the Autumn. I was mightily surprised to see at least four of the teachers who had taught me: Mr Petchy (history), Mr Wallace (physics), Mr Chambers (woodwork etc) and Mr Postlethwaite (chemistry- who by then was one of the deputy headmasters) and I thought some of them were retiring age some 25-30 years earlier, and what's more they were still there seven years later when Sarah left school.

That year I judged Lancaster and Morecambe show and later on a very wet Danby Show, and then later Sarah won decorated "wellie" and vegetable man at Crakehall show where Marnie won the chutney and was second with the cheese scones. A day or two later the road to Northallerton was closed because of the floods at Morton bridge where the Swale had burst its banks.

The milking parlour was finished building before the end of July and Malcolm Hall from Surge began fitting the herringbone parlour and made a great job of it- the only thing wrong was the floor was about two inches too low or the floor of the milking platform was too high – the problem was when he was fitting the arms etc, Bill was having a well deserved week off, so he used me as the measuring stick and I was about two inches taller than Bill – soon after starting to milk in the new parlour we solved the problem by putting some 1 ½ inch planks down with chicken wire holding them in place and stopping it being slippy.

As we started fitting out the rest of the building, we asked various local dairy farmers their ideas. One of the most important bits was the handling facilities, AI service pens at the exit from the parlour. We asked several of the local AI men (there was very little DIY in those days) where the best facilities were and they said Raymond Scotts so we went up there to look at them and then Peter made them to the same dimensions. The one thing we did wrong was not to allow room at the front for heads and to be able to dose or ear tag more easily – it only took us about 16 or 17 years to correct the fault – which made it much easier.

We finally milked for the first time in the new parlour on 8th September, which we celebrated by opening a bottle of whisky. There was shit everywhere for a few milkings as the cows were to teach to use the new system and within 10 days Bill was back to milking on his own, and awkward old cows like Mac Marigold who would only go in one place in the old parlour would go any place on either side and even came in on her own – simply because as a big stretchy cow she had more room to be comfortable.

Although the parlour was up and running there was still much work to be done in the rest of the buildings to be ready for the cows to come in as autumn approached. At this point we only had one little box for calves or calving in, and this led to one particularly amusing incident – probably the best of all the lot and better known as "Let the bugger die incident". Well into September and working at night on the cubicles, Bill had a heifer calving out in the front field who was making little progress. When we finished work for the night and everyone went home, Bill and I thought we had better have a look at the heifer. By now fairly dark, Bill got his bucket of water, ropes and soap etc and set off to the heifer, she had already demolished all the electric fence wires in what were then paddocks, he would creep up on her as she strained and as soon as he got a hand on the calf leg and kept her working, he would call me. I had got my big torch out of the house and waited in anticipation, hearing nothing except the odd swear word, doubting the heifer's parentage and such like. After a spell of total silence, I used the torch to scan round the field, eventually picking up the heifer on her feet in a totally different part of the field and no sign of Bill. I carried on the torch light search and eventually zoomed in on Bill – laid on his back holding up the bucket and proclaiming that he hadn't split the water. When I shouted to ask if he was ok, came back the response, "let the bugger die". We didn't however, let her die but decided we would have her in and we chased her about the field and finally got her up into the corner near the house – fortunately Marnie heard us shouting and came out to see what was happening, so opened the gate into the yard so we could get her round into the one box that was available. We got the halter on and tied her up, and left her to settle down while we had a cup of coffee, or did we need to recover before we started to calve her? When we went out again, she had pulled the hay rack off its mountings on the wall and was walking around the box dragging it with her. Enough of this nonsense, we got on and soon had a bull calf safely delivered.

We finally got the inside of the building finished enough for the cows to use the cubicles for the first time at night in mid-October – and they soon got settled into life in a new shed. We didn't initially fit auto-scrapers, but the passage ways were laid out so they could be fitted at a later date, which we did a couple of years later – the young lad who was the apprentice when they were being fit is now the main man at Storth Machinery who specialise in scrapers and slurry equipment – I usually call and have a word if we are at a show where they are exhibiting.

Talking of slurry, when we had got much of the work done, Peter and Malcolm had a well-earned day off to go to Smithfield and returned having discovered a machine that we had never heard of – a slurry guzzler. Not only that they had arranged with the firm from South Wales to bring one on demonstration. When their salesman arrived before the machine he made the astounding claim that he had never failed to make a sale of the slurry guzzler from an on farm demonstration, and he was spot on – we kept the machine and he went home without it. That machine suited our slurry pit ideally because of the steep fall it had on it which worked with the rear filling auger – all done from the tractor seat without ever having to get involved with mucky, smelly pipes etc. So much did it suit our system that we had four of them in all, right up to the farm sale. One summer we had a visit from the Brompton Agricultural Discussion Group. I had spoken to them the previous winter and shown a slide of the slurry guzzler which again none of them had heard of before. When they visited, I organised a demonstration of it in action, only taking about 60 seconds to fill. Malcolm got his best cap and overalls on, and we stood with bated breath to watch it fill – nothing happened, and it simply didn't fill so embarrassingly had to abandon the demonstration. We later discovered we had got a small stone wedged in the mechanism which was preventing the inner door from opening.

Just a day after the cows had been in for the first time at night, we went to the first speech day of Sarah's at Ripon and heard one of the most inspiring speeches I have ever had the privilege of hearing. Lord Tonypandy who had been a Labour minister of Education but latterly Speaker of the House of Commons. He explained how he had earlier voted against his party on several occasions as they did away with Grammar Schools, his point being they were one way of ordinary people having the chance for their education to lead them to a better life, the wheel seems to have gone almost full circle and there is current talk of them being re-introduced, fortunately Ripon has maintained its status and produces superb results.

A week later we topped the market at Leyburn with Black Welsh Mountain lambs – much to the annoyance of the local professional sheep men. We had set off a few weeks earlier well below market average but by the time we got to this last lot they were appreciated, and all had gone over the weeks to the same buyer, their ultimate destination being M & S.

Throughout the winter of 1986/87 we were continuing to finish off the jobs around the new set up, including citing a new bin to take the feed for the out of parlour feeders which came into operation in early April. As we fitted the transponders through the cattle crush, it was only ten minutes before we heard the rattle of cake as the first cow used them.

In the early part of the year there was notification that as dairy farmers we were all going to be charged for the dairy inspection and the NFU organised a national petition against it, the idea being to have every dairy farm signed up. I don't know why because we were no longer NFU members but I was asked to do our parish which wasn't a big job, but there was one unit that the tanker drivers complained about, the one before us, and their pipes were often dirty and they hosed their wheels off in our yard. Forewarned of the farm, I went in the old farm pick up, you had to walk through the slurry/midden to get to the dairy, where the cows came out round the bulk tank. After reluctantly getting the signature I reversed nearly 200 yards to find somewhere clean enough to turn around, and thought that really, he needed to be charged for an inspection and he needed one about every month.

Just after that we had a North East Holstein Club panel meeting for the first time and had a marvellous night with myself chairing Hamish Logan, Alan Swale and Richard Linnell in a meeting that could have lasted all night. Hamish would be known for his Manorpowis herd, which was very much in vogue at the time, but sadly he lost his life not many years later when he was knocked down and killed by a bus in Edinburgh. The club has held a panel meeting every year since that time – it is still the best attended of any of their winter meetings and over the years has had some tremendous characters and farming businessmen give their time to entertain and enlighten us.

Before Christmas 86 I went to Uncle Harry Liddle's funeral at Greenhow where he had previously farmed for many years – to say it was cold would be an understatement. It wasn't too bad in Chapel, but in a very exposed graveyard, I have rarely been colder in a bitingly bitter wind. Just into the New Year and a parents evening at Ripon told us Sarah was doing well, but not asking enough questions, she must have taken note as she has rarely stopped since!! I had also just before Christmas, started the tradition of taking the men out for their lunch, I suppose a thankyou for all their efforts through that year and for many years we went to the Wheatsheaf at Newton-le-Willows. Not the most attractive of pubs that you would really choose to go out to for a night, they did a very good steak and I think some of the best steak I have ever eaten has been on those days. The Wheatsheaf will have been closed for 10 or 12 years now and is falling into total disrepair and has become a real blot on the landscape in the centre of the village.

We made the old parlour into the new dairy and moved the tank from the old one to turn it into a calf house. Later that spring I bought a smaller tank at a farm sale at Thirn for £110 for 964 litres to take the overflow as we now had a larger herd.

Sean Sproates was born to Dianne and Peter that February, we had a weekend away at Alvaston Hall, near Chester, and had Mr and Mrs Pattinson from Ellengrove, the Holstein UK Board Member for the area, to stay over night when he spoke at the North East Club.

By the spring of 87 we had pretty well finished all the building work apart from a few bits out in the yard to tidy things up, knocking down the old meal house and putting the bulk tank freezer units under the granary steps looking out through two peep holes for air.

We then moved onto another line of work – though didn't quite make it onto the large screen, only the small one.

Chapter Eleven – Television – Filming for it, not watching it!

For several years through the early 1980's, the books of James Herriot had become very popular, and turned into a television series 'All Creatures Great and Small'. They were shown on a Sunday night, drew massive audiences and were shown all over the world. Even now more than 30 years later if you are in a foreign country and someone asks where you are from, they have no conception of where Bedale or Northallerton, or Wensleydale is, but if you ask if they ever watched 'All Creatures' they almost without exception have done and if you tell them it is the area where it was all filmed, they instantly place it.

Jack Watkinson who was our vet from the Watkinson and Naish practice at Leyburn was the veterinary advisor to the BBC in filming the various series of the programme and so we got involved in quite a few ways. When they were first filming, it was before Greg retired and he went off several times to be involved with the shooting of various sequences. Once they hired some of his own hens for one particular bit, the only trouble was they lost some of the hens and not being able to find them all, had to pay him some damages. In another sequence about the first Friesian bull being used up in the dales, which until then had been all Shorthorn country, the story was that the man who bought it had a portrait of it by a local artist who was also a part of the story. Ultimately the bull failed to work in the story and the farmer didn't want the painting. The actual painting used in the filming was given to Greg at the end, and whilst it wasn't very good as it was only done as a 'prop', it sat proudly on his living room wall, and of course, had a story to go with it.

When they came to film the next series in Spring of 1987, Greg had retired and it fell to me to be involved with them, and though it involved a lot of hanging about, it was a fascinating experience. The first time was up at Hawes Auction Mart to film a sequence of a cow being bought at the weekly market. I took Dalesend Unique 7 who was more a Friesian type – deep body on a short set of legs, and although it was early April, it was a bitterly cold day – it usually is at auction marts. I well remember talking with some of the extras who were mostly ladies, being farmers wives who were going to the local market in town. They were all dressed in the clothes of the time and were complaining bitterly about the cold, in particular their lower halves as they had to be dressed in the underwear of the time, stockings, loose knickers etc. which meant the strong wind was blowing up their skirts. Why on earth when they were only filmed for a few seconds from the knees up with their coats on, it was necessary to wear the authentic underwear was beyond me, but that was what was deemed necessary at the time.

The day after I was off again, with Unique 7 again up to West Scrafton to film a sequence on the farm where the cow has supposedly gone to from the market and had developed mastitis. In reality the timescale of the series was not long after penicillin had become commercially available for veterinary use, and in the story the vet was supposedly putting tubes up the cows rectum all night to save her – rather farfetched for a farmer, but the general public knew no better.

On a beautiful, warm, spring day we were in action again, and this time Marnie went with me to see what was going on, and it really was an education and the largesse and wastage within the BBC was there for anyone to see. The particular story was the time about a bull and the introduction of artificial insemination to cattle breeding, with the farmer having some semen collected off the bull for future use. They had already hired our set of stocks which we had used latterly when collecting the young test bulls housed for Herdwise, and because a bull was classed as a dangerous animal, an actor wasn't allowed to handle it, so I was made a temporary member of Equity, the actors union. While they were filming the series, they were based in Leyburn and all the regular actors were dressed and made up there before they came onto set, but any extras were done as needed. To this extent a great big vehicle equipped as a hairdressing salon arrived on site and I was the only person that day to use it, having to have a 'pudding basin' style haircut for the part. Another big lorry was the dressing up/changing rooms, and again I was about the only one who used it that day. I had a personal dresser, and I had to wear apart from the clothes, the old-style lace up long boots which were tied up for me. The dresser then asked me to stand up and walk around to see if they were comfortable, and thinking this might be my only chance ever to have someone doing such things for me, told him they were not quite tight enough, so he undid them all again and tightened them up a little more for a second time. The same applied to the large refreshment lorry that pulled onto site, providing coffee etc. as and when, and at lunch providing a much wider range of sandwiches etc. Apparently if they were filming a night sequence, a full three course dinner was served including wine. So that was three great big trucks apart from the other filming crews vehicles – it took three drivers who all they did was drive from Leyburn to Redmire, as was necessary, level up the vehicle on props and then drive it home again at the end. They did nothing else all day, that was their job and the BBC was very union controlled at that time. Similarly, whilst filming a sequence in which I wasn't taking part, the cameraman was right at the top of a big high set of steps to get an overhead shot and as he stretched the steps wobbled – Marnie put her foot out to stop it and nearly got knocked over by the three crew who then held it – a member of the public couldn't do anything like that when there were men paid to do such jobs!! As I said, the excessive wastage of men and hence the general public's money was unbelievable.

That particular day, when we stopped for lunch, we were all sat outside in the sun together, except Robert Hardy who obviously thought himself a little above the rest of the cast. Carol Drinkwater was not there that day as she wasn't part of the story, but Christopher Timothy and Peter Davidson were quite happy to sit and talk with us mere mortals. Also with us was the actor who appeared in the 'Jewson' adverts for many years. He was playing my boss, the farmer who owned the bull and he was in real life just as much of a character. Lunchtime was dragging on, it was a Friday, but you still don't expect an actor to say "I wish they would get on and get finished for the day, I'm supposed to be going away caravanning for the weekend".

Reinforcing the financial wastage in such productions was when they came to pay Dalesend for the use of various things. Apart from a payment for my time and the use of the cow, there was an extra payment for being an 'actor', another extra payment for handling a dangerous animal, and £12.20 in damages for having to cut my hair in an old fashioned style, apart from various other things such as the use of the cattle stocks. As I said a fascinating experience and an unbelievable insight into the making of such series particularly when both the bits at Hawes, West Scrafton and Redmire probably at most created five minutes of actual television time in total.

At the same time, there was going to be a special excursion train from Bristol to go up to Redmire carrying railway enthusiasts, and there were seats available from Northallerton which we were lucky enough to obtain two, and we had a thoroughly enjoyable Saturday afternoon on the first passenger train to use the line for 33 years. From Northallerton to Bedale you go through some countryside you don't normally see from the road, Newton Grange looks totally different from a field away, higher up on a train, the view from high above Newton-le-Willows across the lower valley and from the top side of Leyburn back over Upper Wensleydale are staggeringly beautiful and in most cases from different angles. This was long before the Wensleydale Railway resurrected the line and were little more than a nuisance from a farming point of view. The line at that time was only used for the stone trains from the dales to the steel works on Teesside and when they ended, was used by the army for a while to move vehicles down to Salisbury Plain from Catterick, though it never struck me as being a very economic way of doing things, particularly when the first load couldn't get under the first bridge after leaving Redmire, they had to go back, unload all the armoured cars etc and then take all the special wagons away somewhere to be lowered a couple of inches. I wonder if their tape measure was like a lot of peoples – a bit had broken off the end and they failed to allow for that when they wrote down the measurement!!

In mid-June that year we hosted the NE Club Show at Dalesend in what is still called the show field – it was the site of Patrick Brompton Show until it ceased some twenty years earlier. Sarah had two calves got ready and trained for the calf show, thus starting her involvement with YMA and then HYB that continues to this day, and from which she and we have had great enjoyment over many years.

In August, whilst Sarah was away in France for a week with school, we had a weekend away to Bronte country. We weren't terribly impressed with Haworth, it seemed that everything was aimed at the American tourist, but we did discover Saltaire near Bradford. An amazing village built for his workers by the mill owner Sir Titus Salt, we spent a whole afternoon there and for anyone who has never been we would recommend it. Later that month it was niece Samantha and Iain's wedding at Ripon Cathedral and reception at the Spa Hotel. Sarah was a bridesmaid after several fittings of dresses.

Having got all settled down after the dairy expansion of the previous year, we decided to go down the road of doing our own inseminating and Bill went first on the course which was five days and held in Stockton, where the MMB (now Genus) had access to the nearly new abattoir to have cows on which to practise. I followed on a couple of months later, and if nothing else, learning D-I-Y taught you a good deal of understanding of what goes on inside the cow. Both of us got our certificates and went on for many years to do the inseminating. The only exceptions were sometimes if we were flushing a cow for embryo transfer work, I might get her done professionally or if both Bill and I were away at the same time, I would get Bert Teasdale, who by then had retired as an inseminator to come and cover for us. I remember one day a few months after being on the course meeting one of the other members of it in Northallerton. After a few pleasantries I asked how he was getting on with DIY – "Fantastic" he said, "never had one come over yet". I thought this was rather strange but felt rather inadequate as that certainly wasn't my experience. A few sentences later all was revealed when he let slip that he had a beef bull running with the cows all the time – which meant that until he got round nine months, he hadn't a clue whether he had got anything in calf.

Into the autumn and I was asked if I could act as the question master for the Women's Institute Quiz for the Wensleydale area, which I did and took Marnie along as the scorer/timekeeper. As we started the first round, I set off with easy questions to settle them down, but wasn't quite expecting the response I got to the very opening question "What's the capital of France?" The first answer from a very nervous lady was "ooh, I wish I'd never come now".

In mid-October of that year, we hosted a big open day for BOCM-Pauls, which obviously featured our now one year old dairy set up, but was aimed for them at winter feeding, and we had a series of speakers on various subjects, one of which was me, and I made some reference within it about the then Managing Director of the MMB holding multiple outside non-executive positions in other companies when I felt there were plenty more major things in house. Someone was obviously listening and reported back very quickly as the day after I had a phone call directly from the lady I was referring to, Detta O'Cathain who told me that being on other food companies boards helped give her the understanding of our food business and helped other companies understand the complexities of the milk and dairy industry.

The end of October was one of those times that sticks in the memory for many years to come. It wasn't too bad up here, though fairly wild, but down south there were fantastic gales which devastated woodland across the bottom of the country, from which it took years to recover. It was made worse by the fact that the night before the weatherman on the television had assured us all that this big storm wasn't really going to be that bad. This atrocious weather coincided with a massive stock market crash and financial tumult. This coincided with many stockbrokers being unable to get to work because there were wires down on railway lines and roads blocked by fallen trees, and in the days before mobile phones and computers, meant that there were great difficulties with communications. I wanted to buy some shares when the prices had collapsed but was unable to do so because the phone lines were very busy or out of action because of the weather

Not that it was anything to do with the storm, but it was at that time that Dutch Elm Disease was identified and became a massive problem all over the country. Mr J got Mr Place from Ainderby Steeple (a member of the Place family, who had had the timber merchants in Northallerton, which was I believe what had become Sam Turners new depot on Quaker lane. The Place family was also the same family as the twins who had been in my class at school at Middlesmoor and who lived in the Vicarage (just down the hill) to come and go round with him and they identified 27 dead ones altogether, which over time we felled and cleared – it still burnt on the fire ok.

In early December of that year we went to Carlisle to observe the first Black and White Sale – the conceptual idea was the work of Gordon Wilson of Petteril, Edward Brown of auctioneers Harrison and Hetherington and the late Michael Armstrong of Wolfa. We didn't consign that year but did so at virtually everyone after that until the herd was dispersed, and the sale goes on very strongly today, and we usually try and attend, as much as a social occasion as anything.

Just a day or two after that there began to appear in the press, mention of a new condition in cattle BSE – Bovine Spongiform Encephalopathy or something like that – and nearly everyone was touched by it, it killed the export meat market and in some quarters farmers were vilified because in actual fact they were feeding back animal by-products to their animals in such things as meat and bone meal. This had been allowed first of all in war time as a means of producing protein, had continued after that date, but at the same time the temperatures required to make it safe had been officially lowered or not adhered to. The actual animal that was infected showed a staggering gait and some violent actions if it became agitated. MAFF very quickly introduced a slaughter and compensation policy which was quite generous to begin with but was gradually reduced in value overtime and then a lot of cohorts were identified within herds and removed. In the early days of the problem there were odd reports of unscrupulous dealers putting a hose pipe into animals ears and turning on the tap which had very similar results – anyone who has ever washed and shown cattle and inadvertently got some water into a cows ear will know exactly what I mean. There was one particular professor who made a lot of noise and no doubt money by publicly informing the general public that a vast number of humans would become infected and die of CJD (Creutzfeldt-Jakob Disease). Fortunately, that never came to pass, and as far as I know there has never been an official or otherwise apology for suggesting and tainting farmers with having caused them. The disease did have great effects on the rearing, feeding and slaughtering codes for animals with the regard to the removal of spinal tissue etc, the age at which cattle could or couldn't be slaughtered for human consumption and it even extended to a country such as Canada being stopped from exporting cattle to the USA after an animal was diagnosed there with it. We lost some animals with it, but nowhere near the devastation it caused in many herds. Strangely enough I hadn't seen an animal showing symptoms for many years, until over in

Northern Ireland last summer (2017) when at an open day there was an animal near calving who was getting very wound up and charging around her pen and attacking the bars – I just hope she was one of those super-sensitive cow who had got excited because there were a lot of people about!!

Just before Christmas of that year it was sadly Bob Husband's funeral, you will remember him from earlier chapters and all the escapades and fun he had and we had with him and then he ultimately lost his leg in the forage harvester. He had enjoyed a marvellous life even after that, had gone all over the world on holidays with his great friend Willy Atkinson who had been the foreman at Hornby Castle, and still managed to dance with his false leg. That false leg caused me problems on one particular night after an event at Dalesend. Bob had had too much to drink and needed help to get him home to the Lodge where he lived. I can't remember who else it was who helped, but I drew the short straw and was on the side of his false leg as we supported/carried him home and every step that false leg hit my ankle – which was fairly sore and bruised by the time we got him there. What a marvellous man and character who will live long in the memory of all who knew him.

Early into 1988, and Adam who had been having trouble with an ear infection throughout the previous autumn had to go into hospital for an operation on it. The doctors should have picked up the problem earlier, it had caused a hole within his ear drum and we had a long six hour wait while our little two-year old had a major operation on his inner ear, after which he had a big bandage round his head for quite a long while, though about the second night he stood up in his cot waving it about after he had undone it all. It caused a quiff in his hair which took ages to grow out, and he still had the bandage on when he first showed a calf (Dalesend Pansy 50) at the club show that June at John Wilkin's. That was the same show, incidentally when we borrowed Martin Webster's big cattle wagon trailer to take the cattle behind the tractor and when we got there a cow had gone through the floor with all four feet – she took some getting out, but a couple of 4x8 plywood sheets fettled the job for going back home. Adam still has problems and always will with that ear and has to have it properly cleaned out twice a year.

The early part of 1988 was one of those times when everything seemed to pass off very quietly and nothing really of note happened, the most interesting thing was in mid-April when I took Sarah plus three other girls to Accrington for a hockey session- why I don't really know, perhaps it was the lure of the name which from a young age and even now when you hear the football results, Accrington Stanley has a special kind of resonance about it.

Chapter Twelve – All kinds of everything

You seem to get spells in life and work when there are quite a lot of changes for no apparent reason, though they are usually triggered by one event. We had, through 1988 and 89 quite a few changes of personnel for one reason or another, some long term and some short term.

I suppose much of it was started by the fact that David Daniels left in May of 88. It was such a shame with such a good lad who had been with us from leaving school some eight years previously. He had done some great work for us over the time and was a particular favourite with that cheeky grin – some of his exploits have already been mentioned in previous chapters, as I believe has his demise. Unfortunately he got into a bit of wrong company and started getting too much drink and was infrequently late but getting more so, and very late to milk a few times and eventually he knew just as well as I knew that the time had come for us to part. We kept in touch after that and I helped him get one or two jobs. Eventually and sadly, his love of motorbikes proved his undoing and he was killed just pass the crossroads at Patrick Brompton.

We were busy silaging quite early in May that year and were busy doing the Plantation field across at Hill Top East, leading into the Grange pit. By then we had stopped running our own forager, though we did the rest of the operation ourselves apart from the mowing, using a contractor to do the actual foraging for us. All was going well when I went into the house to get my tea, but I hadn't been sat down for many minutes when there was a tap on the window, and it was Mike to tell me that there would be no more silaging that evening. Thinking there was a breakdown that would take a few hours to fix I enquired what had broken, only to be told that he had no forager, it had been repossessed by a finance company. He said he would have something sorted by morning, which he did and we carried on as if nothing had happened, although that day I went to support Dan Marriner when his good Gatherley herd was dispersed as Dan could no longer manage the strain on his one leg of the day to day work involved with a dairy herd – another result several years earlier on motorbikes.

A little later into the summer we had to call the vet in the middle of the night as we had a cow that had put her calf bed out. Whilst we were waiting for the vet to come and the cow was laid down, milk fever into the bargain I thought the opportunity was too good to miss and so got the trimming gear and did all four of her feet, which Bill found highly amusing, as did the vet who arrived just as I was finishing the last foot, all was well, cow ok with good feet into the bargain!

We had a bit of fun about then, when Adam who was still only two and a half at the time and decided to lock himself into the bathroom and couldn't be persuaded to unlock it. Fortunately at the time, there was a JCB digging out the remaining bit of lawn between the new cow building and the house, so that we could concrete it, so he was coerced into lifting me up to the bathroom window where I eventually managed to talk Adam into undoing the catch on the window so that I could open it and climb in to be able to open the door and let us both out. Not the kind of job drivers usually expect to do when they come with a JCB. Another lifting job that summer, though one we did ourselves with the Manitou was lift all the furniture up to the second-floor windows in Crakehall Hall for Mr and Mrs Reynolds when they moved there after Mr Reynolds retired as headmaster of Aysgarth School.

We went up to Northumberland to look at a rotating straw chopper in operation, and I thought if it could chop the shocking bale of straw that it was doing, it would comfortably do our job and we subsequently bought a GHL chopper from Ripon Farm Services. We had for several months been using a wheelbarrow type petrol driven small bale chopper borrowed from John Crosier, and while it did a good job was a lot of work with small bales, and a tractor driven one for large bales was a much better bet going forward. I was highly amused a few years later when we had a group of farmers looking at Walkerbrae Eclipse daughters with Herdwise. One of the potential customers saw Bill putting a bale in ready for chopping before afternoon milking and asked how we were doing with it. When I said it was fine, he said they had one but found it was a bit tight with the bale in it and didn't drop down as well it might, so he had to get up onto it and jump on the bales as it went round. He said the only problem was if you were up there for too long it made you dizzy, and I said the other problem was you might chop a leg off!!

At the beginning of August, we got a new young man in place of David, Graeme Wilson who had done a one year course at Houghall college but was not from farming stock and was to teach virtually everything from scratch and he wasn't a very good learner nor showed a lot of signs of developing – so he only lasted a year. He was from Sunderland and I made the mistake one day of calling him a "Geordie" to which he took an instant dislike, telling me that if you were from Sunderland you were a "Makem". On another occasion he told us about the Sunderland Illuminations which I didn't know existed – the only ones I knew were at Blackpool.

In the summer holidays, Sarah went off to France with school again, I don't think she ever learnt much French on her two trips but had a good time. At that time, it was still compulsory to dip sheep, which for us was a problem as we had no facilities for doing so but arranged to dip them at Ainderby Myers. All staff on deck to get the sheep in to the pen at the bottom of the park at Dalesend, and then I said I would manage with Graham to take them to dip in the trailer. Adam was in attendance and I told him to stand well out of the way. We got the tup in first and as I opened the side door to put the first ewe in, he met me full on face to face and I at least kept hold of him and got him back in. By the time we had got the sheep dipped that eye was just about closed and then did so, the next night we had supper in Giovanni's in Ripon where there was a photo taken of me with a massive black eye. When Sarah returned from France a few days later it had gone completely and had it not been for the photograph I don't think she would have believed us.

A week or two later it was Sedgefield Show at which I was the judge. There was a nice turnout of cattle but nothing too special, but the show was always well supported, particularly by Hunday – one of who's herd managers was Phillip Oliver whose parents lived at Sedgefield. There was a special trophy at the show for the best milk heifer on the showground of any Breed. There were only two, my winning heifer which was nothing to get excited about and what I thought was a very poor Jersey. The Jersey judge and I had to agree on the winner, and whilst I would have given ground if it had been a decent Jersey I wasn't going to for a poor one. They got a referee in who was an old retired Jersey dealer/breeder who was to help into the ring and sit down on a seat, immediately where he straight away pointed to the Jersey as his winner which wasn't really a surprise, and the kind of thing which often happened at smallish local shows. While they were giving out the rosettes, I asked the gentleman if it was a good Jersey, to which he replied, "Oh no, it's a pillock but you have to stick up for your own breed". I thought nothing more of it until the following Monday when at Darlington Mart with some geld cows and met one of the Armstrong lads from originally up the tank road who now farmed on his own up in Durham and was on the livestock committee who had selected me to judge at the show, and he said I hadn't known the best of it in the end – the Jersey had been disqualified, so the Black and White won the cup after all. Apparently, the owner of the Jersey who also had the "Jersey Farm Restaurant" just outside Barnard Castle had been buying in ones to show all summer that he hadn't owned long enough to show under his own name. His fellow Jersey breeders had been gunning for him all summer and had finally got their act together with sale catalogues, ear tag numbers and everything else and had put up their notice money with the show authorities to get him put out.

We photographed four cows with Alison Bentall that summer and tried to do a horse as well, but without much success – none of us had much idea about setting horses up for photography. I guess the horse in question was the mother of a yearling of Mrs J's which was entered for a sale at the Great Yorkshire Showground a few weeks later. They were away at the time so asked if I would go to the sale, which I was happy to do and another fascinating experience in a world I had never been involved with – a real bunch of rascals, but at least we got it sold for 1650 guineas. The only other experience I had with horses at Dalesend was one winter when Mr and Mrs J were away at a funeral and as there was no one else about, they asked if I would get the two horses in before dusk, which I endeavoured to do. Setting off with lead ropes and nuts in a bucket I got to the field, but the horses wouldn't come to me or let me get anywhere near them. After a while and almost dark I gave up the battle and left a note pinned to the house door saying, "Tried to get the horses in but they wouldn't let me". Unsurprisingly I was never asked to do that job again. I had never ridden a horse before until a couple of years ago when we were on holiday in China and Tibet. Whilst in Tibet there was a monastery at the top of a very steep large hill that we could visit and had the chance of going on horseback. I wanted to go, didn't think I would make it on foot, so opted for the horse. Fortunately there was a man to lead it, the horse knew exactly what and where it was going, and I was even more glad of the man in control on the way back down and the 'sack of potatoes' arrived safe and well.

I spoke to BOCM Silcock sales reps at West Auckland about what a farmer as a customer expected from them and Bill caught his first ever salmon while away on holiday, or so he said, I'm not sure he didn't buy it on the way home!

In the autumn of 1988, Peter took a sabbatical to go back to college to do an advanced farm management course at Walford Farm Institute. We were quite happy for him to do that through the quieter winter period when there really wasn't plenty of work for the two of them. It was a two-term course through to the following Easter, and he finished up getting a distinction. It had been obvious from very early days that Peter was going to advance himself over the years and not just stay with us for the rest of his working life, and this was one way of improving his CV for the future. After coming back that following spring he applied for several jobs in the management or foreman on larger estates and went for quite a few interviews. I think he thought most management jobs were as good as mine with as good an owner and he became increasingly frustrated by the people who were really only looking for cheap workers with no real management responsibility. Eventually later in that summer he left us to go and work for N.E.E.B as a wayleaves officer, negotiating with farmers when new or replacement lines or underground cables were being installed. I thought it a terrible waste that such a talented young man was in effect lost to agriculture – we still keep in touch infrequently and swop Christmas cards.

Later that autumn Liz Gibson came to work with us for a month to get some dairy experience and she stayed with us and proved a very useful asset for that short time and was a quick learner. The family had originally lived in Crakehall but then moved to Masham. Liz's father was a businessman from the North East, who sometime later was one of the saviour's of the Wensleydale Creamery at Hawes after it had been closed by Dairy Crest, and Liz later went on to marry someone many of you will know, Andrew Fellowes who is now a major cog in the wheels at Carter Jonas and they continue to live at Blairgowrie between Crakehall and Hackforth, where before that Stewart and Linda Burrows lived and prior to that Martin and Shirley Webster before they moved to the farmhouse at Roundhill.

The day after that I spoke at the Northern Dairy Conference at Preston on the 'Practicalities of Progress'. The speaker I followed was something of a research boffin who was advocating attempting to flush cows prior to service as you would with sheep before tupping, in order to encourage more sets of twins that would double farmers income from the resultant calves! I took great delight in telling him that that particular practicality would from a dairy farmers point of view be totally unwanted and a very retrograde step.

That weekend we went out for the day with Mollie over to Helmsley to see one of her horses which was in training near Malton. It began to snow while we were over there and for mid-November came quite a lot of snow and by the time, we got back home there was about four inches of snow and it was snowing heavens high. First thing was Mollies car wouldn't start as she had left the side lights on all day, so she had to stay the night. When I went out to check that Graeme, who was milking that weekend was ok, he was worried that there didn't seem to be many cows to milk, that was hardly surprising, he hadn't shut one of the doors properly after scraping out, and half of the cows were outside, really enjoying themselves galloping about in the snow in the various fields – at that time of the year most of the gates were open. I know the door wasn't properly shut because they all had catches on them so a cow couldn't lick and open them once closed and the latch dropped. We had great fun getting them in by tractor lights and just hoped we had got them all – which I think we did, or any that were missed had to wait until the following morning.

As Christmas was approaching, it was time to make a farmyard for Adam. We had previously made one for Sarah who was much more into farmyards than doll's houses, and Marnie and I repeated the exercise. It was a matter of great pride that we managed to set both our children up with their own farms before we got to be 40, with no borrowed money! Both of them had hours of enjoyment out of them – Adam's along with all the stock and machinery is still up in our attic, awaiting someone to play with it, Sarah took hers home, some of you maybe saw some of the components of it at her 40th birthday party when they provided the table decorations in Bedale Hall.

Again, just before Christmas we finally got all the old, remaining bits of cast iron posts fixed on the outside of the new building beside the house. I got them all wire brushed off and was painting them blue to match the paintwork of the house. As I worked merrily away, all of a sudden, a step broke on the step ladder, pitching me to earth with the pot of paint straight over my head. Just at that exact instant Arthur Barker, my Best Man and Adam's Godfather arrived with Adam's Christmas present – and all he did was laugh, as did everyone else and no one had any sympathy. It took an awful lot of cleaning out of my hair and I still stank of turps a couple of days later on Christmas day.

The spring of 1989 was quite an interesting one from a non-farming point of view. Early in January we went to the Royal Hall at Harrogate to hear Robert Swan speak. Robert was a polar explorer and was not that long returned from one of his expeditions. Being a nephew of Mrs Ropner, he had often helped us at harvest time when still at and just after leaving school. Robert embarrassed me that night – coming onto the stage to begin his presentation, he spotted us in the audience, jumped down off the stage and scrambled across the seats to shake hands and say hello – you were aware of everyone else wondering who on earth we were that the speaker felt he had to do that!!

Adam started playschool for the first time at Crakehall, Marnie's Aunt Evelyn had a stroke and blessedly died in early February. I went down into the Midlands for a two day and overnight symposium organised, and all expenses paid by Surge as they tried to expand their UK presence (something which they ultimately failed to do). William

Hague became our MP for the Richmond division after a by election to replace Leon Britton. He became a very good MP, very well respected in the area and nationally, a fantastic speaker. It was such a pity that he was thrust into leading the Conservative Party when far too young – if he hadn't he would probably have ultimately become one of the country's best Prime Ministers before his retirement as an MP, he was an outstanding Foreign Secretary.

I dug 106lbs of Jerusalem artichokes from the back garden and sold them at 20p/lb to Garners in Bedale. We suddenly got some damp clothes in the airing cupboard and discovered a leak in the cold water storage tank, which had to be replaced with a modern plastic one – when you saw the state of the old one once removed, you had to wonder that it had lasted so long. Sarah went on her first YMA trip up to Manorpowis in Scotland and we went up to Baldersdale to look at the five holiday cottages that Leonard and Mollie had created at Hury, then after another week Sarah had another trip out- to Wembley to see a hockey international. All this in a little over two months – roll on Florida.

Later that spring, we did something we had never done since our honeymoon, and that was to take a long two weeks holiday to go to Florida and Disneyland. It should be compulsory for parents to take their children there for a fun holiday where good weather is guaranteed which of course you cannot do going to Disneyland Paris for instance, and I would suspect won't be that much more expensive. Not only that there are so many other attractions in the area, Sea World, Wet and Wild, Kennedy Space Centre to name just some of them and we had a fantastic time, rounded off by a week on the coast at Clearwater on the other side of Florida – you nearly needed it to recover after the hectic time around Orlando. On the final morning before we set off home, Adam and I walked down the beach in front of the hotel, the tide had been in overnight and left some large, attractive shells which we gathered some of, and they are still in a bowl adorning the centre of our dining room table.

The fun had started however before we even got on the aeroplane. There were a lot of roadworks and hold ups on the M62, so we decided to go over to Lancaster to pick up the M6. There had been a lot of rain, but we weren't expecting to hit flooded roads between Leyburn and Hawes, but we did, and, having no real alternative but to go we managed to get through them ok, but not without water getting in and filling all the footwells. We were able to bail that out as soon as we were clear, but Marnie, Sarah and Adam had to keep their feet up off the carpets. The car was booked in at Manchester to go to a holding park and I asked the driver to please clean it out and dry it off immediately as I didn't want it to sit for nearly three weeks, imagine the growths and smells there would have been. I have to say they had done a great job, you wouldn't have known when we got back that anything untoward had befallen the car. As was quite customary in those times, there was an announcement over the intercom asking if any children would like to visit the flight deck. Adam did and as he was only three and a half years old, I had to accompany him – the views were fantastic, though Adam in a very loud voice asked "Who's driving this thing?" to which the pilot replied with tongue in cheek "Nobody!". Such a pity that nowadays because of security concerns and the fact there are so many silly people about who abused the privilege, it is something that is never now on offer to children.

Just out of interest I have a note just a few days after we came back that we achieved a record price for us for a cull cow – 740kgs at 92.5p/kg or £684.50. A good price some 28 years ago, but would only be average today when you read a lot of the cull beef cows making £1200 and the odd dairy cull getting into four figures and the better end regularly making £1.20 to £1.30p/kg.

Soon after we returned from America we had a good day out for Charles and Emma Ropner's wedding over at Ampleforth – we took Mr and Mrs Reg Hanson as it was too far for them to drive – Mr Hanson had been Sir Guy Ropner's, Mr J's fathers butler. Many of you will know one of their daughters, June who was married to Keith Meynell, the other draper in Bedale many years ago. June is well known for rescuing and looking after many of the abandoned and lost cats in the area, and their daughter Karen and her husband Adrian will also be friends of many readers. Adrian is a self-employed carpet fitter in the area, and very good he is too, having been properly trained by his father in law. He is also the main man for driving and looking after the vehicles for Keith Parlour, the local Bedale funeral director.

Early that summer we did some research work and did a lot of testing the water with a view to bottling water, which was just beginning to take off as a saleable product. Mr J with his experience in starting Dalepak was very keen, but unfortunately the source down in the wood, where there had previously been a watercress bed, which was very good with plenty of flow, was almost too good a natural product and couldn't be used. When you see the amount of bottled water consumed now and all the "poseurs" with bottle in hand taking little sips – it is such a pity as it would have been an absolute goldmine.

At the same time, we changed vets, which in those days was virtually something unheard of. At the time everyone, and particularly farmers tended to use the same bank, accountant, solicitor, and vet almost without question and usually the one their father before them had used. From my early times at Dalesend we had used the practice from Leyburn of Porteus and Watkinson which eventually became Watkinson and Naish and they had done some great work for us. Recently however there had been something of a fallout between the partners and we felt that being at the bottom end geographically of the practice, we were suffering a bit from this disagreement, culminating in having to go early one morning to wake someone up after repeated phone calls to a calving had been unanswered. We changed to the local Bedale Practice of Linscott and Best. They were the original practice in Masham when Mr McDonald retired there and had relatively recently established an office and surgery in Bedale. Brian Linscott, the principal, was a local Bedale man, he still lives in the centre of Masham, and though now retired, the business is still carried on by one of his sons Jonathan, and in fact it is now merged with the Leyburn Practice of John Watkinson, son of the original Jack.

We were looked after by Nick Buck who lives at Langthorne and then after he retired his place as partner was taken over by Howard Best, another very good vet who looked after us very well. Over the years these veterinary practices used a lot of very young good, newly qualified vets, though they also had some very average ones at times as well – one in particular who came to see a sick cow – after examining it I asked what was matter and he said he didn't know- what did I think to which I replied "If I knew that I wouldn't have sent for you" or another one who came on a Sunday morning to see a downer cow in the collecting yard – I was on my own that morning and he wouldn't give me a hand to roll her onto a gate to pull to the fold yard – said that wasn't his job! Neither of them were around for very long, nor was about the first lady vet we had on farm – I think if it hadn't been for the fact that she was a lady vet I would have put her off the farm before seeing the animal – her waterproofs and her box of tools etc were absolutely filthy and had not been washed off after her previous or more than one visit – totally unacceptable and she never reappeared. Two of the success stories from the Watkinson days were Richard Phillips who is one of the senior partners at the Swale Veterinary Practice at Richmond and the now retired Geoff Simms who was ultimately the senior partner at Kebir House at Northallerton. When Geoff first came to Dalesend to look at something, he was also asked to look at a horse which was lame. After trotting the mare up and down a few times, Mrs J asked if she would be able to hunt with it the following week. Thinking she was just a groom, Geoff told her not to be so f**king stupid, the horse would need a considerable rest. That night Jack Watkinson had a phone call from Mr J telling him that his new young vet was not to be sent to see horses in the future. In those days both Geoff and I were both big, fit young men and we would often have a bit of a wrestle either before or after seeing to the patient, and Geoff became a very well-respected cow vet in the Northallerton area.

That was the end of a very hectic few months, but they were about to change dramatically as we embarked on the next ambitious venture.

Chapter 13 – Triple Threat – Canada, Embryos, Paragon

We had been wanting for some time to do something with the herd to lift it out of the ordinary with some uniqueness about it. Over the spring of that year we had been hatching a scheme with the help of Orton Eby in Canada to source some semen from the long dead bull Hanoverhill Triple Threat-Red, get some good cow families over there flushed and bring the resultant eggs over here to implant and leave us with totally new families, and we finally pulled it all together in the summer of 89. Many folks and breeders asked why Triple Threat – long dead, never particularly milky daughters, but we had researched things fairly well – he had at that time the best percentage VG and EX daughters of any bull, and if you looked at the pedigree of nearly all the recent leading bulls or current test bulls he was the sire of almost all the dams or grand-dams.

So, off we went, while everybody was at the Great Yorkshire Show and only going over for the Hanoverhill dispersal sale, Mr J and I went over for about ten days and with Orton did a tour of farms where Orton had already identified cows that might be of interest to us, and he also put together about 50 straws of Triple Threat semen ready for what we wanted to do. On the trip we went to see the Toronto Blue Jays play at the Skydome. The next day at the Hanoverhill sale we saw Alan Swale buy the calf Dixie Rox, who went on to be one of the greatest breeding cows of almost any generation with 66 brood stars. Then the following day they kept bringing extra calves out from the top selling cows as A, B and C lots and all sold well. We went to Frank Donker's at Fradon and contracted a good Warden Maggie cow who's dam was actually a Triple Threat daughter and before that an Astronaut, so it was hardly a milky pedigree, but good type – we only flushed her the once and only had the one daughter that never really bred on, but she was an interesting animal in her own right. Dalesend Threat Maggie we never saw have a heat in her entire life, she was very docile and friendly and you only had an inkling if she was in season and I would usually jump on her back and if she didn't move we would inseminate her, and she usually held, after that if she came over you had a bit more idea three weeks down the road. We also flushed a cow there to something else as she was a Triple Threat daughter – a superb cow that appears far back now in many pedigrees – MVF Triple Threat Amanda, and that did establish a good family for us, we sold one or two sons or daughters at various sales at decent money and still had them when we dispersed. The other family we flushed at Fradon, was Tab Maude. She had been a show animal as a younger cow and had already provided daughters by other bulls and was obviously a tremendous brood cow. We were fortunate to finish up with two daughters, then a younger one at a later date.

One of those two early daughters both of whom went on to be multiple EX cows, was the legendary Dalesend Storm Maude, who is the only cow so far to be All Britain five times, was Champion of both the Royal and Royal Welsh Shows in an illustrious show career and was by one leading judge described at the height of her career as possibly "the Best Cow in the World". We had sold her as a yearling at the Society Genetic Elite Sale at Carlisle to the Wilson's of Tregibby in West Wales, and all the credit is due to them, though of course through all that prominence, she carried our prefix, and was the main reason we were National Premier Breeder for points accumulated at National and Local Shows. I was, and sometimes still am, asked why we chose to sell for the 3200gns which I think she made. The answer is quite simple, she had been Adam's show calf the previous summer and as such was already halter broken and having had a bit more special treatment, she was slightly better grown than her sister, so it was easy really to decide which one to sell. Having said that, at the sale I had one very prominent breeder show a lot of interest before telling me that she wasn't quite good enough in the leg. I have constantly reminded them of that fact ever since!! In a similar vein, at the Club Show for Adam as the Junior calf she was made Champion by Norman Walker, who took a lot of criticism that night for making a baby calf Champion, but he was of course vindicated as time went on. You wouldn't really argue with someone like Norman Walker, who was also the man who told John Pickford and Tony Brough about an in calf heifer called Condon Aero Sharon who went on to be the dam of the great sire Picston Shottle and who herself acquired the record-leading 68 Star Brood Cow. Although the Maude's either for us or the Wilson's never flushed very successfully, we had got a good family established by the time of our dispersal, where several were among the higher priced lots, as were some Echo's that had descended from a Triple Threat heifer which Orton had sent over for us as a yearling at a similar time and then successfully bred on particularly through an outstanding Hilltopper Warden daughter that we did not sell at one of the early Black and White Sales – just as well.

We flushed a Bella cow from Orton's brother at Ebyholme that was an outstanding family in the Oakridge's herd originally. It bred very well, and we had three good daughters one in particular who we showed a little and was an outstanding mature cow. We also flushed a mother and daughter combination at Oaknoll with some success, although the daughter, All-Canadian, Lancer Bunny didn't produce a daughter for us, her mother Warden Jean left us three daughters which all went on and did well.

The final family, and the one we flushed the most was the Rosina's from Craigcrest. A family which had originated down in the States, we flushed the Sexation daughter several times, and we registered eight daughters as well as one or two others we sold as unborn calves, and again left some terrific cattle which went on and continued breeding well, and again leading prices at our dispersal. We did establish a red line of the Rosina's which caused some merriment at home. Years earlier a red calf was considered as bad breeding and a red heifer calf would be disposed of quickly to a non-pedigree herd before it could spread within the herd. They had by this time become quite fashionable and being bred as it was I kept this Rosina, but when it was in the herd as a milking heifer, Mr J came up the drive one day and saw it in the Front Field. He stormed into the office and demanded it should be immediately disposed of as it spoilt the herd. I ignored the order totally and we had a red daughter from it and took it to a subsequent Black and White Sale at Carlisle where it made 3300gns to Andrew Hodge of Cheviotview. When I reported to Mr J that night of a good sale he enquired as to its breeding and when I told him that it was from the red cow he wanted rid of – he said "can't we get some more of them if there is a market".

Also at that sale we sold a couple of unborn embryos by Triple Threat for fairly big money, and it was not until early February the following year that one was to be born. The recipient was looking like calving during the evening and I was up all night wanting her to get on with it and eventually tried to help her out, before having to call the vet who quickly decided on a Caesarean. I rang Bill, couldn't get an answer, so went down to Fox Park to wake him, I shouted and blew the horn and still couldn't raise him so came back and got Marnie up to assist. A heifer calf was soon safely delivered and we immediately worked on the calf leaving Howard Best on his own with the recipient which he wasn't too pleased with but we told him the calf was sold at £6200 and he said we hadn't told him that before he started to which I said "why put you under more pressure". Just as we were finishing off and tidying up this face appeared around the corner to see what was happening – Bill had come to milk!

Subsequently another daughter was the top price at our dispersal sale at 6200gns. So much for colour – and while on the subject of colour, the only real argument Mr J and I had over all those years was about cow colour. Just in discussion one day I happened to say that I preferred a darker coloured animal rather than a white cow. His reply was that I couldn't possibly say that as the greatest cow family up until that time was considered to be the "White Cow family" from Roybrook, it wasn't the fact about the colour which caused us to argue violently, but the fact that I wasn't allowed to think that which greatly annoyed me. I couldn't find it in me to apologise and thought, as we all do in such matters that I was right. I don't know what went through Mr J's thoughts that evening and into the night, but I sat and seethed waiting for him to ring and apologise, which he eventually did, well after both our bedtimes, and was all forgotten by the next morning.

The other thing that the Triple Threat embryos gave us were some young bulls which had good pedigrees, and were well sought after by mostly commercial dairymen who wanted to get some Holstein blood into their herd without finishing up with extreme dairyness and they fitted the bill perfectly. We did sell at public auctions to good prices, but also sold quite a few privately and we had them to deliver to various parts of the country – particularly Scotland.

Through all this embryo work, we had used Linscott and Best as our vets in the provision of the on the ground preparation of the recipients, some of which at that time you couldn't as the farmer do yourself, and we used Paragon ET from up in Northumberland for all the actual implantation work – principally Will Christie and Stuart Mullan, who were good to work with and did a good job for us.

Whilst we were over in Canada buying embryos, we bought a big caravan for a new man to live in but had to leave Marnie in charge of finalising the deal and getting it delivered and set up behind the workshop. We had already taken on Alvin Venables to replace Graeme who just hadn't worked out at all. Alvin was from over the other side of the country, with no agricultural background though he had been to agricultural college for a year. He was a good enough lad, but again never really went on and developed into anything special, but he stayed with us for a while. The one real thing I remember of him was that he didn't swear – he just said "jelly babies" instead, a term we sometimes still use today should it be appropriate. Alvin stayed on with us for a couple of years until "Big Adam" was trained and was a better lad, more on him to come.

During the summer holidays of that year, there was another day of high drama to record. Marnie's sister Kathryn called on the chance to see if Sarah wanted to go and play a game of tennis down at BASA. Fortunately Sarah was next door at Neville Dyson's potato picking – as Kath went back down the drive she was hit by one of the stone trains coming down the dale and her Fiat van was rolled for quite a few yards down the track, but she escaped with just a cut requiring a few stitches on her arm. Whether two of them would have escaped without greater injury we will never know. It was one of the few times that we ever had the cows on the other side of the railway line to graze. This particular day they were over the road in the Plantation field at Hill Top East – a nice bite on it, the judge for the herds competition was due and cows always look better walking up a slope. John Logan (uncle of Hamish and John referred to earlier) was judging that day and arrived to do so among all the mayhem of the train. Every time I saw him after that he used to ask me if Kathryn was alright and wondered "how that wee lassie got out ok". The train had braked so hard on hitting the van that it had in effect welded the brakes onto the wheels and they had to get a special unit out from Middlesbrough to free them. They eventually did and parted the train at the drive to create an opening for us to get the cows home to milk some three hours or so late that day.

With Peter having left earlier in the summer, we got organised that autumn for Malcolm and Chris together with their son Andrew to move into the Bungalow. Where they stayed for some twelve years or so, and Malcolm continued as our only tractor man, also doing every other weekend on young stock at Dalesend.

In mid-December of that year Bill got knocked down in the dry cow yard by Dalesend Pansy 25 and badly twisted a knee under himself and finished up with his knee in plaster from toe to thigh. For the first time ever we were due to go away for Christmas – Mollie had asked the whole family to go up to Hury and use the holiday cottages for a big family gathering. I had to milk because of Bill's injury and so Sarah went up with Muv to stay and Marnie and I would go during the day for lunch and come back to milk a bit later but having done so once I don't think we would do it again, getting home about 7 o'clock to a cold house, getting changed and going out to do all the work, getting done about 10.30pm, having a drink and then to bed, wasn't really our idea of a fun thing to do.

In the spring of 1990 I became president of the North Eastern Breeders Club for two years, a great honour and one I thoroughly enjoyed. Just while talking about such things I was later President of the Yorkshire Club as was Mr J, having previously been President of the North Eastern Club. I think I would be right in saying that we are the only two people who have been, and certainly from the same business.

At that time, Herdwise was going very strongly, and apart from the usual director's role and work as chairman of the livestock committee, I also did a certain amount of support work by speaking at various meetings. In March I went on a three-day trip up into Scotland to speak at two or three meetings for them. The first one was at Campbelltown on the Mull of Kintyre and until we went, I hadn't realised just how far it is to that part of the world. Meeting up with Jim Blackwood and Isobel Parker our two Scottish salespeople, we got there for a meeting that evening. Up in that part of the world, they are so far away from anything that they are almost timeless, and it seems to mean very little to them. Their meeting was due to start at 7.30pm but it was about 9 o'clock by we got people there and started, which meant the meeting didn't end until gone 11pm. Deciding that there was no way I could stay with them on the whisky front and they looked set for quite a session, after a couple of social drinks, I crept off to bed and heard nothing more until about 6 o'clock next morning.

The fire alarm rang, and you could smell smoke which told us it was not just a practise. By the time it was discovered to be the barman's clothes which he had left on something to dry, everyone was awake and it was too late to go back to bed, but too early for breakfast, so Isobel, Jim and I went for a walk round the town to put in some time. Down by the harbour we came across a three-legged dog that had obviously had an accident and a front leg had been amputated. We thought nothing of it until just before we got back to the hotel, we came across another three-legged dog, but it was a cleverer dog because it was a dog dog, and was having a pee against the wall stood on two legs. Of course nobody believed our story, claiming it was the effect of the previous nights spirits but it was actually exactly as it happened, and a month or two later I saw Jim somewhere and asked if he had been back to Campbelltown, to which he replied yes and I would never believe it, he had seen another three – legged dog, and yes they were all different dogs by type, colour etc. Needless to say the "Three-legged dogs of Campbelltown" passed into Herdwise folklore and was quite often referred to along with other stories over the years, such as Malcolm sending out a memo to all staff telling them to save fuel and hence cost by free-wheeling down hills and cutting corners – I don't think it would have added up to much of a saving!!

Later that morning after Campbelltown Jim took me to a farmer customer as we made our way to the ferry. It was absolutely pouring down. That date was the 20th March which meant there had been at that point 79 days so far in the year, and the farmer said they had already had 80 inches up to that point – that's right, an inch more than days in the year to then. I asked him when they managed to get muck and slurry spread on this very wet land and he said about the first week of May, I further asked when they got silage made and he said "oh about the last week in May – we have had so much rain it has washed all the muck in". I know at times we want a good shower of rain in Lower Wensleydale with an average annual rainfall of 27-28 inches, but I wouldn't like to have farmed in that kind of rainfall.

The ferry we were on the way to catch was to take us over onto the Isle of Bute where I was speaking again at another meeting that night. We had to wait for the ferry and so went into the adjoining pub to get a sandwich for lunch and were greeted by a gentleman sitting at the bar, who was the nearest human being I have ever seen to Popeye, he even smoked a pipe very similar to the Disney character. I suspect he was a permanent fixture there and would very rarely have to buy his own drink as with a character like that, tourists and holiday makers would be queuing up to buy him a drink, and I would think if they didn't, the innkeeper would give him one to keep the customers entertained.

Later that spring, over Easter we had an enjoyable short break to Jersey, still the only time we have been, though we keep saying we will go again as we had such an enjoyable time in some great weather for that time of year. We had a hire car for the three days we were there and with a lot of travelling about round much of the island, struggled to do a total of a hundred miles. We went one day to a very large carnation growing farm – massive green house the size of Wembley stadium – at the time still a private business but later became a listed company sending flowers all over the world – Flying Flowers PLC. The underground caves and excavations which had been the prisoner of war camp during the second World War were fascinating. On a farming front they were planting potatoes on little pieces of land, some on the hillsides to which they had to carry everything and do much of it by hand – we saw a grass field being chain harrowed – the little set of harrows pulled by a man with a big belt around his waist. Jersey's with their halters left on between milkings were out in the fields, some with sugar beet pulp sack blankets on to keep them warm. Sarah goes there regularly now to do work ahead of their two summer shows, and the herds are now fewer and much larger with the management style much nearer to our own. Anyone else who has been at one of my talks or slide shows will have seen a photograph of a field of anemones in full flower, being grown for their corms for sale – that was also taken on Jersey at the same time.

During the summer of that year, Sarah was busy doing her Duke of Edinburgh's Silver Medal Award, and as such they were to take to various places for walks. One was over at Grassington, then over to Lancashire for the YMA open day, a bit later another Duke of Edinburgh hike in the area was around Sawley near Ripon, and then a bit later in the summer they had to do an overnight expedition in the Buckden area over in Wharfedale. As part of the scheme she also got a Bronze Medal for Lifesaving and did various other things to gain her Silver Medal, though she never went on to try and achieve the ultimate Gold Award.

Chapter 14 – A Sale, New Tractor, New Lad, New Scrapers – All Sorts!

The summer of 1990 saw us busy with the build up to our next draft sale which we held at the end of July. Prior to that I had another new lad start work for me at Dalesend as soon as he had finished school. Adam Worsdale was from Hunton where his father dairy farmed, and Adam was looking for experience. He was known to us through the Holstein Club and YMA, and for several years was a very useful lad, most of his work being with the young stock at Dalesend.

Our Adam started school that autumn and for some time it was rather confusing with two Adams about – if you shouted Adam sometimes two heads would appear round a doorway and so they became 'Big Adam' and 'Little Adam'. This had to be altered at a later time, though Adam was no longer with us, as our own son became a 6'3" big lad and they were referred to as 'Big Adam' and 'Bigger Adam'!

We also changed tractors earlier that summer, and for the first time didn't actually buy it, but had it on contract hire, something we continued to do for many years. We had become tired of having to put a lump sum to it each time we changed a tractor and a contract hire which covered servicing, tyres, breakdown etc. made good economic sense and meant that it was possible to budget in a figure with a much greater degree of accuracy. The tractor was changed at regular intervals and should there be a problem Ripon Farm Services had to repair it within 24 hours or provide a replacement. After one or two changes and slight increases in hire fees, they seemed to forget about putting it up for years, and I didn't remind them – didn't think it was my job. When they did finally realise, they wanted to almost double the charge and I told them to forget it and went back to buying one, not needing such a big tractor as by then we didn't do any of our own ploughing or power harrowing.

With the sale coming up, we didn't have the manpower to do the clipping ready for it and we had Ellie and Robert from down in the South West to do it. I don't remember how I came to learn or know of them, but they did a good job, and it was a great source of amusement to us that Ellie said she had a pre-conceived idea that Marnie would be "twin-set and pearls with a perm" lady – nothing could be further from the truth, as those who have known Marnie over the years will testify. We had an evening herd visit from the North Eastern Club just the week before the sale on a lovely evening with supper in the garden under lights and the roses on the front of the house absolutely loaded with heavy scented blooms. Stephen Mawson from Baileyground over near Seascale came across to help us for a while around the sale. Still a young lad but keen as mustard he did a great job and we still see him at Carlisle now and again, where he and brother Richard now run a large business with a lot of cows, milk processing, hotel and café. They had been well tutored from a young age by Ken and Kate and had bought cattle from us over the years, and in fact that year Ken bought a good Unique cow early in the sale. For the first time that year we staged the sale at home rather than at Dalesend, taking out some cubicles and feed passage to make room for seating, the sales rostrum in front of the out of parlour feeders, with a raised ring and then turfed on top of the stone we had put in. We sold a few good cows that day and some very promising heifers by Walkerbrae Eclipse who was arguably the best bull we ever used at Dalesend, who just seemed to blend in with our blood lines. One particular heifer was a Lettice, a family which originally came from the old Arbourhill herd after we had bought the farm in the early 1960's. She had calved twins and retained the cleansing and was very thin, though very correct. Bill told Chris Norton she was just a bit "glieked" which Chris had never heard of before but he just told everyone as he got to sell her what Bill had said – meaning she was a bit "pilly-willy" meaning the same thing – a bit poor but only needing to mend up. Someone from the south west obviously decided she was ok, she sold very well, and I was astounded to discover afterwards that she went one better the following year and had triplets!!

Shortly after the sale, and I was ready for a day away, we went down to Pembrokeshire Show which I had been invited to judge. In those times many of the major shows, still had two separate classes for the Friesians and Holsteins and Pembroke was no exception. There were some good classes of cattle, but the thing that I really remember from that show is the class winner of the milk heifer class in the Holsteins. At first appearance a big heifer with a fantastic udder though just a touch coarse in the bone – Cardsland Eclipse Flo who was subsequently sold to Tom Cope at Huddlesford for whom she went on to multi-show Championships and later her descendants went on to do the same for the Bells of Holmland and then David Wright of Berryholme.

Ten days later we had one of the heaviest rainfalls I have ever seen – 2.65 inches in four hours – we had some heifers in the back field to get in as soon as Nick Buck came to inject for embryo work, we waited for a while to get them in but it didn't fair up or look like it so we had to get soaked trying to get them out from the hedge backs and I remember it was so wet there was water on the higher bits, it just couldn't soak in fast enough.

Adam started school in early September, unfortunately Mrs Teasdale the juniors "mother hen" had retired at the end of the previous term, and there were problems with a new probationary teacher who believed in the current teaching philosophy of the times which was to allow them to do what they wanted all the time. He didn't enjoy that first day, in fact had cried virtually all day, but when he came home in the afternoon, he said he had done school, what was next?!!

It had been a very dry spell and on a trip one afternoon to the top of Nidderdale we walked for a long way down the bed of Scar House reservoir, where you could see some of the old pipes which had carried Angram water down, and also some of the old walls that had long been under water. We had also at the time delivered the Black Tup over to near Driffield who that night charged a tree and broke his neck, and then the following week we finally got the auto-scrapers fitted into the cow cubicle passageways, and we also went to the National YMA Calf Show for the first time.

That autumn we did something I had never done before, never dreamt of doing and have never done again since. The Bungalow field was in winter barley and was under sown with grass for silage for future years. It was a really good take and once we got the crop off it sprung to life and so I put a hundredweight of Nitrogen to the acre on, and on the 24th of October we made 81 four foot round bales of silage from 16 acres. It was real wet, heavy stuff, didn't look or smell anything very pleasant when we opened them up to use, but the cows went mad on it. Later that autumn, following BSE and changes to legislation there began a charge for a dead heifer or cow. Not that we had many but from what had been a receipt of a meagre £30 recently it suddenly cost a £10 disposal fee. At the time we took badly to it, though I understand the cost has escalated quite dramatically and will now cost in excess of £100 for a dead cow to be collected.

More fun with Bill – one of our leading cows at the time Dalesend Moss Rose 10, a good Ridgwardine Judo daughter calved twin heifers, until when I sketched them a few days later one of them had changed sex and was a bull, so we had to give him a lesson on sexing calves!! Remarkably the heifer twin to a bull, or freemartin, did actually breed which was most unusual as something like only 6 or 7% ever do breed, though she didn't turn out anything very special.

Sarah went to St. Aidan's at Harrogate to receive her Duke of Edinburgh Silver Medal and then a few days later Bruce Oldfield, the renowned fashion designer spoke at school speech day. He had been at one of the Dr Barnardo's homes in Ripon and an old boy of the school, as was Richard Hammond of the Jeremy Clarkson show Top Gear who was there at the same time as Sarah, though I don't think he was ever honoured in the same way.

At the beginning of December, we had another weather-related experience, which unfortunately impacted on some embryo work. We had a dozen or so recipient heifers lined up for some of the Triple Threat embryos and put nine into the suitable recipients, with three rejected as unsuitable. These heifers had been outside being fed as it had been quite a mild autumn and they were healthier outdoors. Overnight we had some heavy driving snow which froze everything, bringing down power and telephone lines. We got the heifers in straight away on the Saturday morning and got them onto some good food, but the damage we assumed had been done and we didn't have one pregnancy when they were later PD'd. The other problem we faced was no power anywhere for milking, milk cooling or the automatic scrapers, and on the face of it not likely to have any for a while with a massive local area all out of it. At the time we didn't have a generator, and I eventually managed to locate a single unit mobile milking machine at David Alderson's at Scorton and then Bill and I started to milk the 80 or so cows one by one through the parlour which was cold and dark into the bargain. After easing about twenty of them the machine ran out of petrol, but having been to Crakehall for some it wouldn't start again, so we put the rest of the cows through and just eased a drop off the heavier milkers, hoping that we might be able to milk properly the next morning. With no power, the gates front and back in the parlour also were to wedge shut all the time. Still nothing next morning, we got the one stall petrol engine going again, and I eventually located a generator at Simon Leggott's at Cockleton, but when we got it home it was 480 rather than 240, so had to get Ted Nicholson from E & P Electrics who looked after us for many years, and still does at home, to come and convert it, and we eventually got the cows milked – I think they were even more relieved than we were. By this time there was too much muck in the passageways for the auto-scrapers to move so they just kept tripping off, but we managed to get a rough scrape with the tractor. We managed for a day or two until we got power back on, and glad to say we never had any resultant problems such as mastitis. We lost a little milk because of course the out of parlour feeders or the in-parlour feeders weren't working for a day or two.

After that bit of a rough spell we were ready for a long weekend away and went in mid-February, Valentines Day as it happened and stayed at Chipperfield in a nice hotel, (later stayed there quite often as it was the hotel Holstein UK used when down for Board meetings). We went for the day out from King's Cross for lunch on the Orient Express which was a lovely day out as we travelled round the Kent countryside, but the fog was so thick we couldn't see a thing, but it was still a marvellous trip to spend just part of a day in that kind of luxury.

Just after that we were having tea one day when the phone started ringing, and it was the first of several phone calls that evening. People had been watching the local North Eastern television news, reporting on a multi-vehicle pile-up on the A19, and among the cars in the shunt was a number plate many people recognised 7WU. Mr J had this number plate from virtually when he first started driving – I asked him once why that number and he said it was one of the first he had, and he thought it would be easy to remember. It always amazed me that he kept it, bearing in mind when I first went to Dalesend the farm van was JGR 123 or vice versa and he didn't bother keeping it. He was totally unharmed in the shunt on the A19, just in the stationary queue of traffic when something hit a vehicle further back and rammed them all forward into each other.

Soon after that we caused a bit of a stir at the Grammar School in Ripon- by this time, Sarah was in her GCSE year and as part of the English curriculum they had to give a ten minute talk to the rest of the class, on a subject of their choice. Not doing things by half she decided to do it on showing a calf, so I had the calf to take to school and hold while all the class were got outside onto a lawn to listen, and it just about brought the whole school to a standstill as all the other classes stopped to look out of the windows.

A bit later into the spring, one of the North Eastern Club's stock judging nights was being hosted by Raymond and George Sledge at Constable Burton – nothing at all remarkable about that – the funny bit was Adam telling me as we had tea that I couldn't go sledging at this time of year, particularly when there wasn't any snow!

In early July I took Sarah to Wimbledon, as she had been successful in the draw at

BASA. That is the only time I have ever been, another of life's experiences. I realised when there that you could actually have bought an entry ticket very cheaply and then two people could have alternated the actual seat around centre court. We were very high up and the seats then had so little space in front of them that I had to keep going out for a stretch. We saw some of a ladies quarter final with Martina Navratilova playing, before rain stopped play and we witnessed Cliff Richard doing one of his impromptu singalongs from the VIP area.

We had earlier that spring drilled some maize for the first time for many years and going forward it became an important part of our forage ration for the next twenty years or so. Always a crop that at times you wonder why you bothered when it stands still during a cold spell in early June, but then marvel at the speed with which it can grow in a hot sunny spell – this was brought home to me that first summer when, before we went on holiday, I put a post in just to the height of the top leaf nicely into the Twenty Acre, and found it had grown by 26 inches in the sixteen days we were away. Foolishly I left the post in and when we were about to harvest the crop it took me a long time to find it – I didn't think Metcalfe Farms would be too happy to try and chop it through the forager.

We went on holiday to Denmark that year and had a week in a rented cottage and in some good weather saw a lot of the country. Adam of course wanted to go to Legoland which we did, and it was fascinating even in those days, and, quite naturally he wanted to buy some Lego whilst there, and as is the case in such places, it was half as much again as the same box was at Vasey's in Bedale when we got back home. Part of a day was spent at Hjerdl Heydl – a reconstructed old farmstead with pieces they had moved and rebuilt from all over the country, the highlight of which was an old windmill - absolutely massive, which pivoted around a central wooden post that only needed one man to lean on a pole to move it to catch the wind. We weren't as impressed by the Little Mermaid at Copenhagen when you could see it for the people hanging around it and "peeing" in the sea into the bargain, though the Tivoli gardens were very attractive. We then drove up to the north and took the ferry before driving up to Kleppe in Norway to see Colin and family. We had hoped to then come straight back from Stavanger to Newcastle but couldn't do that and so had to drive back down into Denmark to get the return ferry. Calm as a mill pond as we set sail the steward advised us to eat straight away as it was going to get very rough – he wasn't wrong once we got out into the North Sea, but we had eaten a marvellous Danish cold table before that. That was the last family holiday we had for all of us, by then Sarah didn't really want to do boring old things with Mother and Father anymore!! She had by then started part time work at the Staveley Arms at North Stainley and soon after she started, she was there when the boxer Frank Bruno was being feted after opening a new ride at the nearby and similarly owned Lightwater Valley.

It was a busy summer that year – we had decided to go into milk processing to try and help our milk price and Bren Howe built the new processing building to join the existing dairy and with James Jones-Perrott from the Welsh Borders looking after that side of things, we actually started milk processing in mid-October and it was a very brisk learning curve, a real insight into that side of the business and ultimately a fairly expensive exercise, but a lot of interesting bits along the way, including some of the foibles or otherwise of human nature. Just before the start of processing we had a lorry load of plastic bottles delivered – do you know how many there are on a lorry and how light they are – we had them on every trailer imaginable and very unstable, only the lightest of breezes would move them and we were nearly drowned in a sea of packs of bottles. Later we converted part of the Dutch barn into a bottle store. We built up quite a customer base quite quickly and that was when the dirty tricks started, as the existing players weren't prepared to allow a new customer to get a foothold. A group of dairymen in Darlington gave back word after about five days – nothing wrong with the milk but their previous supplier had given them promise of free milk for a month if they went back – from a business point of view they couldn't turn that down. Another local shop who changed to us had a lighted flare put through his letterbox and the most outrageous of all involved Dalepak Foods Ltd. By then a publicly quoted national company (for which JGR was the founder and at the time still chairman) the managing director was told in no uncertain terms that if we didn't pull out of a fairly large contract with a chain of shops we had just taken from Northern Foods, that they would immediately de-list Dalepak. Bearing in mind that they took nearly 40% of their product it was again one that had to be lost. The dairy continued for several years and included several other local dairy farmers as we grew the business, but ultimately was unsustainable and we closed it down. Not long before that we had begun to supply Asda with flavoured milk as a leisure drink which didn't really take off at that time – though it did at a later date – we were perhaps too far ahead of our time.

At the end of July Cascade Court was opened in Wycar, Bedale as the offices of Herdwise, a week or two later Dalesend Moss Rose 10 was champion at Wensleydale Show and then in October we had a group of A Level Biology students from Ripon here to watch us putting in embryos – which at that time was still being done surgically. We set up a viewing platform until on the first incision and a spurt of blood one of the boys fainted, it was almost guaranteed to happen! At the Black and White Sale that year we sold two Triple Threat sons at £2000 and £3600 and then shortly afterwards I sold another to Northern Ireland to Nelson Trimble – he wasn't any relation to the future political leader over there, nor to the future winger in the Irish Rugby Union team. Unfortunately, that bull didn't work when he was old enough and I sent a replacement, but he never did send us back our half of the slaughter value of the original one.

Late in 1991 I went to the funeral of Tony Welbourn at Pateley Bridge. Many of the farmers over a fair area around us will remember Tony who worked for Ripon Farm Services. He was, along with George Reed of Tithebarn, a super salesman, and either of them would have succeeded in selling snow to the Eskimos. Both of these were the only two salesmen who ever came into the house if it was lunchtime to talk, and both of them became friends.

Tony had not been a well man, with a bad chest for many years, but was too young a man to be lost to the area. He had also been involved for quite a few years in exporting second hand tractors to Norway through Colin, which had helped to keep prices up when changing tractors. For those of the readers too young to remember Tony, many of them will better know and remember Chris Gall who succeeded Tony for about twenty years at Ripon Farm Services, before he moved to Paxton's at Northallerton, majoring on JCB sales.

After the disaster with milking cows after the frozen cables coming down and the necessity for the processing dairy to have cover, they had acquired a big static motor generator from a police college somewhere down country, and part of the deal was that we would build the housing for it. The motor was in and going before we got it done so the building went up round it. It was never called into use very much and it was fairly powerful so that in most cases if there was need for it, we had to get Ted from E & P here to switch it over and make sure it was ok, but it could run if necessary all the dairy equipment plus the cattle buildings, scrapers and the house and bungalow.

In the spring of 92 I went with all the Herdwise men on a trip to Holland and Germany to look at daughters of quite a few bulls that we were marketing. At that time there were a lot of bulls beginning to come off the European production line, and many of us needed to be able to get a picture of the type of cattle and their conformation scoring in comparison to the Canadians, as we still had very few UK bred or proven bulls available. We had a good trip; the one outstanding memory was of one of the outside publicists who was travelling with us got off at one of the border check points and we left without him. No one realised for a few miles, it was still in the very early days of mobile phones, but we did eventually go back to collect him.

Katy Cropper the well know sheepdog triallist came in late spring to buy a couple of black lambs. At that time she was doing quite a lot of displays in the main ring at the shows and wanted a "black" sheep in the family to misbehave as she moved them around the ring – I never saw one of her performances, but I believe the black ones did their job.

At about the same time Sarah, along with several more from school did a parachute jump for charity – it was one of those things that is very weather dependant and was on and off a few times because of too much wind before it eventually happened. She landed very exhilarated and wanted to do it again, but that wasn't an option. She was also by then learning to drive, which makes you realise just how time was passing. Though she failed first time, it did no harm and she soon passed and is now a very good driver, covering 30,000 miles or so a year, even if she drives a little too fast.

Chapter 15 – All Change Again – Canada, Italy, University

School was to be over in the summer of 93 for Sarah and there was a lot of activity round about that time. A year earlier in 1992, she had decided to take a year out before university and go to work in Canada, but was looking at places to study agriculturally related subjects the following year. We had taken her up to Newcastle and to Reading and then Marnie took her down to look round Wye College, a part of London University. We had a big batch of heifers calving at the time with Triple Threat embryos so I didn't want to be away, and naturally not one calved in that time. They went down one evening into Kent, spent the next day at Wye (which Sarah thought nothing of, being in the middle of nowhere, whilst having played rugby there twenty five years earlier, I thought was a super place) then travelled across country ready for the Royal Show the next day at which Sarah was judging for the North Eastern club.

We had a classification visit about then from Bill Lloyd, who had something of a reputation for being a little inconsistent, and that day David Hewitt, the head classifier (later Chief Executive of Holstein UK) came to do a check on what was going on. Soon after we started we had a couple of heifers one after another, both with not the best of legs, but one could handle them and the other couldn't. To my eyes there wanted to be 10 points difference in their score but Mr Lloyd got them both to be the same. Before the next one came in David asked me to remember the two heifers as he would like them back in at the end. When we had finished we got them back in, David asked us to shut all the doors and leave them to it. I told them not to be too long or their lunch would be cold – it was because they had obviously had a long discussion over the merits of the two animals. David couldn't alter the classification once it had been done, but there was little doubt he would have liked to.

It was into the summer holidays when we went to see one of Marnie's favourite performers Phil Collins and Genesis at Roundhay Park. Fortunately it was a warm summers evening, we took Sarah and her friends Rebecca and Anna with us and left them to it, agreeing to meet back at the car when the concert was over. A great performer, we thoroughly enjoyed the night but it was pitch black by the time things were over. There wasn't the amount of lighting about the car parks as there would be now, and it was in the days before you could open your car from a distance on the keyring and have the sidelights come on. We took a long time to find our car and when we got there the girls wanted to know where we had been, but we didn't admit to not being able to find it, instead explained we had been enjoying the atmosphere with no rush to get back. A fortnight later we had a few days away, leaving Sarah at home for the first time on her own, though Anna came to stay with her. We stayed at the Beverley Arms Hotel – lovely place and one day went down to Hull and saw the Round Britain Cycle race going past, though by then it had lost much of its attraction to sightseers, though now cycling is very much to the fore again with the Tour de France and now Tour de Yorkshire creating tremendous interest. We also went on the

North Yorkshire Moors railway – very well organised and a long way ahead of our local Wensleydale railway when it eventually became a tourist/heritage line.

We had two calves qualified from the North East to the All Britain Calf Show at the Royal Showground where Dalesend Threat Cher was 11th and Dalesend Warden Idena 13th. They were to go on the Friday morning with Denis Tyreman from Miss Edwards at Hemble, and then we were going down to be there by they were. It was a Friday morning and as Malcolm had the 20 acre worked ready to drill with winter corn, I told him to get on with that and I would do the Herdwise bulls at Fox Park on my own before going away. Taking the Fergi 20 and scraper from round the back, the gate into the Back Field was to open, but I was just too close and it couldn't come properly open. I was in a hurry and going to save two seconds by not getting on the tractor to reverse it – instead of which I hit a forward gear and the tractor trapped me between the back wheel and the end of the gate. I braced myself and managed to stall the tractor but didn't know whether I could retain consciousness until Malcolm got round to me as he was on the first time round the outside of the field so had every corner to work in, so I started shouting hoping Bill might hear me in the buildings. He was washing down after milking with the steam cleaner going, fortunately he let go of the handle and it stopped and heard me which brought him running. I told him when he got on the tractor to make damn sure he got reverse gear first time to release me – fortunately he did. I went and did the bulls, drove to Stoneleigh, and was in absolute agony all weekend, buoyed a little bit by the North Eastern YMA, one of the smallest clubs in the country winning the Tidy Lines Competition.

I was due to go to Italy the week after to look at potential proven sires for Herdwise, and though not really fit enough to go, wasn't prepared to miss it and gritted my teeth. We saw all sorts of cattle and farming conditions, but wondered at some of the quality of the land in the Po Valley which could grow two crops in a year (barley and maize or even double crops of maize) and made good contacts going forward for Herdwise to market some Italian bulls, one in particular from Aquilla. There was John Crosier, Dave Shorrock and Jim Shield on the trip together with our Italian host from Semenzoo and at night he took us to places to show off Italy's food choices. One night we had a "metre of pizza" – as its name suggests, about 12 inches wide and a full metre in length with various toppings on it, so plenty of choice for everyone. Another night to another restaurant where their steaks were legendary. They came under the same kind of regulations as we did from an environmental health point of view, but thought nothing of the fact that you had to walk through the kitchen to get to the table and all the raw meat was lying about and you could choose which piece you wanted to eat. We organised five ribs to be cooked on the bone and Jim impressed upon them the fact that he wanted his well done. Being Italian they took absolutely no notice and when they brought it to our table the blood was still running out. I don't like meat red but it was not to be avoided and it was a fantastic steak, but Jim was having none of it and stood up and left the restaurant in a real pickle and waited outside until we had finished, and we weren't in any rush. I hardly slept while away because of my leg and then as we lifted off for home hit a pocket of air and the plane dropped about fifteen foot at one go, or so it seemed. The day after getting home I went with my leg up to Penny Naish at Leyburn to get some physio and she wasn't too happy that I wouldn't go to hospital with it. I didn't want to because of the circumstances under which I acquired it, and eventually it mended with no more problem, though I still carry the scars to this day on the front of my left shin, and as always, we learn the lessons of health and safety the hard way – if we are lucky – if we don't it can be too late!!

Just after that we had a bit of motoring fun – I had been doing something with big Adam and was taking him back to Dalesend in the pick up. As we went through the dip in the centre of Patrick Brompton we were overtaken by a wheel and almost immediately when the back end dropped realised it was our wheel. Fortunately we just had to cross the road to get some tools out of the garage at Dalesend, and found some nuts to at least get me back home to fix it properly.

During that autumn as the dairy business expanded, we concreted the whole yard as it was getting so much usage. We provided the labour and the dairy paid for the concrete and it left us ultimately with a very good serviceable yard. Whilst it was being concreted Mr J and I went to Canada again, and one night Marnie discovered one of the dairy vans had run across the corner of one of the newly laid pieces, and try as she might it was just too far set to work out and remained as far as I know to this day as a reminder. At the same time we demolished the old gantry to make more storage room for the dairy in the Dutch barn, installed toilet portacabin and offices and concreted a path across the lawn to them. After the dairy had closed and the portacabins gone, this path remained and we called it the path to nowhere. Also while we were in Canada, the central scrapers which had been causing a bit of trouble, suddenly started a lot more, breaking continually and Bill in a moment of both anger and sensibility got Malgar in to fit a new chain – expensive, but it solved the problem.

We went to Canada to look at any other potential cows for embryo work plus a bit of Herdwise business and while there bought a very expensive cow Glavindale Threat Kim from Jimmy Walker of Walkerbrae. We learnt afterwards a few people had tried to buy her around Winter Fair time but Jimmy wouldn't sell her. We hit him on a bad day – he had just come out of hospital that morning from a hernia operation and was just feeling miserable in front of the fire and on his own admission let us buy her at 15,000 Canadian dollars plus half of the embryos in storage from her. The other half of the embryos belonged to the estate of someone who had died very suddenly and they eventually turned up through Harold Nicholson and started an outstanding family for Wilson and Stephen Boow at Dunnerdale with three high scoring EX daughters. We also, whilst in Canada went to see Albert Cormier at Cormdale about a young bull Herdwise were testing, but JGR didn't fancy the look of him and wanted to leave without talking but Orton and I prevailed and got the bit of business done.

Also whilst in Canada, we had a day looking round test daughters in the St Jacobs area with John Maitland acting as our guide. JGR again wasn't too happy with the day

– he hadn't come all that way to look at average cows, but we had to explain to him that that is what progeny testing is all about – it is whether a bulls daughters improve on their dams, and that may well be animals in the lower grades – it is the few fancy ones at the top end which make the marketing side!! The other thing whilst we were there was the Craigcrest dispersal when we were heartened to see our confidence in the Rosina family justified with them averaging nearly double the sale average.

It wasn't a very good journey on the way home. Ok until we landed at Heathrow to discover after a long wait at the luggage roundabout that Mr J's had gone to France. To cap it all when we got to the car it had a flat battery and we had to get it jumped off and it was also very cold and there were a lot of patches of black ice and all the way home, with many hold ups because of accidents, but we eventually made it in one piece after six hours.

1993 brought with it another two big changes the advent of Set-aside and the demise of the Milk Marketing Board.

With the start of Set-aside regulations there was also a requirement to have all maps updated and official, and so early in January we headed to York and the nearest Ordance Survey office to get the necessary updating done and got several copies printed of each, so that we were well prepared going forward and hopefully would avoid any problems as we submitted the paperwork. This was the forerunner of the Single Farm Payment under EU regulations where we were actually paid an amount for a percentage of land taken out of cereal production to attempt to reduce the corn mountains in intervention. It's proper name was IACS – Integrated Arable Control Scheme, and we never thought it was really successful and it soon got swallowed up within the wider Single Farm Payment scheme.

We took a short break in the February half term and stayed at the Royal Hop Pole in Tewkesbury and had a good trip – again for those trying to equate prices over the course of this break it cost us £279 for dinner, bed and breakfast for four nights for the three of us. Whilst there we went to Gloucester one day and had a fascinating few hours looking round the museum of advertising and packaging back through the ages up to the present time. There was Snow one morning but it didn't stop us visiting Slimbridge Wildfowl Trust originally started by Sir Peter Scott but by then set up to attract large numbers of visitors and very well laid out and informative about all the different birds there were to see. Our third visit was to the Beckford Silk Printing factory where we watched them creating the silk and colouring the patterns before you felt almost beholden to buy in my case a very expensive tie – but at least it has been well worn over the years.

A good break before getting into all the meetings that were held all over the place that spring as we approached the end of the Milk Marketing Board. Originally formed to protect farmers from the fragmented market where farmers were paid very little for their milk and it had over the years done a fantastic job in protecting farmers from the vagaries of the market. It had diversified massively over the years into AI and

Management Advice which we now know as Genus and into milk processing which became Dairy Crest. Perhaps by then too big an operation which we all know can create inefficiencies, but in many ways massive improvements could have been made without destroying the principal, but by then we were into an era when monopolies were frowned upon. Mrs Thatcher by then Prime Minister was the architect of its fall, having sometime earlier pulled another rung from under the dairy farmer's feet, when as Education Secretary she did away with school milk.

At those meetings there were presentations from the MMB on staying with them as the newly formed Milk Marque, and from many of the independent milk companies who wished to buy direct, the majority of whom were offering an odd penny or two per litre to tempt you away on the principle that if they divided to rule it gave them more power over an industry in disarray. There were some stormy meetings and it caused serious arguments and even led to fall outs between friends and in some cases families. The argument at that time was that 1p more than basic wasn't a lot of good to anyone, and after all these years since privatisation, that argument is still very much the order of the day. We decided initially to stay with Milk Marque until that was also ruled by EU to be a monopoly, and supplied one or two of the co-ops until we really couldn't or weren't prepared to stand that differential any longer and moved to Arla Foods, not that they are the answer to everyone's prayers, but there is not a lot of choice of buyers in our part of the world as there are in some parts of the country.

Milk of course is very much now an international commodity and prices move very much according to the world markets based on supply and demand and it takes very little for that balance to topple one way or the other causing a very erratic market which makes it very difficult for farmers to plan long term. The problem, or one of them, is still the same as it has been since de-regulation – the price drops very quickly on the down cycle but rises very slowly on the upside and never seems to get high enough ready for the next time. The ridiculous thing is that the consumer hardly looks at the price of milk, just watch people in the supermarket, they only look for the colour of the cap denoting the fat content and the size, very rarely the price, added to which some of the price labels have been swapped around by bored youngsters having to go shopping with parents. All the milk buyers are really worried about is being competitive with all the other buyers and being within fractions of a penny paying the same price – they could easily all pay at least three pence per litre more and not suffer any disadvantage.

Anyway, enough of all this misery caused by the de-regulation of the milk industry, lets have a few more light-hearted bits and proper farming stories. That same spring Linscott and Best got a new assistant vet called Stephen – he was a very good vet, but was almost something from a by-gone age, he would have slotted seamlessly into All Creatures Great and Small, and reminded me of the vet in that episode who was carrying a badger about in a sack on his back, but we had better not diversify the writing onto badgers and TB. That spring we, as always tried to watch the Grand National, but that year it was the race that never was. After two false starts the race was declared void, although many of the horses and jockeys carried on and had a private gallop round. I went down to Buntingford to collect Kim from British Livestock and was pleasantly chuffed when David Gribbon, that doyen of showmen complimented me on that he thought she was one of the best cows to have come into the country in recent years, and certainly she looked every bit as good at home as she had done four months earlier in Canada. A few days after that Mr and Mrs J put on a dinner at Dalesend to celebrate my twenty-five years of being at Dalesend. A few days later we went to Harrogate for Marnie's birthday and watched the Russian Red Army singers and dancers perform – absolutely mesmerising and then we went to Oliver's for dinner afterwards – we hadn't been there for some considerable time, but it was still just as good.

Marnie took Muv to Norway for her niece/grand daughters' confirmation (they make a big occasion of it in Norway though very few go to church regularly, it is all about the giving of gifts and party). They had to fly from Heathrow so I had taken them down, while they were away, Sarah had her first bump in the car, all part of life's learning curve. We had a very wet day of 2¼ inches in 24 hours just the day before what we were going to make our big show season to promote the herd, beginning at Otley show. We had a very ordinary start to our endeavours that day, the best we could manage was a second in the dry class of not many cows with what was to become our lead animal of the year and one of my favourite cows of all time, Dalesend Lettice 23. Adam and I went down to gather them back up from Heathrow the day after – quite a long trip which he managed very well for a seven year old without too many "are we there yets!".

That gave us a couple of weeks to lick our wounds and re-group before Northumberland County Show which we had never been to before. At that time it used to get a good number of top cattle with top local herds, plus ones from southern Scotland and Cumbria. We took a lorry load and had a great day at a very good and well organised show with vast numbers of people coming from Newcastle by train to Corbridge on a Bank Holiday Monday. Lettice 23 had got calved and settled down and Dick Butterfield had no hesitation in making her champion. His biggest dilemma that day was in the senior milk cow class where our Dalesend Unique 13 had torn a teat a couple of days earlier and it was bandaged round the top, but after consultation with stewards and a Society representative made it the class winner and then Reserve Champion to Lettice 23. As a great pair of matching black cows, both by Walkerbrae Eclipse they were unstoppable as the best pair of animals of any breed. Lettice 23 followed this up by being Champion at Malton on the Thursday and then just two days later Bill took a few to North Yorkshire Show at Northallerton and she again stood at the top of the championship line-up. Bill wasn't really a showman as such, but we were all away that day as it was our niece Emma's wedding to Rob up at Romaldkirk.

Next came the big one – Great Yorkshire Show and Lettice 23 looked well, we had high hopes but then she came unstuck. She had always been a very quick, easy milker who soon let her milk down. Under judge Tim Harding of Crichel she stood at the top of her class in the first line up and at that point the milking machine was started up down at the parlour across from the showring, at which point the taps opened and she started to pour milk out, and Tim had no alternative but to drop her down to second.

We came out of the show on the Thursday night and left at lunchtime the next day for Cumberland show just outside of Carlisle which was on the Saturday. We slept in various places, Adam on some bales in front of the cows, where he had a big bull licking him as he slept. Lettice 23 didn't win the championship but did beat the Holstein champion from the Great Yorkshire Show and then a week later was Supreme champion at Cleveland County Show and followed it up three days later with the Championship at Ryedale.

A short break from showing, we came back home on the Sunday afternoon to find a glider had landed in the Bungalow field and while they were waiting for it to be collected, they let Adam have a pretend fly in it. The following day Mr J and I went over to Lancaster for Mr Parker's Bailrigg Sale. That was the herd from which the original Pansy had come and by then had developed into our best and quite outstanding British family. We liked the pedigree of LOT 1 in the catalogue, Bailrigg Queen 15 and never hesitated in paying 3000gns for her and compounded it by buying her eldest daughter for the same money. They went on and bred very well for us as a family, and it is one which Sarah still has to this day.

After one or two other local shows at which we did nothing very much, it was time for our most local show at the end of August. Wensleydale Show has always had a good turnout of dairy cattle and we had a field day that year, winning every class in which we were entered, taking 11 first prizes in total. Ten days later it was over to Westmorland County Show under Phillip Davies of Gornal and whilst we didn't win the top prizes, we picked up twenty one Premier Breeder points, and followed it up in another ten days by taking the Championship with Lettice 23 at a very competitive Stokesley Show – where in those days it nearly took more winning than the Great Yorkshire Show, but rounded off the show season with a poor day at Nidderdale.

The day between Stokesley and Nidderdale, we set up all the trophies for a photo session for the whole show season which had been hard work but a terrific result. We showed at 16 shows, won 52 first prizes, winning 37 trophies and used a remarkable 27 different home-bred animals, so it wasn't just about Lettice 23, and I don't care what anyone says it was a fantastic achievement and all credit to the whole team both at home and at the shows. The culmination came in the February of the following year when we attended the dinner at Ripon Spa where we were announced as the BOCM-Pauls regional and National Premier Breeder. I was sat near Lord Granchester whom I didn't take to when he told me that the competition wasn't for second-rate little herds like ours to win. I had the greatest of pleasure in telling him I was in full agreement, but the fact remained that we had won it and his herd had only been second!!

Some years later we were to be National Premier Breeder for a second time, but have to admit that in that year most of the points had been won for us by the Wilson's of Tregibby with Dalesend Storm Maude.

151

Just before the last couple of shows of the season, Marnie, Bill and I went up to Keld for the funeral of Laurie Whitehead. Laurie had bought sheep down to winter with us for many years, and in all our dealings had been a true gentleman, he had always been very generous to both Sarah and Adam whenever he saw them, and always helped them, particularly Sarah to do some A'level Geography field work on soil depths and topography. Having been at the top of the tree in sheep breeding for decades, you got an immediate sense of the esteem in which he was held at his funeral. The nearest we could get with the car was about half a mile, and we stood at least 100 yards away from the chapel at his funeral, which unusually was on a Sunday.

The day after Nidderdale Show we had taken Sarah to the airport to start her journey over to Canada to work her year out before going to university. She went first of all for the winter six months over to Western Canada near Calgary where she lived and worked with Wayne Vansickle and family at Riveredge Holsteins. The weather is obviously very different to ours in an Alberta winter, but a months winter with temperatures never above -15^{0}C didn't bother them and didn't seem to bother Sarah at all, as she said it was a different sort of cold. With great sadness we only learnt about a month ago (February 2018) that Wayne had lost his battle with leukaemia, too young an age to be gone. Sarah moved from Riveredge over to Oshawa, about an hour east of Toronto to work for the summer months with the Werry family of Werrcroft Farms. They were great with her and created lifelong friendships with various generations of the family that still are ongoing today and Ron and Elsie Werry the senior members, though now retired and moved away from the farm are still going strongly. It was very quiet though at home with only Adam to look after.

In October of that year we went up to the MOET sale at the newly opened Norton and Brooksbank Sale centre at Kirby Thore. It was an ideal place for sales and good to work at as we found at various times over the years when we sold there, but it never really took off, the commercial man wouldn't really come to buy at it as they thought cattle would be too expensive being pedigree – which of course isn't necessarily the case, and it eventually closed as a sales centre a few years ago now.

That autumn Adam had his first taste of rugby when he started to go on a Sunday morning to train with Wensleydale Juniors at the Leyburn ground at Cawkill Park. He enjoyed his time doing so, and it wasn't long before I became involved with the coaching on those Sunday mornings, which he for the most part and me all the time continued until 2001 when foot and mouth brought a premature end to the season. Adam had missed parts of seasons with injuries, wearing a neck brace for several weeks after doing some damage and missing the second half of the 1999/2000 season and the first half of the next after dislocating his hip in a practice session. He had just done re-hab and I think played one game before that dreadful disease closed down the dale in the spring of 2001. By then I had taken the 7/8 year olds from when I first started to the point of being 14/15 year olds who thought it was great fun to tackle/hit the coach as hard as they could. It was taking me until about Saturday night to recover before training the next day and so I decided to call it a day. Adam continued to play whilst at school after his injury but never continued after leaving school, not even when the local club in New Zealand asked him to play. I told him he should have done so once and he could have put on his CV that he had played Rugby in New Zealand – people wouldn't know it was just once and at what level.

That same autumn, Big Adam left to go back home to work with his father as they developed their own herd. He was replaced by Nigel Scurrah from near Masham who stayed with us for a while – he didn't have great stock experience but did a good job for us, and was good with his hands and on machinery or engineering jobs. Many local readers would know his father who had his own mobile machine servicing business and travelled around the area with his old workshop for many years, and had done work for us over quite a few years, primarily when we had the big old engine which ran the corn drier etc. at Old Park House. Nigel went back to engineering after he left us and was one of the people involved with the creation of The Tornado, the first steam locomotive constructed in this country for many years.

At North Eastern Club level, we as a committee were concerned how few members we drew or came to meetings from the Durham area, and so decided to hold a meeting up in Durham to test the waters. We picked a speaker who we thought would have extra appeal and draw people – Brian Bolton who was the manager of the Watergate herd down in Berkshire, at that time one of the top show Holstein herds in the country and known as something of an extrovert himself and as a speaker. He gave us a very good night, including at one point jumping up onto a chair and pretending a mouse was running round it – I think it was to demonstrate how frightened people were to try new things. The only thing was, we had all travelled up to Durham rather than the Northallerton area, but we hadn't one extra person from the North of our region, so we never repeated the plan.

Another first at the time was that the vets started to scan for pregnancy rather than a manual diagnosis, very much the usual practice today though at that time it was still quite revolutionary. Its big advantage was that it could be done much sooner, so that if you had one not pregnant you could start work to get it back cycling much more quickly. The disadvantage was that there was the odd cow which returned at six weeks after she had been pd'd in calf at 30-35 days. My other slight concern which I always felt was that in doing this intervention at around thirty days there was always the danger of disturbing something which explained perhaps some of those 42 day returns just a few days after the scanning had said she was in calf. Do other people have that same worry?

Adam wanted a tent for his birthday that year, and being on the last day of the year, it wasn't really camping weather. Fortunately our bedroom was massive and so the tent had to go up in there for a while, so he could pretend. Soon after that we were at Crakehall Village Hall for Martin Webster, David Gibson and the Cole twins fiftieth birthday party – they had all gone to school together as juniors all those years before, and a few days later the three of us set off for Canada to see Sarah among other things as she had by then come back to Ontario and in addition I had one or two bits of both farm and Herdwise business to see to.

Whilst we were in Canada we did all sorts of things, staying with the Werry's for a day or two and Sarah treated us for Mother's Day to see "Phantom of the Opera" at the newly re-furbished and re-opened Pantages Theatre in Toronto and we suppered at East Side Marios where we used to go when we did the Winter Fair Tour some ten or eleven years previously, and it was still just as good. We visited a maple syrup plantation which was very interesting and they had got all the piping set up to link the trees together and bring the syrup to a central point and it was amazing the quantity being generated at that time of year when the sap was rising. Everything changes so suddenly in Canada at that time of year – when we arrived near the end of March the daffodil leaves were just starting to show above ground, and when we left on the 10th April the buds were almost bursting. Weatherwise we got up one morning to about six inches of snow but it got so warm and had gone before the day was out. I raked the snow off the windscreen with my hands before we set off and did I know about it an hour later – it had been much colder than our snow and gave me an indication of what frost bite must be like. We took a Greyhound coach to Kingston and stayed at the quaintly named Fireplace Hotel, en-route to Ottawa where we stayed for four nights and enjoyed visiting the Canadian Parliament building which had one of the few elevators in the world which doesn't go straight up and down but at a slight angle, and also visited the actual government chamber as they were not sitting at that time. From Ottawa we took a day trip to Montreal which was very nice and very French, I thought much nicer than Quebec City which I had been through previously. We went up the CN Tower in Toronto though didn't eat in the tower, but we did eat in the revolving Skylon Tower overlooking Niagara falls a day or two later. We had been staying in Brantford for a few days, visiting with Orton, Frank Donkers, Paul Eckstein plus some of the cows we had flushed for Triple Threat eggs in previous years and just the day before we set off home went to the Ontario Spring Show.

Back home and a quieter summer with not a lot of showing, but a year after not winning it in her fantastic show season, Lettice 23 was champion at the North East Club show, and then a week or two later Stephen Dalton came to us for a couple of week's work experience from Bedale School and enjoyed it so much and got on so well with Bill that he kept coming at weekends and holidays for a further year before starting work full time a year later, after he left school.

In September I went as part of the Herdwise sire selection committee to France to look at a couple of proven bulls that were beginning to emerge, and not having any knowledge of French cattle or their evaluation standards it was important we went, and we saw all sorts of cattle and systems from the very basic that would not be acceptable under UK regulations to very modern ones, and ultimately Herdwise finished up marketing two Cleitus sons, Davron Clei and Evrex Clei. We used them both ourselves but only sparingly and we had a very good Davron daughter and a decent Evreux daughter, Pansy 90 who though too small, eventually made an Excellent cow.

We were taken to France and shown round by Brian Bolton who by then had left Watergate after the herd had been sold. He did some rally driving in his leisure time and drove very fast all the time, but particularly needed to show his rallying talents to get us back to the ferry in time for coming back home.

We decided to reduce the Welsh Black Mountain sheep somewhat and sold 19 breeding sheep to a lady from Coverdale for the princely sum of £635, not a large figure by todays prices, but not bad for then. At the similar time I decided to change to formulated blend for the milkers and foolishly tried to feed it through the out of parlour feeders. Alright for a day or two when it became apparent very little was being fed and closer investigation showed that the cotton seed within the blend had wrapped round the little augers which dispensed the feed, and it couldn't handle it – if we had left it any longer I fear we might have had damaged motors, but as it was we had to manually empty each of the hoppers to then untwine the wrapped around cotton which was very tight, then get the bin sucked out and replaced with nuts. A hard days work but a mistake we never made again.

Sarah was back from Canada about the same time and then about three weeks later she was to take up to Newcastle with a car load of her things ready to start at University. When we rang her after the first day to make sure she was ok, the first thing she had done was go to see the people involved and change her course to do straight Agriculture, so much for trying to guide her towards the more likely future subjects of countryside management and leisure, but certainly it is something she has never regretted doing. Whilst we urged her to stay at Newcastle most of the time and get involved with University life, she had to come home for various events with which she was involved and just a week or two after starting she finished up third in National YMA Clipping finals building on her Canadian experience and practise.

After the success of maize in the cows diet, we began to grow an increasing acreage and did quite a bit of experimental work ourselves on varieties and with or without plastic, which at that time we were using quite extensively, but gave up after a year or two as it was too expensive. Metcalfe Farms who did both the drilling and the harvesting and BOCM-Pauls who did the analysing of samples were both very helpful over a number of years as we looked for what suited our situation best. Adam used to love going into the maize when it began to grow quickly as he found it something of an adventure down the rows, but by the time maize mazes had become popular he was too old for them. The first year or two while we were still deciding on maize's future roll with us, we ensiled it in an Ag-bag and it produced a superb product which was good to use from whilst the bag was on concrete, but in the second year we needed a bigger site and so did it on grass in the back field and it led to more wastage as you couldn't get it clean along the bottom as you could on concrete. You don't see much being done like that now, the biggest problem was that it was quite slow to fill when harvesting, something which didn't suit the contractors. Interestingly enough, and I haven't seen it in this country, but had seen it on a large scale in New Zealand, it is a widely used way of storing grain and they have developed machines to both fill and empty them. In many cases they just fill them on the headland of the fields they are combining. The system seems to work very well except in one case when I went with Len to look round crops at his friend Richard Peckitt's (originally from Thirsk) when he had a bunch of cattle escaped from a neighbours who had clambered all over and punctured the bag in many places, a hell of a mess which had to be patched up and tidied up very quickly.

We had a good day out one day in half term, but only went as far as Hawes, but very interestingly to watch the cheese making at Wensleydale Creamery, the rope making, particularly the church bell ropes at Outhwaites and then a good look round the Countryside Museum. Shortly after that it was interesting to see Hawes win a National award for the Best Day Out in a Rural Town – well worth it and Hawes is now a very thriving small town with all the tourists, and gets huge numbers of walkers, it only has about two quiet months in the year.

That autumn the Set-aside area requirement was reduced from 15% to 12% which doesn't sound a lot but for anyone with 300 acres of corn it meant nine more acres of corn to sell. I don't think there was any connection though many would say farming has always fallen into that category, but about the same time as that announcement, the first National Lottery was held on 25th November 1994. I bought us all a ticket and probably did so for another week or two, but soon gave up as we never had numbers anything like getting even £10. I still remember those original six numbers – 3, 5, 6, 11, 31, 46 and usually look when they come up on the television screen, but it is amazing how rarely any of them let alone any number of them ever come up, and if I had put £5 per week in since the start up to the end of March 2018, I would had spent just over £6000 on it and wouldn't have won a bean – not a good enough return for my liking.

We had struggled to get Kim back in calf after she had come from Canada, and decided to flush her a few times, so we took her down to David Oldershaw's on the edge of Derby, they had a centre on farm where they could flush cows while they were still in milk and they did get a few eggs for us which we shared with them rather than pay any fees. She remained there for about 18 months until I got a phone call one night to say she would be dropped off by a lorry the next morning, it was the day the BSE crisis really blew up and movement restrictions were feared, just as well they were on the ball. Later we induced her back to milk quite successfully with an unapproved cocktail of drugs which worked and she peaked at about 25 litres. Again we couldn't get her back in calf and eventually she went up to Paragon ET at Hexham where they did IVF work on her very successfully (it is now very much back in use some 22 years later) though ultimately it was to no avail. At the time of loosing all our young stock (more of which later) we had I think it was 16 daughters by 14 different sires – all in calf or bulling heifers – what a terrible loss and we will never really know how good a breeding cow she was. Never a big index cow she wouldn't have been an AI bull mother but we did sell a Prelude daughter as a calf at a Black and White sale for 3200gns to Phillip Green of Eshton which ultimately ended up at Rebecca Jarvis' Braimber herd to complete a 100 tonnes lifetime and I bought an Integrity daughter back from there after Foot and Mouth. We also a year later sold a very smart bull which should have been Champion that day at the Carlisle bull sale for 4200gns to come back to the Cinnamire herd of George Corner at East Harlsey.

That same autumn while we were selling up at the Black and White the bronze statue of Dalesend Cascade with Mr J holding it was stolen, As soon as I opened our bedroom curtains on the Sunday morning I realised it was gone. It transpired later that the thieves had carried it down to the railway, and that one of the thieves involved had been a labourer at the time the milking parlour was being built some seven or eight years earlier. They admitted to the theft when caught for some other country house outside ornaments, and for many years Mr J used to receive the odd cheque for varying amounts in single figures from the criminal damages board – but it would never repay the value of the superb piece which had been sculpted by Sally Armup and which had graced the Herdwise stand at the Royal Show for several years. It was sold originally through a "fence" in Darlington then resold sometime after at the big annual 'fair' at Newark Showground, but never then seen again. I kept waiting for it to turn up on television on one of the many antique programmes, but no such luck. The stone plinth which had been done for Mr J when he owned Stainton Stone and had Dalesend Cascade carved into it, looked very bare without anything on it, and I found an old photo of it which we got blown up and Norman Iveson made a metal cut out of both man and bull and Marnie painted it in his true markings, and whilst not the same, at least filled the space.

At the same time the farm was still running a Saab as my car, and we had to take it to Stockton for its services at Alexanders as the nearest agents, and we would have part of the day to fill in whilst it was being seen to. One particular time was just before Christmas so we were doing some shopping for odd bits of stocking fillers in a cheap and cheerful shop. We were very amused and had a job not to start laughing at two local ladies stood behind us in the queue for the till. One lady said to the other "aren't you looking for a Christmas present for your mother-in-law – what about one of those umberella's, to which the other lady replied "It's a £1, I'm not wasting as much as that on her".

Sarah started work as a waitress at The Friars Head at Akebar in the holidays, something she enjoyed doing and helped her to pay her way through University, before the next summer going back to Canada to work at Werrcroft for three months, and with regard to Adam there is the first mention of what was to become his ultimate profession- gamekeeping. At that time they only shot one day of the year at Dalesend, more of a family day out social occasion round about Christmas/New Year. Bill who from mid December to the beginning of February took a lot of odd days holiday and nearly spent more days shooting than he did milking, used to put a bit of corn round to draw the few wild pheasants out, took Adam with him, and on 28th December 1994, just before his ninth birthday he was with them beating on the annual shoot – and his love of and dedication to that life grew from there, of which more will be mentioned later.

Just before that and a couple of days before Christmas we had a cow down in the parlour pit for the first time after 8 ½ years. Dalesend Daphne 16 was newly calved and just coming through the parlour for the first time after calving and went down with milk fever and then rolled over the heelboard and down, we had little option but to get calcium into her and wait for her to get back on her feet, walk up the steps and out and no damage done.

In the spring of the next year, the Walkerbrae Eclipse group of daughters which included among others Lettice 23 and Unique 13 won the progeny group class at both the North Eastern Club and the Yorkshire Herds Competitions- they were a tremendous group of cattle of which I was immensely proud and never again had as good a group to put forward.

Spring half term took us down to Stroud for two or three days so I could attend the Maize Growers Association conference which was held at Cirencester and on the other day we visited Painswick with its amazing churchyard with 99 yew trees and some marvellous Kneelers in the church, we went over the Severn Bridge and saw some local scenery both sides of the Welsh border. Soon afterwards I gave my 50th pint of blood which was a bit of a milestone, which was marked later in the summer at a lunchtime presentation for all such donors at one of Leeds leading hotels – totally unnecessary and I would much rather have seen they money it would cost spent on the service rather than on the luncheon with all the "hangers-on".

Chapter 16 – Mr Bill takes Canada by Storm and Other Travels

Early in 1995 I was needing to go to Canada again on both farm and Herdwise business and on that occasion Mr J agreed that Bill could go with me to look at some of the families that we had brought over, and also in recognition of the many years of dedicated service Bill had given us, and so in mid-March off we went, and had a marvellous and at times amusing ten days there. The first amazing thing was that in going to get our hire car for the trip in Toronto, they had three John B Liddle's booked in that afternoon to get one. I know Toronto and North America is a big place with a massive population, but Liddle is not the most common of names, and I still find it incredible that there should be three of us in one car rental depot on the same afternoon – it's not as if it was Smith!

We stayed at the usual motel/hotel in Brantford, not far from Orton Eby who took us round most of the herds whilst we were there. They had a bit of a gym and sauna there which I made use of most days and eventually got Bill persuaded to join me. He was soon gasping for breath on the cycling machine but gasped even more on his first experience of a sauna and couldn't stand it for very long.

At the time we had been using a bull on the herd at home called Dupasquier Wind who was a young bull from the prize winning Starbuck Winnie family that were the first family to have a senior and junior champion at the same Royal Toronto Winter Fair. Bill always struggled to pronounce the Dupasquier and usually called him "Dupesquire". On that visit Orton took us to see the cow family and before I could get out to introduce Bill, he had jumped out, shook Oscar Dupasquier by the hand saying, "Hello Mr Dupesquire, I'm Bill". Fortunately, Mr D. spoke very little English having come from Switzerland originally, so he didn't understand or take any offence.

Whilst there we toured round all the following herds – Altona Lea, Raivue, Loa-da-Mede, Willsona, Dappleholm, O'Connors, Browndale, Cherown, Aitkenbrae, Craigcrest, Oaknoll, Walkerbrae, St. Jacobs, Bosdale, Ebyholme, Fradon, Quality, Fieldhouse and Sunnymaple. A lot of fantastic cattle were seen, but on the Sunday many herds didn't want to take visitors, so I took Bill to see Niagara Falls. Bill was navigating after viewing the falls and very nearly got us into America without any paperwork, and it might have been even more difficult to get back into Canada if he had succeeded.

Soon after that I took Adam down to Twickenham with the Wensleydale Juniors for the schools rugby day and just over a month after that Marnie, Adam and I had a last minute invitation by BOCM-Pauls to go to the Rugby League Cup Final at Wembley and see Wigan beat Leeds 30-10. Another of those marvellous sporting occasions you should try and witness.

In between times, there were a lot of empty pallets about the place, from the dairy mostly, which by then we had closed down, so I decided to clear them and hopefully get a bit of cash, so we loaded up the cattle trailer with as many as we could and going up to collect Sarah from University for the Easter holidays, we trailed round Newcastle, only got rid of about three blue ones which didn't get any rebate as they were a designated type, so brought them all back home, and eventually they were sawn up for firewood. Sarah looked after some cattle for us the first time we took some to Kirby Thore and a couple of days before going, she tried to cut off her nose with the clippers while doing some cattle at George Leggott's – first we knew of it was could we go and collect her car and things. Showing seemed to be capable of injuring her – a year or two later when up at Northumberland County Show the day before I was knocking the posts in for our stand when the head flew off the sledgehammer and hit her full on the head. I told her to get up and get on as I had to get back home to milk – no lasting harm done on either occasion.

We had a visit that spring from Devon Breeders Club and an enjoyable lunch in the garden with them, a couple of days later sowed some lucerne in the Wood field as I wanted to get some into the ration, but we were never able to get it established despite several attempts.

Sadly, at the end of May, Marnie's mother passed away after only a short illness, a great loss to the family of a very talented lady. For Sarah to be able to attend her funeral, she had to have one of her first year exams changed and I had to go for her and get her back to Newcastle and she had to have no contact with any of the other students on her course until after she had sat the exam.

More staff changes through that summer after Nigel Scurrah decided farming wasn't really for him and a month or so later after various interviews we appointed our first lady member of staff – Hazel Browne from somewhere over the Cheshire area – a nice girl and seemed capable of doing the youngstock and show preparation side, but only lasted a month before she left, deciding that she didn't after all like clipping cows.

We were still doing some embryo work with our own cows and flushed Dalesend Pansy 30, a very correct (JGR called her the perfect little cow) Rigwardine Judo daughter and she produced 28 eggs and I well remember the following year when the calves were being born, I was away somewhere and when I got back there was a note on my desk from Mr J – bulls, bulls and more b. bulls. The first seven or eight were all bulls, though we did subsequently get one or two nice daughters from that flush to continue that outstanding line.

Things were changing at that time and for the first time that year, all the Black and White cows were in the same ring at the Royal Show. There was also a new era for us as regards the management of our dry cows where the new recommendations were to keep near calving cows on bare pasture, feed them straw and feed a special dry cow cob nut. We were also changing things regards silage storage, tired of the Ag Bag for maize, Malcolm built new walls around what had been the original old bunker silage pits of 40 years previously, so that we could store more maize, one pit in particular being narrow so much less face to deteriorate as we fed out the silage in summer time. After a spell away from them, we went back to using BOCM-Pauls feed in everything for the cows and young stock.

At the end of June, we went up to Baldersdale for Len and Mollie's farm sale before they emigrated to New Zealand, much more of which will come later as we have now been over there four times. The same day as their sale was the Rugby World Cup Final when South Africa beat New Zealand 15-12 with the trophy being presented by Nelson Mandela. More change and movement through that time – David Christie arrived as our new vicar and shortly afterwards we had he and his family for tea and an introduction to farming.

It was fantastic that summer to be invited to judge the Scottish Herds Competition, which at that time was a big event, took a full week and I think we travelled about 3000 miles in all and carrying those animals in your mind to place them in all the different classes was quite a task. The best individual cow was between if I remember rightly, the first cow I saw on the Monday morning and the last one I saw on the Friday afternoon. I do remember that week whilst at Mr Steel's at Kepculloch, a young lady, his daughter had just returned the previous day or two from being tutored and trained in cattle photography by Sheila Metcalfe. Jane Steel has gone on from there, some 25 years ago and developed unquestionably into the best cattle photographer, certainly in Europe if not the world, and ultimately did all our Dalesend work in later years and is still kept busy by the cattle breeding companies even if the number of individual herds still photographing has perhaps fallen as prominent ones continue to go out of dairying.

Sarah was back to University that autumn, no longer in Halls of Residence but sharing a house with four other girls, so we had a load of furniture and such like to take up and get her settled in and then not long after she wanted Adam to go up and spend the weekend with her, which he did and we had a weekend of luxury at the Gosforth Park Hotel. The thing to be really remembered about the weekend was that the Wimbledon football team were staying there ahead of their game against Newcastle United on the Saturday. There was a little shop in the hotel, and I had forgotten to pack my razor so went down to buy a pack of disposable ones. Who should be in there but Vinnie Jones who was in the process of making sure that the lady in charge of the shop knew which room something was to be delivered to.

The next afternoon when we were going out, there was a group of the footballers and their then manager Joe Kinnear coming down in the same lift and Vinnie was telling his manager how there was a knock on his door late the previous evening and who should it be but the lady from the shop and he didn't know how she could have known which room he was in. Mr Kinnear asked if he had behaved himself to which came the reply "oh yes boss". I don't know what bearing these events had on the game, but it will be long remembered by football fans as Newcastle won 6-1 and Vinnie Jones ended up in goal after the Wimbledon keeper was sent off. I couldn't believe how ill prepared as professional footballers they appeared to be as they just lolled about the hotel all morning and ambled as a raggedly bunch towards their coach to the game only about one and a half hours before kick-off. I suppose that is twenty plus years ago when even professional sport was much more relaxed than it is now.

The next weekend we took Adam to Blackpool, also our first visit to the Illuminations, more because the main sponsor and feature of that year was Stobart and there were illuminated Stobart lorries on all the lamp posts. That apart none of us could get very excited about the town or its main event. We did go through them again years later and it didn't really change in our opinion.

We were a bit short staffed through that winter and with stock sales looming, I had the chance of a young lady to help us, whom I had come across once or twice helping Richard Bown at various sales, whom I only knew as Rab. She came to see me on a Saturday and whilst not wanting a full time job, agreed to stay for a couple of months and what's more she didn't want to go away but stayed with us and started work on the Monday. Her proper name was Rebecca Watts and she lived with us from early November up until Christmas Eve when she headed back up to Scotland which was her home. We all got on well and she became another of our adopted daughters, Marnie and she still write to each other at Christmas and Birthdays and we occasionally visit each other. Originally from Ballater up in the north of Scotland, she had worked with the Logan's at Powis, and eventually ended up in that area when she married and settled down with a local beef farmer and they now have two children. Only last autumn (2017) we had a trip up to Dundee to see Bill Gayford who hadn't been down for his few days to see us, and we got in touch with Rebecca to go and visit, but she wasn't going to be there as daughter Katrina was taking part in the Scottish horse vaulting Championships, so we went there to see them and watch what was a new sport to us – basically gymnastics on horse back which we had never heard of before, but very quickly over the next few weeks discovered that it was quite a popular thing to do. A few weeks later as Rebecca and children were heading back north from a friend's beef dispersal sale, they called for lunch and a natter. It's great to keep in touch.

The following week we were up to Scotland for the Scottish Herds Competition Dinner and Awards and the night after spoke at the S.W. Scotland Breeders Club and then in early December we hosted a N.E. Club meeting which was a bit of a change for a winter meeting, and put on a display of the 19 Triple Threat daughters we had by then got from milkers down over, and Stephen Garth from Lancashire came over and did a "top line" demonstration which was still something fairly new in cattle preparation. Sarah brought home with her for that night several cattle leaders, included amongst them, who were on the same or similar courses, were Louise Pickford of 'Picston' and Matt Winter of 'Corringham'. That had been a busy day getting ready for, as we had also that morning flushed Threat Rosanna to Boulet Charles to produce 14 embryos, and just a week or so later we had another good result when we got 19 from Dalesend Threat Bella. In between time we had done some photographing to get some of these early Triple Threat daughters on record. At that time, we still used Norman Walker who did that as well as sale preparation and feet, and he took some outstanding photographs, though he eventually gave up the photo side and concentrated on foot trimming. That particular day it was very cold, wet and windy outside, but Norman had a painted background which we put up at the bottom of the collecting yard and there was a big wide gate and the passage to it, through which there was enough distance to take the photos, plus some artificial light we rigged up. We still remember that day of photographing, Norman had hob-nailed boots on which rattled on the concrete, he insisted on setting up the animal himself before running back to the camera, once or twice a can of white or black magic would tumble out of a pocket onto the floor and frighten the posed animal which meant she had to be re-set. Flour was used quite a lot at the time to build up the rump a little if needed and create a real whiteness, and it was to tidy off before the photo was taken We did eventually get them taken and got some decent photographs!!

In the early part of 1996 Herdwise was sold. We had been aware for some time through the previous year that in many ways it was a mature business and that as there were mergers going on within the worldwide AI industry it was going to become increasingly difficult to acquire and market sufficient bulls of a good enough quality, and had agreed should a suitable offer emerge we would sell the business. That possibility did suddenly emerge in early January, and it was to take over the whole company and its existing staff, some of whom had been with the company for a considerable time and so that made the decision easier. On 25th January Herdwise was sold to Avoncroft Cattle Breeders/Black and White Sires managed by John Williams who earlier had been a very successful salesman and livestock officer with us. Obviously it took a while for all the details to be finalised and exact amounts worked out, the real stroke of luck came when the completion occurred and the final payments made on the 10th April, the day before the whole BSE crisis broke – a day later and I am sure that there would have been massive back tracking as cattle breeding and semen sales went into meltdown for a while as farmers didn't know what was going to happen. At the same time as Herdwise was sold, Mr J's accountants very cleverly, but quite legally were able to roll that along with the fact he was eligible for retirement relief and he was the major partner in J.G. Ropner & Co which was the farm business all up into the equation and the farm became a limited company and we began trading as Dalesend Farms Ltd, which meant that our cattle prefix was always being used at all times.

That spring I had a very enjoyable trip to Twickenham with Dick Brown as the BOCM-Pauls host and George Leggott, one of many trips we enjoyed together. Apart from several times to Twickenham and twice to Dublin, once to the magnificent stadium with the closed roof at Cardiff we went regularly to Murrayfield which was Dick's favourite. When we went up we usually met up with one of his associates Frank who originated from near Edinburgh and knew his way around the city, taking us to some very good Italian restaurants and one time into one of the many teaming pubs on International days. Frank thought he had a great way with the ladies and we had a real laugh one time when he really pushed the boat out and chatted a young lady up with some terrific lines and compliments, only after a while for her to reveal with great glee that he was wasting his time as she was a lesbian!!

We went down and stayed a couple of nights at The Fleece at Cirencester while I attended the MGA conference at the college, a couple of days later I spoke to Deighton Women's Institute, we had a visit in early May from Oxford Grassland Society and two days later we went over to Norway for Elisabeth's confirmation, just after Sarah had been over to the Isle of Man for the YMA weekend. At that time, we seemed to be hosting quite a lot of visits from various agricultural organisations and speaking at all sorts of meetings including WI's, Rotary Clubs, University of the Third Age apart from farming societies. I always enjoyed both the visits and the speaking engagements, particularly the non-farming ones, when you had the opportunity to engage with the general public, tell them some of the unknown to them facts of agriculture, but also correct some of the misconceptions they had either been told or held. At the end of May I spoke at a BOCM-Pauls meeting for the suppliers to Wensleydale Creamery, who were doing work on special feeds for them to produce extra fat and protein for cheese production.

There was much sadness in the spring of the year when Mr and Mrs J's only daughter Carey lost her long and brave battle against breast cancer leaving husband Johny Dickinson and three young children Tobyn, Amelia and Leila, and on what would have been her birthday a marvellous memorial service was held at the St. Michael le Belfrey church in York. Anyone who either uses or has visited Patrick Brompton church will have viewed the marvellous bell tower screen – a huge piece of glass engraved by family friend Jenny Stourton. That is a name many of you may recognise – Edward Stourton a BBC news reader and correspondent for many years was one of their sons.

Early June was Sarah's 21st birthday and we went up to Newcastle and took her plus friends out for a meal and then a few days later we held her actual 21st party in Bedale Hall with visitors from all over, including Elsie Werry and granddaughter from Werrcroft in Canada. I went up to collect them from Newcastle airport and as we drove home was aware of Mrs Werry looking for something which after a while I enquired about. She was expecting to see stone walls everywhere – that was the impression they had got from watching programmes such as All Creatures Great and Small. On the Sunday after Sarah's party I took them up over the tops to Grassington and back over Blubberhouses so they could see plenty of stone walls, and called in at the sports ground as we came out of Bedale where a cricket match was in progress and tried to explain the basics of the game to them.

I was busy through that spring and early summer tidying up all the Herdwise business. The only person not taken on when the business was sold was the accountant who lived locally and understandably as soon as he was offered a job nearby left to go to that, and under the agreement we were to be responsible for collecting all monies owed to us and paying off any monies we owed. The vast majority of farmers paid up their outstanding bills, though there were one or two to chase up relentlessly, one or two were a bit unpleasant and one particularly nasty who said I would always have to watch out because he knew me and I didn't know him and he would get me. I asked him what his problem was as the only one I could see was that he had bought semen from us and we were just wanting payment. He did eventually pay up and so far, he hasn't caught up with me as far as I know.

Many of the bulls we marketed at the time were only leased and there were royalties to pay to the owners. Being a responsible and honest company (as any business associated with Mr J had always been) these were all paid in full, and I must admit to being a little surprised that there was only one of those owners who had the decency to make contact and say thank you on receiving their final settlements, and in some cases we were talking of thousands of pounds. The ones who did say thankyou were the George family of Brynhyfryd.

Another starter as he left school came that summer, Richard Pratt from Bellerby, known to most of you locals as son of Alan and brother of James from Studdah. Originally Richard only came for three days a week but wasn't long before he became full time and he was a very quick learner and got very involved with the cattle preparation and showmanship through YMA and into HYB. He looked after the young stock at Dalesend for almost five years until his job was gone when those young stock were all slaughtered in 2001, but more of that later.

A trip down to the Royal Show with a weekend spent just outside Northampton. We visited the shoe museum there and I have always been a big believer and told people that the wheel keeps going around and things are often in fashion every so often if you stand in the same place. There is no better example of this though than at the British Shoe Museum where you can see them repeated through the ages. It was only a week before the British Grand Prix and we called at Silverstone, but it was deserted, so we went to Sulgrove Manor and saw a display of old costumes and a medieval re-enactment.

The day after we came back, we were happy to show the Werry cousins from Loa-da-Mede herd in Canada round our cows and entertain them for tea – it is always great to be able to repay hospitality. The week after that it was the Great Yorkshire Show, but we had nothing there that year. It was just as well – there was a bit of excitement – Adam broke his arm, but we had to leave Auntie Kathryn in charge of him at the hospital as we were going up to see Tina Turner in concert at Gateshead Stadium – what a performer and what stamina and energy to put on a performance like that for such a length of time. We did go years later to see her perform again at Manchester, when she was just every bit as energetic.

After judging Driffield Show, it was down the week after to judge the Oxfordshire Herds Competition, where I saw all sorts of cows of all breeds under differing systems of management. It was in a spell of very hot, sunny weather and one of the few occasions I wore a sun hat for some protection. One of the first herds we visited was one of the Blenheim Estate herds, about 200 cows in a massive area of parkland right in front of Blenheim Palace. Among other things they had an entry in the progeny group class, but the herdsman had not separated them out from the rest of the herd and just kept pointing one out as we went around. When we got to the end of the field I pointed out we were one short of the required number and as he couldn't picture which one it was or where she was we had to go round the whole lot again in the searing heat to find her – needless to say they were loosing points as we went though they were never contenders at the top anyway.

We had another good day at Wensleydale Show with seven first prizes this time and Threat Rosina 4 was champion but then had disappointment a few days later when Threat Rosanna (out of the daughter of Tikvah Sexation Rosina) who had earlier produced us 18 eggs when flushed came to an unfortunate and premature end. An outstanding young cow – suddenly moved to calve a bit early, and when the vet inspected her he found that she had a dead rotten calf inside her but agreed to do a caesarean on her on condition that he could put her to sleep if things were beyond redemption when he operated, unfortunately that was the case and the early end to a very promising tremendous young cow and the old adage "where there's life, there's death" again came into play – the trouble is, it always seems to apply to the good ones.

Dalesend Warden Idena, Sarah's pet cow was Reserve Exhibitor bred champion at Stokesley Show on the Saturday and then the following Monday I was judging the local dairy classes at Nidderdale Show and that was the end of another show season.

That autumn under the new milk regime, there was incentive to go onto every other day milk collection through Milk Marque and needing a larger tanker anyway and so we installed a new Mueller bulk tank which for those interested in pricing changes through the years was £14,750 through an incentivised payment scheme over three years deducted from the milk cheque. Interestingly it wasn't many years before every other day collection was very much frowned upon and dropped as supposedly it mitigated against the perception of "fresh" milk, but that wheel has again gone round and every other day is now back in fashion and quite acceptable.

In the same autumn we had some excitement for two or three days with some wild cattle. Thompson's from Langthorne had the grazing field below Wren's Hill that adjoined some of the Fox Park land and four of them broke out and were all over the place around the fields and up to the buildings at the Grange to disturb our cows which fortunately by then were fully housed. They got them sort of rounded up and into the 18 acre, two vets, four RSPCA men plus other people and some marksmen – who got three with a drugged dart to pacify them while they were loaded and taken away, though one got away and they later captured it a few days later.

Later that autumn, Mr J decided to give up his office in Cascade Court and establish it in the Red Room at Dalesend and we helped move some of his furniture and a lot of his filing cabinets and paperwork. He ran his office from there for quite a while until we moved him again when they moved from Dalesend up to Hill Top East, and Charles and Emma and family moved the other way.

We had quite a lot of entries at the Black and White that year, went up via Newcastle to pick Sarah up and put on a very good display at Carlisle winning the hamper for the best stand and cattle display but trade was only steady and we brought two young calves home. Just as well, they were Dalesend Stardust Echo and Dalesend Charlie Rosanna who both went on to be multiple Excellent cows. They had been two of what we later called the 'magic' pen of weaned calves in the Solari – there had been six of them and five of them finished up Excellent and the sixth Very Good. Shortly after that the Triple Threats won the progeny group class in the N.E. Club Herds Competition.

To Canada again, this time because we were interested in using two bulls heavily in the herd who had just come in with very promising first proofs and we wanted to see them before committing to using them. Both Startmore Rudolph and Maughlin Storm had been originally proven in Quebec, so we were collected at Toronto airport by both Orton Eby and Frank Donkers who also wanted to see the daughters first hand for themselves and travelled up into that province which neither of us had visited before. That was at the time when there was a great deal of political manoeuvring to keep Quebec as part of Canada and there was a big independence movement in that province, rather like going into Wales, both in Quebec and the rest of Canada, everything was in both English and French. We were quite amused and also pleased with ourselves, the reverse of Orton and Frank. Once into Quebec, Mr J and I both tried to speak some very poor "schoolboy" French, but they appreciated that we were at least trying, whilst the two Ontarians refused point blank to speak or at all acknowledge the "b. French". We ate a meal at night in the motel and the next morning it just happened to be the same waitress. Mr J and I both got a very nicely presented "Full English" while our two companions got a very plain breakfast banged down in front of them and no offer to them of a second cup of coffee!!

We then looked round several very commercial dairy units where both bulls had been used and were impressed enough to use both bulls which went on and did a good job for us, particularly Rudolph and a bit like Triple Threat some years earlier, a lot of the good bulls of recent years have Rudolph somewhere in their back pedigree.

Whilst we were in Quebec, we went to the CIAQ headquarters and bull stud and were privileged to be able to see the legendry Hanoverhill Starbuck – by then 18 years old but still in good order. Back into Ontario and on the Sunday afternoon when we couldn't go anywhere else much, Orton called on his old friend Pete Heffering the man who had bred Starbuck and all the other leading sires of that time. As there was no one else around, we were given a personalised tour of the farm and Hanoverhill herd by the man himself, who by then, while still having a herd there, though not rebuilt to the original standard, spent much of his time in the United States, where he became a leading breeder of horses – it seemed that his innate ability to breed was transferable from one species of animals to another.

Whilst over in Canada we went with Orton Eby to a Lions Club Dinner one night and of course had to buy some tickets for the turkey raffle – it was just before Christmas. I won the turkey and a chicken, and Mr J three chickens, so Orton and family were well catered for over Christmas.

That winter, some of our efforts to make our maize silage clamping better with the revamped pits paid immediate benefit when we won the local maize silage competition run by the Maize Growers Association and went forward to the North of England and Scotland round, but came up against some real professionals and progressed no further. That year the MGA conference was held at Harper Adams and we had an enjoyable couple of days staying at The Lion in Shrewsbury.

At that time Adam was putting in a bit of time going to help out in holidays and weekends at our neighbours Francis Dent's and one particular day he helped them when they were scanning all the ewes. In those early days when he was just eleven, he showed some liking for sheep, which of course was in his family breeding, but must have missed a generation with me. It didn't last very long and he now has even less time for them than I have –"woolly pigs" are nothing but a nuisance, particularly when they jump into any of his release pens up on the hill and eat some of his partridge feed.

Whilst back onto family matters and children it was at the same time that Sarah entered a competition in Dairy Farmer for the David Shead award. He had been a writer/editor of the magazine prior to his premature death and the competition was for young people under a certain age to write an essay on a set subject. That year the subject was regarding the impact of BSE and Sarah was duly made the winner and she and Marnie went down to London for a luncheon at The Farmers Club where she was presented with the award plus the £1000 prize. She has of course, as many of you will know put this to very good use as she wrote for the Holstein Journal and currently edits and produces the Jersey Society magazine and also writes regularly in the Northern Farmer, apart from many other various commissions she has done over the years within her business- The Farm Organisation.

That Spring we sold a young calf at Beeston at "The Genetics for the Millennium" sale – Dalesend Stardust Rosina which was bought by Andrew Stafford of the Saxelby herd and subsequently developed with her daughter resold and a generation or two down resurfaced with the Castlehyfryd Rosina's which superseded Dalesend Storm Maude as the all conquering cow of the time – two descendants that stemmed from the Triple Threat enterprise of earlier times and both came through Dalesend.

Sarah was going for interviews that Spring as she got towards the end of her degree course and went to various places with cattle breeding related communities and eventually finished up starting her working career with Semen World. I spoke that Spring at Masham Agricultural Discussion Group, an exercise I repeated some 20 years later when I spoke and did a slide show entitled 'There's more to life than milking cows'. Adam was asked if he wanted to go to Manchester to visit Manchester United to help make a coach load as part of Phillip Iveson's birthday treat – which Marnie also went on and they both had a great time. It was an experience I also enjoyed along with Marnie, when it was one of the visits associated with the Holstein UK Celebration in Lancashire in 2016 when David Tomlinson of Bilsrow became President. Just a few days after that we went for the first time to the Charity Open Day round the racing stables at Middleham on Good Friday. The one thing that remains in the memory of that day, apart from finding the stable visits so interesting was in seeing Desert Orchid. By then retired from steeplechasing this fantastic horse came up for the event and even then, still knew that he was the centre of attention and in his presence, you could feel that aura which surrounds every great person or animal.

The previous year Marnie had bought me for my birthday a balloon flight, which was something I had always wanted to do. After several false starts because of too strong a breeze and such weather conditions, the evening finally dawned when I was able to have my birthday treat. Marnie and Adam went with me to the base from which they operated just outside Knaresborough but that was called off at the last minute and it was another fortnight before I actually got into the air. There were about ten stood tightly in the basket, once up there the views were fantastic, I would have loved to do it over our own area to see things from a different perspective, but it was still a great way to see some countryside, see traffic hurtling down the A1 and all sorts of other things. We were due to land on Wetherby racecourse to be collected and had gone through all the drill ready for the jolt of landing when suddenly a gust of wind lifted us up and away again just as we were about to land. It took us back towards the town and they had to put the burners on to get us up and over and back into countryside, by which time the gas had run out and we eventually made a "crash" landing in the middle of a field of oil seed rape just coming into flower. Apparently one of the conditions of balloon flights is that you have to have permission to remove said balloon from its landing place. Saturday evening about 8 o'clock isn't the best time to contact people, particularly when it is a farm business tenancy operated through some farm consultancy for an absentee landlord. Whilst we were waiting we carried the folded up balloon and the basket to the edge of the field in what was by now darkness and eventually were collected and taken back to our departure point where Marnie and Adam had waited patiently for hours, not knowing what was happening. In spite of these problems it was still a marvellous experience.

It was at roughly the same time as the Grand National and there were again problems. This time it had to be postponed because there was a bomb scare and it was run on the Monday instead. Adam at the similar time fell of his bike but this time unlike when Sarah did it earlier there was no interrogation by the nursing staff and after X-rays, he had only bruised rather than broken his arm.

Wanting another cow from a different family to try and develop we identified a good cow at a sale up at Kirby Thore and paid £4200 for Parkdown Lindy Tammy 2 an EX cow who later in the sale had daughters sell for 3500 and 5900 guineas, and later in the sale we also bought 20,000 litres of milk quota for 42.5ppl. Once we got her home she couldn't survive amongst the herd and we discovered how bad her feet really were and had to keep her boxed. We never even got her back in calf or managed to flush her for embryos and in fact she went as a casualty, so she was a total loss to us – still you can't win them all.

At the beginning of May we witnessed Tony Blair and the Labour Party win a landslide General Election and wondered what we were in for, and throughout that May I spent quite a bit of evening times painting the outside of the house as we were tidying up round about ready for a party later in the Summer.

As modern technology began to play a part in many businesses, we moved onto auto pay to pay all our wages and other bills with the odd exception of one-off accounts. It was considerably cheaper than the bank charges for cheques and at that time just to fax the one sheet through to the bank was much easier than doing individual payment slips and addressing envelopes. I only had problems with two "businesses" when and after changing. The first was someone who we had dealt with for many years and didn't want anything other than cash or cheques – but he was soon convinced and changed his mind when I told him there would be no further business. The other one which was never resolved was with the Inland Revenue who soon started sending notices of late payment of the monthly National Insurance due on staff wages. I spoke to someone and pointed out that we made the payments on the last Thursday of every month and that it was ridiculous to have a "month end" date of about the 19th when all businesses worked on month ends. I also pointed out that I believed if they checked their records over many years it had always been paid in the month it was due, but they were not prepared to give at all when all it would have needed was a flag on their computer system to tell them payment would be as agreed. We finally agreed to differ on the basis that they could continue to send the notice of late payment on a regular basis and I would continue for the payment to be at the end of the month.

Another sale of good cattle and another Lot 1 to buy this time at Kirby Thore at John Morley's sale, but this one turned out well and bred well for us, and she had our kind of breeding – Gillette TT Raquella cost us 3000gns but she was already classified EX and safely back in calf, so it was less of a gamble. The family developed quite nicely from small beginnings and one of the higher priced animals at our dispersal sale was her great great granddaughter Dalesend Steady Rose sold for 2600gns to the Aytonian herd, where her granddaughter Aytonian Rose 2 was Champion Cow in the N.E. Club 2020 Winter Herds Competition

About that time we took Adam one afternoon/ evening to Whitby to see Endeavour which had been restored and moored there, but after taking a long time to get parked far from the action, we never actually got on board as there was a six hour queue.

Our Silver wedding was the reason for all the tidying up and decorating and we had an 'at home' open house on the Saturday before the event and we had a great day with most of our friends and relatives to see us, and Sarah having finished University the week after was able to look after Adam as we went off on our celebratory holiday to Italy, very well organised for us by Robert Sturdy when he had his own travel business in Bedale. First of all, to the No 1 place on Marnie's wish list Venice, where we did a great deal of walking but resisted the temptation to pay exaggerated prices for a ride on a gondola. That first night we had a marvellous meal on a floating restaurant alongside the Grand Canal and ended up with our feet in the water – at £100 in those days that was an awful lot for dinner for ordinary folks, but we economised during the days afterwards. Up and down the little streets and bridges, we took a trip to see the Murano glass and then after four days we went on the Eurotrain – the first superfast luxury train to Florence – just like being on a super airliner. Arriving in Florence you were immediately aware again of traffic which had been absent in Venice and the vast number of scooters – everywhere, often with three or more people on them and no crash helmets worn. One night after a meal we stood on the Ponte Vecchio and watched a superb firework display – it didn't have to be the fifth of November for the Italians. We climbed the 463 steps to the top of the dome of the Duomo's Cupola with fantastic views over all of Florence and enjoyed walking round the Boboli gardens. It was then on to Rome for another few days – we visited Vatican City, a fantastic place with marvellous architecture but for us such a scandalous abuse of money on all the gold ornamentation that is everywhere. Again, we walked miles, found the Coliseum very disappointing as you couldn't go into it and so got no feeling for the place. Whilst we were in Rome we ate one night in a restaurant where the owner spoke very good English, and on further conversation it turned out to be Carlo who had worked at the Motel Leeming for two years and knew Marnie's Aunt Lillian who had been receptionist there. The other thing we did was pick up a massive cone from one of their large pine trees and brought one home as a memento of our trip. Sometime later the seeds began to drop out of it where it sat on top of the fridge and we put quite a few in plant pots and got about half a dozen germinated and growing and eventually got three large enough to transplant, two of which were on Grange land and have now gone but the one which Paul planted at Fox Park has now grown into quite a useful tree in its own right and hopefully should survive for years to come. The weather whilst we were in Italy was very good, hot and sunny, much better than it had been in Scotland twenty-five years earlier. That wasn't the case at home whilst we were away, there had been 1¾ inches in one twenty four hour period and other very wet days as well, and I well remember as we came back up on the train there were floods and water stood everywhere – it was more like Venice than England in June!!

Shortly after that and purely for local farmers interests in the times when these kinds of things happened, I went to a meeting at Leeming Motel when Mr Padgett introduced himself as the company which had taken over David Hoult's corn drying, storage and handling business at Leeming Bar – trading as Argrain it seems as busy as ever now whenever you pass, particularly with all the tractors and trailers on the road around harvest time.

Although we had nothing very much to show that year, we did just take four to the Great Yorkshire Show because Mr J was the Society President. We were invited on the first day to attend the Presidents lunch and thinking we were unlikely ever to be invited to such an event again we donned our best bib and tucker and had a good time. I did attend the lunch again in the future but that is another story. On the last day of the show we left Richard Pratt in charge of the cattle and somebody else to get them home as we went up to Newcastle to puff out our chests with pride as Sarah graduated with a 2:1 in Agriculture just missing a 1st, which in those days were very rarely given up there, though she did win the award for top marks, then a day or two later we went down to Stephen (Mary's son) and Hayley's wedding, where after a very long photo session, the dance and night were very good with a great band called Crazy Ape.

Into the summer holidays we went one afternoon up on the A66 to visit the Otter Trust, not very well run, we saw a rat run across the yard outside the café and it was a long walk to see an otter. The farm and land is still there but the Otter Trust is long gone from that site. During the summer holidays we also went one day to look at the Royal Armouries at Leeds – very boring unless you are really into such things.

Family...

Our wedding photo - 17th June 1972
L:R - Sid Thompson, Alice Liddle, Bernard and Marnie, Hilda Thompson (Muv) and John Liddle

Our family

The Norwegian family...
L:R - Elisabeth, Liv, Colin and Christin in national costume

Sarah fothering calves at Dalesend from
a young age she was very keen on cows

Young country lad - Adam with the Bronze at
Newton Grange which was later stolen

From the family archive...

Gladys, Bill, Jo, Alice and Ralph Hood
with their parents and Mary Hall

Mary and Bernard Liddle taken 1948/49

Bernard in 1950

Bernard and his Father in
1950/51

April 1992 Marnie and JBL

Schoolboy friend - Martin Holmes

The funny side of life on a farm...

Wagon drivers won't do as they are told!!

That's why the string and fertiliser
bags were across!

That's what happens when you're on
your mobile phone!

From the building site at Newton Grange...

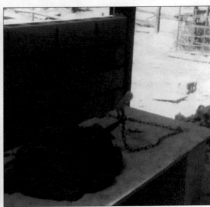

David was a good pointer until he fell asleep!

Malcolm was always losing his trowel...
so we chained it up for him!

Ready for take off

Ripon Grammar School brought to a standstill by one heifer!

Stuart was always hungry... look at the size of his bait box!

Iceland...

Front and back of the doors featuring Adam and Eve in Iceland

Life carried on among the drainage work in the main street of Reykjavik in March 2002

At the shows...

Dalesend win the pairs trophy at the Society Heifer Sale in 1971
L:R - G McGregor, JBL and JGR receiving the trophy from BFS President Captain JR McCarthy
Note the style of showing outfit and the 'sideburns'!

1993 Show winnings with 27 different home bred animals
exhibited during the one season, at 16 shows.

Norman Walker makes
Dalesend Storm Maude
Champion at the North Eastern
Club Calf Show in 1998

JGR, JBL and Mrs J in Bedale Hall at Sarah's 21st

Mr Bill's retirement party at Chinese Charlies
L:R - Wallace, Rhona, Jayne, Bill, Lys, and Geraldine

All Creatures Great and Small...

On set - Peter Davison and Robert Hardy

The budding actor - dressed much as usual!

*The blonde bombshell showing Rosie
at the North East Calf Show*

*In mid summer - Hail Stones still in the garden the day
after they fell!*

These are houses not pigeon lofts on the banks of Porto

Hjerdl Hede Windmill 1991

The Olympic Torch coming through Bedale in 2012

*JBL's one horse ride up to the monastery
in Tibet in 2016 - Good Job the horse knew
what it was doing!*

Newton Grange

Spring 1964

May 2009

Family

Adam and Laura with L:R Freddy, Harriet and Ruby

Sarah launching her own business, The Farm Organisation in August 2008

Chapter 17 – Change of School, Rugby, New Company, Board Member

Into 1996 and Wensleydale Show again saw us with the Champion in Dalesend Threat Bella and we stood first and second with pairs. Later that Autumn her full sister Threat Bella 2 went to the High Flyer Sale at Kirby Thore and made £3000, while our own Lettice 44 (out of Lettice 23) made £1900 and her heifer calf £500.

Just after Wensleydale I judged Northumberland Herds Competition, and the one thing which remains in the memory is one particular farm visit. The steward, who was an NMR area manager warned me before we got there that I was in for a surprise but wouldn't enlighten me. It was the last visit of the day and already into the late evening when we arrived. The cows were all out happily grazing, not at all ready for milking. There were some good cows amongst them, but the striking feature was their uniformity, they were all exceedingly small – almost pigmies, and in that respect not the sort of cow I was looking for. The owner was in no rush to get on and I enquired as to his milking time at night, but was stunned by his reply – "oh, about 10 or 11 o'clock – there's nothing much on television then so I go out after the news headlines and get back in about 12.30 or 1 o'clock and there's often a good film on then. As we left the farm the steward told me that he also didn't milk until about 10 o'clock in the morning, the first time she had called to collect milk samples there was no sign of any activity about 9 o'clock other than the milk tanker arriving. When she made enquiries the tanker driver filled her in to the fact that he was collecting morning and night milking from the previous day and that the farmer would be out in a minute, take his dog for a walk, wash out the tank before going back in for his breakfast before he milked. Very strange and whatever suits different people, but at those timings, there couldn't be much social life outside the farm.

At the beginning of September Adam started senior school at Richmond – a very large jump from Crakehall with about 40 pupils to senior school with about 1600, but at least in the first year, they got 'run-in' by the first year students spending most of their time and lessons at the old Richmond Grammar School before moving up to the main school for the second year onwards. I had played rugby at the old school some 40 years or so previously, and not long afterwards Adam went back to my old Alma Mater to play for the Richmond Under 13's at Ripon Grammar School.

Just a day or two after his start at Richmond, I judged Wolsingham Show, not a massive turnout and nothing very special – again the one abiding memory was the eeriness as the whole showground came to a standstill of absolute silence in memory of Lady Diana, who's funeral it was that day.

There were a lot of changes going on at that time. We finally ditched the NFU for our insurances after many years. When their renewal notice came in, I thought it was very much on the high side and rung them to tell them, so my mood wasn't improved when their response was that if they'd known it was competitive they could have made it about £1000 less. That finished them as far as I was concerned, but I decided to play them along and asked them to requote which came in about another £500 less and when I rung to tell them we were moving elsewhere they knocked about another £500 off. What a way to do business and I know of other instances where the same thing has happened. We changed at that time to Gale and Phillipson who had an office in Northallerton and met their agent – Edwin Southwell, a descendant, I think nephew, of the late Guy Southwell of the renowned Hunthill herd some thirty years previously from whom Dalesend had used several herd sires. Although Edwin has moved insurance brokers once or twice since as they have been taken over by larger firms, he likes to maintain personal contact with his customers, and whilst probably not always the cheapest, he has always been very good to deal with and apart from the farm, looked after Mr J personally and the Wensleydale Property Company after it was formed.

At the same time as we approached winter, we put an extra two units on either side of the parlour, which we had allowed for when it was installed ten years or so previously. At the end of the week we hosted a Young Members field day practice at Dalesend, and that particular day, Mr and Mrs J asked if we could look after two trainee vicars whom they had been hosting for a couple of weeks. They hadn't a clue what was going on in clipping, haltering etc, but when we went up to home for lunch they came into their own. Marnie had cooked sausages to make hot dogs for us all, and they were first into them – I told them that I was pleased to see they had learnt the first rule of 'vicaring' – first into the trough and eat well!! They were called Matthew and James, so they were soon nick named the two Apostles!

With Adam now away to senior school and Sarah working, Marnie began to help out on a voluntary basis at Mowbray School at Bedale. Previously she had done two sessions at Crakehall and found it rewarding, and particularly fulfilling at Mowbray one of the early specialist schools for pupils with learning difficulties. It wasn't long before she was asked to work there and for the next fifteen years, she did so on a part time basis, mostly with Linda in the art and cookery department. To help those children and others with behavioural problems was obviously challenging but she found it tremendously rewarding. I wouldn't have had the patience with them, but Marnie obviously was very good at it and even now you can be in Tesco when there is a big shout out when one of them recognises her. One of the highlights of the year was just before the summer break when they took a group away for activity week, travelling all over, Scotland, Wales, England and Ireland.

That autumn, the Patrick Brompton Buying Group which had been in existence for many years was to celebrate its 150th meeting. It had been a very vibrant organisation with a strong membership who largely played by the rules of going with the majority of business with the designated official supplier. In the earlier days it was much simpler in that a supplier quoted for twelve months and the prices also, but in more recent times with rampaging inflation and bank rates, many firms were unable to stick to their prices. In recent times smaller numbers of commodities were bought as a group and it had and was becoming more of a social gathering about four times a year. When the group was originally started, Mr J was the chairman for many years and George Heeley the secretary and members included Harold Webster, Peter Knox, Major General Clutterbuck, Colonel. Van Straubenzee, Jim Harrison, Mike Keeble of Clifton Castle Estates, Tom Archibald, Derek Heath, Bill Cowley among others. After George's death I took over as secretary and continued to do so up until 2012. Members took it in turn to supply the drinks for the meeting – beer, lager, lemonade and the payment for being secretary was that you didn't have to stand a turn for the drinks. By the time of the 150th meeting most of the remaining members were the next generation from the originals and we were under the chairmanship of Martin Webster. It was agreed that we should make this particular meeting, something special and include everyone's wives and so we had a celebratory dinner at what was then Plummer's in Bedale, which of course is now and has been for a long time Pannetti's and is still very good. The Buying Group continued on in an increasingly subdued way for another 15 years, and when Dalesend Farms was sold, and one or two other members had given up farming it was decided to close it down.

A night or two later we went to hear Robert Swan speak at Aysgarth School (having been an old boy) on about another of his Polar expeditions and he was just as good the second time, and the week after that Adam went with school to Old Trafford to see New Zealand beat England 25-8, yes that's right rugby at Old Trafford, and then a fortnight later I went with Dick and George to Twickenham when they fought out a 26 all draw.

Christmas Eve was a very wild night, I mean from a weather point of view, not entertainment wise and I spent much of it trying to keep the fire going in the dining room or stopping it blowing smoke back in, or was that the night I stacked logs round the edge of the hearth to stop it being able to draw too much air, and it was burning so well that it set the logs alight. None of that was a real problem, but it put a tree down across the Newton Road from Hill Top East side. I went with the loader and got it moved off the road, thinking I would saw it up in the next few days. You can imagine I wasn't best pleased the next day when, as we went up to Hunton to Kath and Peter's for Christmas lunch, I discovered that most of it had been sawn up and gone. I discovered the man who lived in the end house of Lynas Terrace had been given a new chainsaw for Christmas and had decided to try it out that morning, you would have thought he had more to do that morning with two young sons.

Adam got an air rifle for Christmas that year and Bill gave him a lesson the next day after which he was away beating two days with Bill before New Year. That was the start of his shooting career, and he now has quite a collection with telescopic sights, night-time viewers and such like – I'm not sure he really needs them all even as a gamekeeper, but he seems to thinks so!! Sarah that same time of year went to the British Cattle Breeder's Conference as a prize for an essay – "2000 Breeding – Art or Science?".

Early in 1998, we had to let Stephen Dalton go. He had been very keen on the breeding side and worked well with Bill, but unfortunately he had got mixed up with a few lads in Bedale who easily led him astray, and he was getting a bit too much "wacky-baccy" on a night. It was at a time when milk price wasn't so good, and we didn't replace him and I did the alternate weekends and holiday myself, with Sarah's help who enjoyed the dairy business and was quite happy to milk if I was away on a Sunday afternoon at Newcastle for the rugby, and later if I was away on Holstein UK business. With Richard at Dalesend doing one weekend and Malcolm doing the other, things carried on without too much hassle.

There were a lot of meetings in the spring of that year, odd ones were perhaps of note more than others and maybe of more interest to readers. The Hackforth and District Rabbit Clearance Society was still operating, and we usually met once a year to discuss any problems and from time to time hire a new rabbit catcher. We all paid an annual fee based on acreage and then so much an hour for mole catching and it worked very well, and like the Buying Group would be one of the oldest such organisations still operative. It was a common sight through winter to see someone walking behind a plough gathering worms to use for the moles and most farmers were well on top of them at that time of year, though the same cannot be said now as the regulations on the poisons that could be used have changed significantly, and as you travel about you can see the problems that has caused – there are moles everywhere. One of the only solutions now is trapping, and I am told that marshmallows, are one of the best baits to use to attract them. Bill was away one day that spring to go to London for the mass demonstration and march with the Countryside Alliance to protest at proposed changes to many countryside pursuits. I spoke to Craven Grassland Society and then a day or two later a night over at Carlisle for a judge's reason giving school, and down to Wells for the MGA conference. Having been nominated and elected to represent Yorkshire and Durham on the Holstein UK Board, I attended Scotsbridge House for a director's briefing day. At the end of March, I have a note of attending a meeting with Mr J at Tilly's to discuss the setting up of Wensleydale Property Company, which will surface again later in the book. In the Easter holidays Marnie and I had a few days down in London where we stayed with Emma (Mollie and Len's daughter), among other things we visited the Planetarium and Madame Tussauds all of which was very interesting, and one night we took Emma to eat at Sticky Fingers, which at the time was owned by Keith Richards of the Rolling Stones, though I think it is no longer in existence, certainly not under that name or ownership. Later that spring Sarah moved out to share a house at Hopperton with two other girls – thus in effect closing an era, even if she did occasionally for various reasons spend a few days back under our roof.

At the end of April, another enjoyable chapter began when we went over to Ireland for the Breed Society AGM at which I officially joined the Board. At that time the Irish Republic were still members of the Society and they gave us a wonderful few days of Irish hospitality, we visited good herds such as Cradenhill and the Barratts at Laurelmore, Michael Buckley, the retiring Society President, went to Paddy O'Keeffe's, the high priest of grassland dairy production, who tried to tell us in the very wet weather the cows were all outside on nothing but grass – I thought it funny that in those conditions their muck was quite firm, and when I cornered the herdsman he said the boss hadn't a clue what was going on and they were using ten big bales of hay a night and sleeping in if they wished. We had a medieval banquet at Bunratty Castle one night at which Richard Linnell had to sing his song to be released from the dungeon, and the next day while we had a Board Meeting, Marnie and others went to Galway Crystal and the Cliffs of Moher. The next day, we had visited the National Stud at Kildare and been well looked after by Tom Kelly at his Monamore herd, it was very late by we got to the hotel for dinner at 11.15pm, typical Irish timekeeping!

We hosted the North Eastern Club for the linear classification competition at the end of April and then a couple of days later went to brother-in-law Eric's retirement party at Studley Cricket Club. We established the old cast iron rose trough opposite the kitchen window, went to the Crown at Boroughbridge for dinner for Marnie's birthday, I was master judge up at Hunday for one of the Northumberland Club judging nights and then a few days later Newcastle Falcons won the Rugby Premiership in the early days of "professionalism". They have never quite hit the heights again since then apart from winning the Cup a year or two later and have in fact had some fairly barren years including relegation, but they are, under Dean Richards slowly building things again, playing some very attractive attacking rugby and as I write this (mid-April 18) still in with a good shot of making the top four play offs.

The day after that was a momentous day for the Breed Society. Work had been going on for some time behind the scenes to develop the technology and I was asked as a Board Member to take part in the potential testing of "Tele-Reg" and on 18th May registered our first calves by telephone. When I first came to Dalesend, they had to be sketched and all the black filled in on the sketch before sending the tear off copy to Scotsbridge House, and then latterly you just put the outline of the markings in, so it was a massive jump forward to not have to do that. Ultimately 'tele-reg' incorporated the BCMS cattle passport application as well. Since then of course things have moved on even more quickly and many registrations now are done on the internet, and you don't now have to have a registration certificate for the animal, it can be held by the Society on the net in a paperless form.

In mid-May we attended Patrick Brompton Church when the beautiful glass screen in memory of Carey was dedicated – I have referred to it before – beautifully engraved by Jenny Stourton and the wood surround and fitting done by Nigel Luettke of Kirkby Fleetham, a very big job, glass within stone of the bell tower so all the shock and movement could be absorbed without any risk.

I attended my first Holstein Board Meeting in England in early June at the late John Pickford's at Picston. There were some remarkable coincidences between John and I – our birthdays were the same day – just two days after this meeting, we both joined the Board at the same time, and our daughters both did the same course at the same time at Newcastle University. Sadly, John died long before he should and was a great loss to the whole British dairy and pedigree scene, though the farm and herd are still being superbly run by he and Helen's two sons. The meeting itself was about Breed Development and the changes it was thought should be developed as the Breed moves forward.

The end of June was a busy time as we took Adam up to Hawes one evening to play cricket for Crakehall juniors, it was a horrible, miserable, drizzly night, then just a couple of nights later we both played for the North Eastern Club against an invitation farmers team at that lovely little cricket pitch as you approach Stokesley from the A19, though I fear it is no longer used by the look of it the last time I was along that road. That night we were struggling against a few regular cricketers, though we were helped a bit by Cecil Hutchinson being our umpire and Adam and I managed to bat out time as the rain began to fall to claim an honourable draw, though we found out the next day that Adam had broken his finger during the match.

We took Threat Kim up to Paragon at Hexham to start IVF collections and met Sarah up there as she worked and had lunch with her at the Hadrian at Wall. We were also at that time collaborating with neighbours to clean out Newton Beck, which was badly overgrown and silted up, meaning drainage from adjoining fields wasn't good. On the Saturday morning we were all walking the stream with the contractor Mr Alderson who was going to do the work the following week. As we walked up the side it suddenly started to rain lightly, at which Bryan Cockburn the Bedale butcher and owner of some of the land became quite agitated. I said to him it was only a light shower and the rain wouldn't do him any harm to which he started talking about pork pies. When I pressed him for the reason, he explained that Saturday morning was the day of the car boot sale at Bedale which had a massive following. If it was fine, they baked hundreds of extra pies, if it was wet when they started they just baked the usual number. The worst scenario was exactly such a shower as this in mid-morning which sent everyone scurrying home rather than walking down the town and buying pies or sausage rolls and on a Saturday morning it wasn't ideal to have a lot unsold. I often think of that on a Saturday morning, particularly if it starts off bright and sunny and then comes on to rain late morning. Adam still rates Cockburn's as his favourite pork pie and we usually take some up for him when we go on a Sunday.

Early in July it was the Royal Show and at that time the Holstein Society judging competitions were held on the second day, with teams from all 26 clubs competing in the three age groups for both linear and ordinary judging for teams of two. Sarah was representing the North East Club and went on to win the Senior Linear and with Claire Tyreman (daughter of Denis – herd manager for Miss Edwards at Hemble) being fourth, they were unstoppable in winning the team competition.

As most farmers with cows know, mid to late summer is a bad time for flies, particularly in the milking parlour at evening milking. I came across a firm who made and sold fly tapes on big rollers which you could put round the top of the parlour pit and just roll it on with the winder as often as you wanted to. They weren't a lot of money and Adam and I put it up in the parlour one Friday evening and Adam was keen to see if it worked. It was sticky both sides and he insisted after 24 hours that we count the dead flies – it certainly worked – there were 904 of them! We later put a couple of them up in the young stock building where the young calves were in over summer, and it certainly helped keep the numbers in check. Sometime later we did try for a couple of years using a system set up by Lambert, Leonard and May when you released some little maggots which they sent about every six weeks which then developed into a fly which supposedly attacked the more traditional fly and kept them under control. The first year we thought it had been effective and did it for a further couple of years but it seemed to be of little benefit going forward, plus it was more expensive than a year's tapes, though I still think you can go down that route if you so wish. The most amusing story I have heard about flies in the milking parlour came from Kingshay Farming Trust. We were members for several years and they did in the early days do a lot of good independent small-scale research and survey work. One such survey was asking farmers about fly control at milking time – all sorts of replies came in with a wide assortment of control methods, the best one was a man who had altered his milking times until it was after dark. He didn't put any lights on, but just wore a miner's helmet with the light on the front of it – and no I don't think it was the man up in Northumberland with the little cows who milked at the most unfriendly time of night!!

A few days later we had some cattle up at Carlisle at one of the club sales and as Richard Pratt and I came home in the afternoon we got held up soon after Barnard Castle by a queue of traffic with very little coming the other way, there had obviously been an accident and we were at a total stop for some considerable time. Having left home about 4.30am that morning we weren't really ready for this delay, but eventually when we began to move again the scene of the problem was just past Mainsgill farm shop and imagine our shock to see 7WU, Mr J's car sat on top of the wall, having also had a brush with a lorry. He had been up to the sale and left before us and in the heat of a July afternoon I think had just dozed momentarily. Fortunately, neither he nor anyone else was injured and after a night in hospital as a precaution he was soon back to himself.

That next month was the HYB Calf Show which that year was hosted by David Alderson at Scorton Road Farm and was the start of the Storm Maude story when as mentioned earlier Norman Walker as the judge took a lot of criticism for making a baby calf champion, though he was of course vindicated many times over the next few years. And if I don't tell you here, then Adam and Sarah will no doubt make everyone who will listen aware that I had missed her, and it was they who found her!! We had a good night as with the cows Dalesend Warden Idena was Reserve Champion and Exhibitor-bred Champion and Dalesend Queen 2 (who had been Adam's show calf a year or two earlier) was second and Reserve Exhibitor-bred Champion.

A day later one of Dennis Percival's round balers caught fire while they were baling straw in Jasper and both Bedale and Leyburn fire engines were called out – no damage other than the baler and a piece of hedge burnt, they had managed to get the baler loosened off the tractor. It does seem to be a problem in balers that get overheated when doing a lot of baling and straw gets onto the runners and eventually can take fire.

Just a week later we had Mark Sanderson (son of Robin and Anne) of Morton-on-Swale to work with Bill for a week or two during his summer holidays as a part of his veterinary studies and he is now practising somewhere down in Shropshire. His grandfather was Marnie's Uncle Cecil, who before his retirement to Patrick Brompton had farmed at Spennithorne for many years and was very well known in the area – John Thistlethwaite had worked for him as a boy before he came to us and told the story of hoeing potatoes in the pouring rain one morning and the water had filled their wellingtons and was running over the top. Uncle Cecil, when they got to the end of the rows told the men he would have to go as he had some cattle at the market, but if it came on to rain heavily they had to come inside and find something else to do. Talking of Uncle Cecil and water reminds me of the time I was going up to Arbour Hill and Uncle Cecil was out for his daily walk. There had been some snow and it was melting fast and just passing Northfields, I came over the hilltop into a big puddle and absolutely soaked Uncle Cecil who had stepped onto the verge when hearing the car. I daren't stop and say hello but watched in the mirror as he waved his stick angrily after me, and I spent long enough at Arbour Hill to make sure that he had got back home before I dared to venture back that way. I never did tell him, I thought it was better left him not knowing.

Towards the end of the summer holidays the three of us went for a long weekend at Barton Grange calling at Hopper Lane Hotel on the A59 for a bit of lunch, and it wasn't until three days later that I discovered my cards had been stolen out of the front pocket of the car whilst we were there. Fortunately the thieves had only used it a couple of times for small items and then been foolish enough to withdraw a larger amount of cash than the daily set allowance which had caused the card to be rejected and the bank soon sorted the job out so we were back in action. Whilst at Barton Grange among other things we enjoyed time at Beacon Fells Country Park, Fleetwood, the furniture museum at Lancaster and visited Dunsop Bridge – supposedly the centre of the British Isles, I wouldn't like to argue with them, they have all kinds of signs up telling us so.

Early September was a busy few days, more from a social aspect than a work aspect. One morning Bill was milking in a very laid-back manner after a good night out and he himself recalls it was the nearest he ever came to "reneging" through drink. I helped him get finished and told him to go home and sleep it off, which he happily did and was ok by the time of afternoon milking. A day or two later we went to Nicola Kerr's (Sarah's school friend) after wedding party at Ripon Spa and then the next day it was our God-daughter Victoria Barkers 21st birthday lunch, and a few days after that I have a note in the diary for the farmer readers who like to keep abreast of prices that we had sold 213 tonnes of wheat at £68/tonne.

The 23rd September 1998 was a very significant date from a Breed Society point of view when the merger of the Holstein Friesian Society and the British Holstein Society was announced at the Dairy Farming Event – it had been a long time in the formulating and I had only been involved in the later stages of the discussion as an ordinary Board member, with a working group from both societies having done all the hard work over the previous couple of years. It was widely welcomed by all but the hardest of diehards in both societiesHhHHHHH and despite some problems along the way, it is difficult now some twenty years later, to remember that we did have two organisations. There were a lot of meetings around that time as the details were put in place and just before Christmas we had an Extraordinary General Meeting to approve the official formation of Holstein UK, elect a new Board which was larger than ideal for the transition period and I was elected onto the Advertising and Promotion Committee. At the same time, we were holding talks in this part of the country, as was happening all over, as the different Breeders Clubs discussed their amalgamations. Myself and Gerald Carter of Bricknell and now the boss of the highly successful ShowTime venture, who was at that time the Northern Board Member of the British Holsteins, acted as joint chairmen involving discussions between Yorkshire HFS, North Eastern HFS, Northumberland HFS and Northern Holstein Club, and it very quickly became apparent that Northumberland felt that geographically they were too far apart, and the members of the old Northern Holsteins would become involved with the local club. The recommendations from the working party was that the Yorkshire and North Eastern Clubs should join to be one and this was sent back to the clubs for their consideration, though we weren't surprised when both clubs decided to reject the idea and go their own separate ways. They have done ever since and still continue successfully, but I am still of the opinion that ultimately a merger will come about. As the number of dairy farmers and hence breeders reduces everywhere, the potential number of members to attend meetings falls and it is more difficult to attract good speakers from further afield. There are less herds able to host judging nights and the work that entails. Interestingly the two clubs do now work together on staging judging nights in springtime and usually stage one each, though the results of the two clubs are kept separate to go forward to the National Judging. Similarly, after the formation of the North East All Breeds Calf Show, the Yorkshire Club stayed independent for a while, but now are equal participants in what is a very good days competition.

We bought Olympian Jabot Pamela for 4000gns at Kirby Thore at the Olympian dispersal – our first venture into more index-related genetics – she went on and bred reasonably for us, but never really established an exciting family – we flushed her and the last three heifers to come across from Dalesend before they were all slaughtered in 2001 to calve at the Grange were her daughters and we had walked them across the fields because transport on the road was not allowed without a lot of paperwork.

The next month we had cattle at the monthly sale at Carlisle with a reasonable trade and the sale that day was followed by the Northacomb dispersal of Robin Baty. Many of you will know or know of or come across his son Cameron who has his own very well established and respected cattle preparation business and did all the sales at Wright Marshalls at Beeston. His father developed a very successful pick-your-own unit and farm shop on the side of the roundabout where the Corbridge road joins the A68 Carlisle road.

Round about Christmas 1998 and into 99, Adam spent most of those holidays away beating or shooting with Bill, and if at home he was helping Bill make up time for being away between milkings, and then Adam had a day up at Grinton gamekeeping, which we had bought for his birthday at a charity auction. The night before that I had taken Richard to the Fellmongers Society dinner at Richmond where he won an award under their apprenticeship scheme recognitions, a well won award and an interesting night to attend one of these very ancient organisation's events.

That January I had to get the vet out to a calving in the middle of the night. The cow had got on well, but had a leg back and was so far on and was straining so hard that I could not get the calf back enough to get the leg up, and nor could Brian Linscott who was himself on duty that night. We did something that night I have never done before or since and I don't think you will find in any calving manuals. I got the Kramer loader in and we put a rope round her back feet and Brian told me to very quickly lift her up and then straight down again or she would be dead as all the stomach etc would go forward onto the heart, lungs etc. I did that and hey presto the calf popped back in again and Brian had a live heifer calf out before I had got the rope off her feet and the machine out of the way.

I don't know why (though I suspect Sarah for Semen World was showing them round some northern herds that day) we had Frank Regan and family from the famous Regancrest herd for lunch, and then the day after down to Stoneleigh for the Maize Growers Association conference, and about then we had brought Kim back from Hexham as she had stopped producing IVF embryos and despite being on a starvation diet, she was fatter than ever. We tried to induce her back to milk again but not very successfully this time, and eventually she had to go, and we bowed to the inevitable and sold a very expensive geld cow. That spring the HUK Spring Selection sale was held at Carlisle where we sold Dalesend Storm Maude to Tregibby for 3100gns, and as if to help pay for the loss of Kim in financial terms, Vodafone got the mobile phone mast erected up the back lane on the hill top. It was in the summer before when I was just going out to milk one afternoon when a car pulled into the yard and a man got out with an armful of maps and introduced himself and they were looking for phone mast sites. I said I hadn't really time to talk then but he should come back as it was obvious, they had found a site on our land or he wouldn't have come. I thought that reasoning was fairly simple, but he seemed to think it quite amazing that I had very quickly come to that assumption. Just as he was going, I asked in round figures the kind of figure they had in mind for rentals and his answer prodded me to ask him how many they wanted. In fact they only wanted one but it paid very well and later Orange also affixed their apparatus to an extended mast and it was a very substantial contribution to our income and a far better return per acre than any kind of even the most intensive farming could generate. At that time I decided that we could not go on supporting Milk Marque any longer and I calculated at that time that conservatively in the five years since de-regulation it had cost us £68,000 to remain with them and this couldn't continue and in the fullness of time after giving notice we moved to supplying the Co-op.

Mid-April Marnie and I went down to Norfolk for a Holstein Board Meeting plus the annual convention. We had some trouble with the car as we went – it lost all power but we just got there in time for me to run into the start of the meeting and got the car mended whilst we were there, it was only a bit of pipe on the air intake which had broken off. The meeting and convention were based at the very plush Dunston Hall Country Club, but we also attended the Norfolk Club Golden Jubilee Ball at the fantastic ancient St. Andrew's Hall in Norwich and they also held a special show at the Norfolk Showground – it was heavy driving snow and bitterly cold in the middle of April.

A week later we took further steps to make the dairying business more efficient. The use of water on a dairy farm is a major cost, particularly when you are paying for it through a meter, and so in spring of 99 we had Dales Water Services sink a borehole for us in the yard. They had to go down 40 metres to find a good supply, piped it through a salt machine to remove the calcium from it and piped it back to serve not only the farm, but the houses as well, including back down to Fox Park which was on the same line. Obviously there was a fair cost involved in the scheme and the cost of salt tablets was about £1600 per year, plus service costs and the occasional change of other chemicals in the purifying plant it didn't come for nothing, but it is a lot less than the £10,000 or so that mains water was going to cost us. The water was very heavy in calcium and the one problem it caused apart from the build up in the kettle was the effect it had on the heating elements for all the dairy hot water. Despite putting in super electrodes with supposedly a lifetime guarantee, they didn't last very long and we always kept a spare one in stock and changed them ourselves before getting the next one from E & P Electrics if it hadn't already gone to Martin Webster's who had the same problem.

Mid-May saw us to Twickenham to see the Falcons lose 29-19 to Wasps in the cup final, and then in mid-June we had a super day out down at Lincolnshire County Show where I judged the exhibitor-bred classes on the second day and the powers that be really look after you like royalty.

Shortly after that Mr J said we should think about the prospect of going organic as the milk price was much better. I soon found out that someone had been going to dinner parties in some local houses advocating such a move. It had quite rightly always been the case that it was no good just dismissing something Mr J suggested, you had to do your homework correctly and set out all the proper arguments. This I did ahead of a meeting with someone from the Soil Association, on stocking rates, yields, cost of organic feed etc. which as far as I could see just didn't add up. In addition, we would have had to cease doing embryo work at home as the wording stood at that time. I asked the man about mastitis and he advocated a warm water massage of the infected quarter for 20 minutes six times a day, and I asked if he would like to come out and explain that to Bill or should I do so. He said that if it didn't respond well then you could resort to conventional treatment to which my retort was "Nay, have the courage of your convictions and let the 'bugger' die". Needless to say the idea never got any further and it is still amazing to me that if you speak to a non-farming organic devotee today they don't know that the standards set for somatic cell counts and cleanliness are only about half the level as is required for non-organic milk.

July and August were fairly busy, though quite social that year, we were down for the Royal Show and on the second day I acted as one of the stewards at the Young Judges competition, a fascinating insight into just how many permutations there are in placing four classes of six animals. A week later I judged Durham County Show – no longer the strength of show it once was, and I believe has now ceased to exist. The North Eastern Club was over to Lancashire to visit a pedigree herd which has not been in existence now for many years. It really was very untidy, and my abiding memory is of Bill continually saying or asking, "I wonder what it is like in his house?" – we never got invited in, so we never got to find out! A few days later I went across to view the Holmland dispersal sale of the Bell family, having got to know Tony fairly well through our days on the show circuit over the years, and we still now always have a chat should we meet up at some event or other. The star of the sale that day was a young Flo calf from the Cardsland family from Pembroke referred to earlier, who was bought by David Wright for his Berryholme herd and went on to develop a line of illustrious major show winning champions. The final dispersal sale of the Bailrigg herd of Tom Parker from where the Pansy and more recently Queen families had originated for us was also at that time, but we didn't purchase anything at either of those sales. A few days later I spent an enjoyable three and a half days over in Cumbria judging one section of the Border and Lakeland Club herds competition and then on the final day, the three judges of the various sections all visited the winning herd from each to arrive at a Champion herd and we had little hesitation in awarding that to the Dunnerdale herd of Wilson Boow and his son, Stephen. Whilst over in Cumbria, there was a short spell of near darkness in the middle of the day when we had a 75% eclipse of sun.

Again, at that time, not that it involved me too much physically doing the job, we put mattresses in the second half of the cubicles. We had done one half the previous year and found it much easier to bed up and keep clean, without the need to be continually filling up with box muck, a job which no one enjoyed doing too much. It entailed cleaning out the old muck in the beds, putting in as necessary some stone and then a skimming over with a few inches of concrete to give it firmness for the mattresses and also create some gradient to the front of the cubicle. A good job done even if Malcolm got his calculations slightly wrong at one point and a selection of them seemed very steep back to front, though the cows didn't seem to mind. It was amazing to see them put the final covering over the actual mattresses as one long uninterrupted length so there was no way the cows could get feet under it. It was fastened along the heel stone with the cover laid out in the passageway, then took several men to all at once fold the whole length over to be fastened at the front out of the way of anything loosening it.

During the summer holidays we had various parts of days away with Adam. Sarah by this time had moved to working for Semex, covering much of the same area, but just with a greater selection of bulls to offer prospective customers. During those part days away, we went up Nidderdale and walked from Scarr House back over the tops to Middlesmoor and back down onto the bottom road back up to the reservoir, where we had left Adam happily riding his bike rather than walking with us. We visited the Sion Hill Birds of Prey Centre, the World of James Herriot at Thirsk, walked from Kilburn up and round the White Horse, and also visited the Forbidden Corner at Middleham.

By that time I had become a little tired of paying exorbitant prices for seed corn, and we began to buy it direct from Martin Webster. He always grew a small acreage of first generation seed of both barley and wheat and got it properly dressed and we paid the royalty that was due, but it was still only about half the price. The only slight inconvenience was that we had to go and collect it which sometimes didn't fit in with our plans, but it was a small price to pay, and we continued getting it from Roundhill right up until the farm sale some fourteen years later.

At the end of September, we went over to the south Lancashire/north Cheshire area for another Holstein convention. There were two that year because both were already arranged when the societies merged, and so we had a good few days over near Warrington which had originally been set up by the British Holstein Society. We had a Board Meeting to start with and with Marnie now working part time at Mowbray School, she came over by train later to join us. She thought she would never make it on the very slow cross-country train which seemed to stop at virtually every small town on the way.

Whilst at that Board Meeting there were various changes within the Non-Executive Directors (NED's) for the next year, and I became NED for Finance, a role I filled for the next four years, and saw quite a few major changes during that time, including the purchase of Livestock Services from the Scottish MMB to create Cattle Information Services, wholly owned by Holstein UK, the amicable divorce with the Republic of Ireland becoming a Breed Society in their own right, many meetings with and about various possible arrangements with National Milk Records, working closely with Orchid about the formation of computerised management systems for whole herd management and information, the resignation of Tim Brigstocke as Chief Executive and the promotion of David Hewitt to that role in which he did a terrific job for the next eight or ten years.

At the similar time was the date when we actually started to supply milk to the Co-op instead of Milk Marque, and on the same day Adam had to be fitted with a neck brace after damage sustained playing rugby, which he wore for a considerable time. Also at that time I was in the position of needing to change the farm car – Adam pestered me to think about a Freelander and to keep him happy I agreed to take one for a day's trial – which soon convinced me I didn't want one. It vibrated all the time as you travelled, and when I told the salesman on my return his reply of "Oh you soon get used to it" was the final nail in the coffin, and I finished up with a Peugeot 406 on contract hire to replace the white Renault that had come to the end of its hire period we had taken over on the sale of Herdwise. Another thing to come to an end at the time was my favourite cow Lettice 23 who had come to the end of the line – we couldn't get her in calf and her old legs had finally got the better of her, but we had had a great deal of fun with her over the years. Later that month at the Yorkshire Club Herds Competition we won the Progeny Group Class with daughters of Hanoverhill Inspiration.

Various things around Christmas including going for the first time to the Co-op Milk Suppliers dinner at Durham Castle which was very enjoyable, though the rooms provided overnight were rather cramped and we struggled to keep warm in freezing cold rooms!!

Adam had been complaining for a day or two about his leg hurting but that didn't stop him going with Bill to pheasant beat up at Agglethorpe and came back complaining very badly about his hip – straight to the doctors who had him straight off to the casualty department and between them they were eagle-eyed in spotting a dislocation which they kept him in for ready for an operation the next day – millennium eve. There was a vast amount of publicity being given to and money spent on preparing for the "millennium bug" which was supposedly going to ruin computer systems and controls at the point of passing into 2000. This country spent millions in preparing for it and I believe I read somewhere the Italian nation spent about £35,000. They were proved correct as it appeared nothing happened of note and things just carried on. The ridiculousness of this thinking was highlighted for us at the Friarage Hospital at Northallerton when we went to visit Adam after his operation on that evening of New Year's Eve 1999 which was also his fourteenth birthday. The National Health Service was fully briefed for the expected collapse of all their systems as the clock ticked by. There were about six of them no doubt very highly skilled and very highly paid specialists to be in attendance on New Year's Eve, they sat about all evening waiting for the doom time, were partying as you would expect on such a day, and some very expensive sandwiches and cakes shipped in for them – nothing happened and they all went home the next morning. Adam's operation had been successful and we were going to stay and see the New Year in with him, but about 10.30 he suddenly announced he was going to sleep and settled down to do so, we left him to it and came home to see in the New Year on our own. Adam was home five days later with crutches and a wheelchair, was back in ten days later to have the clips removed but went on from there, through re-hab at Bedale Leisure Centre and with exercises to get things rebuilt and going again and doesn't appear to have suffered any long term damage.

We went over to Carlisle for a very pleasant evening at the awards presentation from the Border Counties Herds Competition I had judged the previous summer, then a day or two later took Kim back up to Hexham to try and collect oocytes from her, but never had any success in getting them fertilised. Talking of Kim we were down at Shrewsbury last Saturday (21/4/18) for the Perfection Collection Sale and I was talking to Dylan Jones of the Puertomadryn herd in North Wales and he was telling me the Kim he bought at our dispersal is dry and coming to her 8th calf and they also still have one of the Scants they bought in 2011, so they have done very well and he was delighted.

In early February, Holstein UK along with Orchid launched their new management system OneStop and I took Mr J and George Leggott with me across to Andrew Williamson's Ingleden herd near Penrith to see a demonstration of it. We did go onto the system soon afterwards but George's memory of it has nothing to do with computers. We stopped at the Little Chef near Appleby for a bite of lunch on the way home and after we had eaten and about to go, Mr J, who's love of chocolate is well documented got a Mars bar for each of us but had no money to pay for them, so I did the treating – George still laughs about it even now.

Adam had always been quite keen and particularly during his recuperation from the hip operation to watch the American wrestling on television and asked us to take him to see some live at the Community Centre at Northallerton. We duly did so, and he enjoyed his evening, though it was absolutely pathetic – it was slow motion and set up you could see the moves coming before they happened. Adam then had another check up and was consigned to crutches for another six weeks which would make three and a half months in total.

In early March 2000 I went, purely from a nostalgic point of view to the last ever Gill's Machinery Sale at Leeming Bar. They had been holding an annual sale to dispose of machinery they had taken in part exchange over the year, and farmers were allowed to enter other machinery as well. We had done so on several occasions and usually been very satisfied with the results. It was always a very sociable occasion drawing people from a massive area and was one of the first 'farming day outs' of the year, so people were ready for it, but some years it was held in horrible wet, cold, snowy weather with a lot of puddle about.

On Society business at that time, there was a suggestion by National Milk Records that they were going to start issuing parentage certificates and in effect cut out the need for pedigree registration. As a defensive measure, Holstein UK entered into discussions to purchase Livestock Services from Scottish Milk. Michael Armstrong as Chairman, myself as Finance Director and Greg Watson as the Deputy Chief Executive and Company Accountant held several meetings, mostly up in Glasgow and principally with John Duncan who was then Chairman of Scottish Milk and Jack Lawson who was Managing Director of Livestock Services and it took some time before the deal was done, but eventually it did and became Cattle Information Services and under the control of Sue Cope it has cut out a great business within the Livestock Information industry and developed many new initiatives. Jack Lawson who will be known to many, particularly up in Scotland, continued as a director of CIS for many years and helped in its development and growth. Many will also have heard him doing the main ring commentary at AgriScot, a role he also undertook for years over at the Royal Ulster Winter Fair, and things under his direction always ran like clockwork. Sue Cope who has played a massive pivotal role in the development of CIS has recently taken a step up to become Chief Executive of the parent body Holstein UK. Having been one of the prime movers in the purchase of Livestock Services, I felt it was only right that we should be one of the early users of their services, and it wasn't very long before we changed to them for our milk recording and continued happily with them until our dispersal.

Bill had shingles and was off for a fortnight, and then for another week or two only milked either end of the day, but he did get over it quicker than many people do – that was just as well as I was very involved with meetings and Holstein UK business. Big Adam came back and did some milking for a while to help us out. We bought some clean quota at that time at 38.3p, and I think that would be the last time we did so apart from some much later when we sold some to create a capital loss and replaced it with some at about 0.5p to show we had and were actually using it.

At a similar time Tesco opened a new store in Catterick and it wasn't long before we paid a visit to do our weekly shop, something which became a regular trip all the time we were at the farm, though now we are nearer to and regularly use their store at Northallerton. I didn't get off to a great start with them on that first visit when I asked them why they had no fresh cream and they tried to tell me that UHT and Elmlea cream were in fact fresh cream, and they weren't too impressed when I told them that as an active dairy farmer I knew a little more about dairy products than the average shopper, and that they should know their facts before starting to advise customers.

Wensleydale Property Company, by this time was up and running, the first three being properties the company took over from one of Mr J's other companies – Iceflow, but by then he was looking for other properties to add to the portfolio. We looked at properties at Stockton, Thirsk and Washington, and after one such visit to Hartlepool Mr J took me all round the area where he was brought up and spent his early life, a fascinating two or three hours in an area I didn't really know.

April that year had not been a very good month and was the wettest month, not just comparable to April's, but of any month of the year, since I had been keeping rainfall records at Newton Grange. It meant there was plenty of growth that spring and a good time for planting things which included the planting of the Millennium Yew Tree in Patrick Brompton churchyard on 23rd April. Plenty of silage in May and then just when we got into June, we had a very wet weekend and from 4 o'clock on the Friday evening to 9 o'clock on the Sunday morning we had 2.4 inches of rain. It would be a weekend when things were happening – the two local clubs had a joint judging night at George

Barker's 'Folly' herd at Northallerton when the heavens absolutely opened, and the day after it was Robin Dickson's 'Upsall' dispersal sale over at Carlisle. Robin and his wife Pat had been great club supporters for many years and developed a good herd of cows – the star family at that time which created great interest was the Gem family which commanded all the leading prices that day. They are still on the go today and Sarah recently bought a calf from the family at the Bowberhill dispersal sale.

Before that we had investigated over in Stockton at one of the properties taken over by Wensleydale Property and whilst there made use of it. The tenants were a Chinese restaurant which went as "Chinese Charlies" and they did a super buffet of hot and cold food which varied between day and night time but was very good which ever it was and in future years we went there a few times and in fact we held Bill's retirement party there as he and Lys had always enjoyed Chinese food. It no longer traded latterly, and we sold the property a few years ago.

Calf prices at that time were down in the doldrums and I don't know how the first connection was made, but we started to sell our bull calves to Gordon and Christine Thompson from High Catton, a relationship which continued right up to the end of our farming. Gordon had a small holding and also helped out on various local farms and Christine had her own milk round and so they usually paid for the calves in cash, which on that first occasion were £8 a piece, but meant that I could then use the cash to secure another bargain with a discount, though as we got more calves about and they got dearer that didn't continue. It wasn't long before in conversation it came up that Christine sold Longley Farm products and so they used to bring me a selection of yoghurts or my preferred option Fromage Frais when they came. They usually used to come on a Sunday morning and took any calves down to four days old (sometimes that included Thursday and Sunday within the four days) and took everything whatever shape and size they were and it meant we weren't blocked up with calves drinking quite a lot of milk and eating quicklettes to get them good enough to go through local markets where everyone knew they were mostly Holstein blood. Gordon didn't worry about that too much, he sold them all dead weight with a slaughter house very close to them and said he could stand the loss of an odd one of our calves, when he couldn't have stood the loss of a fancy Belgian Blue or Limousin calf at £250 plus, which would always be the risk when buying in from auction marts. They will crop up again in the next chapter on 2001.

In June Dalesend Vaakje 12 a Denver daughter was Champion at North Yorkshire County Show with Lettice 52 standing Reserve to her and a week or two later Dalesend Storm Maude started her illustrious career as Reserve Heifer Champion at the Royal Show and talking of Maude, just after that I had a Mr Armstrong from Northern Ireland wanting to buy Storm Maude 3 which I wouldn't sell him although by about the third time he was offering fairly big money. She was younger than the other two, was much thicker set and we were really struggling to get her in calf, and I didn't think she was good enough at that sort of money. He still wouldn't give up and when he was coming over for the Eshton dispersal sale rung to ask if I would pick him up and show him the heifer, which I did – so over the tops to Skipton and back, twice one evening and when he saw the heifer shook my hand and acknowledged that I had been truthful with him rather than not wanting to sell or jack up the price – it is nice when people will admit to your honesty with them.

At the end of July we had a lovely evening when we were guests at Mrs J's 70th birthday party on board the Ullswater Steamer, what a marvellous setting on a beautiful evening, only spoilt by the fact that Bill was away on holiday and I had to milk both before we went and we had to come back home that night so I could milk next morning.

A couple of days later, Adam really showed what his future ambitions were when he started going to help and learn some gamekeeping skills with Brian Metcalfe. Brian worked for Martin Webster at Roundhill and lived down on the farm of Mr Hutton Squire which Martin farmed at Holtby but looked after the gamekeeping over that land and some of the other local farms and woods of a local syndicate. Adam went nearly every weekend and holidays and at certain times the evenings and he certainly learnt the hard work aspect of the job, but absolutely loved it. It was quite a trail to take him to Langthorne and away down the mile-long lane to the base every day and gather him up at night at whatever time it might be. It was all a labour of love as he got paid very little or nothing at all apart from beating days.

Into August and we journeyed up to Dumfries where I was judging their annual show, which at that time was one of the leading one day shows in a heavy dairying area, with good entries of a tremendous quality. The one class that stood out was the Senior milk cow class which took some sorting and at the end of the class it was revealed that first, second and third were all from the Errolston herd of the Davidsons. The sadness of that was six months later they were all slaughtered. As we came home that evening down the A66 we saw a bunch of heifers in a field of wheat about a month away from harvesting. Realising the potential danger to heifers of this sort of experience, we spent some time trying to find the farmer and eventually it transpired they were from a farm a couple of miles back, so we went. Marnie jumped out of the car to inform them, only the lady of the house was in and showed no concern at all, "Oh, they're always getting out, I'll let them know when they come in." We weren't too impressed with the indifference to someone trying to do a good deed and not even getting a thankyou – we comment every time we go past and wouldn't do it again even if all their cows were out!! The day after we went down to Sykehouse Show near Doncaster where I judged on the Sunday – quite unusual at that time to have a show on a Sunday, there wasn't a great show of cattle. Sykehouse Show was quite unusual and the only one I know of who booked a judge for two years in a row. I would doubt if they have any dairy cattle classes there now, as it is pretty much a non-dairying area.

Between barley and wheat harvest that year, Malcolm began to dismantle all the bull pens in the old dairy buildings at Fox Park. They had stood empty for about five years after we had sold Herdwise and before that the regulations with regard to young bulls from overseas having to come here before proving etc. had changed. Now Paul Ropner, who lived in Salt Lake City, Utah decided he would like to convert it into a house which he did over the next year or so, creating a beautiful house with some stunning views up Wensleydale, though they are not just as good now as the woodlands he has planted around the paddocks have grown quite considerably.

From a Holstein UK perspective we had been negotiating the separation with Southern Ireland. Having been, as the Finance Director very involved in the discussion with their two Board Members who had become friends as well as associates, Tom Kelly of "Monamore" and J.J. O'Sullivan of "Lisduff" it had been quite awkward to reach a conclusion that suited both parties, but we had eventually done so, subject to approval by both our Board which was forthcoming immediately and the Board of the I.H.F.A. I was called at a couple of days' notice to go over there to make a presentation to them about the intended settlement. In organising the trip, the travel organisation suggested flying from and returning to two different airports at quite a distance apart, which I pointed out to them wasn't terribly practical as my car would be in the wrong place. To be able to go from an airport which could also accommodate our return we went down to Birmingham airport and we had a couple of days holiday while we were there. Flew into Cork and hired a car and we stayed overnight in Kilkenny – still much the same as it had been some thirty-seven years earlier when over playing rugby. The next day Adam and I had a good trip to a trail for Quad bikes and we also went to Waterford to go around the Waterford Wedgewood factory, fascinating to see the high-end production of crystal and other quality products. Back up then to Dublin where Marnie and Adam had a good day exploring the city while I was all day at the I.H.F.A meeting, but it was worthwhile as they agreed and accepted the settlement as it was, and so back home via Birmingham, back home a couple of days before judging Kilnsey Show and watching them doing the famous fell race up round the Crag.

At the end of September, it was over to Lancashire for a Holstein UK Board Meeting and then the convention based at the Norbreck Castle Hotel in Blackpool, to coincide with Alan Swale becoming President. The one thing people remember about that particular event was the lack of quality in the hotel, and to this day it still appears to be a mystery as to who selected and booked the hotel – the Lancashire Club were apparently not consulted on it or would have suggested alternatives but despite that I am sure everyone enjoyed the usual hospitality.

A week or two later we had Norman Walker for the first time to do some foot-trimming with his rollover crush. He only had an average day that time – only doing 91 in the day. We used Norman regularly after that until we got our own static turn-over and with someone helping him all day to put cows in and out and me keeping him well supplied with tea, he regularly did over a hundred if needed, and when he came to do a tidy up before the dispersal he did about 130 in a very long day.

One time in Summer when he came, Norman's wife was rather unwell, so during the day with the raspberries at full ripeness I picked him a punnet full to take home for her. When I saw him a few weeks later I enquired if she had enjoyed them – he went on to tell me that they were on the front seat and as he turned in at home there were only two left, so he thought he better eat them too!

There was some pretty awful weather that autumn, with a lot of very heavy rain, I described the 30th of October as one of the most horrible days ever weather-wise. There was a lot of very wet corn about and we had to hire Howard Dyson's mobile dryer to get some of the worst dry enough to take down to Donaldson's, there were floods all over the place, two fields we never got baled and there was a lot of winter corn never got sown. Both Sarah and my cars got water into the air intake which on Peugeots, as both were, are low to the ground and mine blew up the engine while Sarah's needed new CAM rods.

That autumn we used sexed semen on a batch of heifers for the first time and thinking we would do our job as best we could we actually managed and programmed them as we would a batch of recipients for embryo work and got an inseminator in to do that job when they were all to do at once. We were very disappointed when we only had one pregnancy from about sixteen heifers, not only at the wasted cost of what was more expensive semen but also the loss of time on the heifers. A while later, Cogent who at the time were the sole suppliers of sexed semen visited with their specialist as they had done to several other farms having problems and it emerged that three of us in particular who had all used embryo experience to try and obtain good results had achieved the opposite and that brought about the advice at that time not to programme animals for sexed semen. I am sure that technology and expertise has moved on considerably since then and both the use of sexed semen and its results on both heifers and cows is considerably improved and it is now successfully used in embryo work for which it was not recommended back then.

We discovered through a member of a different branch of the Liddle clan that my grandfather's brother had at one time been a gamekeeper – so it had obviously jumped several generations to land with Adams obsession. Adam at a similar time had finished his rehab and cleared to play again, almost exactly a year since he had injured it. He barely got back into training or played a game before all was cancelled at the back end of the season the following Spring.

We went to Tesco's on the Friday night before Christmas and discovered they had sold out of bread and toilet paper – it is always remarkable the amount of stockpiling that goes on at that time of year. The next morning (Saturday) I went to Bedale early to get one or two things, fortunately not at Cockburn's the butchers as they were queued out of the door, past Headquarters the hairdressers and halfway along the front of The Food Weighouse.

During the year of 2000 there had been much written, mostly critically about the Millennium Dome in London (now the O2 arena) and we thought we had better go down and see it and all the things happening inside it before it closed down at the end of the year, so two days after Christmas we drove down with a horrible journey taking seven and a half hours before finally finding somewhere to stay and eating at Café Rouge at Canary Wharf. All the next day we had a fascinating and most enjoyable day at the Millennium Dome, and we thought it was very good and much of the criticism unwarranted. We drove home that night on a remarkably frosty evening when it was amazing to see how the temperature fluctuated quite dramatically as the topography of the land changed.

The final day of the year saw more drama when the milking machine packed up on me halfway through evening milking, by which time it was also snowing heavily. Malcolm Hall of Surge who was still looking after us at that time lived at Pickering but he battled through drifts up above Sutton Bank to get to us and found the shaft on one of the vacuum pumps had gone, he finally got it fixed and me milking again just before midnight. That brought to an end a fairly interesting year, but nothing like the next year was going to be.

Chapter 18 - 2001 – Not a Space Odyssey

At the start of the year, we planned to improve our dry cow management even further by making another dry cow yard behind the old Dutch barn and corn drying area to keep the far off dry cows separate from the close calving cows and feed them accordingly, including the installation of yokes along the feed area, and with a concrete area to be cleaned regularly to keep their feet in better order than being totally on a bedded area. Norman Iveson made and installed the metal work which was somewhat individualistic to join up to the existing building, and once that was done Bren Howe did the building work and it was soon finished and immediately into use at a total cost just under £20,000.

I spoke to Bedale Probus Club early in February on "Farming round the world" from my travels and slides, the day after that we had a regular Farm Board Meeting, at which it was suggested by some of the younger generation that we should consider possibly going down the route of contract farming or a farm business tenancy. After some discussion, Mr J, as the chairman asked me what I thought, to which I replied that I was really the wrong person to ask, but I would make just two points, the first being that I would immediately be out of a job if that course was taken, apart from the effect it could have from a taxation/inheritance tax position, but secondly I asked him if the previous Christmas Eve he remembered ringing me to ask if I could go down to Dalesend as water was dripping onto the landing from the attic above. When I got there, I found the ball cock not shutting off and just put a new washer on it to solve the problem and asked who would have seen to that under the proposed ideas. His response was immediate "Point taken, next item," so the subject was never raised again until 2011 when we looked at a possible contract/share farming scenario.

In late February, we hosted a judging practice for the whole of Yorkshire Young Farmers with a massive turnout from all over the region at which we had Paul Harrison of "Chishillways" up at Hexham as the Master Judge and also training them in reason giving as much as actual placings. We had been down to Cirencester for the MGA conference, the previous week followed a day later by the National Holstein Show at Stoneleigh but the day after the judging was into school half term and we went down to the Midlands and stayed a couple of days at Bicester. We visited Cadbury World at Bournville, thinking it would be very interesting for us as well as Adam, but it was very poor. We then went to London and stayed at a Travelodge, went to the Salvador Dali exhibition and the British Army Museum which were much more of interest, even to a non-painting, non-soldier like me. We couldn't unfortunately get on the London Eye as it was all full at the times we could go. We met Emma, ate at Belgo and wandered round Covent Garden that evening. The following day Sarah came down on the train to join us, we went to Harrods, had dinner at a Chinese and then went to the Phoenix Theatre to see Blood Brothers – very good. The next morning we did something I think I had never done before nor done since – we had breakfast at a Burger King before going to Twickenham, which was the point of the whole trip out to see Newcastle Falcons win the Rugby Cup Final in the dying minutes of the match 30-27 against Harlequins.

Imagine on the Monday when we were back home, the shock horror when news broke that Foot and Mouth had been confirmed at a pig farm in Northumberland, virtually next door to Paul Harrison's who had been with us and those Young Farmers from all over Yorkshire on the farm less than a week earlier. We kept our heads down and didn't let anyone know, and certainly no one asked about the previous meeting. Whilst I know Hexham was identified as the source of the outbreak. I, and I know many others don't believe this. There had been talk for a few weeks of many lame sheep up in the North West and South West Scotland which had been blamed on the very wet winter we had been enduring. Foot and Mouth is not as noticeable in the lameness in sheep and this together with reports of young lambs dying (one of the signs in sheep of foot and mouth disease is early lamb death or very weak lambs) and it wasn't very long before that area of the country became the real centre of the outbreak, centred around Longtown Cattle Mart, and again it wasn't until they began tracing sheep movements that many of us non-sheep men realised just how much movement of sheep there was – particularly store lambs which could be sold several times in a couple of weeks. These were recorded movements and there is also little doubt that a lot of sheep were moved without that control - remember at that time it still required numbers to be notified and 'checked' to claim the Hill Farm Sheep Subsidy and it was generally accepted that many sheep were moved about and counted more than once at a variety of locations, and even after movement restrictions were introduced, there were some night-time movements to get sheep back to where they were supposed to be.

For the next few weeks all the attention was concentrated particularly on Cumbria and Dumfries and Galloway areas, and we had many friends and associates within the pedigree cattle industry who lost a lifetime's work overnight through no fault of their own. Immediately the disease had been confirmed, virtually everything in rural areas and agricultural communities came to an abrupt stop – farm meetings, rugby matches, farm visits, even going to places where other farmers might be, in case there was a cross over of infection should any exist, a meeting of the NED's of Holstein UK was held as a conference telephone call rather than us travelling down to Scotsbridge House. We moved some new calves from home across to Dalesend in a cattle trailer and walked three near calving heifers back across – that was all on our own land so no problem.

Suddenly there was a jump of the foot and mouth and it was confirmed at both Danby Wiske and Bellerby. As I had mentioned earlier Richard was from Bellerby, and as he had quite a bit of outstanding holiday I told him he had better use it up and stay at home, and then about ten days later the farm on the other side of them was confirmed with foot and mouth and they were to be taken as a contiguous cull and their own "Studdah" herd were slaughtered on the day of Richard's 21st birthday – a day to be remembered for all the wrong reasons.

Life was just in limbo at that time, I have a note in the diary at that time when there is little else but foot and mouth mentioned that on 11th April that Pansy 102 calved as a heifer, she was well bred and turned into a very good cow, the significance of her calving was that 10½ years later she would be Lot 1 in our dispersal sale, dry and due with her eleventh calf – who says Holstein cows can't last. She was by Comestar Leader and had already bred for us two VG and two Excellent daughters. Nothing else much happened for the next ten days other than routine jobs, and then the ultimate blow landed.

It was Saturday early afternoon, and Marnie was re-decorating Sarah's bedroom, and was starting to wallpaper after lunch. As I had always done in such circumstances I was there when she hung the first piece to make sure it was straight – either with a plumb line or spirit level – on old farmhouse walls the corners are very rarely straight all the way down. She had got the piece cut and pasted as I hovered to check it when the phone suddenly rang. It was the Ministry of Agriculture to tell us that Butterwell Farm had been confirmed with foot and mouth and that as our land at Dalesend joined them, all the cattle at Dalesend were to be slaughtered as a contiguous cull, and that the RAF who were supervising the slaughtering in this area would be in touch about doing so the next day. It was then and still does to this day amaze me that there was never any suggestion of taking out the cows at home as well, even though we moved men, machines and cattle quite regularly and openly between them – not that I would have wanted that to happen. At the time, many people asked me why we didn't lodge an objection and argue our case, and my answer was quite simple and twofold – (i) if we had made too much argument it may have dawned on them about the herd and encouraged them to take that as well and (ii) with the main road Leyburn to Bedale creating a break line, we were the last contiguous cull eastwards and if we had won the argument and the cattle survived only to actually then succumb to the disease a few days later, that would have taken out another swathe of farms, and that would have been even harder to live with going forward.

Being a Saturday afternoon it wasn't easy, though all organisations were on high alert and the Holstein UK offices were being manned twenty four hours a day and they updated all our pedigree certificates and dispatched them by special courier to be with us by 10.45am next morning and it was arranged for Chris Norton of Norton and Brooksbank to arrive to value them all at 11.30. Marnie and I were up most of the night (I don't suppose we would have done a lot of sleeping anyway) sorting out all the paperwork on calves being carried, remembering there were quite a lot of embryos in utero, and including all the Kim heifers from IVF within the in-calf heifers. I was amazed that Saturday when MAFF suggested that no one should go and feed the cattle on the Sunday morning until valuation and slaughter, which I told them was absolutely ridiculous and completely alien to any notion of livestock husbandry to leave that number of cattle unfed for several hours beyond their normal feeding time. I eventually got them to change their minds, but only on the understanding that I would have to stay there until being disinfected after slaughter in the evening. I did fother a little later than normal so that I could breakfast before going down there, and Marnie packed me up with lunch and snacks and various flasks of coffee to keep me going through the day. Chris came and did his valuations starting at 11.30 and finishing at 2pm, followed by Robert White, the local butcher from Morton-on-Swale who will be known to many people over this wide local area, who still then had a slaughter house but had been seconded to MAFF to do the evil deed as and where necessary. Charles Ropner came to help when we started the process and we started with the biggest in-calf heifers first and worked down to the youngest calves and finished off with the four Black Welsh Mountain sheep. Fortunately we had the race to use and Charles and I fed them in at one end and Robert and then the RAF staff moved the carcases at the other and it was about 8.30pm by we had finished, at which point all our clothes, wellingtons etc. had to be changed for clean ones we had brought with us, so that the others could be burnt along with the cattle. The next day wasn't very pleasant either, we had MAFF vets to do a routine check on the cows – it was a cat and dog vet who didn't really have a clue about cattle – this was followed three days later by another cow inspection – this time by a Hungarian vet, seconded over here to help. No wonder there had been problems earlier in the epidemic with this sort of veterinary input. In between those two vet visits, all the cattle were loaded onto lorries and led away for disposal – an agonising sight.

After about a fortnight we had part of a day with a MAFF valuer to see about the hay, straw, wood etc. which would have to be disposed of by burning and also discuss the disinfection procedure that would need to be followed. We had another valuation lady from MAFF a few days later who seemed to cover much of the same ground, and we decided that as there was now only Bill, Malcolm and myself left, we would leave it to MAFF to organise the "clean up" and they went to great lengths constructing a reservoir for all the washed down water to be pumped into after the steam cleaners etc., which had to be all double fenced round etc., and then ultimately had to empty it out and spread onto stubble before sowing later that autumn.

In the meantime, I had the unenviable task of meeting Richard Pratt to inform him that on top of losing their own cattle, he had also in effect lost his job with us as there were no young stock to look after. Ultimately things worked out well for all at Studdah, their buildings were in the process of being converted into houses within Bellerby and they extended their dairy unit down the lane and replaced their herd with the complete herd from the "Browtop" herd from over in Lancashire and Richard along with his brother James and wisely directed by father Alan have taken that herd forward to be one of the leading herds in the area.

In amongst all this, Bill was approaching his retirement later in the year, and we began to advertise for a replacement and had all kinds of applicants at all different levels from some who were really over-qualified and were more fitted to a large herd manager role where they did very little actual milking to one who rung up to enquire and who's opening question was "What's brass like". Needless to say, we didn't even see him for interview. We saw several potential candidates twice, the first time at Dalesend as we didn't want to risk them coming among the cows as the foot and mouth rumbled on in other areas of the country. Eventually we settled on Bill's replacement – more of which later.

There was a further foot and mouth scare towards the end of May when there was a lot of activity over at our neighbour Francis Dent's with what could be clearly seen as MAFF officials in all kinds of protective garments but eventually they decided over the next day or two that it was some other problem and he was declared clear. About that time Adam started going to Cobshaw to game keep again having not been for about four months, but school wouldn't allow him to go there for his two weeks work experience at that time, so he went instead to work with Howard Braithwaite at their nursery at Leeming Bar, and for a non-gardener I think he found it quite interesting.

At the end of May, when all of this was going on, Bedale had a special market one Tuesday – that was to mark the 750 years since it had originally been granted a charter to hold a weekly market.

By then the Foot and Mouth epidemic had run out of steam, and in this area, things were gradually returning to more normality, though in many cases, things were never going to be quite the same again. In our own case, whilst it had been a harrowing experience and one you wouldn't want to suffer again, we were more fortunate than most in that we kept the cows and one thing Foot and Mouth taught us was how quickly numbers build up to former levels, we only bought about a dozen cattle over the next two years to maintain our numbers until our own heifers calved in again. Round about the time of the epidemic, people used to ask me how we had managed to keep going as they would have been unable to cope. Two in particular said that to me and I told them they had both suffered much worse, which they didn't accept, but one rung me that night and the other a few days later to acknowledge my thinking. One had lost a son with leukaemia and the other a daughter with cancer. I told people that we kept going by thinking that we had just had a draft sale, and financially, a very good one at that, as the compensation was very good (should there be another outbreak sometime in the future – it will never be as good again, nor will a lot of the abuse and wastage of the clean up be allowed). During and in the aftermath of the tragedy, there were only three times when I got upset about it, though there was always that sadness at the loss of young animals and the wonder as to what something would have turned out like. The first time was very soon after having the cattle slaughtered when one ignorant, fairly local farmer said "Well it won't bother you – they weren't your cattle you were only the manager" – needless to say he got a not very polite mouthful. The second one came in late summer when Marnie and I were up much of the night to calve one of the best cows at that time, Dalesend Threat Bella with her third calf. About two in the morning after a very difficult calving with a very large calf, it was inevitably a bull, though it was alive, but it suddenly dawned on me that her previous calf had been a bull, her first calf had been a heifer who had been lost with Foot and Mouth, which meant that it was going to be at least another year to get back to where we had been two years previously as far as her breeding was concerned – it was almost a soul destroying moment in the tiredness of the night. The third time was several months later, one Saturday in Northallerton. There was a gentleman who had a sweet stall on the market – he had for many years also stood on Bedale market on a Tuesday and I had often got a few sweets and had a bit of banter with him, though by then he no longer stood at Bedale. He always had plenty of talk about him and often had a bit of a dig about farmers and all the money they were making. This particular day in Northallerton was just at the time that it had been in the national press that someone had received a massive six figure compensation payment for a bull which had been slaughtered, and the sweet man whilst I waited to be served started to go on about all the money farmers had got from Foot and Mouth and when he had finished looked at me and asked what I thought. I just looked him straight in the eye and told him if he wanted to line 163 animals up and put them down a race to be shot at the other end, he was welcome to it. An elderly lady who was waiting to be served and obviously knew very well his "gift of the gab" turned on him and gave him a real mouthful telling him she had told him many times his tongue would get him into trouble. An hour or two later as I went back past the sweet stall, giving it a wide berth, the man spotted me, had at that time no customers, and he called me over and gave me a full apology for his earlier insensitivity not realising that we had even lost any cattle in the cull, or what was involved in it. At least he was a true gentleman in realising the error of his ways and he has now been retired for a few years, though I enquired of his successor with the stall only recently who says he is fit and well and looks down at the market most early Saturday mornings.

Apart from Foot and Mouth disease and all its ramifications, there was a lot else happening that year. We had a General Election in early June won by Tony Blair and the Labour party, which precipitated the resignation of William Hague as leader of the Conservative party. Mr Hague was our MP here in the Richmond constituency and was a very good man both locally and nationally, but he had been almost forced into the Tory leadership when too young and at a time when they had little hope of being elected. He later went on to play a senior role in government and was Foreign Secretary for some years before retiring as an MP in 2015. A very inspiring speaker and well-respected historical writer, he was to my mind lost far too early to politics in the UK.

As school drew towards a close for the summer, they had a charity dressing up day at Mowbray School and Marnie went dressed as Baby Spice with blonde wig and all in place. A few days before that we were going to Panetti's for supper and I rather stupidly suggested that she daren't go out in the wig, which only resulted in her taking on the dare, but it gave us a great deal of amusement. Being such a good eating place and well used by locals, there were quite a few people in that evening whom we knew, but it was amazing how many people ignored me or looked the other way, as this blonde sat with her back to the room so her face couldn't be seen. It was only a day or two later that word was out in the locality that I had been seen out on the Saturday night with a new blonde mistress! Great fun.

A few days later we were invited to a lunch at RAF Leeming given by 24 squadron to all the people they had been involved with during the Foot and Mouth outbreak, and we had an interesting few hours with them. Just a day later Bill was honoured with a 35-year long service medal at the Great Yorkshire Show.

The week after that, and although the Foot and Mouth epidemic had been over for some time, there were still restrictions in place, one of which was that we were not allowed to move cattle across the road at our drive end. Because we had no young stock to graze and the Corner Banks field at Hill Top East is un-ploughable or cuttable, we had put the dry cows over there for the one and only time, but some were getting close to calving and needed to come home. We got the paperwork from MAFF to be able to bring them across which had to be supervised by a vet. When the lady arrived she insisted that we should make a straw pad, fully disinfected for them to walk across – I tried to tell her that it was more likely to scare the cows and they wouldn't just calmly do as they were told to walk across it, but she wouldn't be told and insisted. When the cows came out of the track down from Hill Top which was fenced all the way, they immediately wanted to gallop and shot both ways towards Bedale and towards Newton-le-Willows, and although we had every available person on duty we couldn't hold them and they took a lot of getting back and went on a lot of roadway they needn't to have done and then we had to gather up the straw and burn it – when nothing had been on it and then wash down the road with disinfectant and water which was my original plan, but the lady knew best – ridiculous.

As we approached the end of July, we were getting to the end of Bill's marvellous 37 years of service and devotion to the Dalesend herd – a wonderful chapter of all kinds of things both serious and amusing – I have already relayed some of them, more will crop up over the years, and they are likely to be all rounded up into one short chapter dedicated to him at the end of the book. Bill and Lys had got a bungalow in Crakehall and they were moving things down there for the first time at the end of July, with Bill's last day of work coming some fortnight later, and a fortnight after that we had his retirement at Chinese Charlie's at Stockton – a great night that everyone enjoyed and also had a particular twist to it, apart from some comical gifts we gave Bill – a spare sugar beet pulp bag to fix to the back of his lawnmower to collect the grass, we have photographs of him previous to that straddling such a bag as he mowed his lawn, a spare lance for the pressure washer that over the years he had used to diligently to keep everywhere spotlessly clean, but the big twist for Bill was Wallace.

Wallace and Bill had been great friends from being boys and continued it through shoots and visits over many years. They had fallen out a few years earlier over something as silly as a shooting date which one or other had got wrong on the calendar. Neither would back down nor ring the other one despite many talkings to. As Bill's party approached, I asked Lys if she thought Wallace would come if we invited him, she doubted it but gave me his telephone number. It took Wallace but a few seconds to agree to come down unbeknown to Bill and go straight to Stockton and he and his wife were sat there when Bill walked in, and immediately turned to Marnie and I and said "You b*****s you've got your way in the end". That was all it took, and they carried on as if there had never been a fall out, and it was just as well because it wasn't too long before Wallace was very poorly and sadly died. I have told this story several times to people who have had a similar kind of fall out over very little with a lifelong friend and urged them to patch things up before it's too late!!

With Bill retiring and moving it gave us an opportunity to move staffing and housing round a bit. Bill had originally come into the bungalow at the Grange and then when his family expanded moved down to Fox Park when I started the herd off down there and was unmarried and had remained there all those years. In starting off afresh with a new herdsman, I wanted him to be on hand at Newton Grange, but this meant persuading Malcolm, Christine and Andrew to move down to the vacant Lodge at Patrick Brompton. We did one or two bits of work down there before he moved in mid-August and we did one or two other jobs in the Bungalow before Richard moved in there. Richard Lapthorne joined us as a herdsman a day or two before Bill retired so he could pick up the pieces. He already had a house in Crakehall and came from looking after Guernsey's on a robotic system at Brymor near Jervaulx, where they used much of the milk in the manufacture of their well known and much appreciated ice cream. Two or three weeks after starting work, Richard, Helen and Victoria came to the bungalow, along with their very new daughter Charlotte. It was quite a change for them at such a stressful time with a new baby and unfortunately Helen and Victoria just could not settle in the quietness of the countryside after always having lived in a village, even to being too quiet for them to sleep without street lights at night and in a little more than a month we had to regretfully allow them to move back to their own house in Crakehall, which fortunately they had not at that point got let. For the next ten years or so Richard travelled to work all the time, on the understanding that if I was away on either business or holiday, he came back at night to check the cows before bedtime and during the night if anything was calving. Apart from that I continued to do the night time requirements.

Adam had badly twisted a knee playing rugby some time earlier, and it was beginning to bother him and in the autumn of that year he had keyhole surgery on the cartilage of his knee, that meant a week off school and no sport for a further month. Unfortunately he didn't do quite as he was told by the surgeon as regards not overdoing it, and it still bothers him today, particularly through the shooting season when they can walk 12-15 miles per day, six days a week over fairly rough going. Before that, we had taken Adam for his last schoolboy holiday to Centre Parcs at Elveden Forest down in Suffolk where he did clay pigeon shooting and field archery amongst other things. One day whilst he was doing one of those things, we went off to Bury St. Edmunds and Marnie said it felt as she imagined it must if you were just let out of jail.

I was doing quite a lot of travelling about again after the restrictions of Foot and Mouth and with my work with Holstein UK and seemed to hit a bad patch motoring wise that autumn. Having had two speeding tickets a little earlier in the year, I was going a little steadier to avoid another, but then got hit twice in two days with a parking fine, one on a Saturday afternoon outside the Valley Gardens at Harrogate and one the next afternoon up at Kingston Park for the rugby. That one I successfully escaped by writing and pointing out that there were no signs saying you couldn't park on the grass verges, and suddenly they had decided to stop everyone parking there and I guess they had so many complaints they withdrew the tickets and put signs up for the future.

Even before Foot and Mouth struck, we had been exploring ways in which we might do away with having the young stock at Dalesend and avoid all the time which was spent moving men, machines and animals backwards and forwards between the two places, the one big problem was the financing of such a scheme. If we are honest the Foot and Mouth epidemic helped enormously in bringing this plan to fruition – we had no youngstock or not very many for twelve months and the Foot and Mouth compensation saw to the financing part of the problem. Immediately we had lost all the young stock the ideas were just formulated to put up a large single span building behind Newton Grange to house everything under one roof. We obviously had to go through the planning process for such a large building and that in itself almost caused problems, though it did delay things for a month. When it came back to Newton-le-Willows Parish Council for their comments, the council, which was chiefly made up of retired school teachers and army colonels, suggested to Richmondshire that it would be more environmentally friendly if it were five or six small buildings rather than one large one! Fortunately the District Council Planners told them this was 21st Century not 19th Century agriculture, but because the parish council made the comments it had to go before the full council rather than a farming matter such as that which would normally have gone through on the 'nod'.

We had had some very heavy rain at times through the summer and early autumn, one day in August having 1.7 inches of thunder rain in just one and a half hours, flooding everywhere but it was a good open autumn, allowing us to get on well with the new buildings, we started excavating for a level site on 5th September, Waddington's put in the foundations on 25th September and just three months later we had stock in part of it. In between times we had the shed erected and then ourselves did all the fitting out of floor, walls and divisions within it, though we were fortunate we didn't need it all done for that winter because we only had that years calves and no older heifers. Malcolm was in charge of the day to day work inside the buildings, and the initial part housed two loose calf pens for calves on milk, plus four or five larger pens for weaned calves/stirks, along with one bull pen, plus two larger pens with yokes for older heifers. The electric supply to the farm came across where the building was to go, so we had to get it laid underground at great expense, though we had to do most of the work ourselves – digging the trench and then filling it in after NEEB had installed the cable. It had to be filled in after inspection and I got into bother for having put a couple of dead calves into the trench and was ordered to remove them before clearance for in-filling – I can't see that they would have affected the supply. Much of the autumn was spent laying concrete, and every pillar for the inside fittings was in a sleeve, so that if we wished we could take them plus all the concrete panels out to leave a total flat, open floor – true flexibility. We had been keeping all the calves in what were the dry cow yards through summer and autumn but with the winter coming needed to make space for the cows to come into their quarters. We had had to keep the bull calves from March onwards as movement restrictions prohibited their movement, so it was some relief when just a couple of days before Christmas we got youngstock moved into the new building, even though some of it was "bodged" up with gates to contain them. Talking of bull calves, right from the "lock-down" we had agreed with Gordon and Christine that we would keep them for them and that they would take them when able to, without ever agreeing how we would work out the price – again a sign of the benefit of people having trust in each other, and we came to a mutually agreeable price as a job lot for the 36 bull calves they took on January 9th in a wagon load - what a relief that was.

That autumn Keith Colley took over as our BOCM Pauls adviser after Dick's several promotions to a higher level within the company. Keith looked after us from then until our dispersal, we became good friends as well as business associates, and continue to meet up now and again to set the world to rights – not that it takes any notice.

It had been a busy autumn while all this building work was going on, in the house we had got the central heating changed from an anthracite burner to oil, we went to hear Stuart Tate give a very interesting lecture on Hadrian's Wall to raise church funds, and the North Eastern Holstein Club had its first meeting since everything stopped in February with a supper meeting at the Swaledale Arms. Marnie took a student for work experience for a week at Leeming Motel, we went to Hopperton where Sarah lived to see if the steaks were as good as they were supposed to be at the Mason's Arms – they were, and so were their garlic prawns for a starter – over the years we called there a few times for supper on the way from all sorts of places with not far to then travel home – yes, the steaks were every bit as good until the couple running it moved on!

Over winter we put in a dirty water system adjoining the slurry pit and laid two underground pipes to moveable sprinklers in the Front and 20 acre fields. With Richard having moved back to Crakehall, the bungalow was empty until we let it to Doug and Elsie Ponton who lived there happily with their two dogs for several years. Mr Bill had a shoot on the farm as part of his retirement present after Christmas, then a couple of days later we took Adam to Chinese Charlies for his birthday and up to watch the firework display from the Gateshead side of the Tyne for New Year – fantastic, and we saw them the following year as well, but now the powers that be have stopped any being placed on boats in the centre of the Tyne on health and safety grounds – what spoilsports.

We had one or two funerals to go to just at the turn of the year – three actually, which again proved the old adage that such things occur in threes.

I went with Dick and George up to Murrayfield for rugby – there and back on the train in the day, but a good day out. Sarah and James went up to Aviemore for a week's holiday but couldn't ski as there was no snow. I was still heavily involved with meetings for Holstein UK, mostly revolving around the ongoing dispute with National Milk Records, in between times we were taking down all the extensive fencing round the dirty water lagoon MAFF had erected at Dalesend – I wish we hadn't volunteered for the wire and parts as there were more staples that you could ever have imagined, and Richard went on a DIY AI course.

One of the decisions we had been working on all summer and autumn, was what to do with Dalesend now that the young stock were all coming back to be reared at home in the future, It didn't really fit any agricultural purpose that we may have had for it, and situated as it was in the corner of Patrick Brompton the obvious use was as building land for housing, so we employed at great expense Malcolm Tempest to come up with some plans and submitted them for outline planning permission. The problem was at the time the buildings had been put up as agricultural buildings and were still regarded as greenfield sites, and also the land was outside the then village limits for housing and so was refused, at the same time at what had been Lyon's garage on the other side of the village was also refused – it later got permission for development of very smart, stone built offices at one end of that area and ultimately I am sure we shall see housing on the larger area towards the church. Ultimately, we were allowed planning permission to convert our buildings into light industrial and or office units, which in subsequent years became fully let and the Dalesend Business Park has 29 units of varying sizes and has proved to be very successful. We were advised by the powers that be at the time of that planning consent being granted to keep very detailed records of all the attempts to hire out the buildings and the costs involved because if we couldn't make it work and proved as much in a few years' time we would almost certainly get housing on it as it had now become a brownfield site and was then only one step to housing rather than the two steps at one go from greenfield to housing – how crazy a way is that of planning in operation.

We did have some problems a couple of years later when it was a struggle to let the two large silage pits and an oil company wished to put in some storage tanks and operate from there – this required approval for vehicles to be based there and planning from the local council. Many villagers objected at meetings which was their right, but what wasn't their right was through the course of the summer for one or more objectors to resort to trespass and on several occasions at night time, open gates, lift gates off their hinges and such like where the heifers were at Dalesend, mixing them up, letting them out into corn crops and once in particular getting them out onto the road and into the village in the middle of the night. Fortunately, no one or no animal was hurt, but it left a very unpleasant taste and we had gates chained and bolted and crooks turned upside down so they couldn't get gates off. Finally after the Parish Council Meeting to discuss the proposal – from which I was banned as I did not live in the Parish, Mr J decided that he couldn't stand the unpleasantness anymore and informed the company that they couldn't go ahead – miraculously the cattle were never out again – day or night. Whoever it was, if they happen to read this, do the decent thing and admit you were involved – I won't worry about it now - life is too short to be vindictive, and the business park is very successful – we transferred it into the property company several years ago.

In the spring of 2002, we went on our long-awaited trip to Iceland. My wish list to visit there went back forty years when the A level geography group of which I was a member was to go on a school trip with Mr Crawford. Limited to only twenty, I was first reserve at number 21, but no one pulled out, so I never got to go. The family were sick of hearing the story and eventually Marnie bought me a day trip for Christmas one year – all went well until not long before the due date when they rang to say it was cancelled because there was not enough interest. We decided that wasn't enough to put us off and we booked a long weekend for March and we had a marvellous trip. Arriving at Glasgow airport for the flight the fire alarm went and everyone had to evacuate the terminal – you could smell burning and fire engines arrived, but it was amazing how people reacted and started complaining about being outside and their flights might be delayed. One such complainant started on me and I soon shut her up by asking her if she wanted to go back in and be burnt or stay outside until it was safe. I think she saw my point and calmed down and we were soon on our way as it was a luggage belt that was rubbing and had overheated, but as always there is no pleasing some people.

We stayed in Reykjavik and sampled its marvellous food, watched the chocolate making as we had a cup of coffee in the adjoining café. We went on a trip round part of the country one day and stopped at a garden centre where they were growing tomatoes and bananas in March in Iceland!! The same place had a pair of beautiful wooden doors at the entrance, as you went in, one had Adam and the other Eve beautifully carved into them, the great thing was when you went inside and turned round it was the naked backs and back-ends of them that really finished it off. We saw geysers and glaciers and went to the Blue Lagoon and swam in the lovely warm thermal pools while it snowed on us. They were also doing a new drainage scheme through the centre of the town, but people just carried on walking under swinging cranes and walked wooden planks or bits of steps across the trenches to get into shops- imagine what "Elf and safety" would say to that over here.

It was a busy spring on our return, the Yorkshire club dinner was held at the Buckles Inn and was spoilt by a very poor speaker who upset a lot of people, but all credit to the club, they realised the problem and sent a letter of apology out to everyone the next day and people were satisfied by that prompt action. The North Eastern Club dinner was only a couple of days later at the Golden Lion in Northallerton and fortunately there was no such controversy. Around this time, we were busy at spare moments helping Sarah getting a house ready at Cottingley near Bradford before she and James moved in.

It was the Genetic Elite Sale at Beeston that Spring where we bought Airfield Gibson Anne from Ken Procter who from a yearling heifer developed into a good cow and bred nicely for us. The other heifer I wanted to buy was a Cousteau Sharon from Antony Brough of the Tallent herd – one of the very first daughters from the Sharon family to go to auction just as Shottle was beginning to make a name but I couldn't get Mr J to understand what I was trying to tell him and he wouldn't go on after a few initial bids. Literally a few days later he came up to the office with a copy of the Holstein Journal and told me about an article in it – that was the sort of family we should be investing in – I had a wry smile to myself as I explained to him that was the Sharon family I wanted him to buy into at Beeston – his response wasn't too polite or repeatable in a book such as this !!

Just into May and we went up to Newcastle, walked for the first time over the new Millennium Bridge over the Tyne and had lunch at Tosca's tapas bar for Marnie's birthday before going to the final Falcon's game of the season, which was the end of an era for quite a few of that team who had won the championship just a year or two before, Tuigemala the ex-Rugby League player, Pat Lam, Dodie Weir, George Graham and Garry Armstrong, all tremendous players in their respective positions and most of those names are still well known today some sixteen years later. After that it was into another very busy spring and summer.

Adam as part of his Design and Technology course at school had made a papier mache hat decorated in Falcons colours. His hero was Inga Tuigemala and when we went to a game we arranged for him to autograph it. When we collected it at the next game we found the whole team had actually signed it – it is still wrapped up in our attic.

Chapter 19 – A Lot of Changes and a Very Sad Loss

As we kept getting more cows and fed more silage through the summer as well as the winter, our silage space was somewhat restricted by the two original silage pits having roofs on them – that was ok in earlier days when tractors were much smaller, but with the growth in the size of the machines, it was impossible to get enough depth of silage with it rolled sufficiently, and so we decided to remove the two roofs, which wasn't that big a job. We cut all the bolts off from the inside and dropped the sheets down onto the floor – one side was tin sheets and they were easily gathered up, the other side was asbestos and by its age would be just that, so we all wore masks and once all down, scooped it up with the JCB bucket and into a trailer, there just happened to be a big hole somewhere which needed filling with some soil on top!! Norman Iveson then came and cut down the posts to about 3ft above the walls and put a safety rail all the way round. Much better and shortly afterwards much better for ensiling, rolling and sheeting up.

By now it was just over twelve months since we lost all the young stock and our numbers were inevitably falling slightly – one of the first pedigree sales of any note that spring was the Ingham sale at Kirby Thore where some good cattle from good Canadian families had been brought up from the "Deane's" in Norfolk. We weren't necessarily wanting immediate milk and were quite happy to buy in calf cows or heifers and we bought from such good cow families as the Bevins and the Newlands Sheik Maggies – 12 in all, and they calved out and started some good families for us with the exception of two of them. Later in the autumn as they got closer to calving, we had got the remainder of them into the dry cow yard the very morning that the hunt came through in the afternoon. I don't know who was in charge of the Bedale Hunt that day, but they came through the yard and round the back at full tilt, totally spooking the heifers on the concrete and leaving two of them doing the splits from which they never recovered and had to be put down – the hunt paid good compensation through their insurers. At the same sale there was a small herd dispersal at which I bought a mature dry cow with some tremendous milk records. Very correct with short legs and a very deep body, she calved later in the autumn with a Simmental bull calf when she was supposed to be in calf to Black and White, I had only paid 480gns for her and with £40 back from the vendor plus a bull calf worth about half of her purchase price, she only stood us at £240 or so and she went Excellent a couple of months later into the bargain, and also peaked at 70kg/d.

Just into June and there was knock on the backdoor one evening after tea. A rather shaken looking young man asked if I could help with a tractor as he had had an accident, so off we went down the road and turned up the back road towards Francis Dent's where I saw his problem. He had taken the sharp bend too fast and gone off the road into the ditch which put his car onto its side to go behind the road sign for the junction and stopped just after it. He had climbed out of the passenger door and was unharmed. How the car had found room to get between the hedge and the signpost I know not, but I soon had him pulled out, upright on the road and it started up straight away, more bothered about the bulling he was likely to get from his father than the odd dent in the driver's side – he had only got this, his first car a day or two earlier – the best way for the boys to learn as long as they come to no harm.

In mid-June Mr J went off for a fishing trip – to Alaska, and just a few days later one of our better cows and Sarah's all time favourite had the only heifer calf she ever had in I think it was eight calvings, by a young bull, you would struggle to make up such coincidences – Woodmansees Alaska.

I went down for a Holstein UK meeting and the annual convention that comprised a fascinating morning at Whitsbury Farm and Stud where they paraded the stallions for us, took us through all the foaling sheds and explained the whole stud business and finished with a parade with a specially prepared brochure and commentary of all the mares with the years crop of foals. We had a good herd visit to Robert Cooper's at Normead, including a tour of all his environmental work, including bird boxes in the lee of the Marlborough Downs. A night of whippet racing followed, and we also visited Tim Harding's Crichel herd where they ran a competition to pick the best six cows from a big field full of almost 200 cows. I must have been the only one to spend enough time among them or lucky enough to see all the ones the judge saw as I ended up winning which was a trip for two to Italy courtesy of Genus.

Mollie was over from New Zealand at that time, and Marnie spent quite a bit of time taking her to various libraries and record offices as she continued to work on the Thompson family history. At that same time I was down to Essex for a Holstein UK classification workshop at the "Thurlow" herd managed by John Copeland who had previously been a classifier, followed by a superb lunch courtesy of the Vestey family who even today still own large parts of that county in addition to their extensive beef operations in South America. Talking of lunches, Mark Marley of Fishers Seeds took Martin Webster and I on a tour round their site at Melmerby and then out for lunch at The Angel, Topcliffe, which followed an earlier lunch at Panetti's with Dick and Keith to discuss likely prices and requirements for feeding for the coming year. You will be beginning to think that I never did much work and was always out eating, but they are just the highlights of a busy schedule, and you have to eat lunch somewhere and was always or at least usually working lunches.

A week or so later we were down at the Royal Show to see Dalesend Storm Maude be Reserve Champion and be one of the winning Burke Trophy pair at the Show. That same week we took all of the feed troughs out of the milking parlour which I had wanted to do for some years but Bill hadn't wanted to, but Richard like me was quite happy to do so, and we incorporated more feed into the roughage feed and used the out of parlour feeders even more, putting in an extra stall from the ones which we had bought from Rob Dickson's at Upsall after he stopped milking, he having bought them from Northsea Holsteins after they ceased, and we used Dennis, a very clever electrician to look after them and keep them going – they were rather specialised computer controlled feeders and he also looked after automatic car washers, which again are a fairly fussy sort of electrics.

Marnie went off on activity week from Mowbray, this year to Holy Island. As always that was the same week as the Great Yorkshire Show – we had a couple of cattle there and Adam and Sarah were looking after them – we did no winning, but that paled into insignificance as the week unfolded. I went on the Tuesday to see the cattle judging and other bits of business and as I came home called at The Lodge to leave our exhibitor tickets for Malcolm and Chris who were going on the second day. I saw Chris as Malcolm was out playing quoits for the Greyhound at Hackforth. Imagine my utter shock just as I went to bed that night to get a phone call from Chris to tell me that Malcolm had collapsed and died as he threw a quoit – what a loss at just 56. Time had passed very quickly in those 15½ years he had been with us, but as I wrote in his eulogy the best I could do was repeat what I wrote on my notes when I interviewed him then – "He'll do me". The best tribute I can pay Malcolm is to print in full the eulogy I gave for him at his funeral a week or so later for which Mr and Mrs J flew back from their holidays in Cornwall.

Malcolm

"Malcolm will be remembered by everyone here today and many more besides, in different ways and for different reasons. Son, Husband, Father, Father-in-Law, Grandfather, Brother, Uncle and we all share in their loss and our thoughts and prayers have been with them over the last few days, today, and into the future. But on a wider scale, we knew him as Malcolm, Malc, Super Malc, Percy, Percy Dobbs, Dobbles – the names have evolved over the years to fit the various situations.

The fact that Malcolm only lived in three houses in his life and worked for only two farms in 40 years tells you pretty well everything about the character of the man he was. He was born at Ainderby Myers where his father worked and he continued to live in that house in which he was born after he married Christine, moved to Newton Grange about 11 years ago, and had lived across the road at the Lodge for just less than a year. He was a countryman in the true sense of the word, working quietly in it and tending for it as he went about his work and, in his leisure time involved in some of the local pursuits of this immediate area.

Malcolm wasn't just a tractorman, although that was his main work, he could turn his hand to most things, building, joinering, plumbing and stockmanship, though we never did get him to either milk or lead a bull. Nor did he do electrics no doubt put off by the first night of electricity in the cottage at Ainderby Myers when he plus Alwyn, Janet, Dennis and Keith raced upstairs to see who could be the first to put on the light – he got tripped up and split his head open on the bedpost.

Some of the buildings at Newton Grange stand testimony to his building skills, and he was just as proud to lead a cow if we had a judging competition night at home, or stand beside them at a show – they were every bit "his" cows as they were anyone elses. He loved his day at the Great Yorkshire Show and sadly just missed it by one day this year. Similarly he loved to take bull calves to Darlington market – best cap and overalls on – what fun we have had with him over the years with various colours of overall – and he always came back with the full tale and ten foot tall after a good trade.

In the community, Malcolm had been for many years a member of Hackforth Village Hall Committee and was very much involved with its enlargement and refurbishment several years ago. He was also very much involved with the Millennium celebrations there and more recently with the Golden Jubilee festivities. He had for a long time, organised the monthly domino drives for the Hall funds.

He was very involved with Greyhound Inn at Hackforth and its quoits club, a player for many years in the Lower Dales Quoits League – and a member of that leagues committee. He had always declined chairmanship of these organisations, preferring to work quietly in the background rather than up front until this year, when he had ironically, become Chairman of the Greyhound Quoits Club because nobody else would do it. He was also Captain of the Hackforth Darts and Dominoes Thursday night team.

During the last few years, Malcolm gave considerably of his time in helping the Hackforth Leukaemia, now Children's Cancer Fund, of which Christine was the Treasurer. Usually in the background helping at functions and stewarding the annual fundraising walk. They, along with others, have raised thousands for these causes.

Malcolm was also a very, generous giver to virtually any charity – you wouldn't find a better buyer of raffle tickets for whatever cause – but never in his own name – firstly for Andrew and, more recently "put Tom's name on them" (his grandson) – and what's more they were always very lucky.

Not a sportsman in the true sense of the word – I often used to tell him quoits, dominoes, and darts weren't real sports, he was still interested in the results particularly cricket. He always had the radio on in the cab and kept me up to date with how England were doing, or more importantly, Yorkshire, and usually through the summer knew how Newton and Crakehall had done the previous Saturday. More recently with my interest in rugby and Newcastle, he had always found out the score by Monday morning and gave me some stick if the Falcons had lost.

Don't, however, run away with the idea that Malcolm was all sweetness and light. Like the rest of us he had two sides but fortunately one didn't surface very often. He could at times be the most stubborn and obstinate man you could ever meet. If it was a job he didn't want to do or thought should be done differently, he would dig his heels in and his John Deere 6600 wouldn't move him though he would eventually come round, and by the time he had finished it, it had been his idea all along.

At times also, his attention to detail and striving for perfection could drive you to distraction if you were wanting to get on – spirit levels and that final bit of tamping of some concrete that he felt was only 99% - even when the next load was waiting. Nor did he think tourists had as much right on the road as a farmer going about his work leading corn.

It is many of the small jobs that many of us will miss him for, be it on the farm, at home, at Hackforth or even this Church. Many who come to this Church at Christmas time or a wedding will not realise that it was Malcolm who put up the circle of candles or flowers just above us, or that for years it was he and I who cleaned out the gutters each autumn. He was a man, dedicated to his work and the countryside, happy in what he was doing and never wishing to chase after greater things. He would sometimes come to work on a cold, wet, horrible day in November or February – ask if there was anything special to do, and then say "well, I might as well have a day's holiday then" and off he went – and he would spend it – at an auction mart, or just part of the day, sat in his car in Bedale, with a Cockburn's pork pie for his lunch, just watching the world go by.

Malcolm was not into a lot of modern technology, he enjoyed the CB in his tractor because it kept him up to date with the locality, and like me he only mastered the basics of a mobile phone – but how I shall miss that never changing response if I rang him from the other end of the country, or the field next door – just a simple "hello" he never did use two word if one would do.

I wrote in my diary on the 12/01/1986 – saw Malcolm Percival about coming to work for us – "Shan't bother to see anybody else - he'll do for me" – and he certainly has.

Malcom - we are all here today for many reasons the one main thing that draws us all together is in paying tribute to your life.

We have all been the richer for your knowing, and we are the poorer for your going.

AMEN

With the loss of Malcolm, we had to quickly re-think our farming practises, and whilst taking our time to get it right, the immediate problem was spraying which Malcolm had done for years and was the only person with the correct paperwork to be able to do so and we asked James Wilson from Hutton Hang to step into the breach which he did and continued to do so very effectively for us for the next ten years – he was a perfectionist in his work with the sprayer and working very closely with Andrew Fisher, our agronomist, he kept right up to the minute in both sprays, technologies and legislation and got to know the fields very well, and latterly, they almost cut me out of the loop – not that it really bothered me.

One Saturday we went out for the day and ended up at Pateley Bridge for a bite of lunch before deciding to go for a walk along the River Nidd to Glasshouses. It was a lovely day when we left but suddenly the heavens opened, and we got absolutely soaked before we got shelter.

A few days later I judged the cattle at Penrith Show – a good turnout for the first real show in that area since the autumn of 2000, as nothing was held in that region in 2001.

In early September we left on the Genus trip to Italy which I had won earlier in the summer. The flight was at some ungodly hour from Stansted so we went the night before and stayed at Harlow – didn't sleep as we had to get-up about 3 o'clock for a very early flight to an ex-Italian air force base now used by the lo-cost airlines but eventually arrived in Cremona, where we had a very enjoyable three or four days touring round all sorts of farms – very interesting and also to the Cremona Show which was a big event. We went into town one evening but didn't find our way back, couldn't see a taxi, so asked a policeman. He was very concerned for us as tourists and said, "jump in" and the two of them took us back to the Hermes hotel. On one farm just as we were getting onto the mini-bus, I spied a pomegranate bush in the farmyard and after asking was able to pick one just to say I had done so. I always thought the feathery bit on the top was where it attached to the tree, but that is the other end of the fruit that was originally the flower. Pomegranates always bring back childhood memories when we would occasionally be allowed one between us and had to eat the individual seeds with a pin as mother said the bits of tissue within the fruit were very bad for you and would make us poorly – I think that was an old wives tale. We stayed at Harlow overnight on our return and then on the next day called at Thaxted a lovely and very old Suffolk town.

Into that autumn and I had been to a Holstein Club meeting at night, but still had the cows to check outside before going to bed, and that proved to be some way off. I saw immediately that the automatic scrapers had tripped off and re-set them once or twice, but they immediately tripped again, so I had to go and investigate. I found the problem right at the far end of the shed where they went under the doors, only to find Lettice 59 wedged halfway under and unable to move and totally surrounded by what the slurry scrapers had brought the length of the building. With the door to open and scrapers to press at the same time, I had to get Marnie to help me and we soon got her scraped outside so the doors could be closed again. Having just calved a day or two earlier she was down with milk fever and so was unable to get up, so we had to get the JCB and pull her round into the silage pit until morning and then give her a couple of bottles of calcium. By then it was well after midnight and we still had to get ourselves cleaned up and dried off before we could go to bed. A happy ending – she was up by next morning and stood at the door ready to be milked and forever afterwards was renamed "the slurry sniffer".

With the sad loss of Malcolm, we were short of someone to do odd bits of routine jobs and so advertised for a part-timer and took on Richard Herron from Sinderby who was shaping up to be quite promising when after a couple of months he had to give up as his wife had quite serious health problems and he needed to look after her and their children. Later that autumn, Chris Knox who was farming and still is at East Farm, Patrick Brompton came to help us two or three days a week and continued to do so right up to the time of the dispersal some ten years later. Chris was very useful being so close and reasonably flexible as we were with him and could come extra days if required and we could manage odd days without him if he had something else on. He usually came Monday's and Friday's which were the main cleaning out and bedding up days for the dry and calving cows and all the young stock. Mind you, he didn't get off to the best of starts when after only a fortnight he caught a car in Newton-le-Willows with the bucket of the JCB on his way to Dalesend. Fortunately, it was Ruth's (whom we knew quite well and worked at the dairy) sister and so it was easier to deal with and quickly get seen to under insurance.

In half term we went to Norway for a few days, I remember having fresh crab and prawns for supper one night and getting back from Norway in the dark on a Sunday evening to find our car with a flat battery, and it took a while to get someone at that sort of time to jump us off, after which we were ok as it was the side-lights I had left on, but came at an exorbitant price.

In early January 2003 we had a special classification visit, still trying to catch up on cows that got missed because of Foot and Mouth and their calving times – we had a good day with three rescored Excellent, ten new Excellents and eleven new Very Goods, a couple of days later had a visit from Tim Davies of Kite about possibly using them, before deciding it was too expensive and then a week later had a free DEFRA consultation because of Foot and Mouth and a first meeting with Greg Ricketts of Andersons who I had various dealings with over the next ten or twelve years, some constructive and others of various types. To bolster our milking numbers we went to the Lancaster Club Sale in January and bought Bilsrowan Convincer Star for 1080gns and Dunnerdale Spirit Kate for 1020gns, neither of whom owed us anything by the time they had left the herd some years later, and the day after Mr J had his second replacement hip operation, and I also have a note about that time that one night Adam had shot 27 rabbits and 5 hares around the farm.

We had, since Richard had joined us as herdsman been considering going into complete diet feeding. Richard felt that to increase yields we needed to go down that road. Though I was far from convinced, we had costed out, and got clearance with Mr J to alter buildings and purchase a tractor and Keenan for the system and raised it again, when Richard said he couldn't see the point of spending £50,000 plus to take an hour longer to feed the cows every day, and so we continued as we were, though we did tweak things somewhat. Though still feeding up the central feed passage filled with the JCB bucket from one end, we began to block cut maize and grass silage, brewers grains and sugar beet pulp nuts and turn them over to mix before feeding and that seemed to do the job. Quite a lot of visitors over the years said they wished they had stayed with a simple system rather than spend a lot of money on machinery that was quite costly to run and ultimately was to replace (sod's law that was always at the same time as the milk price headed south). Interestingly enough a year or two later we went to a specially invited group by BOCM Pauls to a meeting where the main speaker was Alex Bach from Spain. During the day Keith had been round each of the participating farms to gather a bucketful sample as fed that day, they were placed round the room and the speaker inspected them all for quality of mix and declared ours the winner – the only one not fed with a mixer wagon!!

In early February, again because we had been a Foot and Mouth victim, we had a free Environmental Assessment which was done for us by Karen Stanley of FWAG, whom we had used before on one or two farm woodland planting schemes. Part of the assessment was on muck and slurry and our capacity to store it. For this Karen got the measurement of the slurry pit and enquired as to how deep it was. My answer was that if she fell in I wouldn't go into rescue her as it was too deep – so she assumed it was large enough to store 'X' weeks of slurry, which, if it was wet it certainly wasn't.

In mid-February we sadly had to go to Dennis Lamb's funeral. Dennis had followed his father Jimmy in farming at Carnaby Farm at Patrick Brompton which adjoined Old Park House when we farmed it and was also a member of the Buying Group and had always been a very good neighbour. Unfortunately, there was no one to follow on, as Dennis and Barbara had five daughters. Dennis was quite a character, though couldn't swear like Jimmy who was an even more unorthodox type.

That was half term and after such a long time with Sarah and Adam at school over nearly twenty years of observing school holidays, we had to continue doing so now that Marnie was working at Mowbray. We went down to Devon and stayed at Plymouth and walked out onto the Hoe where all those years previously (about 425) Sir Francis Drake had played bowls. We visited Launceston with its small round castle and had a good walk round Tintagel and its fantastic cliffs and scenery. We visited the Eden Project but were disappointed that the tropical biome was closed for annual maintenance, before coming back over Dartmoor and Exmoor on our way home.

In early March of that year we planted the Jubilee plantation at the far end of Jasper and Road End fields at Hill Top East. So called because it was the Golden Jubilee year of the Queen's Coronation, it was an area that was always damp and could flood badly after heavy rain, it was done under the Farm Woodland Grant Scheme and generated some income for the next 15 years or so. Marnie brought a group from Mowbray to plant and put their names on some.

The end of March it felt like the phoenix had risen from the ashes. Pansy 132 became the first heifer of our own to calve since the calves and young stock were slaughtered in 2001 as a Foot and Mouth contiguous cull. She was born after that and so calved at just on two years old – not very common in those days though now the expected calving age.

A day later I was lucky enough to go to Dublin with Dick and George and saw one of the greatest England dominations of a rugby match under Johnny Wilkinson's guidance when they took Ireland apart to win 42-6 on their way to even greater achievements later in the year. That night we had our first and, in my case, only visit to a lap-dancing club in the heart of Dublin – it was something of an education to watch the very attractive young lady's gyration around a pole. Dick said we must have the same story for our wives which George and I just laughed at as we had only been observers rather than participants and our wives were unlikely to be worried about it, not that Dick was anything other than one also.

March had also seen Sarah buy a cottage in Newsham just off the A66 – it suited her well, situated very much in the heart of the area she covered for Semex, and sometime was spent that month decorating and helping to get her moved in. It was also the month of Uncle Cecil Thompson's (of Spennithorne and latterly Patrick Brompton) 90th birthday party at Solberge Hall where we had a super lunch do. Marnie had gone to do his lunch for him one day a week sometimes after Auntie Betty died and then after he went into the Millings in Bedale she had visited him on a regular basis on her way home from school. The day after that I was over to Cockermouth to judge the inaugural pedigree black and white sale. They tried for a year or two to get it established but it never really took off, and so far as I know is no longer held.

Before turn out that spring we put a fence up the side of the Plantation field and along Newton Pasture and the West fields, so that we could move heifers more easily from their new home at Newton Grange to either Hill Top East or Dalesend, wherever we wanted them grazing, and some years later we built proper holding and handling pens in the corners of Corner Bank and Road In at Hill Top and the Reeds and L. Drive fields at Dalesend to go along with the existing one in the Park. Over the years the races and pens made stock movement and management much easier as the number of times heifers were to get in over the summer for worming and fly treatment in addition to IBR, BVD injections etc. seemed to become more frequent. About that same time, it became a requirement for operatives to have training to handle a telescopic handler and so we put Richard, Chris and Adam through the two-day course at £208/head. It was a short two days as the instructor forgot to come until lunchtime on the first day and was finished soon after lunch on the second day, which was just as well as we were hosting the N.E. Club Linear Judging Competition that night. I didn't need to take the handling course at that time as I was an old codger and had 'grandfather' rights – they ceased long ago but I never did the training.

We had a visit from the Devon Holstein Club in early May, and gave them lunch in the garden before they went on to visit Tim Gibson's at Crakehall (one of the pioneers of robotic milking – Mr Lely and a long time contributor to Dairy Farmers "cowmen comment" pages.). Then at night over to the Feather's at Helmsley to have dinner with them before going the next afternoon down to Newark to attend the Newark and Nottinghamshire Show Dinner, before judging the black and whites the next day. In between time Jim Westaway, who many will remember in earlier days as manager of the Wiseburrow herd down in Somerset before becoming a classifier for the society, came to install and instruct Richard on the I-Stop computer programme for herd management, which worked very successfully for the next eight or nine years.

That summer, as our young stock numbers were getting back to capacity and we needed more accommodation for the larger heifers, we took another two bays of the shed put up two years previously and put in cubicles for about forty in-calf/bulling heifers. As was our thinking with the original shed, everything was done so that it could be, if required at a later date a level, open space, the yokes and the cubicles were all movable and removable, and the feed passage and cubicles were split in half, and bedding in the cubicles was on chopped straw as were the cows.

Early June saw me spend two or three days down in Norfolk judging their Milk Records Herds Competition and it was interesting to visit different systems and breeds of cattle. This was between the Suffolk and Norfolk County Shows in by then a non-dairying area, but I was amazed at the interest and keenness to support their local county shows and the discussions about what I may have seen that could be going to the show. It is even more of a desert area for dairy farmers now, with only a few large herds remaining and I think both shows now probably struggle to maintain their numbers. Just after that we went to the Holstein Genetic Elite Sale which that year was held at Lancaster and we purchased a Scant heifer from Cogent to give us a family with some "numbers", and while the numbers never really materialised to be leading edge, it did develop a good family for us, one or two members sold well at our sale and have gone on to do very well in their new homes.

A very busy summer and among it, we took Adam over to Newton Rigg one Saturday to have a look round with a view to possibly going there to do a degree in game management a year later. This was followed by a day or two over in Northern Ireland for the Holstein Convention, where among other herds we visited was the "Inch" herd of Jim Morrison who the previous year had won the Pedigree Premier herd, and what a herd it was, even if only relatively small – I don't think up to that time I had been in a herd of such uniform consistency.

A few days later the first commercial train ran on the Wensleydale railway after it had been virtually closed for some time. The Wensleydale Railway Association have continued to run the line, but it is a struggle for them to keep going and without people digging deep into their pockets I think it would long ago have ceased as a commercial proposition – it was always only ever going to be a scenic ride rather than be used regularly as they tried to suggest for people to come down the dale to shop in Northallerton and join the main railway service. Their dream of re-opening the line westward to join the Settle-Carlisle railway was never anything more than "pie in the sky" thinking. From our personal point of view, we would have preferred to see it closed, as it was nothing but a nuisance in crossing our farm drive.

Work was continuing within the cattle building as we got back to full numbers, we re-laid one bit of bad passageway for the cows, had the concrete grooved at the bottom of the collecting yard and did some in the barn where the heifers were finding it a bit slippy. In addition we put up some girders and fitted concrete panels around the outside part of the silage pit which had been earth banked, and then we filled in behind them with soil to level it up and make it wide enough to store the tyres on to make sheeting up easier. We also took out an extra wall in the AI pen which had been a passage through into the cow cubicles to make it rather larger and more useful. One afternoon's time was spent recovering the lawn mower from the park at Dalesend which had got away from whoever was mowing the lawn and had shot over the hedge and into the ha-ha. We got it lifted out and back onto the lawn with the telescopic arm on the JCB.

The Great Yorkshire Show that year Sarah looked after, prepared and showed a cow for Metcalfe Farms from Leyburn to be Reserve Champion, Pansy 135 as an in calf heifer was in the winning inter-breed group and Adam was third in the showmanship, just before he started working for Mr Elwood at the Akebar Park for the summer. Soon we were into harvest and though yields were fairly good, the price wasn't, with barley at £65 a tonne – not a lot of profit in it at that, and prices have been very up and down in the years since then.

In amongst harvest I managed to get a day away for the judging school which that year was at Calcourt Farms down in Wales, and had previously talked with and organised with Mr Jones for Adam to go down with me and spend a day with him round the Long Mountain Shoot which included land around Lake Vyrnwy, and then shortly afterwards Adam got the first pheasants in for the Dalesend shoot – the first time they had ever done so, and he had made a release pen down in the Low Wood.

That August when I was down at Scotsbridge House for meetings, Marnie went down with me and went by train into London to see Emma. We stayed a night either side in Milton Keynes – what a soulless place, then made our way back cross country to Stamford in Lincolnshire for lunch and across the Humber Bridge – what views. The All-Breeds North Eastern Calf Show was held at the end of the month at the old Auction Mart at Thirsk, which is now all houses, with Paul Harrison as the master judge, Adam was Champion Handler much to many's surprise but Paul said in his reasons he didn't have the best or easiest calf to handle but had stuck to his job and never got flustered. That same day we had a novelty 'oldies' handling competition which some took very seriously and didn't take very kindly to me being the designated fool that day to cause mayhem in the ring in a wrongly buttoned white coat, wellies with one trouser leg in and one out, and leading the calf like a dog, but it was all good fun. That was I think the first All-Breeds Show and I note there were 89 calves– quite a turnout, and that was before the Yorkshire Holstein Club also joined in.

We took on a young man called Mark to milk on every other weekend afternoons – he was from Teeside, had no real milking experience, but just wanted to be involved with farming. He was ok for a while until the travelling got too much for him, but he turned up again some time later as a driver for Warren's when they came to collect a dead calf or a casualty of some kind.

It was also party time, Mary and Eric celebrated their Ruby Wedding at Studley Royal Cricket Ground, we had all the family from Norway over to stay, and had eleven in total for supper one night before all the youngsters went off to party at Amadeus, that famous Northallerton night club after the three younger Norwegians had been at Leeds to see a football match in the afternoon, and then the day after we all went to Kathryn and Peter's Silver Wedding party at Elmfield.

Shortly afterwards we hosted the Patrick Brompton church evening Harvest Festival in the young stock building which was very successful with 80 people attending compared to 28 at church the previous year. It was a great night, with a silver band providing the music, some calves in pens, and others bringing hens and sheep and Percival's who did all our contracting work putting all their machinery with corn drill etc. in one of the pens. It was quite magical, during the sermon or other parts of the service to see a small child get up and go and stroke a calf or a lamb. It was all rounded off by the church ladies providing soup and apple pie for supper. Typically it was soon suggested that we should repeat it the following year but I refused, saying that if we did it every year it would loose impact and other places or businesses could do their own thing – harvest doesn't just mean farming, but no one took up the baton and it went back to church for a year or two before we hosted it again on a terrible night of torrential rain, but still attracted a massive congregation of well over a hundred people.

At the end of October after a busy autumn and before the onset of the winter routine, we had a weekend way in Northumberland, a marvellous county of open roads and great views, but yet plenty of places of interest. We stayed at Bellingham on the advice of Sheila Eggleston who runs Eggs-Port Ltd, a company with whom we have done several amounts of business and from whom we got the previously mentioned fly tapes for the parlour. We visited places such as Hexham, Otterburn, Alnwick and the Castle Gardens, the views from Carter Bar at the border with Scotland and a good exploration of Kielder both the forest and the reservoir.

Sarah had been away for some time to visit both Canada and then on to World Dairy Expo at Madison – expenses paid for having the most improved sales performance of the year for Semex.

As winter began to close in, we finally got heifers into the new cubicles in the big barn at the end of October, and it didn't take them long to settle in onto their diet of straw and nuts – very simple, but cost effective and it was easy to roll a big bale right up the front of the feed barriers and feed nuts on top of the straw. That was if you thought to shut the locking yolks to stop heifers putting their heads through which made rolling the bale hard work. We also bought another wooden cake bin to store the nuts in right next to the feeding alley which made it much easier than having to bring them round from the other bin.

Adam by now was in the Upper Sixth at school in his final year before A-levels and as part of his engineering course they visited an aluminium extrusion plant at Newcastle and whilst there they got to do some hands on work and he made a small model of the Tyne Bridge. He had by this time also passed his driving test as previously mentioned but it wasn't long before he had his first bump, and quite a nasty one at that. Marnie had not long before got a fresh car, a nice red Fiesta, and Adam went out one night just after tea and it wasn't long before we were down at the scene where the back road from Newton-le-Willows joins the main Leyburn/Bedale road. The road joins at something of an angle and has never been good to see back to Leyburn, but he had either missed seeing or mis-calculated a car which hit him amidships and shunted him into the opposite verge. Fortunately, nobody was injured, other than Adam's pride, or the written off Fiesta.

That autumn was also a very busy one, rugby wise. Apart from the regular matches up at Newcastle, the World Cup was being held in Australia and after watching many of the matches on television, Saturday morning 22nd November 2003 was no exception, except that England were in the final. Everyone knows of the excitement and closeness of that match, culminating in Johnny Wilkinson dropping a goal for victory. Marnie wasn't too keen on going to help, though she had promised to do so, at the church Christmas Fayre, but managed to keep the radio on to keep up to date with the game, but was frowned upon when she let out a great shout as that drop-kick sailed over the bar – nobody else in Patrick Brompton School Room was the least bit concerned or interested. Only a week later we had been given complimentary tickets for lunch in one of the hospitality suites at Kingston Park for the Falcons v Wasps match. At the time of them being booked no one had any idea that England would have won the World Cup let alone that it would be paraded for the first time after being won and that would be at Newcastle where it was carried out and onto the pitch by Johnny Wilkinson and Lawrence Dallaglio the England and Wasps captain. Quite a special occasion and special to be a small part of it.

I took delivery of a new Peugeot 306 car in dark blue on the 1st December and it was soon in use that day as I had to go to York to represent the Society at the funeral of Frank Abbey a long time Board Member and former President.

Just a day or two later we had an eventful evening when Queen 6 put her calf bed out with the second calf in it as she had twins. The vet was called and whilst we were waiting, we did one or two bits of jobs in the middle of the night, and eventually got the job done, though it was to no avail, though things were ok, and both calves were alive, they were a bull and a heifer which meant the likelihood as a freemartin was that the heifer wouldn't breed.

Adam had his first ever shoot at the Grange since he had taken over from Mr Bill and had put some birds down – he was like a dog with two tails!! About the same time, went up to Chris Iveson's draft sale from his Myersgarth herd at Wensley and though trade wasn't hot for cattle, the quota auction at the conclusion was absolutely mad so we didn't buy any.

We had the farm staff luncheon for Christmas at the Wyvill Arms that year – very good it was too and talking of Christmas I got pulled into the digital age when Marnie got me a mobile phone and hand's free kit for the car. Having said that I haven't moved on very far from the basics some fifteen years later. Marnie had an important day just before they broke up for the holidays when the famous local artist, he of the square sheep, McKenzie Thorpe came to open the new art room at Mowbray school.

Auntie Gladys Lofthouse, mother's youngest sister sadly passed away and we went to her funeral at York between Christmas and New Year. We had always swopped holidays with David, Eleanor and Jimmy coming up to Middlesmoor and us going to Strensall when we were younger and the taste of the goat's milk at Strensall still lingers in the memory.

That brought the curtain down on what had been a very busy and eventful year, and weather wise it had been one of the driest on record – having for us less than 20 inches in the year, compared to our rolling average of 27/28 inches. Despite that it had obviously fallen at the right times, as the barley averaged over three tonnes to the acre and the wheat had just made four tonnes.

One of the winter jobs that year was taking up the fencing along the main water pipeline that runs from Thorton Stewart reservoir down to Northallerton, where they had been putting in a new pipe to augment the existing one. It paid well in compensation as all those sorts of schemes do and it ran across our land from Newton Pasture, below Fox Park up and over behind the Grange and into Neville Dyson's on its way to Crakehall. As they were finishing I enquired as to what they did with all the fencing and they said they would just bulldoze it into a heap, crush it and bury it, posts, gates and the lot – no wonder water comes more expensive than it needs to. I agreed with them we would take it all up for having the barbed wire, sheep netting, posts and galvanised 12 foot double gates for about half a mile of double fencing, through four or five hedge-lines – a useful value which lasted us a long time and some of the wire netting we still had and sold at our sale some eight years later.

It was a busy start to the new year, Adam bought his first shotgun, the first of many and he now has quite an arsenal of high-powered rifles of all kinds with fancy night scopes, imaging etc. They are all properly licensed, accounted for and legally kept in a secure cabinet, it seems to be a common part of being a gamekeeper to have more guns than any one man can use. Talking of guns, it was only a month or so after this that we attended the funeral of a lady from Newton-le-Willows, Margaret Tindall who was a regular at St. Patricks at Patrick Brompton, who helped with afternoon teas when they did them, and was a great supporter of the Church. A very small and on the face of it a rather shy and timid lady, but it wasn't until the eulogy at her funeral that we discovered she had spent sometime in the police service in Kenya at the time of the Mau Mau uprisings. She had carried a gun, slept with it under her pillow and apparently wouldn't have been afraid to use it. A less likely gun-toting lady policewoman one couldn't imagine!!

Back to Adam and he had of course had his 18th birthday on the last day of 2003, and not wanting to cramp people's styles on that particular night, we had a family meal out a few nights later – another surprising choice – Tandoori Nights at Richmond, but a good time was had by all, and somewhere most of us would not otherwise have thought of visiting.

Marnie had a few hectic days around the same time as Mowbray school had an Ofsted inspection, but it was soon over with and all was very good, and then a few days later the school took part in a special service at Ripon Cathedral.

While this was going on, I was fairly well occupied with Holstein business and speaking engagements as well. Down to Telford for two days of meetings firstly at a HUK Board meeting and then attending the dairy day of the Cattle Breeder's

Conference. We had a classification visit from Peter Gray on the Friday of that week, followed by the North Eastern Club awards dinner at night, and then straight after the weekend I was at a Border Counties Breeders Club to sit on a panel with representatives from First Milk, NMR and a Kite Consultant. We got off to a good start and then midway through someone asked a question on labour in dairying. The lady consultant said that it was no problem, all you had to do was pay 10p/hour more than Tesco for stacking shelves and you would have as many milkers as you could ever want. When I as the farmer member of the panel asked about milkers such as that knowing what to do if a cow had E-coli mastitis or was badly off colour at that milking – she didn't help her cause by asking me what 'E-coli' was and the audience started to laugh. That was her finished for the night and she never spoke again.

We had to go to another funeral at the end of the month – "Wacker" and Mrs Williams who lived at Lynas Terrace as you went towards the village. I have already mentioned "Wacker" previously as one of the men I gave a wave to as I went past when Dick Agass was with me and he couldn't comprehend as a Londoner that you gave people a wave in passing. I also previously mentioned him when Adam was little and asked why everyone called him "Wacker" – he had a reputation from earlier days of being a bit of a fighter, and for a while Adam asked me the same question, every time we saw him – just because he liked the story. The first time I met Mrs Williams was about the second day I was at Dalesend as a student. She was a friend of Mrs Suggitt's on the corner where I called for some cigarettes and her dog – the biggest, roughest looking Alsatian I had ever seen came bounding up to me and started barking at me - they are still not my favourite dog and I still tend to give them a wide berth.

Adam went to his first Keeper's shoot at the end of the season for the Arbour Hill shoot and then to the dinner at the Queens Head at Finghall. Same night we went to the cinema at York to see "Lost in Translation" the film which launched Keira Knightley and we called for our supper at Hopperton.

That somewhat brought an end to a degree of gallivanting about for a while, as we suddenly hit something of a labour shortage situation.

Chapter 20 – Many other Changes – including a new use for Dalesend.

At the beginning of February Richard had to go into hospital for a hernia operation – he had been nursing it for a while and awaiting his turn to go under the knife, but it meant a lot of filling in and more milking for me. The same day Chris rung to say he couldn't come to work that morning – he had spent the weekend in hospital having his heart checked – it was ok but he hadn't to lift his arms above his waist and he had damaged tendons and was on cortisone. Two days later Mark rung to say he wouldn't be able to come and milk anymore at weekends as he had changed jobs and would be working most weekends. All of a sudden, we had a lot of stock work and only me plus the family to do it.

I did very quickly manage to get Alastair Wilkin from Danby Wiske to come and do some milkings for us, when he wasn't tied up with other people for whom he worked various part-time jobs. We will come across Alastair a bit later in the book when Sarah rents a bungalow from him. I had known him from when he was judging as a young farmer competitor and knew a good cow when he saw it, but was also a very knowledgeable young man who has since appeared on quiz shows on television, having competed on both Countdown and The Chase. Only last week at the Arden Arms at Atley Hill with their Christmas programme of events he was billed as their "resident quizmaster". It was a very cold spell of weather that February, the parlour was frozen up once or twice and he made me laugh one morning when I went to check everything was ok – he had a big bucket of hot water in the pit and he kept dipping his hands into it to keep them warm.

We managed to get by with the help of Alastair and Chris got back to short half days after about a fortnight and a week into March after five weeks Richard got back to sort of half work and after another two or three weeks was back to full time which was a great relief to me.

Other things were still going on through February, we had a visit from a lady VAT inspector, but all was in order and she wasn't here too long – a shorter time than the previous inspection when we also had the Dalesend Dairy as part of the farm in its early days and was more complicated – though I had taken great delight in selling her a pack of bottled water.

I don't like particularly paying reference to various funerals but they unfortunately keep cropping up and I mention them when they are local people that others will remember, and at that time I went to Harold Terry's funeral at Scruton. Harold had for many years been the rabbit and mole catcher in the area through the Hackforth and District Rabbit Clearance Society, and was a familiar sight in the area if you passed someone ploughing, he was often a few steps behind in among and fighting the seagulls for the worms for his mole-catching.

We had to get a new cooker about that time, Marnie went to Newton Aycliffe to see about it and again so you can put prices into perspective it cost £300 – comes expensive when the old one had only lasted us for 32 years – about £10 a year!!

Early in April Marnie and her superior Linda brought a group from Mowbray to see cows being milked and what happened to the milk as it went to the tank. They were doing a food course within Home Economics and went from us up to the Wensleydale Creamery at Hawes to see the cheese being made.

I spoke to Ainderby WI in early March and then down to Scotsbridge House for a

NED's meeting to learn that and discuss the way forward as the potential tie up of CIS and NMR had broken down, and this was then followed by a CIS Board Meeting. Just after that we had cattle at Carlisle for a club sale, won a class with Dalesend Unique 46 but were not prepared to take just 900gns for such a good uddered heifer and brought her home and she went on to become an EX90 cow. This was the very early days of the Border Counties Spring Bull Sale – we had a very good bull in it Dalesend Reputation who was out of Dalesend Charlie Rosina by STBVQ Rubens PI ET – a very smart, correct bull which sold well at 1700gns to Mr Roberts from Shropshire, who went on and did a good job for him. The week after it was back down to Scotsbridge House for a Holstein Board Meeting at which I resigned as the non-executive director for CIS. Two of our Board members were also Board members of NMR, our main competitor and it seemed to me totally un-business like to discuss CIS business and accounts with them present and I asked for them to leave the meeting. The matter was put to a vote and the other members thought it quite alright, leaving me with little alternative but to do the honourable thing, though several members told me afterwards I was a silly old Yorkshireman for having such high principals!!

After all that busy three months at the start of the year, we were ready for a break, and while Adam and Sarah went off to Somerset for the HYB weekend, we went off to Portugal for a long weekend. We flew from Heathrow to Porto for the trip and had a very relaxing time but also have some still very vivid memories of the city, which is almost divided into two halves by the Douro river, with wealth on one side and poverty on the northern slopes. We visited the railway station to see the renowned tile murals on the walls, as we walked on the Sunday morning in the poorer side of the city it was obviously wash day as the smell from the drainage channels only covered by stone flags was of 'Lenor' and whenever we smell that anywhere now, we chorus 'Portugal'. Parts of it were a real shanty town like pigeon lofts on the side of the cliff which you saw from the river as we took a cruise up and down the river, (that was after seeing the dead pony floating in the river as we crossed the gangplank). We ate some very good, typical Portuguese food, mostly fish based, sole and salmon, Fruits of the Sea risotto and Marnie particularly enjoyed their sardines and also their little "custard like" tarts. We had a fascinating tour of the Taylors port wine lodge and saw all the other famous 'port' names on the south and hence wealthy side of the river, found a very cheap but very good wine in a little backstreet shop and I bought a belt at another little leather workers shop.

A fortnight later we drove down to Twickenham, Adam and Jenny went with us to see the Falcons win the Powergen cup 37-33 against Sale in a terrific match which saw the lead change hands nine times.

The 22nd April 2004 saw the first action in the conversion of the young stock buildings at Dalesend into a light industrial/business park from its original use as the rearing unit for the farm, after Foot and Mouth three years earlier and the subsequent erection of a new building up at home. There is no great desire now to alter the Dalesend Business Park to housing as it has generated a very useful income for years now, though there was a lot of hard work and problems on the way to converting it and filling the units, all 29 of them, and it now generates a considerable income per year. The farm sold it into the Wensleydale Property Company after several years as our accountants were concerned that it might compromise our status as farmers for Agricultural relief. At that original date, what we did was lay a new concrete floor in the old byre so that it was at least level, and it did in fact after more adaptation become the home of our first tenant HGM Services belonging to Stephen Howitt who is still there with his very successful property maintenance business. From the inception we had worked with George F White as our letting agents and in those first few years Dianne Atkinson worked tirelessly to find the tenants and get the scheme off the ground before she left to become the Headmasters secretary at Thirsk School.

Courtesy of George White's we enjoyed a very welcome afternoon of racing at Hexham. A glorious, sunny afternoon despite a cold wind, with very enjoyable hospitality. You don't normally think of going uphill to a racecourse, but you certainly do at Hexham, right up out of the town onto the hilltops, but the view of virtually the whole course from the hilltop is superb. On the Sunday pm we went to rugby, which was the only spoiler as the Falcons lost 16-15 when they should really have won. All this was fitted in around milking and other jobs as it was my weekend on, though Sarah helped by milking both afternoons.

A week later the Falcons were playing at Rotherham Titans, who were at that time in the premiership. Not knowing exactly where the ground was, we went in good time and planned to get a bite of lunch somewhere near before the game. We didn't see anywhere we liked the look of and eventually had to make do with a burger at a Wimpy bar. What was amazing was that you would have thought the Pied Piper had been out as the locals were homing in on the place for their Sunday lunches. It looked as if it was a regular occurrence, all these "grey" people descending in their droves for lunch.

At the end of May, Adam finished school when they broke up prior to taking 'A' Levels and that Friday evening he was to take up to Grinton where they were all having a "field party" by the River Swale. No doubt they had a great night camping out – we left them to it and on the Saturday went up to Durham University to look round the Oriental Museum, had a bite of lunch in Sedgefield and then finished up in Stockton for our supper at Chinese Charlie's (one of our tenants of the Wensleydale Property Company).

A week later Marnie and Sarah went to the opening of Archer's Ice Cream near Darlington. They milked Jersey cattle and to diversify making more use of the richness of their cream, they began in a small way making ice cream and this business has grown and they now have a well-attended on-farm ice cream parlour and a very successful one at The Station in Richmond at which we sometimes treat ourselves when viewing the Stations art exhibitions. They have a good selection of flavours and we certainly rate it the best of the artisan ice cream makers in the northern area which boasts quite a number. Many dairy farmers may well have sampled it as they have provided the blue and white ice cream on the Barclays Bank stand at the Dairy Event. The name Archer will crop up again later as Sarah was involved working with John on the promotion and marketing of veal.

Adam was planning to take a year out after his exams, and had pretty well got fixed up to go to a large estate in mid-Wales for six months, but this fell through and he was left with nowhere to go with only about three months to the start of the shooting season. We put an advert in the back of the Shooting Times and he was inundated with phone calls from all over the UK and Ireland from the north of Scotland to the tip of Cornwall, Norfolk and the west coast of Ireland. He looked at one or two relatively local ones, but thought none of them suitable, so one Saturday in mid-June he got fixed up with three estates rather further afield and we set off to take him to see them. First stop was Lord Daventry's just outside Nuneaton, then just into Wales over the Gloucestershire border and then back across the Severn Bridge and down to the edge of Exmoor before calling at Darrington near Ferrybridge for supper on the way home. Just a short run out – 680 miles in total that day. As we came back, I asked Adam which one he would choose if all three of them offered him a job. "I think that old boy at Nuneaton might just have a bit more time to teach me things" was Adam's reply and so he finished up at Lord Daventry's just some two weeks later.

The reason for the opening at Nuneaton was that Owen the gamekeeper of many years had retired two or three years previously and they had replaced him with another keeper who had not done a good job and they had got rid of him before appointing a new one who had simply failed to turn up to start the job. Most jobs in the gamekeeping world are changed during the close season and particularly from early February to the end of April/mid-May before poults arrive for rearing and so Owen had agreed to come out of his retirement for a year providing they got him some young legs to do the running about for him – hence their jump at the advert in the Shooting Times. It was a great experience for Adam as it was a traditional family estate farming about 2000 acres managed by one of the national estate agencies with a resident agent "Hugo", the farm work all done by one of the national contractor agencies, but then there were estate maintenance workers, nannies, butlers etc. and so there was a learning curve of how all these different hierarchies knitted in together. We took a load of things down with Adam on the Wednesday for him to start work the following day the 1st July. Marnie and he went in his old red car and I followed with our car and trailer and some hastily gathered together furniture and we got him moved into his palatial three bedroomed house within the estate, with his resident guard dog – a big but lovely Alsation by the name of Billy, whom Adam got very attached to and was sad to have to leave at the end of his spell there.

He had only been there a short while and one Saturday afternoon he was up at Owen's bungalow when the Dowager Lady Daventry called with a bowl of strawberries for their tea. She talked away to Adam finding out about him for quite a while before suddenly saying "it's all very well young man, pleasant as it maybe to talk with you, but I have two horses running tonight at Towcester – must dash." Just before Christmas Adam was in his house for lunch one day when there was a knock on the door, and it was the good Lady with his Christmas present – two old style handkerchiefs in red and blue in a brown paper bag – wished him all the best and left with the retort "I don't do wrapping". Adam certainly did learn a lot in the short time he was there, particularly the problem of game management on the urban fringe, the estate woodlands criss-crossed by public footpaths and literally only a few hundred yards from the centre of Nuneaton. We went down to see him odd weekends and one night I called on the way back up from a Holstein UK meeting at Scotsbridge House. It wasn't much of a detour off the M1 and took him out for his supper. Just as we were finishing our steaks, he got a phone call and we had to go, I dropped him off and he would ring me later on the way home. The problem was that Owen had gone round to check some of the birds and found quite a few that had been beheaded and left to die, with the heads chopped off with the electric fence posts that were round the release pen to keep foxes or other predators away. A day or two later when he and Owen were doing something, they found discarded needles and syringes around the area – obviously someone on a high who had caused such suffering to innocent pheasants.

At a similar time, we were short of Chris Knox for a few work days after he squashed a finger between two girders as we were doing the walls up the side of the old silage pit and he finished up in casualty with an overnight stay, but no long term damage was done.

Again, it was Royal Show time and we were chuffed when Dalesend Storm Maude won the Holstein Championship and went on to be Interbreed Champion and lift the Burke trophy for breed pairs. Not a lot our doing, but she does carry our prefix.

The week after that we finally bit the bullet and got a proper new fence put up the side of the drive in the front field. The old fence had been there for longer than I had and had been patched up and new bits added over the years, and, if you were expecting visitors to come to look at and hopefully buy cattle, it wasn't the most welcoming or encouraging sight. We used Len Porter to do the fencing, the first time we had ever used an outside contractor for such a job, but we simply hadn't the time or staff and the materials tend to be no more expensive because of the volumes they buy in. They made a super job of the fence including new double gates in from over the railway, until a week or so later Doug from the bungalow came across to say their toilet etc. was backed up and wouldn't go away. I being the drain man on the farm tried my best but couldn't get it going and then realised that they had got a post right into the drain without breaking the pipe, but effectively blocking it. Len's men came back straight away and moved the post and blocked up the other hole and the problem was easily solved.

Adam soon had a break from Lord Daventry's to come back and help at the Great Yorkshire Show and on the middle day won his class in the handling competition and was Hon. Mention in the Championship.

The last two weeks of July were fairly hectic and seemed to involve quite a lot of eating as well. I was over at Cumberland County Show to judge the cows, and quite unusually Sarah was also there to judge the calves and handlers, not very often a father and daughter officiate at a County Show on the same day. Back for the evening wedding party for Robert's wedding at Margaret O'Gradys at Wren's Hill, then two days later it was the staff barbecue for the end of the school year at Mowbray school and at the end of the week we hosted the North Eastern Club for its end of season barbecue and events night and then the night after it was the annual charity barbecue at Londonderry Garage.

The following week it was my final Board Meeting of Holstein UK as my time came to an end. Hitherto I had never missed a meeting in my time representing the area but with Richard away on holiday it was looking like it might have to, but Marnie and Sarah decided that wasn't going to happen, and between them looked after the farming for the day.

The last day of July was a sad day in attending Michael Armstrong's Wolfa dispersal sale over at Penrith. Michael had been Board Chairman for much of the time I had been on the Board and always done a great job and we had spent quite a bit of time working together, particularly when we were negotiating to purchase Livestock Services from the Scottish MMB to become the Society's recording subsidiary, now known as CIS. Michael was very ill at the time and was probably not fully aware of what great trade he had, and it was with even greater sadness only two weeks later that I attended his funeral. A great loss to the Breed and agriculture for one to be taken so young. That afternoon as I rushed back home for milking, I got copped for speeding on the A66 as I came over the hilltop and the drop down towards the Barnard Castle turning. The policeman who waved me down at the bottom was not moved by the fact that I had been to a funeral and had to get back to milk, having clocked me at 97 or so miles an hour. Fortunately, I must just have eased my foot off the accelerator enough to get under the 100mph, which at that time was an automatic driving ban.

Talking of funerals, it was only another fortnight before going to Arthur Jackson's funeral at Patrick Brompton. Mr Jackson had worked for the council during his working life and in retirement for many years been a church warden alongside Steve Smith, but his main claim to fame was the marvellous condition in which he had maintained the church yard for all that time – with a walk behind lawn mower, none of your ride-ons as is done nowadays.

At the end of August and into September we were extending the dairy housing by two bays to give us an extra 28 cubicles and a longer collecting yard to accommodate the extra cows, though we didn't extend the parlour, but instead fitted a Goosen "cow-moover" which worked very well in moving cows up as you milked. We were looking at a new type of vented ridge for the extension and Richard and I went down to Geoff Spence's to look at his before finalising the order. It had only been a few bits of showers here, but there had been a virtual cloud burst down at Brompton and the ford you have to cross to go to the farm was in spate and Geoff had to come and get us on a tractor. Whilst we were waiting for him, we were kept amused by two lads having great fun trying to race backwards and forwards through the water on their bikes. They were soaked through but were enjoying it and yes we did put the ridge up, and later you could see that it worked because after chopping straw in to bed the cubicles you could see the dust from a poorer bale coming out of either side above the roof.

A note for the farmers who are interested that as we harvested the wheat at this harvest, it was only worth £60/tonne, so it didn't add up too quickly despite good yields.

It was Marnie's turn to make a fool of herself in the "old codgers" handling class at the Calf Show at Thirsk, replete in long blonde wig and toy dog called Rosie and they were unplaced in a class of 29. Adam had come home on the train to win the Senior handler and be Hon. Mention Champion Handler, the day after being Reserve Champion Handler at Wensleydale Show, and Sarah turned out a Gibson calf out of Pansy 102 to be Reserve Champion Calf.

We went down to Norfolk for the Holstein convention where Gavin Patterson was the incoming President, we had a tour round the Norwich City football ground where he was a Director and a meal at Delia Smith's restaurant (she was also a Director and one of the main financiers). The day after we visited the Wright family's Pinebreck herd where we saw some tremendous cows which spent much of the year outside on very sandy land with tremendous legs and feet and also viewed their very large and interesting outdoor pig rearing unit.

Back for a day or two and then to judge at Nidderdale Show – the final local show of the year, and then later in the week took Mr J down to the Dairy Event, which we greatly enjoyed and then we took Adam out for supper while we were down there, Mr J amused me greatly as we arrived back home. As I turned into Dalesend he said I had driven very well but he just had one comment to make – I drove about 5mph too fast all the time – a bit rich from someone who drove down the M6 at about 110mph and said don't touch your brakes when you see a policeman so he can't see you were speeding in his mirrors!!

A day or two after that Richard severed the tendons in his index finger when a cow kicked him and he was signed off for a month, which meant there was just me left to do the cows during that time. We had got the building finished and the cubicle mats fitted, all that was left was to get the actual cubicles put in, it was by now mid-October and time for the cows to be in, so instead of going to the National Calf Show, Marnie and I stayed at home, did all the jobs and got the cubicles put in, and were able to keep the cows in, just as the weather turned. The next day there was one of those moments that you just don't visualise happening on a farm in North Yorkshire. Mike Heugh who did all the shed erection work for Norman Iveson, arrived to get his old crane which had stood in our back field since finishing the shed extension a month or two earlier. It took him some time to get it started and mobile and when I asked him where he was going with it for another job he said he had sold it to go to Ecuador – that's right, South America!! You just don't expect that kind of an answer.

Richard was back to milking after about three weeks which freed me up a little and I found time to go to Big Adam's herd dispersal sale at Leyburn Mart and just a couple of weeks later George Barker's "Folly" dispersal sale at Northallerton. We went down to Nuneaton and stayed overnight with Adam just before he had his first shoot day at Lord Daventry's. We went up to Dundee to visit Bill and Marg Gayford and then to Perth for Rebecca's (Rab's) wedding party, and then Adam came home by train for Ben's leaving party before he went off to join the Royal Navy.

The 14th November was one of those landmark days that you always remember. A lady rang me up a few weeks earlier to see if we had any weekend work for her son, Stuart Clapham who was still at school, I said yes if he wanted to work, as we were short of a bit of help at the time. After seeing him and knowing of the family I said we would give him a go and he started that November Saturday morning. He arrived just as I was about to go in for breakfast after finishing milking and gave him a job or two to do while I was in the house. When I came out afterwards, I was encouraged to hear the sound of a brush on concrete. He had done the jobs I had given him and was brushing down the passageway of his own volition rather than just waiting for me. That was a good sign and he developed on from then to become eventually a full-time member of staff – he will keep cropping up in the story as we move forward. Again, for those who like to be aware of prices at the time, his opening pay was £3.50 per hour for 8 till 11am on Saturdays and Sundays, and he soon started to come in the holiday's as well.

There was some very unusual weather at the turn of the year both locally and internationally. On Boxing Day the southern hemisphere was struck by that terrible tsunami where thousands lost their lives and the devastation was unbelievable – there were still some of the results there to be seen round the coastal areas of Sri Lanka when we were there some twelve and a half years later. Just into the new year we had a terrible storm with very high winds one Friday night and it took out quite a lot of the roof lights in the dairy building, including over the milking parlour. It wasn't very pleasant milking on the next morning as it was raining heavily and also running down the roof and dripping onto the cows and me, but fortunately it didn't hit any electrics to cause trouble. As soon as the jobs were done and breakfasted, I resolved to go to Sam Turners to get some replacement clear roof sheets as I thought we wouldn't be the only ones to have suffered in that way. I got as far, or nearly as far as Morton bridge to be met by a flooded river Swale with a lorry floating in a field, so had to go back via Scruton and Kirkby Fleetham to get over the Swale which was a fearsome sight in full spate, and got the required sheets and back home, so that Norman Iveson and Mike Heugh could put them on that afternoon, so it was rather better for the next milking. Some of the damage was done by slates ripped off the granary roof and a large section of it was to repair later, and the rest of the sky lights in the main part of the shed were replaced by Waddington's later into the spring.

When we took the Christmas decorations down on Twelfth Night, we discovered that the Christmas tree lights had begun to melt the holders onto the bulbs – so they had to be thrown out – a shocking expense having cost £3.40 and only lasting for 31 years!!

Mid-January we went across for an embryo auction at Garstang, really to see what the trade was like rather than to buy anything specific, but when some Spottie embryos by Dundee weren't selling too well I bought them for 560gns each. We eventually only finished up with one daughter but she developed into a tremendous cow, was Reserve Junior Champion at the Royal Highland Show and at our dispersal sale she sold for 3700gns, her daughter for 4500gns and about a dozen embryos from the two of them totalled over 5000gns. You don't win them all when you buy into something like that, but that gamble certainly paid off.

For Christmas that year Marnie had bought me a personalised number plate S55 JBL, with the S a bit distorted to almost look like another five and it was mid-January by I got it onto the car. The number wasn't a vanity project, it was because she was embarrassed by me never remembering the number if we were checking into a hotel if away for weekends. It does the job and now when you sometimes have to put the number in to get a car park ticket it is easier than having to go back to the car to remember the number.

One morning when getting the cows in to milk the scrapers were tripped off and a cow down in the passageway with back legs right out – and guess what it was , as always in those situations a good one, Dalesend Storm Maude 2 the EX full sister to the Royal Show winning cow at Tregibby. You could see immediately that there was no hope of her ever getting up again, either she or another cow had been in season during the night and put her down. Being the cow she was we got the vet to remove her ovaries and got them straight up to Paragon at Hexham – they managed to recover 57 oocytes and tried to fertilise them but didn't succeed in getting any of them to develop on. Adam finished at Arbury when the shooting season ended and we went down to collect him and his things in early February, he did one or two jobs about home for a couple of weeks before he flew off to New Zealand to stay with Mollie and Len and work on the nearby farm of Richard Peckitt who originated from near Thirsk.

A good trip to Dublin with Dick and George and quite a collection of Paul's customers from all over the country, plenty of good food and some Guinness.

By now we were beginning to burst at the seams with young stock as we were back up to full stocking after Foot and Mouth and the building extension and we decided it would be more cost efficient, certainly in the short term to winter the yearlings off farm than the high capital cost of another building, and we looked at various possibilities, one of which was at Richard Andrew's (Rob Andrew the England rugby international fly-half's brother) but we decided Middleton Tyas was just too far away and we looked for somewhere nearer to home – we didn't need to look far for the following winter as Chris decided he would winter them rather than buy in store cattle to fatten, and it worked very well from the autumn of 2005 up until our dispersal in 2011.

We were due a holiday and with Adam in New Zealand it was a good enough reason to go there and visit Len and Mollie. When travelling somewhere as far away as that you need to go for a good spell, and we were away for three weeks in total. After 24 hours of travelling time we arrived in Auckland, me getting fined before we got out of the airport. You cannot take any food into New Zealand and I thought I had eaten all the satsumas I had taken with me, but one was left among the things in my hand luggage and that was soon picked up by the cameras and it cost me 200 New Zealand dollars and I couldn't even have the orange. We had the best part of a week in North Island and did a lot of driving about. New Zealand has two great advantages for travellers – they speak English and drive on the same side of the road as we do. They think their roads are busy, but apart from Auckland which is home to about a third of the total country's population, there is more traffic on our back road to Newton-le-Willows. We visited the fascinating Kauri Wood Museum up the Northland peninsula, took in the Bay of Islands and the hot springs of Rotorua. We weren't too impressed with either of those – they were rather tourist orientated. We drove down to Napier with all its Art Deco buildings and on to Wellington through forests with plenty of birds of prey, before catching the ferry over to South Island. The first night we planned to stay at Hanmer Springs but had nowhere booked – the place seemed very busy and we couldn't find a spare bed anywhere – discovering it was one of the big weekends when the passes were open for the first time for a large scale mountain bike race. We had something to eat in a pub and nearly got into a dispute with locals over Richie McCaw the All Blacks rugby captain and world acclaimed back-rower. There was a live rugby match on in the bar and at the bottom of a ruck he was trapped and interfering with play, so one of the opposition got hold of his legs and pulled him out of the side – for which he promptly got red-carded and I was foolish enough to say that it was McCaw who should have had the red card. There was little else on the rugby channel for the next few days when eventually they got the man himself on and the first question was about the incident – he just had a little laugh to himself and said "you win some and lose some", he knew very well. After having our meal there was no option but to sleep in the car that night and so we drove out a few miles and found somewhere to park up. Not the best of places to sleep well and I wasn't too amused to be woken up in the middle of the night, having, I thought just got to sleep by Marnie exclaiming at what was outside, and I rather blearily saw the Southern Lights. Can't say I was too impressed and straight back into the car for more fitful sleep. We were awake early the next morning and got on the road well before any other vehicles were about and we were the first people to stop at the coffee shop at Springs Junction on the way over to Greymouth. We got our coffee and were keenly waiting for our cooked breakfast to arrive by which time another couple were just coming in, when one of the kitchen ladies put her head round the door and said to the waitress "do you know what day it is – we shouldn't be open yet". The clocks had changed overnight, it was their autumn and so the clocks had gone back. What was really funny was that they put the other couple back out the door, locked it and told them they would have to wait until the new 7 o'clock. Luckily, they didn't do the same to us as they were already cooking it. We couldn't really see the point they were already up and at work!! We then went on to Westport and Greymouth calling at Buller Gorge, crossing it on the swinging bridge and then the next day drove back across to leave the car at Timaru airport where Mollie collected us.

We stayed at Mollie and Len's for a few days and saw them shearing at Richard's with Adam packing wool, before we took off again via Lake Tekapo with the fantastic view down the lake through the church window above the altar. There were signs asking you to go outside in front of the same window to take photographs, which of course the Japanese totally ignored. We headed for the base of Mount Cook – I suppose drawn by the connection of Great Ayton that we shared, and then called at Wanaka, Arrowtown and Queenstown. Even then, Queenstown was a tourist centre with its bungee jumping and jet skiing in the gorge, but it has expanded greatly since then and to us is now a glorified Blackpool. For young people it is very much one of their centres and a few weeks later after we were back home, Adam rung up one breakfast time (our time) and I asked him if he had been to see any of the British Lions rugby matches as they were touring at the time. We argued about where the next match was. I said it was in the capital, Wellington, to which I was told in no uncertain terms that to anyone under the age of 30, Queenstown was the capital of New Zealand. We stayed in Dunedin for a couple of nights, the first day was Good Friday, it was wet and miserable and the only place open was the South Otago Museum which we found very interesting – much more alive than our museums and of course their colonial history is much shorter than ours and so more easily related to. We took a trip up the Otago peninsula and watched the little penguins coming ashore and making their way in land to their nests – they are fascinating to watch. As we headed back up towards Mollies again, we walked among the Moeraki boulders on the Koekohe beach, (the next time we called it had become commercialised and you had to pay to get down the steps from the café to get to them, but we went a bit further along and found a free car park and walked back along to them). We called at the Totara estate where the first shipments of chilled lamb were sent to England in 1882.

A couple of days later Len and Mollie took us to the local Fairlie Show which was a similar show to say Stokesley, Wensleydale or Nidderdale Shows and much the same sort of things were going on. There was a Scottish marquee where they would tell you what clan you were from (remember many of the original settlers in the second half of the 1800's came from Scotland). A big burly man in his kilt waved me in and as we entered asked my name and immediately said he needn't bother looking that up as he knew we had been thrown out of Scotland as sheep stealers. I told him that I already knew that and hadn't travelled all that way to be reminded of it.

The day after was Ladies day in Timaru to which Mollie and Marnie went and I went with Len to the Temuka sales yard – a totally different experience to a UK auction and much of the dealings, cattle selection are done by agents who operate all over the country. The next day Mollie took us for a ride out in the afternoon for our final day in the country, and we stopped for a coffee on the way home beside Highway One. When we set off back home Mollie said she would have to go down to the next junction to go the other way. It was just an ordinary two-way road with no central reservation, there was nothing coming either way as far as the eye could see so I told her not to be so daft and just turn the way we wanted to go – their roads are so busy you see!! We left the next day from Christchurch and having cost me money with the satsuma to come into New Zealand, I was a bit put out to have to pay to leave it. As it so happened the date was 1st April and I thought that it was an April Fool's joke, but no, at that time there was a fee of about 40NZ$ per person payable as you left.

Back to reality, while we had been away, Richard, Stuart and Chris had been getting ready for spring, harrowing and rolling grass and fencing. We had always struggled a bit with grazing heifers at Hill Top East as there was nowhere to alternate with Corner Banks Field to give it a rest. I had for years watched a field across the road from it belonging to the Peacock family, not be greatly used either by grazing or in one year they got about ten bales of moderate silage off it, so I resolved to visit them to see if we could rent it from them and after a lot of discussions and various on and offs they finally agreed to rent us it, which we did so for the next seven years. The soil and grass was so soft and loose on it with being unstocked and the grass just rotting down each year that it didn't produce a lot that first summer and the heifers broke it up quite badly, but we gradually improved it, built up the fertility, sprayed and harrowed and rolled it, until by the seventh year it was serving our purpose very well, it was a 10 acre field and we were still only paying £500 per year for it. It was an annual negotiation that took about half a day, we nearly lost it because we had significantly improved the watering hole of the natural spring having put a trough with overflow and concreted down to it so it didn't get full of puddle, but I hadn't asked permission to do so, but I managed to talk them round to allowing us to continue, but they wouldn't allow us to put in a gate at the other end of the field nearest to Hill Top, rather than where it was, because if you didn't get all the animals out onto the road first go, the odd one would race up and down the hedge side with the majority of the heifers on the road. After we gave it up after 2011, it was virtually unused for several years, though I believe now someone else has sheep on it.

That spring Richard converted part of the old Dalesend Dairy building into his office and we took out the old bit of office to enlarge the calf house, we got the inside of the extended collecting yard walls rendered to make them easier to clean and match the original, completed concreting of the extended silage pit and made a small holding pit for sugar beet pulp nuts or brewers grains as we continued doing our own mixed ration for the central feed passage and were only giving the cows supplementary feed through the out of parlour feeders having removed the feed troughs from the parlour.

We changed the JCB loadall in early May and then at the end of the month changed the Toyota Hi-Lux pick up from a 2 wheel drive to a 4 wheel drive – so we shouldn't have the same problem on getting stuck or struggling in muddy gateways anymore. Unfortunately I don't have a cost in for either of those exercises so cannot give you actual figures for comparison, but I do know they would be substantially less than it would cost you to do so in today's market place.

On a nice Saturday towards the end of May, we had a ride up over the tops to Middlesmoor and walked across the footpath from Ivy House right up to High Riggs where Uncle Jack and Aunt Clarice Challis used to live when we were up there – it is now derelict, and I don't think anyone has lived there since they moved down to Halfway House many years previously. Such a shame, it has a marvellous setting in the middle of the moor, and I would have thought in this day and age could have been very valuable holiday accommodation. We also visited Howstean Gorge. That and High Riggs were somewhere Marnie had never been to before. We saw my old schoolboy friend Martin while we were in Middlesmoor – they were busy in some of the holiday cottages as it was a change over day. Martin had some years previously converted the old sawmill and house buildings into holiday cottages after he moved down to live in Pateley Bridge.

A day or two later Adam was to gather up from Manchester after he got back from New Zealand and just another few days later and we all went up to Sunderland greyhound racing. Some of Sarah's friends had arranged it for her 30th birthday present, with one of the races named In honour of her. Great fun was had by all, little money lost and the first time I had been greyhound racing for forty plus years since we went with Ken Bradshaw from Ladybridge.

Mid-June was the North East Club trip to Picston down in Staffordshire which was a general open day as they had won the RABDF Gold Cup the previous year, and it was great to see John's two sons carrying on his good work. A day or two days after it was North Yorkshire County Show and what a day it was. The morning was very hot and I came home for lunch, leaving Sarah and Stuart to it, when I got a phone call to say could I go back for the cattle as they were letting them go home early because of the heat. Got one load and then the heavens were opening and there was a massive hailstorm among the rest of the thunder rain – great big rough hailstones like gravel. In all it came 1.1" of water in 25 minutes and when I went back for the second load of cattle there was water standing everywhere and I had a job to get round the roundabout to head for Otterington because it was flooded. The weather had been even worse towards the other side of Thirsk, with bridges washed away and streams bursting their banks.

Early July saw both Marnie and I have school reunions on the same day, Marnie's over at Malton and mine at Ripon rugby club. First one I had been to and they are a bit un-nerving when you see how old some of your contempories look, what they are doing, or have made their fortunes and already retired in their fifties, but still an interesting night, even though I probably wouldn't go to another one. A day or two later I took Mr and Mrs J down to the Royal Show – a surprise for Mr J who was called into the ring during judging to be presented with the 2004 National Premier Breeder award, something he was unaware of – most of the points were amassed for us by the Wilson's of Tregibby with Dalesend Storm Maude, but still a remarkable achievement to win it for a second time some eleven years after winning it the first time. That was only a couple of days before the terrible terror attacks in London of 7/7, the real start of world problems of that nature which just seem to have escalated ever since.

The Yorkshire Show which followed that week was quite eventful. Marnie was away with Mowbray on their school activity week at Etal up in Northumberland and Sarah and Adam were away at the show, so all was quiet at home. Stuart had finished at school and was working quite a few days before he started work full time, including getting scooter training before he got a scooter under the "wheels to work" scheme, but he had days at the show playing with the school band who were performing there along with other schools. At the show there was a rumour doing the rounds that I was retiring, and Sarah was taking over from me – a likely tale as I wasn't old enough, couldn't afford to and she hadn't the experience. We had a bit of fun and I got some invitations printed for a non-retirement party and gave them to an ally to hand out, mainly to the two or three people we suspected of starting the rumour – it seemed to do the trick and never heard a lot more about it. At the end of that week we went down to Ashby-de-la-Zouch to judge their show which is a good show, usually well supported by local exhibitors and we ate at a smashing Italian out in the open courtyard on a very balmy evening.

The following week was one of our highlights when we were invited to one of the Buckingham Palace Garden Parties. It was fascinating before hand to receive a letter asking if we would be able to attend on a certain date should Her Majesty invite us (she obviously doesn't like refusals) and we naturally accepted. Went down the day before, had a meal with Emma and Cliff the night before at Chez Gerard, drove up Horse Guards Parade and found a designated parking spot for attendees, had a walk in Hyde Park and a picnic lunch before going to the Palace. It was the day 21st July of another security scare when a suspected terrorist, a Brazilian national was apprehended and shot on a bus. As that happened there were sirens going and blue lights flashing all over the place, and it was quite un-nerving to see armed police officers on the roof of Buckingham Palace watching for any potential problems as the Garden Party went on. There were a lot of people there, and as ever at such occasions many toffee-nosed officials. I obviously was too near the official party and one of them snootily enquired "Are you being presented?" and wasn't too amused with my reply "What with – I didn't realise we had won anything". A great afternoon was had by everyone and certainly something we will never forget. The other amusing thing was that as we left to go back to the car, another guest had obviously hired a Rolls Royce for the day, got there very early and parked as near as was allowed to the Palace, but the car wouldn't start for him to go home and he was there with the bonnet up and the AA arrived to see to him – so much for show-offs!!

Stuart started work full time at the beginning of August. I had a bit of trouble persuading Mr J that we should employ him full time, he didn't really think we had enough work for him, or need, but I said that when you had the chance to get someone as good you did so, and found work to justify the cost, and for quite a while he did go off and work days with Sarah to clip cattle etc., and that spread the cost. Having said that you have to work in with these youngsters and keep them onside with modern lifestyles, but I was a bit put out (though I knew beforehand) when after only a fortnight he was off for four days at the 'V' Music Festival, and that was while we were harvesting and leading straw. That year, wheat was worth £64 per tonne.

We had a super night out with the Yorkshire Holstein Club with their "Cruise on the Ouse" from which you saw York in a totally different perspective, followed by an open night at Butterfield's "Ingleview" herd, and then a day or two later Marnie took Adam to Newton Rigg for his HND interview before he started there the following month to study game management. We also went to a N.E. Jersey Club meeting at Archers and sampled the ice-cream as well. Dalesend Pansy 135 was Reserve Champion at both Wensleydale and Stokesley shows that autumn.

We had a short break after harvest and went up to Kilconquhar on the Dee estuary – a bit of a "freebie" really, under false pretences. They were selling time shares and you got a free stay at the hotel while you saw what was on offer – we went to the various meetings etc. but had no intention of buying. While we were up there Adam went back down to Arbury to see Owen, before he went off to Penrith to start his course at Newton Rigg. Talking of education, Stuart started his day release classes at Bedale Ag Centre at a similar time. The Ag Centre at Bedale was an outreach centre of Askham Bryan College, and was I think the very first such one in the country when it first opened some forty or so years earlier. It had been very successful over the years, but as the interest in farming in young people fell away around the 1990's and into the 2000's, its agricultural classes became less, it eventually moved those to the new facilities they had established at the new Thirsk Auction Centre and it is sad now to see that it has gone altogether and the site now boasts a row of houses.

Early October and I bought Braimber Integrity Kim from Rebecca Jarvis in a private deal. We had lost the Kim family with the Foot and Mouth slaughter, having originally sold the mother of this cow as a calf at the Black and White sale to the Eshton herd and when that was dispersed by Phillip Green, Rebecca had bought her and she went on to complete 100 tonnes at Braimber. We took heifers up to Chris Knox's at East Farm at Patrick Brompton for wintering for the first time.

I went down to Cornwall, to speak to a discussion group there, staying with Rodger and Ella Laity overnight. On the way back on the Saturday we stayed overnight just south of Birmingham at a very pleasant golf and country club. I went to the gym and sauna before dinner and thought nothing of it when I slipped getting into the shower in the changing room. I thought much more about it two days later sitting in agony at the Yorkshire Club Dinner and finished up in hospital on antibiotics intra-venously and spent a week in there getting the infection out of my leg. It was obvious I had made a slight break in the skin when I slipped, and my leg hit the dish of the shower unit and had got some dirt into it. We had two bulls entered for the Wexham Cup at Beeston that week which I obviously couldn't go to, so Sarah took them and did well to get both away at 1500gns each.

We had nothing in the annual Black and White sale at Carlisle that year, but attendance had become something of a ritual anyway and without any intention of buying anything, I acquired a three month in-calf heifer from Peel Park originating in the Gail family with six generations of VG or EX behind her for 1000gns. She calved a heifer calf by Weeton Jackson went VG as a two-year-old and gave just short of 10,000 litres as a heifer, but we never got her in calf again, hard as we tried. The Dalesend Jackson Gail went on to be an EX90 third calver, sold for 2700gns at our dispersal sale to Angus Dean and her daughter a VG85-2-year-old by Smiddiehill Emulate sold for 4200gns to Messrs Showell from Warwickshire. You have to get lucky sometimes!!

The OTMS (over-thirty months scheme) which was a result of the BSE problems of some 10 or 12 years previously was coming to an end, so I thought we had better have a thin out of some cull cows before it did so, and so took ten to Darlington one Monday, trouble was, everybody else was thinking along the same lines and trade was terrible.

Sadly, at the end of the year I went to David Gibson's funeral, just older than me and far too young to pass away at just 61, with leukaemia. David had been in Bedale Young Farmers at the same time as us and had always farmed very well following his father at Hunter's Hill at Crakehall, and he was then followed by his son Tim who will be known to many people all over the country as Mr. Lely and who wrote in "cowmen comment" in the Dairy Farmer for many years.

Just before Christmas we were well stocked with cattle and needed to thin them out and sold 11 milking cows to Jeremy Hutchinson from Scorton and they eased the load a bit over Christmas, and went on and did very well for him, though he is now another farmer who no longer has dairy cows.

Adam was home for Christmas from college, went out with school friends in Richmond on Christmas Eve and got breathalysed twice on the way home when he had had nothing to drink other than blackcurrant and coke. His generation are much more reliable than ours was – if they are driving, they don't drink alcohol – we had the problem of getting used to it after the breathalyser was introduced. He went over to Manchester to see in the New Year with Theo and some more friends from school,

Theo went on to be part of the duo "Hurts" who have had both a top selling record and albums. After being back at college he then came back home for the North Eastern Club Dinner at Romanby Golf club and the next day it was "keepers" day at Dalesend for the end of the shooting season.

January 2006 started with us pulling out the old rough bushes on the hillside of the heifer grazing field at Hill Top East. It tidied the place up, and if nothing else made it easier to check and count the heifers in summertime, as it was sod's law, wherever you were in the field there would be an odd heifer either intentionally or otherwise in among them and hidden from view. Later that week we were in Northallerton and had a coffee at the new café that opened in Sam Turners. Very well used, they have had to greatly enlarge it now, we often have a bite of lunch there and on a wet Saturday lunchtime you can nearly guarantee there will be one or two farmers you know there.

Early that spring we decided to change from offering minerals ad-lib to cows and heifers to using boluses. Minerals over the years had become more expensive and I had never been convinced that when offered ad-lib you were sure they were being properly used, some cows never took any while other cows always seemed to be there and were no doubt getting luxury uptake, which in excess could be counter-productive. We looked into it in some depth, consulted with a couple of farmers who had been using boluses alone quite happily for several years. Our feed advisers said the cow feeds we were using should contain sufficient minerals for the milking cows and younger heifers, and so we began the practice of dosing them with a mineral bolus at drying off that would cover them through the dry period and the first few weeks after calving. We continued this for the next almost six years until the cattle were sold – were very happy with the system and saved considerable amounts of money on minerals. The only thing we did still offer was the Himalayan rock salt lumps, as much as anything to give the cattle something to do and keep them amused.

Down to stay at Worcester for a couple of nights to go to the MGA (Maize Growers Association) annual conference, this year at Hartpury College, always a useful meeting which over the years has taught me a lot about maize growing, then back up home for a couple of days before a trip to Murrayfield with Dick and George.

At the end of March which had been with us the wettest March on record, we were away one Saturday and while in Marks and Spencer both Marnie and I went to the toilet. It was the dearest "penny" I have ever spent, it cost me £201. Whilst I was waiting, I looked at a jacket, some trousers and a shirt, which Marnie encouraged me to buy!!

That spring we got involved with Richmond School on a "bridge project" in which a non-academic student could work out of school one day a week in their final year at school to prepare them for full time work after that. We had a couple of students over the next year or so, but it really didn't work, they tended to be rather unreliable in their timekeeping, didn't come in holidays etc. We didn't have to pay them, but it was quite costly in time and effort in trying to help them.

At the end of the spring term, Adam finished at Newton Rigg to go off on his practical work where they had to so something associated with gamekeeping for a minimum of four months. He chose to and found a job on a pheasant egg and chick producing farm near Copgrove and spent a very useful spell with the Phillips family. He wasn't too impressed when he came home after the first day at work – he had collected 905 eggs from under the tin sheets, brash etc. put out round the pens for the birds to lay under. I was amazed and must admit to my ignorance until then, that hatching of eggs, be they hens or any other birds are not all natural in timing. They simply store the eggs until a certain date – based on when they want the day-old chicks to be available, at which point they are loaded on to incubators and controlled from that point on, so they get large numbers all at the same time. Adam also went rabbiting with Carl and one night shot 77!

We had a visit over to Norway to visit Colin, Liv and family at Kleppe, via Sola airport but we had to go via Schiphol (Amsterdam) which took almost twelve hours for a flight of about 1½ hours if we could have gone direct from Newcastle to Sola. Whilst over in Norway we went to see an old house which Colin had bought as a project to restore and create two properties from and he showed us an enormous bee's nest he had discovered up in the attic – fortunately it was no longer in use or we would have given it a wide berth.

A trip to the National Holstein Show at Stafford saw Dalesend Storm Maude beaten in her class for the first time and the end of her illustrious career. A few days later we went to Robert Burrow's Stardale sale. Robert was "retiring" and handing over to his son James and they had a fantastic sale of the milking herd with the quality of the cattle conformation matching their depth of pedigree. Quite remarkably James has now become the third generation to develop a great herd of cows under different breeding systems prevalent at their respective times. His grandfather did it with mainly natural service herd sires, Robert with widely available proven AI sires, and James is continuing the dynasty with mostly young genomic sires, tapping into the strength of their dominant cow families such as the Vaakje's.

We hosted one of the North Eastern Clubs judging nights in early May, and a couple of days later Stuart passed his driving test, so it wasn't too long before he had a bump which steadied him up, Adam was stopping down at Copgrove in a caravan quite a few nights rather than travelling home every day. I judged Otley Show that May in torrential rain, and following on from the wettest ever March, we had a total of 3¼ inches in the middle nine days of May which meant there was plenty of growth, but rather delayed silage making.

Marnie took a class from Mowbray up to Swinton Castle, where they were holding a Japanese day and the children learnt of the customs of another country and then just a day later she went to a staff members leaving party at Masham where they sat around on cushions and ate Turkish style.

Early June was quite a busy spell – I went with Sarah down into Cheshire one afternoon when she was Master Judge for a Western Club stock judging meeting at the Wardle herd. We called for coffee at a farm shop and I bought a ceramic picture which was the first time I had seen them. They are now some twelve years later all the rage, so was well ahead of my time. We were at the time just starting to extend the young stock building at home to be able to store more straw and were putting two extra 20' bays onto the end – it is amazing how a 20 foot bay seems so much more roomy than a conventional 15 foot one. As usual a superb job done by Norman Iveson and on this occasion, we didn't concrete the floor when it was only for straw storage, and simply put stone down – mind you, that isn't a cheap option anymore. I stewarded the N.E Club young stock herds competition one day and had a hairy moment when I took Peter Waring of Winton fame and currently in 2018 the Holstein Society President to judge at Kevin Clarkson's at East Witton. Theirs is a long narrow farm and the heifers were at the far end – Kevin got us loaded up onto his four wheeled "motor bike" and went off at a tremendous rate of knots – it was ok for him – he knew where all the dips and bumps were and wasn't too concerned about Peter and I hanging on for dear life, it took us a while to recover when we got back to the farmstead. A day later we went up to Durham County Cricket Ground to see Elton John in an open-air concert. He was very disappointing – sang very few of his songs that people knew and couldn't get finished and away quickly enough – his helicopter was up and away before we got walked back to the car, let alone get out onto the road.

It was a very fruity year in 2006 and I note in the diary that we picked altogether 21½lbs of gooseberries and a little later in total 30lbs of redcurrants – most of them were frozen and will last us for a number of years – the redcurrants are beating us even though Marnie makes a batch of jelly every year for the church Christmas Fayre, but there is a limit to how much between us we can use.

In early July we had a busy few days of officialdom. A visit from the Rural Payments Agency for an SPS Inspection under the Single Farm Payment Scheme. He was a decent enough man who had a job to do, but it was a full inspection and he walked and checked and measured everything to check field sizes etc. It took him a day and a half to physically do that, and then a further day to come back and see me and go through his findings. Some fields were fractionally too small and others the opposite way, at the end of it all the difference in acreage was 0.2 hectares in a total of about 170 hectares – about a tenth of 1%, was it really worth it. Now of course much of that is not necessary as they have us all under surveillance with the "spy in the sky" satellites. The next visit he was to make was to a big holding of just over two hectares - hope they didn't have 0.2ha difference – that would have been a 10% variance. Units as small as that it could be argued should not be eligible for such payments anyway. At the same time as the RPA man paid a visit, we also had Martin James, our accountant visit to do a physical audit of our stock numbers - new European requirement under business law for limited companies and fortunately everything matched with the numbers provided at our year end some two months earlier after allowing for arrivals and departures over that time.

We had cattle at the Great Yorkshire Show that year but didn't set the world alight – a second, a third and a fourth, and then on the second day I was the Master Judge for some of the Young Farmer's classes which took all afternoon including the reason giving, which was of varying standards. A week later Sarah, Alan Goldie and myself went down to Noremead near Swindon for the Judges Conference.

Roll that in with a day at an Inland Revenue Sick Pay training day at Harrogate because of a lot of new legislation on such matters, and it was not the most inspiring three weeks or so.

Chapter 21 – Illness and Various Trips

I had a bit of trouble at the Auction Mart one day when selling geld cows and there was an obvious fix on between the buyers. When I spoke to one of the directors whom I knew quite well about it he asked me to come with him to the office and immediately got £30 from petty cash to make up for it – proved the point, he knew what had gone on, it wasn't the regular auctioneer who was away on holiday, but that was the last time we sold any cull cows there, after that we sold them through Andrew Heaton who collected them on farm and so saved several hours going to the mart.

The end of July was a busy time with visitors, we had Emma to stay for a couple of nights, she and Marnie went to Northallerton to visit the new M&S Food store when it opened that week, and then the day after Colin and Liv arrived from Norway to stay for a week or so.

In among all this it was the North Eastern Club's end of season barbecue and President's evening at the Donaldson's at Barlees. By this time plans were getting quite well advanced for the junior section of the club to host the national weekend the following year and much fund-raising was going on. That night someone had brought a ducking stool and people paid money to see one or other youngster get soaked, but then all got together to put up a larger amount to get a senior member ducked and guess who they chose or who was daft enough to do it, and of course then a lot more joined in and took great delight in seeing me stripped down to my pants get well and truly wet, and a banged head on the side of the tub into the bargain, followed a couple of days later by a bump up the back of the JCB when leading straw which gave me a bit of a jolt.

Whether it was either of those two things or something totally unrelated we will never know, but a day or two later I had a very bad headache, not something I usually suffer from, the doctor gave me some tablets, but they didn't do a lot of good. Colin went off to Nantwich Show with Sarah where she was judging the handling classes and, as I did a few years later, found the cheese show which is one of the leading ones in this country, absolutely fascinating. Christin and family also arrived from Norway so the house was nearly overrun, I was sick a couple of times and spent much of a couple of days laid down with eyes closed, mended a little to spend some time sat out in the garden with Arthur and Anne when they came up to see Colin and Liv. Arthur himself had been very poorly and had major surgery but was by then on the road to recovery.

By the Saturday after sleeping in the chair very fitfully for a couple of nights, we finally went to the Friarage to Accident and Emergency, where they did various blood tests, x-rays etc before sending me to the observation ward overnight until they decided what was wrong with me. The young Irish doctor who first examined me made a lot of notes and said having been a front row forward all those years ago my neck and shoulders would be all shot at anyway and was amazed to find after x-ray that they were undamaged. The day after I had a brain scan which showed nothing wrong (many would disagree, thinking there had been a lot wrong with my brain for many years). They then did a lumbar puncture, which they were not too happy about and so transferred me to James Cook Hospital at Middlesbrough. I had always been under the impression that ambulance beds/stretchers would be very comfortable with great shock absorbers but let me tell anyone who hasn't been in one, they are not. I think laid out there it seemed to take forever and I felt every little bump in the road all the way there. Once there they did more tests and finally decided that I had a bleed on the back of the brain – in the Meninga – a complex collection of nerves – and they called it viral meningitis – not the "killer" type which strikes very quickly and dangerously particularly with children. They put me onto medication, it needed something to make up for the terrible food in there, before after a couple of days sending me back to the Friarage. The only trouble was they forgot to send the medical notes or the medication back with me, and eventually late at night they got them delivered by taxi – but by then there was no-one to interpret the notes and it was the next night before they got me back onto antibiotics, so nearly two days wasted and I had gone backwards again.

There are some people in hospital a lot worse off than yourself and are desperately ill, and there was one such elderly gentleman in there at the time, but he did provide some very amusing moments that you cannot help but be amused by, even though they are so sad. We had jelly one night with our evening meal and he complained he couldn't eat it until I told him to use the spoon rather than his knife and fork. One night he tried to get into my bed for company and then on another night it was just as well I am not of a nervous disposition as he told us in the middle of the night how in the last war he had been a parachutist and had been dropped into Germany and had killed many Germans.

I finally was released from hospital after eleven very long days, and took a long time to get fully back to fitness, and even now I do not like looking down for a long time such as walking down a hill or a long flight of steps as I go a bit light headed, though very quickly recover.

A few days later I was due to judge Halifax Show and Marnie drove me down there and like a lot of smaller shows, there was only a few cattle there, no steward for the cattle classes, so Marnie did that as well, and we managed ok, though it was hard work.

At a similar time there was a bit of freshness in the canine world, Mr J got a new whippet pup, black and white whom he christened Dale, and a day or two later Adam got his new pup whom he christened Penny although she had some long pedigree name. She was a Cocker Spaniel and under his tutelage developed into a very good gun dog – he was able to take her back to Newton Rigg with him and continue her training there, and she used to just sit and gaze up at him as if he was her shining light, which of course, he was. As I write this some 12 years later Penny is not very well and failing rather quickly, virtually deaf but still a marvellous nature. Penny was the first but certainly not the last as Adam like many gamekeepers seem to have far more dogs than they need, and he has about six at any one time, but none have ever been or will be quite as good as Penny.

The steam train was running up the Wensleydale railway for the summer season, and I wanted to get a photo of it, with home in the background, so one Saturday went off into the Railway field over the line to await the train, but was most put out. First effort I was too close and this enormous train blocked out any view of Newton Grange and the following day I tried again and from the far side of the field near the road everything was too small and the picture too diverse to have much meaning, so I didn't try again.

The water board were putting another new pipe across beside the other one to carry the supply to Northallerton, so we had more disruption and another substantial payment, no wonder water rates are so high.

The end of September saw Dalesend Alaska Idena (Warden Idena's only daughter) being Champion at Stokesley Show and just two days later be Reserve Champion and Exhibitor Bred Champion at Nidderdale and she was also Champion Cow in the Yorkshire Herds Competition. On the day of Stokesley Show, after it Marnie and I went to York to see the Queen. No not Her Majesty, but Judy Dench in the film and very good it was too.

I went with Keith Colley down to an invited BOCM Pauls meeting to discuss development of new feeding strategies as they unveiled their latest thinking. It was held at Leicester Tigers stadium, which was also of interest and I had a talk with Austin Healey, part of the World Cup winning squad, as he sat outside after training that day.

We again hosted the Patrick Brompton Harvest Festival Service in the barn, featuring the Bedale Brass Band to provide the music and Howard Petch to deliver a superb sermon, followed by a supper of soup and apple pies. A massive turnout of about 150 people despite the torrential rain on the night.

In mid-October I went down to Cirencester for a college reunion. They had been holding one for our group for several years, but this was the first one I had been able to attend. I picked up John Foss somewhere in South Yorkshire and across to Dave Hampson's at Marple in Cheshire and then went down with him. We had a very good evening and meal and then on the Saturday went on a private visit to Prince Charles's Highgrove Estate where the farming was run by an ex-student. All organic it was very well run, a superb flock of Lleyn sheep which was the first time I had seen them – they have now become more popular and widespread, some terrific crops of red clover waiting to be silaged, the one disappointment was the herd of Ayrshire dairy cows.

After a couple of days up in Scotland at the end of October visiting old friends Bill and Marg at Wormit and visiting Rebecca and family we came back to stay overnight at the Travelodge on the Quayside at Newcastle. Next morning as we had breakfast there it overlooked the fairly new Law Courts and it was quite fascinating watching all the escorted prisoners' vehicles arriving ready for that day's events. That wasn't why we were there!! The purpose of our visit was the night before when we went to the Arena stadium to see Don Williams and Rita Coolidge and the star of the show Kenny Rodgers in concert. He was fantastic, had the audience eating out of his hand and although getting towards the end of his career, sang all his well-known hits and put on a great show.

The last day of October saw us start our first ELS (Entry Level Scheme) which was for a five-year period. We could easily meet the criteria because of the hedgerows, overwintered stubbles after maize and "ridge and furrow" in the Park at Dalesend. The vast majority of the woodland around the farm also qualified on an acreage basis and for an annual payment of about £5500 we couldn't afford not to be in it, and it ran quite easily for the full course. It ran out just at the time of the sale of the majority of the land, but we continued on for a second term on the remaining area, the qualifications were more difficult to meet this time, but overwintered stubbles before spring barley and low-input grassland allowed us to meet the necessary requirements. That ran out last year and there is now a new scheme which is totally different, basically we can't meet the objectives of the standards and so are not going forward with it, and I believe not many people are doing so, there may have to be a re-think.

The first week in November was always "fishing week" for the Ropner family – they had a regular week for so many rods on the Tweed near Kelso and went every year. This particular year was very successful, and they got 19 salmon in their three days which was by then as many days as they went for. Sadly, salmon fishing on the great rivers such as the Tweed has now declined quite markedly and this year 2018, their beat had only had 3 caught in it in the month around their visit – the leading family fisherman now is the youngest son Dominic and I am told his youngest daughter Willow, is the fishing star of the future.

November was a time of both joy and sadness within a matter of days. Emma (Mollie's daughter) and Cliff became parents to twins Jake and Daisy and just a few days later Liv passed away suddenly overnight in Norway. Neither Sarah, Peter nor I were able to go over to the funeral because of other commitments which left Kathryn and Marnie to go on their own until up stepped Adam to ask "do you think Mother and Auntie Kathryn would like me to go with them". That he did and after he and Kathryn came home, Marnie stayed on for a while to give Colin and the girls a bit of support, before coming home via Bergen – having time to fill in she had a walk round the old town and was as ever looking upwards at what was around her, she didn't see a bar trapdoor open and fell down into a cellar – fortunately no damage done.

I spoke to Border Counties club on "a bit of this and a bit of that", went to an MDC meeting on classification, helped with a caesarean on Dalesend Storm Radiance, a good young cow who never bred again after the operation and so the family never got going. I also had a meeting with our MP, William Hague at his Richmond Surgery about our 2005 Single Farm Payment which had some heavy penalty deductions wrongly applied. He was very helpful and wrote off quite a few letters to various involvee's and we eventually got our dues. Strangely enough we are battling at the moment over our

2016 payment. It was or is to do with the Woodland grant scheme which they claim we were not eligible for, though we have had it for many years and so deducted the amount and that meant we also fell into a large penalty deduction as well. In total we are talking about some £4000 and it is just dragging on with the Rural Payments Agency as are many others from then and even earlier years. Our case is strengthened by the fact that our 2017 year was paid in full on the same basis as all the other years and as I write this our 2018 payment should be coming any time so we wait to see what that is and they say they it will be unaffected and not delayed by the 2016 dispute- time will tell!

Just before Christmas I went to Auntie Nellie Hepworth's funeral – the last one of fathers generation, his sister and the mother of Beryl and Pat, they had followed mother and father onto the farm at Great Ayton, when they moved to Humberstone Bank before going to Middlesmoor. Many local readers may not know Beryl but would know her husband Vic who for many years operated a mobile feed mill that toured farms in the area and farmed a small holding on Ham Hall Lane at Scruton.

Just two or three days later before Christmas we had a computer problem which fed the cows and though our man who looked after it quickly sorted the issue, I had failed to back up the records for months and so it was totally out of date and many cows were no longer with us or their feeding had changed after calving etc. The next couple of days and much of the nights right up to Christmas lunchtime when I got finished, were spent inputting every individual animal and all its details. I got it sorted and back on an even keel, it was all my own fault and after that I made sure I kept things up to date and had a backup disk in place.

Adam was 21 on the last day of the year, but not wanting to have his party when a lot else was going on that particular night, he asked for his party to be on the following Saturday, which we held at Bedale Golf Club- they did us proud with a terrific meal and everyone seemed to have a good night and dance. We had the four Norwegians Christin and Kjell Erik, Elisabeth and Tore to stay for a few days (Colin didn't feel he wanted to come and party after his recent sad loss of Liv) and we had them plus about another 20 friends and fellow students from Newton Rigg sleep in the house overnight. All of the youngsters on the floor of either the dining or sitting rooms in their sleeping bags – a good night was had by all and they headed away happily during Sunday after a full lunch, many of them back to college to start the Spring term the next day.

The early part of 2007 was busy but relatively uneventful, there was a short spell of extra work while Stuart was away skiing in Switzerland – it was something he always looked forward to and went quite regularly, having first started with school trips. It had obviously been a very mild and growy winter as I note in the diary that I cut all the house and farm lawns on the first of February, I think the earliest I had ever done so and have no real plans to repeat – far too early. Marnie took the children from Mowbray to see Arthur the Invisible and not too long after took them to Magma at

Sheffield, we went to see the new James Bond film, Daniel Craig in Casino Royale and then in February half term we thought we had earned a few days away and headed down to Devon and stayed at Torquay for the weekend, there was dancing in the lounge one night, I wasn't impressed at having to pay £5 to get a second cup of coffee, we went to look at the Babbacombe model village which was fantastic in its detail, visited the Orchid farm at Burnham, ate at a very good Italian restaurant at Paignton, particularly their zabaglioni, then the following day to Brixham Harbour and ate at a very good fish restaurant called 15, where we were highly entertained by the next table of noisy people who were busy discussing the merits of squid and calamari and which was the best, without ever realising they were the same thing. We were back from there in time to go over to Carlisle for the dispersal sale of Robert Musson's "Threelimes" herd. Robert was another great friend of Orton Eby over in Canada and had bought an odd heifer from us at the Black and White one year. We didn't go to buy anything, just some moral support. For any younger readers, if you were involved in Holstein Young Breeders, you may remember when Robert's daughter Jo was the national co-ordinator of the movement for a few years.

As springtime approached, it was getting towards grass harrowing time and we were still great believers in the benefit, particularly to longer leys and permanent pasture of having a bit of opening up and some dead grass pulled out. Conventional chain harrows didn't seem to last long and were awkward to move about, and so we bought a new set of Opico spring tine harrows on a folding frame, and I note that at that time they were £2,300, and on checking the sale records from our machinery sale after five seasons use, they made £3000, so a good return at plus £140 per year for a job well done, and proved their increasing popularity over the more traditional chain harrows. Finally, at the end of March we got the old moist grain tower taken down at the Grange. This was a sore sight for a long time, but anyone I approached was not interested or wanted silly money for doing so as there are an awful lot of nuts and bolts and all the sheets "super glued" as well, but I struck a deal with the local scrap men that they could have the metal if they took it down – I guess a win for both sides, and later we got the concrete base all covered up and blended in with soil as we completed the two narrow maize silage pits which had been the old original earth pits in the early days of grass silage some sixty years earlier. Just at that time Stuart brought his new pup "Archie" for the first time, he became something of a regular and a friendly feature in the yard for the next four or five years and was the star of the HYB "Field to Foto" competition later that year when he jumped off his "set" and disappeared.

In early April Marnie and I did something we had been planning to do for many years but had never got round to – to see the wild daffodils of Farndale. For anyone not from this part of the world, they are quite famous and are a fantastic sight at the right time of year. Being wild they are much smaller than the conventional garden daffodil, but in Farndale they are everywhere in fields and woodlands alongside the paths. The biggest problem is finding somewhere to get parked before you do the walk, and the second problem can be the walk, a lot of stiles and gates and if you do the full round trip as we did, and I think we did more than we need have, it is a long way, we reckoned we did about ten miles and it took up five and a half hours, not all walking, some of it was admiring both the daffodils and the scenery. I was about knackered by we got back to the car but had built up an appetite for supper at Sutton-under-Whitestonecliffe.

Max had given up coming by now, having got an apprenticeship with a builder, but he was replaced by James, who proved little, if any, better and he didn't last very long before we and Richmond school gave up on the project. Stuart went on his DIY AI Course and the first cow he served was Dalesend Pansy 92. She didn't hold to that service and by my records was never got in calf again, which was a pity as she was a hell of a good cow, not just my words or memory of her, she was EX93-4E, though I have no record of any daughters but she may have had one or two lost in the Foot and Mouth young stock slaughter of 2001. He soon got the hang of it and became very proficient. That meant three of us could now do AI, and with Richard and Stuart doing most of it, I gradually did less and less. Bill in his day as he got towards retiring did less and less and got me to do more and more, saying his arthritic old hands couldn't manipulate the cervix as easily. At the time I poo-poo'd him and told him it was just to save time, but I had got to the stage where I knew what he meant, as the flexibility in my hands declined. At the same time Stuart and the Bedale Brass Band were busy rehearsing for and then recorded a CD in West Tanfield Village Hall. I don't think I ever heard the result, but it didn't, sadly, make the big time and shoot them all to International stardom.

That spring the volunteers on the Wensleydale Railway were busy tidying up the sides just near the drive and were shedding up the saplings which they felled and all the brash. In total I got 38 25kg cake bags full of chippings and put down in the raspberry cage and they were far more successful at weed suppression than was plastic sheeting.

The early spring Bank Holiday saw us take a couple of days up in south-west Scotland and among other places we visited were the Logan Botanical Gardens near Stranraer. Being on the west coast and so near to the Gulf Stream, there were many plants growing there that you would not expect to see flourishing in Scotland.

Much of our spare time and effort that summer was in preparing for the National HYB weekend being hosted by the North Eastern Club. We had held regular meetings of the organising committee and we were to host the "Field to Foto" competition on the Sunday after having the judging competition at Mile's Littlebridge herd on the Saturday morning, a visit to the "Forbidden Corner" in the afternoon, with the Friday evening being at Metcalfe Farms' Washfold herd at Leyburn. Much time had been spent by a lot of the youngsters in halter breaking, first clip over of the forty or so heifers required for the competition and Ted Nicholson of E&P Electrics put in a special electric supply with isolator switches and all the necessary safety features for the clipping competition which also included the National Clipping Finals. The electrics at such events had always been a problem with surges when the stewards say go and everyone switches the clippers on at the same time, or when they are top-lining them ready for the showmanship and the hairdryers all go on at the same time, usually resulting in blown fuses. To tidy the place up we had finally got all the concreting done between the dry cow yards and the young stock building which had been hardcore. It was ok in good weather but got rather messy in wet weather with the constant use, fortunately finished about a fortnight before I record a very wet spell when we had 4.8" of rain (120ml approx.) in a forty eight hour period. Whilst we had concrete there, we made some stands for rope holders for show rings which proved very useful at various events over the next few years.

The plans for the actual HYB weekend were that the youngsters from all over the country would come to Newton Grange for four o'clock on the Friday afternoon and leave their cars to save them having to drive about all weekend. As a special treat we arranged for the Wensleydale Railway to lay on a special train to stop at the crossing of our drive to pick them up and take them on the very scenic route up to Redmire, where they would then be bused back to Washfold. I was highly amused as we were organising this that the railway were very concerned about the safety aspect of loading the train. I said we would put a few big square bales for them to jump up onto to join the train but was roundly told that that was definitely out of the question as a definite safety risk. Eventually they said they would see to it, and brought a rickety old set of wooden steps with a handrail on with a man at either side to hold it steady, far more likely to be an accident and much slower than a couple of big bales would have been. A look round the impressive (even then, much more so now) set up at Metcalfes at Leyburn and the one competition of the night the National HYB Tug of War, resulted in a home side victory for the N.E. Club followed by a barbecue supper before they boarded coaches to take them up to stay for two nights on Durham University campus. Imagine the dismay as travelling on the busses to Durham the news was announced that there had been a Foot and Mouth scare, centred on the MAFF research site at Pirbright, meaning we weren't allowed onto any of the farms and things had to be hastily re-arranged, the only thing left from the original plan was the Forbidden Corner visit and the "Deal or No Deal" quiz competition before the disco on the Saturday night. Fortunately, Sarah was involved with tennis and the Bedale Athletic and Sports Association at Bedale where the club ladies provided the lunch as planned rather than at Littlebridge and was also the setting for the "Field to Foto" competition on the Sunday. We managed to gather up various pet dogs, including the aforementioned "Archie" and they had to prepare them, set up a photo site and take a photo of such animals as well posed as they were able. Still judged by the original choice of judge in Jane Steel, the ingenuity and skill with which they adapted was great to see. For the first time ever, the HYB weekend was to feature an overseas team, and it was great to entertain a team from Italy, and it was they who proved the most adaptable in getting the dog to sit the best and produce the best shot. So, all the effort in cleaning up the place and Ted making all the electrics safe and secure was completely wasted, but everyone had a great weekend.

We had a request just before that from a Scotsman who was wanting to buy a substantial number of milkers of various ages and we got them all clipped and washed and turned out separately in the Front Field where they looked very well when he arrived. Imagine my dismay after a quick walk through them when he said sorry, but they were no good to him. I did feel rather better when he gave me the reason – they were too good in the udder as he was putting in robots and wanted udders with a bit more "variation" in them for the computer controlled teat cups to pick up more easily.

Adam had by now finished his course at Newton Rigg and we were very proud later to go for his graduation ceremony at Penrith when he had gained a triple distinction in the three elements of his game management course. Before that he had already got a job and in early June moved up to Hownam, just over Carter Bar into Scotland to start as an underkeeper for Eskdale Shooting Services. Another of these coincidences which keep cropping up is that at the graduation ceremony, the presenter of the awards was unable to attend at short notice and so the stand in was Mr Joe Harris, a local landowner with a fairly large estate between Penrith and Carlise. The coincidence was that he was Mr J's schoolboy best friend, but coincidences were further compounded just a couple of weeks later when he was shooting up at Eskdale and got his vehicle stuck on the moor, and Adam had to pull him out! When we took Adam up to Hownam he and Marnie went in his car but had a couple of hours to wait for the previous occupants to leave, and then had to "muck" the place out – literally. I followed later with the car and trailer with some furniture in it and had to get someone to come and guide me into his house in the middle of nowhere.

Later that week it was very wet, we had 4.8" of rain in 48 hours and there was water everywhere, and it was quite widespread over the country, and there were grave concerns about floods. As I travelled down to Lincolnshire to judge their Herds Competition, there was a detour from the M1 onto the A1 making it very busy, as there was concern over a reservoir dam somewhere in South Yorkshire and they had discovered a small crack and water seeping out and were very wary of it bursting and causing a disastrous surge of water down the valley and across the motorway. Fortunately, it didn't happen and the weather gradually improved. The Herds Competition was very difficult to judge, as many of the cattle had been kept inside on "end of season" straw because of the floods, one herd's dry cows were outside being fed in a ring feeder and I lost my wellingtons in the deep puddle getting to see them and had to be rescued by the farmer and the steward. Fortunately, by the end of my judging stint we had moved to a bit drier area and were able to see a great herd of cows, outside on reasonably dry ground at Messrs Winter's Coringham herd.

At the end of that week we went up to Hownam again to see Adam and do a few jobs in the house, and then the following week Marnie was up in Scotland again for Mowbray School's activity week which they spent on Bute – took 9½ hours to drive there. As always that was the same week as the Great Yorkshire Show, we did nothing much there, but Stuart finished up as the Champion Handler on the second day.

Mid-August and we went down to Islington for Emma and Cliff's christening of Jake and Daisy, their twins. It was a multi-christening affair of all nationalities and it was marvellous to see quite a lot of the relations of other children mostly of Caribbean descent in all their very fine and colourful dress – both men and women.

I caused amusement for a day or two among staff and family about then, when moving the combine as we did the winter barley. I was pulling the header up the Grange drive and missing a hole on the road with the JCB, I got a wheel of the header trailer off the side – at the highest drop into the Front Field. Fortunately, no damage was done, except to my ego, and we got it rescued and combining soon continued. I can at times be quite good at making a fool of myself in embarrassing circumstances and did the same later that autumn. We were using brewers' grains in the milking cow ration on a regular basis having made a pit beside the silage pit to hold a lorry load and had got a heavy rubber/plastic sheet to cover them with. After we got a load and then pushed up with the Loadall, I was up the back of it beside the silage pit wall, when I suddenly sank into them, wellies and all, and it took both Richard and Stuart to pull me out and then recover my wellingtons which by then were full of the stuff. Easily emptied and washed out and left to dry. Whilst talking of brewers' grains, there was more enjoyment one day after we had a load delivered. I was in the office and saw the empty lorry set off down the drive at a great speed only for it to shoot off the side and only the strainer post in the fence stopped it rolling right over – it transpired the driver was on his mobile phone and not watching what he was doing. A heavy rescue lorry from Colin Brown's at Langthorne had to come and get him mobile again, fortunately no damage done.

Stuart had been Champion Handler at the Great Yorkshire Show in July and then in October he went off to Canada, having been selected to represent the National HYB on the Semex "Walk of Fame" at the Royal Winter Fair in Toronto. The other British representative was Henry Sanderson and the two of them had a great couple of weeks, though I gathered they had to work fairy hard for the honour and privilege of going.

Just before Stuart disappeared for a fortnight, we had a short trip over to Norway to stay with Colin for a few days, he took us to see Elisabeth playing in a handball match, not played a lot in this country but quite a popular sport over there and it is quite fast and furious. Colin took us for a long walk up a hillside beside a waterfall which was very picturesque and quite hard work. As we came back down again, a helicopter flew very low over us and Colin said he could almost touch the skids underneath it and he would then have felt as if he was James Bond!

We had struggled for a while to have the balance of staff at weekends right, and in November of that year Andy Stonehouse started to milk on alternate weekends. Andy worked with his father at Pickhill, and it worked in very well for both him and us and gave us two pairs of hands each weekend. Andy milked on the mornings of Richard's weekends, which meant he could start a bit later and come in to feed up and do the young stock and then manage on his own in the afternoon. Stuart came in to help me on my weekends on and then I managed on my own in the afternoon. Later as Stuart became more proficient, we swopped over, and he got up to milk and I started later to do the feeding. It all worked in very well and gave us a degree of flexibility, whilst allowing everyone a slightly improved element of free time – something most dairy set-ups are still trying to achieve some twelve years later.

Mid-December saw me away twice, up to Northumberland to judge their winter Herds Competition and then up to speak at the South of Scotland Holstein Club. We then had the farm lunch at Panetti's that year and the next day Spottie calved for the first time, and she gave us some enjoyment for the next few years, being Reserve Champion Heifer at the Royal Highland Show and right up to the sale she had a character all of her own and if you were near her as she ate, she had the habit of getting a mouthful of silage and throwing it up in the air and all over you as well as herself.

In the new year of 2008 we took part in the first ever North Eastern Club Winter Herds Competition for an individual cow and heifer and a group of six animals, and were delighted a fortnight later to learn that we were placed second in the group and second with the best cow with Dalesend Stormy Pamela. At a similar time, I had to break into Dalesend as Mr and Mrs J had locked themselves out. It was a grand feeling to act the 'criminal' – break a window to be able to open it, climb in and then open the door from the inside.

That January I was invited to join the Leyburn Dairy Group and attended my first meeting at Nigel Dinsdale's. The group meets on the second Tuesday of each month from October to March and goes round each other's farms when the host has to be on his mettle to answer the probing questions of his peers, and usually one meeting goes out of the area to a go ahead dairy farm doing a superb job. The group continues today, and I am pleased to still be welcome some eight years after stopping dairying and enjoy the banter and challenges that the industry faces, even if we can no longer host a meeting.

Soon after that I went with Mr J down to near Wakefield to Morrison's head office where we met Ken Foster as JGR having established Dalepak and Richmond Ice Cream within the food industry, wanted to explore what other opportunities might be emerging, and a couple of days later Marnie and I went to York to see the film "Sweeny Todd", very gruesome with blood everywhere with Johnny Depp in lead role – Marnie and I howled with laughter at it, but don't think we were supposed to, everyone else seemed to think it was a horror story. We called at Sweet Basil on the way home for a very good Thai meal.

In the February half term we took a trip down to Lewes in Sussex – a lovely old fashioned sort of town and made some interesting trips to the Kew arboretum at Wakehurst where they have established the millennium seed bank, to Rye – another picturesque and "olde-worlde" town and of course, historically, one of the 'Cinque ports'. To Dover to see the white cliffs, but otherwise a horrible place, over run with traffic for the ferries, Brighton where we saw great piles of wood piled up on the beach which had been washed up from a recently sunk ship, Chichester and Arundel.

Later in the month Market Rasen in Lincolnshire had an earthquake measuring 5.3 on the Richter scale, and just a week or two later we were down in Lincolnshire for their Herds Competition Dinner at the Petwood Forge Hotel. We had stayed years previously when we found the hotel in Sleaford that we were going to stay at looked horrible, so drove past and found the Petwood instead, which was a very good hotel that had some of the most enormous rhododendron blossoms I have ever seen.

Machinery and animals don't that often go together, but they did in March when new legislation meant that anyone transporting animals more than I think it was 60km needed an Animal Transport Certificate of Competence, I arranged for the test to be done and Sarah and Stuart and myself who were the most likely to need to drive to say Carlisle all took it, along with two from Hornby Castle and three from Martin Websters. It was one of these computer-generated tests overseen by an outside man from some government quango – everybody passed. Many people don't know or aren't aware of such requirements unless they get stopped or have an accident. Not that long after a breeder had got stopped on a routine check on his way into Carlisle market, fortunately he lived under the required mileage, and so was ok.

Reverting to owning our main tractor rather than contract hiring it and to make sure there could be no criticism of whatever we bought, I took Richard and Stuart with me to look at a John Deere that wasn't really suitable and then across to the Russell's Open Day at the Eden Camp and I finalised a deal on a three year old TM135, Ford or as now called New Holland for £22,500. It did our job very nicely for the 3½ years until we sold it at our farm machinery dispersal sale for £16,900. That was £5600 over that time, much better than the £1000/month wanted to continue the contract hire which would have needed £42,000. You have to win sometimes!!

Marnie's uncle Cecil sadly died in spring 2008, he appears earlier in the story of John Thistlethwaite and hoeing potatoes. He liked a little gamble on the horses, usually favourites, and when he was living in The Millings in Bedale he used to walk down to his 'office' as he called the bookies or to go to the bank. I met him outside the bank one day and had a word, and when I went to the Nat West the following day, he was again sat on the seats outside. I sat down beside him and asked if he had been there all night making sure his money was safe, and he just grunted at me.

In early May it was Dick Barry's funeral at Carlton in Cleveland. Dick had been a member of the Patrick Brompton Buying Group on behalf of the Faceby Farms which he managed, and I represented the group at his funeral. Still only a young man, he was very distinctive whenever he answered the telephone – the number and then Dick Barry here. A day or two later it was the funeral of Mrs Wilson at Patrick Brompton where she lived for many years after their retirement from Hutton Hang, now very well managed by grandson James, who latterly did all our crop spraying for us. You could put money on it that I would get a telephone call from Mrs Wilson at harvest time to complain about us spreading straw on the road as we led straw to Dalesend, and she blamed it all on us, even though the number of loads going up the dale at that time was very large.

At the end of May, I took JGR up to Hexham Abbey to attend John Moffitts Memorial Service. He was a contemporary of Mr J and with his Hunday herd and chairmanship of Premier Breeders as it became from CBS, they had always been rivals but both had tremendous respect for each other. He had been one of the great agriculturalists of the second half of the twentieth century and will be remembered not only for the herd which he developed, but also his marvellous collection of agricultural machinery, particularly his "Ferguson" collection, also for the enormous contribution he made to many agricultural organisations over those many years. Sad to say, that herd, like Dalesend is no longer in existence.

A little later in the year I and Bill went to Darlington for Stan Dixon's funeral. Stan had lived next to Suggitt's Corner at Newton-le-Willows as long as I can remember and had looked after our cattle feeding for many years until he was ill some years previously. He had worked originally for Lever's who then became Silcocks and then BOCM-Silcock.

The saddest of all funerals we had to attend that year was up in Scotland. Phil who shared a house with Adam up at Hownam turned over and rolled a Kabuto up on the hill and was trapped underneath it, and Adam got back to him first, but he passed away in his arms with a ruptured spleen, a terrible thing for a young man to adjust to, but what really upset Adam was that when he finally got back to the house, there were some police waiting to inspect Phil's gun cabinet and remove his guns – and that was before they had even been to inform his parents of his loss. He was a grand lad, at 6'7" he made Adam look small, and that first shooting season, the two of them in effect lost a man between them in weight as they went from well-looked after students to working young men. Phil was also a keen fisherman and had represented Scotland in junior angling competitions in earlier years. The enquiry into the accident and the health and safety issues rumbled on for Eskdale for several years after, before ultimately being cleared of any wrong doing. Phil's passing was no doubt one of the main reasons that they very soon moved Adam to a new beat at Longcroft, where he still lives today.

Having got all those out of the way in one go, let's get back to rather happier things. That spring Mr and Mrs J swopped homes with Charles, and they went up to Hill Top East, and in June of that year Stuart and I moved Mr J's office from the red room at Dalesend up to Hill Top East. His big glass desk was very heavy and was to take apart to get through doorways, but he soon got his office re-organised. They also had a party "Goodbye to Dalesend" before they moved.

Shortly after that Marnie and I had a weekend away to Aintree for the Grand National. We have always been great believers that you should try and attend as many of these grand occasions as you possibly can, and we had a good couple of days, even if it was a very long walk from the coach park to the grandstands and was a bitterly cold, if fine day, Comply and Die at 7-1 was the winner that year. That night we stayed at Cottons Hotel for a bit of luxury, the next morning had an interesting walk round the gardens at Tatton Park, even if it was too early in the year to be a lot of colour.

On Marnie's birthday, or the day before we went up to Gateshead, walked across the Tyne to lunch at the tapas bar before going to the Falcon's final game of the season which they just won 28-25, and then the next day to the tulip festival at Constable Burton Hall, and collected a cow from Leyburn where she had been on the farming stand at the Wensleydale Festival of Food and Farming. I used to do a spell on the farming stand for several years. It was quite fascinating to talk to people with little or no knowledge of agriculture and even be so basic as to tell them which was a sheep, pig or cow. Fortunately, most of them were eager to learn, and if we are honest, we wouldn't know very much about what goes on in the back streets of Leeds or Bradford. There is still a massive educational requirement we as farmers need to get more involved with as we move forward with all the focus on global warming, vegetarianism and veganism and many of the mis-leading let alone down right wrongs which are heaped upon agriculture – remember, the people who do the complaining always have full stomachs, you rarely hear a complaint from someone who is hungry!!

The day after I sent Stuart up to Carkin to help them and Sarah get ready for the N.E. Club stock judging later that night. He was getting paid by us anyway, but it was not until several years later that I learnt he had never been offered anything for the work he did up there, nor had any thanks for it – typical!

Whilst we were busy silaging, Marnie and others took a class from Mowbray to visit Thomas the Bakers at Helmsley which they all found fascinating, and just the week before they had had them up to Reeth to do some sketching. In the May half term we had a long weekend away and stayed down in the Midlands and had a great day looking round and admiring all the restoration work that has been done at Chatsworth and the following day a fascinating visit to the National Tram Museum in Derbyshire, where many old machines from towns all over the country had been restored and looked tremendous in their newly painted liveries. We came back via Lincolnshire and over the Humber Bridge.

Patrick Brompton church at the time was struggling, as all village churches do to meet their financial commitments, particularly the "quota" to the diocese, and in St. Patrick's case the insurance which had to be of the highest order because of its Grade 1 listed status. As long as 12 years ago, the two combined came to about £15,000 and that's before you switched the lights on as you went in. A lot for a small parish and congregation to find apart from the actual running of the church on a day to day basis, and always galling to the local people that so much goes out of the parish, and the ordinary local non-church goers are unaware of, and think the church is always "on the cadge". As a PCC at my suggestion we decided to hold a charity auction, and I finished up having to do most of the chasing of things for the auction, but we finished up with a good list and a glorious summer's evening at Dalesend to host the event with a wine and cheese evening. I had a slight fall out with David Christie, the vicar, who thought we should have some small lots for ordinary people to bid for, as he thought poorer people wouldn't be able to afford a day's pheasant shooting, or a day's salmon fishing for example. I didn't take a lot of notice and it was too late to change the list after it had gone to print and been promoted. I had called in a lot of favours from people we had used over the years, and with Robin Jessop wielding the gavel, we raised a superb £4,600 for church funds, which the vicar didn't seem to object to.

We couldn't show at the Great Yorkshire Show because of Blue Tongue restrictions, brought in after it was confirmed in the south the previous autumn. The boundary between the regions was between us and Harrogate, so instead we ventured north for the first time in years to the Royal Highland Show and were rewarded with Dalesend Dundee Spottie being Reserve Junior Champion under Paul Harrison, but there was for my liking too much messing about going on with milk cows, injections, batteries and leads onto cows teats and blocks on feet shaved down so they walked straighter rather than because there was anything wrong with the foot. The perpetrators do not seem to grasp the fact that it would only need one photo on the front page of a national newspaper for the impression to be given that all cows are treated like that and that milk is not as wholesome as they might think.

We had some excitement just at the time of second cut silage at the end of June. I got a phone call from John Wilson of Crakehall to tell us some of his Highland cattle had escaped along the beck side, through the Reeds and into the Park at Dalesend. This was a Sunday morning not far from lunchtime and just as we were about to start mowing the Park. We were told they were very wild and uncontrollable, only having been let out the day before by John's son, whose cattle they were. A field of 25 acres like the Park is not the best of fields to try and round up a few cattle, but we did have a proper handling pen between it and the West Field. Metcalfe Farms had two big mowers to cut the grass, and having opened the gate into the pen, they cut round the outside in tandem – it worked a treat and they went straight in. There was a bit of fun about getting the animals into the race, none of them would go into the pen, but Sarah and I did so, and they again obliged. Next thing we knew a vehicle came straight across the Park over cut and uncut grass – he was a vet with a gun and approved to shoot the bull – first thing he did was get a good bulling for not going round between the swathes like everyone else. He seemed to think he could shoot it dead while loose in the race – and I asked him how he was going to safely do that, and why it wanted shooting dead anyway to which he had no answer and he soon went away with tail between his legs. By that time John was back with his trailer and the bull soon ran in and away he went back home, and we got our lunch, even if the Yorkshire puddings were a bit "well done".

Fertiliser that year was quite expensive, but I saw some "seconds" advertised in the Farmer's Guardian and got a wagon load at well reduced prices. The first few bags we used while still fresh was ok, but it got gradually harder, lumpier, and more set the longer it sat. After second-cut I decided we would have it used up and spent most of a very uncomfortable day riding in the tillage spreader breaking it up as we went along – it was my fault so only right I did the horrible job while Stuart drove the tractor – but we eventually got it used – I don't think the spread pattern would be too good but I have no one else to blame but myself. I note a little later that barley that year was £110/tonne.

Cattle prices were reasonably good at that time and we sold 11 young cows and heifers for £17,000 to David Oversby from Grassington. David had at that time just started processing his own milk and has since then developed the business tremendously into what is now well known as "Dales Dairies" and only recently took over one of our local processors Hauxwell Dairies and continues to expand. Since before Sarah started her own business, she has made regular visits to Grassington as she does the matings for David's dairy herd and has also bought a fair number of cows either with him or on his behalf at a variety of northern sales and privately.

Round about that time, Doug and Elsie Ponton who had been in the Bungalow for a few years, decided to move to Northallerton. They had had quite a bad a car accident previously just outside the entrance to Dalesend, and neither of them were yet able to drive and so they were rather stuck out in the countryside and wanted to be rather nearer to civilisation. It wasn't too difficult to find a new tenant as Sarah was wanting to move back into the area from her home up at Newsham as most of her friends and activities were in our area. She had been working for Holstein UK on their journal magazine for a couple of years, but at that time decided to set up her own business. After some upgrading of various things in the bungalow she moved in, and on 2nd August 2007 had the launch party for 'The Farm Organisation', which as many farmers all over will know or have used, as she writes, promotes, prepares, buys and sells animals for people and anything to do with mostly agriculture, but not averse to non-farming work, including catering for anything from an on-farm snack lunch to a full blown wedding reception and anything in between, very ably helped for most of that time by Sarah Jarvis.

Shortly after that we vaccinated everything against 'Blue Tongue' as advised, but I was never convinced it was either necessary or beneficial, it was just more work and hassle. A day later we had a visit from Kite Consulting who had the contract with Arla to do Carbon footprint assessments and it was gratifying to find they worked ours out to be 0.85kg per litre against a national figure at that time of 1.1kgs.

There was some heavy rain at the end of August, and as we were obviously not going to be harvesting for a few days, we decided to go up to Adams, but by the time we got to Catterick there was already a lot of water about and flooding from the Swale, being over its banks and it got worse as we went north until by the time we got a phone call from Adam telling us not to go as we wouldn't get there, they were cut off by floods and they were also cut off further up the hill and they couldn't get to feed or see to the birds for two or three days, and they lost quite a lot in the meantime.

Apart from the Royal Highland Show that year, we only ventured out twice and were rewarded with Dalesend Lettice 74 as Reserve Champion at Wensleydale and Dalesend Silky Rena Reserve Champion at Stokesley. At the Yorkshire Club Dinner and Awards that autumn, Spottie was 1st Heifer in Milk and a group of Allen daughters won the best three heifers' class. This was followed later in the N.E. Club's winter herd competition by Silky Rena being the Best Cow and Lettice 74 2nd in the Best Heifer, added to which Dalesend Silky Rena also won the Best Cow in the summer Herd Competition.

An interesting visit to the Mouseman Museum at Kilburn one Saturday, a superb performance from Northallerton Male Voice Choir in the church were among the highlights that autumn. The choir contained a few farmers I knew, Peter Corner from Harlsey, Brian Phillips from Warlaby and Keith Blenkiron from the road to Yafforth, together with Richard Kershaw, now the Managing Director of Yorkshire Timber whom we had got to know through his daughter and Sarah being in the same class at Ripon Grammar School.

More problems in early November, when probably our best cow at the time Dalesend Stormy Pamela, a highly scored second calver with a long pedigree was down with the splits one morning. We tried lifting her for a couple of days and put her out in the Back Field, even though it was November – the cold was likely to do her less harm than the splits. At that time there had been some promotion of water chambers to lift downer cows, and after quite a bit of time on the telephone, I eventually tracked down the nearest one I could locate – over near Lancaster. I had to go and collect it and then we spent the next few days messing on with it and her with no success or improvement at all and went back to lifting her with a hoist. Although she did brighten up and tried to stand once or twice, it was all to no avail and we had eventually to send her in. A week later I had the water bath to take back and the total cost for the week was £375 - a very dear bite for no return, and there was my time in collection and return, plus two men for several hours on several days! You never hear anyone mention them now, I can't say I'm surprised on our experience. I still think if a cow is going to get up, she will, and something down overnight from that sort of injury, is very unlikely to make it.

A day or two later we hosted a Dairy Co open day at Newton Grange, which was on silage utilisation, with a good crowd of thirty plus. Nothing very revolutionary, just re-asserting the best of principles on pit/face management and the correct use of forages and the feeding out of it. Very relevant for the time of year, and by their assessment, we seemed to be doing most things reasonably right.

Marnie was very busy that autumn with the youngsters from Mowbray, going with them up to Newcastle Aquarium and to the Angel of the North for photography/art projects and then soon afterwards took some of them up to the Sage at Newcastle to see a play.

We had one of our best days classifying in late November, with Geoff Bone in charge of the computer, with seven new EX, nine rescored EX's, and 21 new VG's including eight 2-year-olds. By this time we had got into the habit of sorting out what were to do as we milked the night before, milked the rest about five the next morning and then classified about 6.30am, so the cows had natural milk on them prior to a normal morning milking time, and it suited the cows, the classifier and ourselves to do it like that, and I think the results helped to prove that. A very quick change and then to Les Ward's funeral at Kirby Sigston – a grand chap, same age as me.

The week after we had a very good N.E. Club meeting at Thirsk, when the speaker was Mark Nutsford of Riverdane fame. Mark will be known to many as the developer of an outstanding herd of cows which he has sold as a unit two or three times and then rebuilt from his own heifers. He also established a very successful and well used embryo breeding business that is widely used by many of the top breeders today, and also started and developed the AI company King Street Sires. What many people will not know and we didn't until Mark spoke at that meeting, was that he originated from up in Cleveland, learnt his trade with Northsea Holsteins and one or two other top herds, and you have to admire the way he has built his business from very small beginnings.

We had some very heavy snow in a few hours in early December, followed by rain. About five inches in total, the most we had had for several years, and everywhere very wet and "puddly", but followed by a few frosts it dried up nicely enough for us finally to finish concreting the middle piece of the gap in-between the dry cow buildings and the young stock one. We had planned originally to do it over several years to spread the cost but had grown increasingly tired of the mess left when the hard core got very wet, and so finally took the plunge and did it. A piece like that which took all the machinery with silage trailers and feed lorries delivering 20 tonnes at a time in some cases, meant that the concrete had to be a good depth and reinforcing put in as well. It is common now to go on to farms, where the concrete is beginning to break up from when it had been laid long before everything became so big and heavy. It is very expensive, you see a load of ready-mix coming in with a load of about £650 of concrete and know it is not going to go very far, but once done it made things so much better, easier and cleaner and we never regretted for a moment shortening the time over which we were going to do it. This last piece, right up the centre was the easiest to do, there was no shuttering or such to do.

We had a very good farm Christmas lunch at the King's Head at Masham before I went off to a NVZ meeting at Jersey Farm at Barnard Castle, then after a quiet Christmas, I took the motorbike, some big blue drums to make into feeders and Mr Bill up to Adams. He gave Mr Bill a grand tour of some of the shooting areas before we had a sandwich lunch at Kirk Yetholm (the end of the Pennine Way) before we came back home. We got the cows ready for and had the judge for the Winter Classic, where a fortnight later we learnt we had come 2nd with the group of six cows, Silky Rena was the Best Individual Cow and Lettice 74 was 2nd in the Best Heifer class, and then the next night we went to Darlington Theatre to see the Ukrainian National Ballet do Swan

Lake. Not a usual ballet as you would understand it, but still very good and rather better that I thought it might be

After hearing William Hague, who was our local MP who later was to become Foreign Secretary, speak at Aysgarth School, the next day was the All Breeds Calf Show at Thirsk Auction Mart which had been postponed from the autumn because of the Blue Tongue restrictions. We went in good time as I was to steward the Judges, but Marnie finished up doing that while I did the commentary as whoever was supposed to do it didn't turn up. They never turned up after that and I have now been doing the commentary ever since. The trouble that day was that it was bitterly cold with quite a strong wind and both calves and people were absolutely frozen. We went straight from there to Clifton Moor at York to see Slumdog Millionaire which was very entertaining and then supper at Sweet Basil, by which time we had just about got thawed out. We had had a good day at the show into the bargain winning two of the calf classes and Stuart being Reserve Champion Holstein handler.

A few days later it was sad to go to Miss Heugh's funeral at Patrick Brompton. A staunch Methodist, Freda Heugh was 98, but couldn't quite make the century for which she was aimed. Known throughout the area in earlier days on her sit up and beg bicycle with wicker basket on the front, she was always smiling and happy with a great optimistic outlook – a real character.

Richard, Stuart and I had a bite of lunch in Leyburn one day before going to Bolton Castle Farms to see the Heatime Collars in operation and then to John and James Simpson's at Gildersbeck to see their roll-over foot-trimming crush and automatic calf feeder. We did subsequently invest in the Heatime system through Semex and installed a roll-over crush which was very well used, but never did go down the automatic calf feeding route, and were working towards pasteurised milk with a specially designed small pasteuriser mobile unit – and in fact had one ordered which had to be cancelled at the time of our dispersal some two and a half years later. Another day out a week later when I took Mr J over to Lancaster for a trip out for the Lancashire Holstein Club's January sale which is always their special one, and this one was extra special being the 600th. Over the previous 50 years he had become great friends with many of their leading breeders, and though he wasn't very mobile, many of them came to have a word with him. People like Jim Burrows, Tom Drinkall, The Townleys of Mearsbeck and Knowsley gave him a very enjoyable day out.

The early part of 2009 was busy in many ways. The sad bits first as we said goodbye to Maisie Newcombe, Malcolm and Dennis Percival's mother who had helped in the house at Dalesend for many years and had lived in several of our houses over those years. Just a day or two later it was Stan Donaldson's funeral at the Chapel in Wycar, Bedale – a marvellous service in memory of a very devout Methodist and a superb solo by Brian Phillips. We had sold virtually all our corn down to Flood Bridge straight off the combine, both wheat and barley for a lot of years. Never did we set a price beforehand, always fixed at the time of settling up a matter of days after finishing combining, and never an argument about the price, just a bit of friendly negotiation. It was an annual pleasure trip to go down there to settle up always timed to coincide with ten o'clocks, so Stan and Brian didn't waste valuable working time, and usually a scone or a piece of teacake from Mrs Donaldson. We continue up to today still to take our corn there, though a lot less of it, and Brian continues farming in the same very efficient manner, ably helped now by his nephew Matthew, and they have recently moved into another direction with the erection of a large egg laying unit.

Shortly after that Marnie and I went to Barcelona for a long weekend in the half term holiday. The weather for mid-February was fantastic, warm and sunny and we marvelled at all there was to do and see in that marvellous city. Our hotel was just off the Ramblas and we admired watching the living statues all around the square, the amazing fruit stalls and fish and meat on sale in the La Boqueria market, we took an open topped bus ride around the city, saw the Olympic area of a few years previously, marvelled at the Sagrada Familia started by Gaudi and still unfinished after 120 years, and I guess there is a vested interest in never getting it finished. Visited Park Guell full of his offbeat designs and visited the Picasso Museum. A great trip, much enjoyed and a place we would go back to again.

In early March I was honoured to be elected as President of the Yorkshire Holstein Club. I believe I was only the second person to have been President of both the Yorkshire and North Eastern Clubs, the other one being Mr J.

At that time we decided to get Len Porter to make us some proper permanent catching pens and handling facilities for heifers in the bottom corner of Corner Banks at Hill Top East, the Reeds, the Drive Side at Dalesend and improve the ones between the Park and West Fields. Quite expensive to do, but well worth it for the greatly improved efficiency as we seemed to spend more and more time injecting or treating animals for or against everything. At two of them we also made a funnel to help guide them into the pens.

Another night away and a great experience when we went over to Manchester to see Tina Turner in concert – what a fantastic performer – the energy she puts into her act is quite staggering, particularly for someone of her age. Afterwards we ate at a Cantonese restaurant which, at least to us, was unusual in that they started a 30% discount on the price at midnight to encourage extra diners. It was great some nine years later to go down to London to see "Tina- The Musical" which was about her life story, and the young lady who played her had the same kind of energy to belt out those great songs.

Adam was home for a few days holiday, and while he was here, sat patiently and waited and eventually shot the crow which had been plaguing Sarah at the bungalow, arriving on various windows early in the morning and pecking at the putty around the windows, and making quite a mess of them.

For many years we had used the horse box as our farm trailer, but as we moved more stock about and we were selling regularly at Carlisle, we took the plunge and bought our first cattle trailer – an Ifor Williams, which for those who like to take note of such things was £3350 with nothing to part exchange as they kept the horsebox at Dalesend. It was a rather capital expensive spring as we also put in the roll-over crush at £6750 and changed our small JCB loadall. By that time, we like everyone else had become very dependant on that particular machine, used each and every day to mix and feed cows, and so it had to be kept up to date and be fully operational, but it cost up to £23,000 to change it, though that did include the silage block cutter and a sweeper brush – both helped our efficiency in maintaining good clamp faces, and keeping the place tidy now that all was concreted both front and back, and Stuart if he had a spare ten minutes would put the brush on and have a clean-up.

Our God-daughter Vicky Barker's wedding was an enjoyable day in a very busy spring, in a mild and dry period, with the swallows arriving very early on the 14th April and us drilling maize on the same day, I think the earliest we had ever done so. A sunny day out in early May took us for a ride out over to the upper dales and we had some very moderate "Chunky-Funky" soup as they called it at Tan Hill pub as we checked out a hotel as a base for summer school for Mowbray near Hawes Water where they also looked after and nurtured the fast declining red squirrels.

We were still doing some embryo transfer work at the time but decided to have a change of operator and started to use "Spike" from Lambert, Leonard and May. He wasn't a vet but worked under their supervision and came with a very good reputation which in our work with him was fully justified. He was never prepared to compromise in making adjustments to timings of either donors or recipients to make a visit fit in with others in the area, and regularly travelled massive distances to make the timings right. He was also very definite in his use of recipients and was not prepared to implant an egg unless she was a 100% correct. That attention to detail worked very well for us and by our dispersal sale some two and half years later we had built up a useful stock of embryos which sold well at the sale.

At a similar time, we had a request from a commercial dairyman over Skipton way for some good cows, and they visited and picked out four young cows and we agreed a total price of £11,500. Granted they were good cows with some breeding which we really didn't want to sell, but just short of £3000 each at home was too good a price to turn down. What amazed me was that they neither milk recorded nor classified, so the pedigrees were going to be wasted – they just liked good looking cows, and who were we to argue!

At the end of May we went across into East Yorkshire for me to be Master Judge at a Yorkshire Club night at Peter Waring's, Winton herd. The day after, on the Saturday we had a ride out towards the coast, called at a nice garden centre started by two elderly brothers who had tired of trying to make their fortune farming – in talking with them, they had been a few times up into our part of the world and taken inspiration from Braithwaite's here at Leeming Bar. We went across the Holderness with some very good arable farmland but as we headed down towards Spurn Point it was disappointing to see so many derelict farm buildings and farmsteads where farms had been amalgamated and the house sold off to non-farming families. The day after as we made our way back home, we called in at a fund-raising event for the local church, which was a walk through the woods on Lord Manton's estate. I thought it was a good fund raising idea and suggested it at one of our PCC meetings but it was thought to be too much hard work and people just looked for problems from a health and safety point of view. Before we had tea at Hovingham we visited a pick your own farm and got some strawberries and asparagus.

We like all other farmers by this time were becoming more aware of the need to be much more careful with our slurry application, use of nitrogen, sprays etc, and I decided to have some slurry injected after first cut silage. The 27 acre was a good field on which to trial this, big enough to do some and miss bits to see if there was any difference. The slurry pit was full, and we got AWSM to do the slurry injection and their tankers to haul it to the field. We had had a very dry spell and they struggled to get enough liquid mixed in, even with a big stirrer, but the job was eventually done. It worked out quite expensive in contractor application charges and we couldn't really see a lot of benefit from it getting nearer to the roots to start with, for all their claims of not needing any further fertiliser, and we had a very moderate second cut from it, needless to say we didn't go down that particular route again. Our usual way of emptying the slurry pit had for a long time been using the slurry guzzler which either Stuart or Mr Bill did for us, but as we got more animals it became an endless job, especially in a wet spell and at times we were having to spread when really we should not have been on the land, either from a travelling or environmental point of view, and I was beginning to look at other possible storage and spreading opportunities.

A quick trip down into Derbyshire one Sunday for Bill and Roberta Higson's Ruby Wedding party was most enjoyable as was a trip up to Scotland for the Highland Show a few days later, staying with Adam overnight on the way. At the foot of Carter Bar, the police camera flashed, and Adam gave me a good talking to when we got there – "Father everyone knows there is a speed camera there, apart from, apparently you!". Luckily, they must have decided I wasn't that far over the limit as no summons ever arrived, and it had definitely gone off.

Holstein UK had decided with the demise of the Royal Show, to take the National Judging School Finals around the country, rather than base them at another show. The first time was the previous year when they were held at the Noremead herd down in Wiltshire, and we were invited to host them in 2009. Whilst it meant a lot of work in tidying up and getting ready for them, in addition to getting all the cattle halter broken and taught to lead properly, it was a great honour to be asked to be the hosts. There were three classes of six animals, plus five for the linear, including the one to demonstrate on, and another six for a demonstration class. With a spare for every class, it was over thirty to get organised and clipped and then the day before and the morning of the event to wash and then get top lined and turned out for the two hundred or so young judges who came from all over the country to judge and it was a fantastic sight to see all three classes being paraded at the same time in the yard. Marnie did a buffet lunch for the judges, stewards and other Society dignitaries who were here – all in all a marvellous day.

We were very fortunate on that day with the weather – it was very hot and sunny at the end of a spell of hot and dry weather. Just as well because two days later the heavens opened. We learnt what it was like to be in the eye of the storm when we had 1.5" of rain in just forty minutes – including some very big hailstones. It rained so hard that the gutters on the main cow building couldn't get it away fast enough and it was coming across the concrete and over the sill to get through the back door, though I managed to keep it at bay until the rain passed. It was white over with hailstones and in fact in odd places where it had come against a wall there were still some left the next morning. In the garden the rain/hailstones had shredded the lupins, begonias and geraniums and out in the fields the maize had taken something of a battering, though it was still early enough in the season for it to recover.

A trip down to Ashby-de-la-Zouch Show – not a big turnout, but what was there were very good, and there was a terrific turnout of handlers in the senior handling class, particularly from the Jersey breed. That was followed immediately by the Great Yorkshire Show where I had official duties to perform as the Yorkshire Club President, also standing in for Phillip Davies as the National President who was unable to attend. We did nothing particularly with our own cattle in the show, were 2nd with the Exhibitor Bred Group and 3rd with an Exhibitor Bred Pair of any breed – emphasising once again – our role as breeders, not buyers of show winners.

An enjoyable evening was held the week after at the North Eastern Club barbecue which was held at Neil Bellerby's and included a class of goats to judge from Neil's large goat milking enterprise. I don't think many of us knew what we were looking for, but it made quite a change. At the end of July, a carload of us went up to Brian Davidson's at Errolston in Scotland for the Holstein UK Celebration Open Day at which Sarah was doing the lunch for about 300 people.

We had been struggling for a while with our vets, not the main partners who were all very good, but their younger vets were not up to the job, and the principals are not always available to attend for either routine or emergency visits. I know the younger members of the profession have to get their experience somewhere, but when they ask you what you think after they say they don't know, which was the reason for requesting a visit in the first place, it is rather disconcerting, as was the refusal one Sunday morning from a young vet, when I was on my own to give me a roll-over with a downer cow. Enough was plenty and we moved to Bishopton Vets from Ripon, a very go-ahead practice with specialist large animal vets apart from ones dedicated to horses, pigs and small animals. We had met with and talked to Phil Alcock about moving to them and the move went smoothly, and we very soon got into an amicable working arrangement. They also had a lead vet for each dairy farm and a second vet also, which meant that for most of the regular work you were always seeing the same people and they got to know the herds profile. We had only been with them less than a fortnight when we had an emergency calving of a heifer, with an upside down, backwards calf and a leg through the uterine wall as it was delivered. Internal bleeding needed very fast attention, the student vet was sent to get things from the car but was very slow, Neil decided to go himself and was back before the young lady, got the heifer's bleeding clamped off and all was well. Needless to say, the young lady student never re-appeared as a fully-fledged vet at Bishopton, but the young newly qualified one – Neil Eastham became our lead vet and is now a partner in the practice.

Sadly at that time we attended Mrs Teasdale's funeral, she had been Sarah's junior school first teacher, was a real "mother hen" who looked after the new starters and really taught them without them ever realising they were being so taught. Her husband Bert had for a long time been an AI man, and had, even after he retired still come and done the odd insemination for us if both Bill and I were away. I actually met him in Bedale, just last week (January 19) and he was in very good fettle and said he still went up to his and now his daughters own small holding every day, despite being into his 90's.

We had over the years had several cows produce over 100 tonnes of milk, which in the early days was marked by a special certificate but more latterly had been by the presentation of a model cow. We had several of these which had been given to various people as mementos, and JGR complained that he himself had never got one. Just then Dalesend Pansy 87 just managed to squeeze 100 tonnes and by then you could get them painted in the actual markings of the cow, though they were by then to pay for. I ordered one and after a while rang to see why it had never arrived. Holstein UK referred me to the Shebeg potters on the Isle of Man who did them and when I spoke to the gentleman he said he was glad I had rung because the request had come for it but without any paperwork either about the cow or its owner and so couldn't get in touch. By chance, he just had the one model left as he was retiring and not doing them anymore but painted that one for us after I sent him photographs of the cow, and so we were able to give Mr J his own model cow from the Pansy family.

Early September saw us down into Cheshire for the Holstein UK Convention which was also to mark the Centenary of the Society, and opened with a special celebratory service in Chester Cathedral and followed with a visit to the Cogent bull stud, Messrs Robert's Townhouse herd, and the Centenary Society Sale at Beeston where we had a very good trade with the very showy yearling heifer Dalesend Queen 28 which sold for 3600gns to Jim Warnock of the Capelleferne herd in Kent and a Dolman Rosanna heifer at 2000gns down into Devon. It was straight from Chester up to Carlisle for the annual bull sale where there was little trade and we brought them home.

I took JGR down to the Dairy Show at the National Event Centre at Birmingham, he enjoyed his day but was tired by mid afternoon and we came home in good time. Later that week I was down to Floodbridge to settle up for that season's corn – for those interested it was £80/tonne for the barley and £88 for wheat that year, there was a lot about and yields had been good all over.

I went down to Cirencester for our college reunion, picking John Foss up near Darnsley on the way. We had Vic Hughes, the ex-Principal who had been Farms Director when we were there and Dai Barling our crops lecturer as guests at the dinner at night and the next day visited Kemble Farms for a very interesting tour of the farm with 750 milkers and the first bio-digester unit I had visited – now of course quite common place.

Spottie had not been doing very well for a few weeks, had gone off her milk somewhat, was not eating very well and loosing condition, but nothing outwardly to be seen. After several unsuccessful examinations, it was finally decided, she must have a wire in her stomach and so an operation ensued. Fortunately, they found the wire before it did any serious damage internally, she got over the operation quickly and continued on her own imperious way.

Sadly, in early October Marg Gayford lost her long battle with cancer and we went up to Dundee for her funeral. Marg was a marvellous lady, very opinionated, but very soft at heart, and respected you if you stood up to her. We keep in touch with Bill on a regular basis and either he comes down for a few days or we go up to visit him. Bill and Marg first came into Marnie's life when she was a little girl and they were a young, married couple looking for somewhere to have their caravan when Bill was posted to RAF Leeming, eventually becoming a Flight Lieutenant.

Dalesend Jessie 45 was in October as far as we could ascertain, the oldest milk recorded cow alive at that time. She had always had a grey tinge to her, but it was by now very pronounced. The Society were highlighting longevity in one of their journal issues, and so Sarah got her all ready and took her up to Beamish Museum in Co. Durham where Jane Steel photographed her among some old vehicles, and it made the front cover of the subsequent magazine. We got a spare copy of the magazine which we got made into a picture, properly framed at the gallery in Leyburn and gave Mr J it for his birthday when he was in hospital. About that time, in half term, we had gone up to Scotland to do a bit of decorating for Adam, then overnighted on the way home at the Gosforth Marriott, where the Worcester Warriors rugby team were staying prior to losing the next day 14-13 at the Falcons. We had a walk along the beach at Druridge Bay and then a totally new experience for me, a walk round the big IKEA store. I wouldn't say I enjoyed it, all you had to do was follow the arrows round to be able to get out, I much enjoyed the rugby better in the afternoon, although it wasn't a particularly good game.

We fitted a brush for the cows at the start of winter and the cows gradually got to like it and use it, though odd cows seem to monopolise it, and although we had studied the various makes and bought what we thought the best, it was a bit too heavy for the cows and I think if we had put in another one, it would have been another make.

We had some metal detectorists from up about Hartlepool who used to come quite regularly. Usually two of them who always called to make sure it was ok and which fields they could go on, not that, as far as I know, they ever found anything of note. One of them was a keen fisherman, and he arrived at the door one Sunday morning with five good sized cod he had caught the night before. Marnie filleted them and into the freezer they went, and we enjoyed them over the next few months.

Another of those occasions when I made a fool of myself. After giving all the milk cows their IBR booster one morning, we were washing off at lunchtime as we finished. I had my wellingtons in a bucket of water and as I took it out, got tangled up in the handle, and eventually the bucket won and I ended up on the floor, got covered in water and absolutely soaked. Nobody helped me, Richard and Stuart just fell about laughing.

November that year was an horrendous month, I believe the heaviest individual month's rainfall I ever recorded at 7½ inches, more than a quarter of our annual average, it was a good job we had got the maize off and all the winters corn drilled before it got started. Right at the very end of the month we went to our godson Richard Howe's wedding at Crathorne Hall when it was absolutely pouring down, there were floods everywhere, we couldn't go by Northallerton but got there and back by a very circuitous route. We had another good classification visit in among all the rain, with Alistair Bell in the driving seat, resulting in another five new EX cows, 10 re-scored EX, 17 new VG's including another eight VG 2-year-olds, and then just a week later at the Yorkshire National Milk Records Dinner, the Rena's won the Best Family Competition and the Comestar Outside daughters won the Progeny Group, and a successful autumn was concluded at the Central Yorkshire Grassland Society Meeting, when we won the award for the best baled silage with some fourth cut.

Just before Christmas we went to Newton-le-Willows Village Hall for a party to celebrate the village being voted the Calor "Village of the Year", not that we had anything to do with it, though much effort had been made by those who had in pursuing various "green" initiatives and such like. Talking of parties we had a few more family ones around Christmas as Mollie was over from New Zealand and she, Emma and the twins came up for a few days, and then into the New Year we went over to Lancashire for their Club Dinner as the Yorkshire Club President, calling to see Samantha at Lytham St. Anne's on the way.

The early part of 2010 was quite a busy time as we made our plans for the farm for the next couple of years as we tried to move forward. We decided to try and be in the forefront of dairy producers in getting greater control of disease risks, we were vaccinating against IBR and BVD, were fortunate to be in a four-year TB area, and decided to try and become Johnes free and tested as such. Joining the CHECS scheme that was mostly based on the Scottish schemes we had our first herd blood test which proved very satisfyingly that we didn't have a huge problem, and subsequent later tests carried that forward so that at the time of our dispersal nearly two years later we were only the final (blood) test short of being certified Johnes-free. Sadly, as far as England is concerned little progress has been made on several health fronts in the intervening period. Scotland on the other hand has continued to progress various health schemes and is way ahead of us, and now requires pre-movement testing for animals to go over the border and I can't say I blame them. Going back forty years or so Britain was called the "stockyard of the world", we and many others used to export all breeds of cattle all over through Frank Chapman and The British Livestock Company. Some now think that we will be able to do that again, and certainly apart from embryos and perhaps the odd highly tested show type cattle, there is unlikely to be much change into Europe in the foreseeable future as we are "light years" behind much of Europe in such matters.

We had a visit from the dairy auditor for Arla at that time, and all the paperwork, management protocols etc were in place and approved, there were only two problems he found and one of them was my own fault. We had been moving cattle the day before, and had some more to move the day after, so I hadn't cleaned out or washed off the cattle trailer. He of course looked at it and didn't accept the reason or me saying it was one of the very few times we had not done so, which was quite true. His other problem was there were some pot holes in the drive which he didn't like and so we had to put some stone in those and send before and after photos of both it and the trailer to get the clearance certificate. What either of them in reality had to do with the quality or cleanliness of the milk we produced I still have not quite grasped, but as a requirement it had to be adhered to. What the episode with the drive spurred us on to was to do something more permanent about it, which we had been thinking about for some time. Most of the pot holes are created by the milk tanker, which once there is a small one, causes a 'bounce' and movement of the milk within it, which then makes it bigger and creates another one a little further on. Although there was plenty of stone already on the drive, we didn't feel that tarmacking it would last very long, and we did get a price worked out to concrete it, doing the work ourselves, but with ever heavier lorries coming into the yard and the requirement for reinforcing and depth of concrete required, it was going to cost in the order of £30,000, which was more than we wanted to spend, even if we had done it over two years. I had seen adverts for and heard of a system in effect – rotavating up the stone and mixing dry concrete in with it before applying water and rotavating in again before allowing it to set and in effect create a "concrete road". It wasn't to be used for a few days to allow it to set and we managed to get the milk tanker in via Fox Park and it was only spoilt by a young vet racing in at the road end, despite there being cones up and a rope right across with a sign on it, but no harm was done and although we only had it for another two years it seemed to do the job. It obviously wouldn't last as long as proper concreting, but at a third of the price we could have rotavated it up and redone again another twice to be no worse off, and as far as I am aware it is still good some nine years later.

At the same time we all went to Beckwithshaw to visit a dairy farmer who had a pasteuriser for feeding his calves, and he seemed very happy with the results, and that was a system we eventually decided to go down, though I had ultimately to cancel the order when it was decided to sell the herd some eighteen months later.

I also did some research work and made enquiries about the installation of a wind turbine and had a visit from a technical man from one of the major installation companies. The ideal site was already taken by a telephone mast up the back lane, but I took him up on to the top of the Wood Field which I thought would be ideal, but with his technical apparatus he said it was far from ideal and was borderline for pulling in enough air speed to be viable. The other problem of course, although we were about three miles away "as the crow flies", we were still in close proximity to RAF Leeming and without a lot of expensive legal argument, he doubted whether we would get planning permission, and so we never pursued the matter any further. I have never been a great believer in the efficiency of windmills as power generators, but economically at the time there were very generous financial incentives to erect them. These have now been significantly reduced and they are no longer a great financial project at an individual farm level.

I went with Dick, George and others up to Murrayfield to see a 12-12 draw with Scotland – not a great match, but it was still a good trip, and just after that took Mr J to Carlisle for a club sale where we had cattle entered. I sent Stuart and Sarah with them and came later so I could bring Mr J which proved to be his last outing to a cattle sale apart from our own dispersal. It was overkill to have four of us involved, but under the circumstances didn't really matter. Trade wasn't very good despite winning a milk class with a Lustrous which made 1800gns and was about third top price. We brought one home, plus a bull from the spring sale - trade for them set off reasonably well, but by it got to the later lots where ours was, everyone had got fixed up and there were no buyers left.

At the end of that week I acted as Master Judge, or one of them, at the Yorkshire Young Farmers Stockman of the Year competition, which I found very disappointing in that it was badly organised, the cows were very late coming, had not been clipped, washed or anything else – not very good as a promotional exercise.

Sadly, the next week, we had to put Dalesend Jessie 45 (referred to earlier with regard to photos at Beamish) to sleep. She was beginning to get very arthritic and was losing condition, but she was, after all 20 years and three months old, a quite remarkable old cow, though she never produced vast amounts of milk or bred anything very much. They say when one door closes another one opens, and on the same day, I submitted our monthly VAT return online for the first time. Interestingly enough only some nine years later in spring 2019 we are on the point of all VAT records and returns for any business with a turnover above £80,000 having to be totally online – not just the actual return. In many cases it will mean farmers having to purchase a special package or pay someone else to do it all for them – more cost and the onward march of "online" everything!!

At the end of March later that year Stuart had a day off to celebrate his 21st birthday and just a fortnight later he and his girlfriend Abi had a joint party in between their birthdays. It was a good night and I was very pleased to be asked to propose the toast to them.

Early April saw us hosting a calf rearing skills workshop for Bishopton vets, for which we received the princely sum of £110, but it took very little effort on our part, and hopefully it was of benefit to others as well as Stuart and Richard who sat in on parts of it.

I had for many years kept every sale catalogue and herd brochure, nearly all marked up from the newspaper reports thinking I would have use for them in the future. Except in odd cases, that future never materialised, and we had run out of storage space and every cupboard was full of them. Under much pressure and a wet weekend, I finally succumbed and sorted through them, only keeping a few of them, and on the Sunday afternoon we took 10 feed bags and two box fulls of them to the recycling centre.

That was just at the time when the volcano erupted on Iceland and there was supposedly volcanic ash everywhere in the atmosphere and all flights were cancelled all over Europe for several days. We could never see it and I don't know whether it was as bad as it was made out to be, but it caused mayhem for a while. Not that it bothered us as we weren't flying anywhere at that time, but we did have a small travel hiccup at the same time. One Saturday on my weekend off we went for a ride out over the tops to Settle. A beautiful spring day with everything looking very picturesque in the sun. On our way back home, we stopped for a stretch in Kettlewell and continued on our journey home, planning to call at Street Head for our supper. When we got there Marnie suddenly realised she had lost her handbag, so we decided she must have left it on the top of the car in the car park when she lit her cigarette, or in the café where we had been, so back to Kettlewell we went, but no sign of it anywhere and no one had seen anything of it. Back over to Street Head for a belated and worrying meal before we could do anything about it when we got home. When we did so, phone message from Sarah – she had had some "odd bod" lady on the phone about a handbag and left a contact number. When we rang it, she told us her young son on cycling home had found it in the middle of the road halfway to Starbotton. They would take it and leave it at the General Stores in Kettlewell, where we were to collect it next morning, a good job there are some good, honest people still about and he deserved the finders fee Marnie left in an envelope for him.

At the end of April, I went across for the final Weeton dispersal sale, trade was not as fast as it had been at the first part, but still topped at £7500. A few days later we hosted a combined North Eastern and Yorkshire Clubs judging night – over a hundred people here, so it was a good job Marnie had taken an extra day off to get the food ready for supper – they cleaned it all up. A couple of days after that we had a General Election which resulted in a hung Parliament and eventually, we finished up with a Conservative/Liberal Coalition which was ok for some things but ultimately became a reason for doing very little. An advisory committee meeting at Askham Bryan, the same night was followed the next morning by an R.P.A. full check of all ear numbers. Fortunately we had always made a point of keeping passports and paperwork up to date and made a point of replacing ear tags when we noticed ones missing, so we passed with flying colours – it seemed a lot of work and time for four of us for most of a day, but I suppose someone has to have checks as we are all receiving public money, but you always feel that you know of other farms where they do not keep on top of things and need an inspection, but they are supposedly picked at random.

We had for some time wanted to improve our newly calven cow management and also gradually increase cow numbers without altering the parlour or collecting yard. The calving cow yard had always suffered if we had some heavy rainfall which tended to flood it out, which meant a days job to move all the sloppy water and then muck out the bedded yard which was soaking, so we decided to roll all that into one, by knocking it down and using the walls to build up the floor level to get above the water and extend it through into the dutch barn in the yard, using three bays of that. We also led in quite a few loads of stone from the fields that had been picked many times. We removed the roof from that part of the dutch barn and Norman Iveson made an individually measured roof to span right over the lot and also locking yolks along the feeding side of the yard which we then split into two halves to take calving cows and newly calved or show cows. They were at the nearest end to the main cow building and we usually housed sixteen in there which could come round the inside of the cubicle house and into the collecting yard and make two sides of the parlour. It meant we could make sure cows were ok after calving, or if they needed any further treatment, they could be fastened in with the yokes without upsetting other cows. In addition the shed had a cleanable walkway at the front which we could clean on a daily basis if necessary, and also we could fasten the cows onto the bedded area, and on routine vet visits just run the other cows from the main herd requiring the vet across and into the yolks – making that much easier and quicker in vets time – we also adapted a feed trolley with a cover for the vet to put all his tackle on to and just run along behind the cows. Cows were on straw at this critical transition period and could spread out to be more comfortable than in cubicles the day they calved. Even in the short time we operated the system before the herd dispersal, we saw great benefits to newly calven cows and particularly to newly calven heifers. I had and still do think we ask an awful lot of heifers, even more so now when they calve at a young age. One day they are an in-calf heifer, they then calve, get put in many cases straight in among a lot more older cows and begin to produce milk, go into a milking parlour, all at that time of maximum stress. For the first few days they don't know where they are or what they are supposed to be doing, and although cubicle trained still spend far too long those first few days standing, particularly with hind feet down in the passageway, putting a lot of extra stress on the hind feet, causing bruising and quite often lameness from an ulcer some time later. We always tried within the new building to move if possible two heifers, but if not then a cow and a heifer into the main herd at the same time, so at least they had a mate.

Through that summer, a lot of work was going on around this development, most of the building work was done for us by Derek Brown from Barnard Castle, who also took up and re-laid the far passage of the cubicles which had become rather rough because of the effluent which occasionally seeped through from the adjoining silage pits. Once the structure set up we used blocks rather than panels for parts of it, particularly where it fronted onto the main farm yard and Derek organised a local man from up in his part of the world to face it with cobbles to match in with most of the original buildings, using more stones we gathered up from all over edges of fields. What a marvellous job they made of it, topped off with slates bought from Edward Price, and it wasn't out of the way price wise, in fact it was less than we thought it would be for proper craftsmen. Derek and his men kept us well amused for a few weeks – they weren't the earliest starters – always calling for a Mc Breakfast at Leeming Motel as they arrived and Derek was into motor racing and got a fancy machine that he soon damaged, but they did a good job.

To try and solve the water problem once and for all we had Marcus Metcalfe here to put in a new settling/collection tank at the end of the concrete, and it was amazing in a heavy rainfall how much surface water was generated over the roof tops and large concreted area. He got in a machine to work with lasers and make and install a drain under the yard and across into the Bungalow field down behind the drive side hedge. It certainly took all the water away to a soak away. It worked for a while, but like all soakaway's, by the very name struggle to cope with very heavy rainfall. Still it was better to spoil a bit of the field than continually flood in the yard.

The final pieces of the jigsaw were to fit a calving pen that could be accessed from both calving and calved yards or out into the front yard if needed with cattle going to a show or sale. Having got the front feeding area complete we invested in a "pusherupper" for the front of the Loadall and it certainly increased intakes with the new calved cows and we pushed the forage up to them four or five times a day.

I had a bit of fun with Mr J while we were doing this building. When we did the original dry cow yard years earlier I got the roof sheets put on upside down to leave a slight gap between each sheet and an open ridge and contrary to many people's thinking, it very rarely rains in, snow occasionally does. When we put the big, new stock building up after Foot and Mouth, I wanted to do the same but Mr J would have none of it, saying it would rain in on cattle and they would be wet and cold, but despite several attempts, I couldn't convince him otherwise, and ultimately he concluded with "Just because you have an obsession with fresh air it doesn't mean everybody else has to suffer for it", and that was the end of the argument. When we were doing the new yard, Mr J wasn't at all well and not at all mobile, so, rather naughtily I did the roof with upside down sheets on while he was in hospital. When he was rather better and came down for a look as we finished the building work he immediately noticed the different roof, which he though was fantastic and a revolutionary approach to air flow, something which is often ignored in cattle housing. The cows had their first night in the new shed in mid-September, and although it was only in use for only fifteen months it was a great success and worked very well for us.

As mentioned Mr J by this time was struggling very badly health wise, and some of my time was taken up with him, a couple of times when silaging I picked him up and drove him round the fields and to the pit to see what was happening, and the same again at harvest time. After his first stroke his speech was badly affected but he gradually got enough back so I could just about have a conversation with him when face to face and I could feed it back to him to confirm what he had said. The problem came when he had nothing to do at night, but he knew my number off by heart and we had many jumbled conversations – most of the time I hadn't a clue what he was trying to say – I just said 'yes' or 'no' and hoped they were in the right place!!

During the summer whilst we were very busy with the building work, a lot else was going on and off the farm, with and not with our own cattle. I have never been a great lover of Dexter cattle – I have always wondered what their purpose was agriculturally, and they seem to be the most able breed at bawling their heads off, particularly at shows. Stuart arrived back in the yard one morning from checking heifers to report a wild Dexter cow among our heifers in the Reeds. Off we went to get it in, we knew it was from Wilson's next door field, and after some effort we got it into the handling pen along with all our own heifers and let all but a couple of them out. The Dexter was charging around in a demented fashion and we decided that rather than just leave it there and ring John to come and get it, we would take it back, so Stuart stayed with them to stop it trying to jump out whilst I went back home for the trailer. When we got it loaded into the trailer with a struggle as it charged about, we decided that rather than take it back to its mates, we would return it to its owners – Big Sheep and Little Cow, the toy visitor farm at Bedale who were just using the grass eatage at Crakehall. When we got there the man seemed very uninterested in his escaping, mad animals and continued dehorning calves which were too old to be being treated as they were. After some badgering as to what he wanted doing with it, he said "put it in our trailer and I'll see to it later", so had to back our trailer to his, concoct some makeshift hurdles as his trailer had no gates, got it run across, shut the door and departed with the animals head well over the back door as if it might not be long before it escaped again.

Wimbledon was being played at the time and it was in one of the early rounds the longest ever tennis match was played going to 60-58 in the final set – they must have been absolutely knackered by they finished. On the Saturday of the Dexter and marathon tennis week, we went to Northallerton, had our lunch at the Golden Lion, and then at night took a picnic supper to Harewood House to see Russell Watson in concert. He was superb on not the best of nights weather-wise and we were very impressed by his supporting act, a young lady by the name of Camilla Dallerup, whom we were sure we would hear more of in the future. We did, she sang at various sports occasions and later became the wife of Chris Robshaw the Harlequins and England rugby union captain.

The following week, an interesting day at the home of the RABDF Gold Cup Winner of the previous year. Geoff Spence from Brompton, Northallerton, producing some very good figures – a lot of cows on a relatively small acreage. This was the first time,

I believe, that we had a local winner of such a prestigious trophy. In subsequent years most of the winners seemed to be from the South West many of the Open Days we attended, but we had a local winner again this year (2019) for the 2018 year in the very large, well run unit of Metcalfe Farms Ltd up at Leyburn. The Gold Cup Day at Geoff Spence's was the same day as we had Andrew Birkle, (future Chairman of Holstein UK) to stay overnight as he judged the Yorkshire Club Herd's Competition and I stewarded him the following day at Pratt's, Nicholson's and Andrew Jennings.

A week later we had three cull cows at the mart at Leyburn, and as I went up with them, I noticed that the sign had been taken down on the Pheasant Inn at Harmby and a new one put up as it was re-decorated and starting to sell another make of beer. Cows were a good trade and as I came home I called to enquire after the old sign and finished up buying it for way over the top at £40, thinking it would make an unusual present for Adam with the profession he was in. Marnie subsequently rubbed it all down, touched up odd bits of the background black paint and then re-varnished it and it made a very good Christmas present later that year. The next day I had to go to the dentist and finally had one tooth removed that they couldn't patch up anymore. Touching wood, that is the last time I needed anything doing other than routine check and polish in the ensuing nine years, which after all the troubles I had some thirty or forty years earlier was a great tribute to Mr Abrahams skill and expertise – he was a smashing man and managed all Bedale's teeth problems on his own, rather than now when there are two dental practices with goodness knows how many dentists!!

Mike Heugh started putting up the new cow yard building in early July and on the Saturday, my weekend off we had tapas on the Terrace at Wynyard Hall for lunch, the day before Marnie went off to the Orkney Islands for the week with some of the Mowbray children.

Nothing particularly exciting at the Great Yorkshire Show that year, and at the end of that week we had rubber matting fitted through the milking parlour and the top end of the collecting yard. The idea was to relieve pressure on cows feet, and you could appreciate when seeing a cow walk on it how much it pressed down that otherwise much of that stress was being transmitted through all the leg joints, and a great help on cows turning as they left the parlour. The fact that it was more comfortable for the cows was emphasised by some of the cows lying down in the collecting yard until they felt like being milked and simply got up and wandered in to be milked.

A pleasant evening at Ripon Races one night as a retirement party for one of the staff from Mowbray. We went for supper to Valentino's in Ripon, but it was full, so we called at the Black Bull in West Tanfield on the way home. The following night it was another retiree's party and we had a super combined picnic supper at Thorpe Perrow before watching an open-air version of a Midsummer Night's Dream except when it started, we quickly realised it was The Merchant of Venice. The following day was spoilt for us by the sudden death of our favourite Dalesend Red Rosina who had just calved a heifer calf the day previously - no problems but by the blood behind her at milking time that morning we assume she had torn something internally. That night the new vicar, Brian, was inducted at Patrick Brompton.

Earlier in the summer, though only a matter of weeks, we heard from Norway that Colin wasn't very well, and he began to fail very quickly. Marnie resolved and arranged to go to Norway as soon as she broke up for summer, which she did on the Monday, and was eternally grateful that she did so to see him for one last time before he passed away peacefully on the Wednesday night. What shock and what a loss of such a young life at 64 of someone who up until that time had never ailed a thing. A quickly arranged trip for Kathryn and me to fly over to Stavanger and to Kleppe for his funeral in early August. We came back the day after, but Marnie stayed a while longer to support Christin and Elisabet in their grief.

Whilst away things had carried on ok, Richard keeping the stock side in order and Stuart seeing to harvest, the straw in particular and even got his girlfriend Abi in to help him one night which didn't go down too well in some quarters, but I thought it was great and showed the youngster's commitment to the cause. Barley was only worth £68 per tonne that year, so again, didn't add up too fast, despite good yields. Bill had been leading the corn and emptying the slurry pit.

That was the end of a very busy spell, which included Bill Gayford coming from Dundee to spend four days with us, visits to the Durham Botanic Gardens, Emma, Jake and Daisy staying for a week, selling the old pick up for £4500 privately to be able to take the new one as a straight purchase with all the discounts. Both of them are still about in the area and we sometimes see one or other of them on the road. We had the All Breeds Northern Calf Show at Thirsk and for the first time the Yorkshire Holstein Club were also involved, and I continued my role as commentator.

If you think that was busy and hectic, bearing in mind most of these extra activities were on top of all the normal day to day jobs, then that was as nothing compared to what was about to unfold for the next twelve months.

Chapter 22 – The Presidential Year

A year earlier during 2009 I had been nominated for and then elected to be President of Holstein UK, Europe's largest cattle breed society, and was President Elect for the year until autumn of 2010. That year did not involve much work or time, standing in at the Great Yorkshire Show for the President Phillip Davies from Gornal who was unable to attend, also his inauguration as President which was low key as there was some changes of dates and there had already been an event coinciding with the Society Centenary Year during which Ken Proctor of "Airfield" was President, and attending the odd Society meeting in readiness for my role, and several local meetings to plan the Holstein Celebration for which the North Eastern Club had formed a small sub-committee, consisting of Kevin Clarkson (club chairman), Peter Miles (club President), Peter Corner (President elect), George Leggott, Karen Hutchinson, myself and Sarah who also acted as the secretary of the committee.

It was the practice of the Society to hold a 2-3-day convention in the area of the incoming President, including the Society AGM which was the only real business of the event. At this time the Society had been without an events co-ordinator for a while and had just appointed Lynette Smale to take over, though being new to the job, much or most of the organising apart from the actual booking by members was done by the North Eastern Club, including producing a small brochure on the area and the programme. The first job was to find a suitable hotel and vet them, though there weren't many alternatives in the area that could provide not only the number of rooms required, but also had facilities to cope with dinner for up to two hundred and fifty on the second night. We eventually settled on Blackwell Grange Hotel on the outskirts of Darlington and they did a very good job for us. We decided to start at lunchtime on the Monday to give delegates chance to travel after the weekend and met at Newton Grange for lunch. We had a big clean-up for the week beforehand and the day or two before getting everything set up for the visit, including flowers, banners, tables and chairs from Newton-le-Willows Village Hall, and getting thirty cows all clipped washed and numbered ready for the judging competition of picking 6 from 30 judged by Ken Proctor. The cattle made a good show, prize of a trip to Italy with Genus was won by John Jamieson of "Firth" with the winning lady Judith Waring of "Winton" winning a Lewis and Cooper hamper.

After the visit we all went to Blackwell Grange for a very good, hot buffet meal and were then entertained by Northallerton Male Voice Choir, who put on a terrific performance for us. The main contact in arranging this was our Club President Elect Peter Corner who sings with them, and the choir also has well known farmers Brian Phillips and Keith Blenkiron in their number, which also included Peter Kershaw the Managing Director of North Yorkshire Timber whom many locals will have dealt with over the years.

On Tuesday morning delegates had two non-farming options to choose from, a visit to the racing stables of Mark Johnston at Middleham. This was the most popular of the two options and people were amazed how much time and effort the top trainer had taken and took in looking after them himself the whole time and answered every question asked of him. He was of course aware that there were a few potential customers amongst his visitors. The other option was a fully conducted tour of Richmond Ice Cream company at Leeming Bar, now the largest ice-cream factory in Europe, which had originally been started by Mr Ropner just after milk quotas came in. We, as the farm did a feasibility study on it as ice-cream was outside milk quotas. What the feasibility study told us was that there was so little milk used in commercial ice-cream production that it wasn't worth us getting involved, but, having established Dalepak Foods PLC, Mr J decided he wanted to pursue the idea and bought a small ice-cream two man business, "Cardosi" from Redcar. From little acorns have mighty oaks grown. Although no longer actively involved in the business, the contacts were there for our visit to perhaps a greater degree than most visitors get. The factory was in full operational mode and we were right down on the floor watching all the very technical machinery which filled, packed all the ice-cream cones etc., though interestingly the Malteser in the bottom of one line of ice cream cones was put in by hand.

After those two fascinating visits, everyone met up again in the Village Hall at Bellerby for another cold buffet lunch before we went on to visit the Studdah herd of Messrs Pratt which was in terrific form. They have done very well in recent years, winning in both Yorkshire and North Eastern herds competitions. For those who didn't want to look at cows again, mostly ladies, went for another non farm visit to the fascinating Bolton Castle, with those fantastic views up Wensleydale.

Back to the hotel and an hour or two spare before the AGM which was as usual a very quick affair as everything is pretty well organised in advance. When we were looking into getting an after-dinner speaker, someone suggested Rosemary Shrager as something completely different. She was at that time at the cookery school at nearby Swinton Castle near Masham, and also had featured on the television reality show "Ladette to Lady". She was written to and her agent came back with yes at a fee of £6000. Nothing was done for a week or two when Sarah received a phone call from the agent to say she had received no reply, to which she was told it was rather more money than we wanted to spend, and it was immediately reduced to £3000, and being told that was too much it was cut again to £2000, and this was just for 20 minutes, so we didn't pursue the matter. It was then decided that a more appropriate speaker would be Howard Petch, the former Principal of Bishop Burton College, and at least a connection with the club, his brother being David Petch of the Aytonian herd. He was and is a marvellous speaker and gave a masterful speech that night, moving effortlessly from serious to humorous from agricultural and non-agricultural matters. You can tell how good he was when you had people such as Peter Dixon-Smith of "Lyons" and Bill Towers of the "Aldingham" herds, both men who have been involved with many organisations over a lot of years saying they thought it the best after-dinner speech they had ever heard. Howard was very happy with the £400 donation we made to the Farm Crisis Network with which he was heavily involved. We were able to do this due to a very generous grant from the Yorkshire Agricultural Society's educational programme towards the cost of the convention.

The following morning, we travelled across the county to the Aytonian herd of Messrs Petch where we looked round the herd before having another buffet lunch and the delegates dispersed all over the country after a very good couple of days. The catering at all three venues had been done by The Farm Organisation, so that it was different each day, and there was no competitive element in one host attempting to better another.

Whilst our youngstock building at home was all cleaned out and we had the chairs and tables, we hosted the evening Harvest Festival again on the Friday of that week, and following on from the success of previous occasions, we had a fantastic turn out despite it not being very well publicised.

With my commitment to Holstein UK for the twelve months, with the full support of the Ropner family, whilst still holding down and doing a full time job, as well as at the same time also being President of the Yorkshire Holstein Club, and Treasurer of St. Patrick's, we had to be very thorough and organised in the farm operations. To that end I did a two-week programme of my activities which was updated every week as things were added to our itinerary going forward. This I copied, and provided I was there, had a meeting every Monday morning with Richard, Stuart and Chris to go through what I was doing, when I might be away and they needed to juggle their work to accommodate me and what jobs were to do at that time. Without the help and co-operation from them, it would have been impossible to do the job as I wanted to do it. Because of the fact that I was still managing the farm, there were occasions when we travelled either to or from events at night, when it might have been better and more relaxing for us to have taken a little more time, but that is a price we were happy to pay, bearing in mind that sometimes visits also had to fit in with Marnie's work at Mowbray, though again I have to say the Headmaster Jonathon Tearle was very understanding and helpful in letting Marnie swop days about to fit in with our schedule.

It wasn't long before we were straight into business and I have to pay tribute to Lynette and Heather Lewington at Holstein UK who made all the hotel reservations, air flights etc. for us over the entire year, they were always absolutely spot on.

Our first official visit was in early October to the South West Dairy Show. We couldn't leave home until late afternoon as Marnie was up at the Durham Oriental Museum with a group from school. A long drive down to Somerset, and by the time we got down towards Bristol we were ready for some supper. Marnie as the excellent navigator she was, followed the M5 straight through the heart of Bristol which was all very well until suddenly all the signs dried up – they got us into the centre but no-way to get us out. After a couple of circuits of the city, we decided to call in for supper at an Italian restaurant we had spotted on the first trip around. We had a very good meal at "Prego", and fortunately the young waitress on our table was about the only local there, and she said "just go down to the end of this road, turn left and you're out onto the road you want to go to Shepton Mallett, which we did and we got easily then to the Thatched Cottage at Shepton Mallett where we were booked in overnight. We were warmly greeted at the Show the next morning, had a good day, did the presentations as necessary – the one thing we had to get used to was that in that part of the country they give a blue rosette for 1st prize and a red one for 2nd, the rest of the country do it the opposite way round. A long journey back home – round trip of almost 600 miles.

Saturday morning saw us back on the road again after being up to Newcastle the night before to see them scrape a 22-16 win over Bourgoin in the European Champions Cup. Down to the Royal Showground for the All Britain All Breeds Calf Show. Opened the proceedings as President and on and off presenting rosettes at the conclusion of classes. The standard of showmanship and quality of calves at this event continues to be fantastic, and the level of improvement through some of the other breeds has to be seen to be appreciated. The work that all the youngsters put in with their stands and promotional work is phenomenal and it is just a pity it is not seen by more people than those directly involved with the participants. It really is worth the effort to go see what is happening and to support the development of these young members who are the future for all the breeds.

That night we stayed at the Ramada Warwick which interestingly was very much Indian orientated including the restaurant, menu and service. I enjoyed a very good curry, and we looked after some of the main visitors and guests for the show. The Showmanship on the Saturday was judged by James Tomlinson of "Bilsrow" and the calves on the Sunday by Ashley Fleming (Potterswalls) from Northern Ireland.

We supported the Yorkshire Holstein Club in their attempt to get a sale going which the next week was held at Thirsk. The idea was good, it is very good to get to on major roads and fairly central for both vendors and potential purchasers, but it failed to materialise into results and there was a very poor turnout of potential buyers and trade was very flat, though we did manage to get Dalesend Design Jean 2 and Pansy 182 sold at 1500gns each. They didn't try to hold any more at Thirsk as it is now no longer a dairy area but have reverted to occasional sales at Skipton.

Off again the week after down to Carmarthen for the Welsh Dairy Show. We left early afternoon and had a good run until suddenly on the M50 we came to a complete halt and did not move for about 1½ hours – a car had caught fire a little ahead of us and it seemed a long time to get it out and removed with both sides of the motorway closed. It was only a little Fiat on the back of the breakdown truck when we saw it pulled in at the first service station which we needed to visit after the blockage. That night we stayed at the Spilman Hotel in Carmarthen ready for the show the next day at the United Counties Showground. The show had a real buzz about it, was very busy and a good turnout of cows judged by Tom Kelly of the "Monamore" herd in Ireland with Tregibby taking the Championship and a special presentation to Mike Davies, ex-Herdwise man who was retiring after many years serving the Welsh agricultural industry. Travelled back across country via Abergavenny and Ross-on-Wye a scenic ride, but very slow, we thought we were never going to get back to the M5.

A couple of days at home, one of which included photographing with Jane Steel and then on the Friday evening across to Carlisle for the Northern Dairy Expo Show judged by Paul Harrison from "Chishillways".

A reasonably quiet week to follow which allowed Richard to have three days holiday to fit in with his two girls and school half term holidays. The out of parlour feeders had failed to switch off the auger one night and emptied a lot of cake out onto the floor, so it was all to shovel and bag up one morning and then keep tipping into the hoppers as necessary, and another day we had a visit from the Scottish Agricultural Colleges Dairy Study Group which included Hugh Neilson of "Overside". They came for lunch and we had a very useful discussion and look around. The Saturday night of that week was the Yorkshire Club Dinner at Millstones restaurant on the Blubberhouses A59 road and we attended as both Yorkshire and National President and Presidentess!!

Bonfire night saw us flying over to Belfast for the Northern Ireland Club's Annual Dinner and awards night. The previous weekend when talking to their secretary about the arrangements he said, in typical Irish fashion "We tried something different last year and it didn't really work so we're going to do it again." The something different was to do all the presentations before dinner. I could see this might cause some slowing down in the proceedings, so we had a bit more substantial tea than we would normally have done after we had had a tour of the city on an open topped bus as we had left home at six am to catch the only suitable aeroplane time wise. The dinner was not at the Ramada where we were staying but at Temple Patrick. It had been arranged that Mark Logan would pick us up at 6.45pm but it was about 7.15pm by he did so and after some standing around and talk at the venue, the head waiter came to the Club Chairman to tell him dinner was ready "oh, not everyone's here yet and we have the awards to do before that". Marnie presented a fairly long list of trophies and awards and then they had to go into another room to do it all again to be photographed instead of doing it at the first presentation. Fortunately, it was a hot buffet meal, so it didn't take too much fault as it was about 9.30pm by we had the supposedly 8 o'clock meal. This was followed by my speaking and then the evening's entertainment by one of their local breeders Wallace Gregg with some very entertaining stories and jokes. As a result, it was about 1.30am by we got back to the hotel, booking an early morning call as our flight was at 7am. They failed to give us the early morning call, fortunately I woke realising we were running late and as we hurriedly dressed and packed, they rang to ask if it was us the taxi had come to collect. Fortunately, at that time on a Saturday morning, Belfast roads were not particularly busy, and we made the airport and our flight back to Newcastle with a few minutes to spare. Back into Newcastle at 8 o'clock we breakfasted at Dobbie's Garden Centre just down the road towards Ponteland, had a good tour round the Northumberland country lanes, ate for the first time of many at Fratelli's in Ponteland for tea before going to see Falcons beat Ospreys 18-17 in a rather uninspiring match.

Monday of the following week saw Spike from Lambert, Leonard and May here to put some embryo's in and at night to a Yorkshire Club Committee Meeting before leaving early on the Tuesday to drive down to Scotsbridge House for a Holstein UK Board Meeting. Tom Phillips in the Chair and much of the time spent discussing the possibility of joining the Dairy Event and the Holstein Show into one event. Overnight at the usual hotel at Chipperfield and into the meeting for 8.30. I had to leave at 11.30 before the meeting finished, home by 3 o'clock, unpacked, re-packed and then we drove up to the Strathclyde Hilton, just south of Glasgow, for the Scottish Club dinner, not massively attended but a pleasant evening and reasonably early to bed after only travelling about 420 miles in the day. The next day was quiet – just a drive home by lunchtime, Marnie went to school in the afternoon and then I went to an Askham Bryan College advisory meeting at night. A quiet end to the week, going to Barbara Leggott's birthday party on the Saturday night and then getting ready for another busy week to come.

Tuesday was an early start to drive down to the NEC just outside Birmingham to attend the Holstein Society's Breeders Club delegates meeting followed by the HYB co-ordinators meeting – neither of which were very exciting. Left before the last one finished, drove back home, picked Marnie up and up to Lauder to stay at Adam's overnight ready to go to AgriScot at Edinburgh. AgriScot is a very well organised show in a relatively compact arena and the cattle show is run like clockwork which means that other things and happenings in the main ring can be put in the programme of events and they will happen at that time. I knew I had a presentation to do at the climax of the Holstein classes and on enquiring what time that would be, the Chief Steward, Andrew Dunlop, who, if you don't know him is a very big man, jabbed me in the chest with his finger and said "3.20pm and don't be late". I wasn't and it was within a couple of minutes of that time. A superb show, tremendous turnout of senior milk cows, a slow journey back home held up by an accident and a diversion.

Friday of that week was the N.E. Holstein Club sale at Leyburn, where we had three entered, I wasn't expecting too much as general trade wasn't very fast at the time, and was pleasantly satisfied that the three averaged £1550 with not a lot of cost. It is much cheaper to sell at Leyburn than, say, Carlisle because the entry fees are smaller and the cost of actually getting them there and the time involved is much less, we reckoned you could take at least £30/head less and still be ok. The only trouble was, they only had one sale each autumn, and sadly now through lack of support that has gone by the board.

North Eastern Club again the following week after a family party at Haxby at the weekend for Cousin Jane Lofthouse's 70th Birthday party and then an Arla/Asda meeting at Nick Brown's near East Witton on calf rearing. At night Colin Laird, the current President's Medal winner came to speak to the club about his time in the HYB movement and also about their Blythbridge herd.

Mr Bill wasn't renowned for asking questions but was first in this night and asked Colin what you called a Muslim with rabbits strapped to his back – Colin shook his head and wondered to which Bill replied "Bin Lampin". It transpired that earlier in the day, he and Brian Craggs had been picking sloes to make their sloe gin for the shooting season only to find on their return to Brian's there was some of last years left which they had to finish!!

The next morning it was over to Carlisle Racecourse for the Harrison and Hetherington Conference, which was very good with some excellent, practical, farmer speakers. I looked forward to it becoming an annual event, but as far as I am aware, they never held another one.

At the end of November, Sarah started to do some work on veal in conjunction with the Archer family with their Jerseys which they launched at the Richmond Food Fayre - not a lot of sales, the first thing is changing people's perception that veal calves are tied up in cages and fed nothing but milk – that used to happen, but was banned many years ago and they lead a more normal life, they are just slaughtered at a much younger age and lighter weight. Particularly with the Jersey calves, it meant the bulls did at least have some life, even if a short one, as they would otherwise probably have been shot at a day or two old as "bobby calves". They did manage to create a market and later Adrian Harrison of Thornton Rust also joined the party, but after a few years they decided to close the business down, despite having some notable clients in Fodder and Weeton's in Harrogate, Castle Howard Farm Shop, Fenwicks in Newcastle and the Jesmond Dene Hotel. The problem was that it cost virtually as much in slaughter and packaging costs as a fully grown beef animal, so that cost per kilo was much higher for a product that sold at only a slight premium, and while some customers wanted half a side one week, they wanted very little the week after and you still had it to deliver which made that cost much higher. By all this had gone on there wasn't a lot left to share out between the three partners who had put the effort in. It was though a very interesting exercise and veal is still available, mostly I think produced by the Buitelaar group, but it is much larger animals up to about eight months old and larger weights, plus they have their own slaughterhouses and distribution system as a multi-national company.

At the same time, Mr J who had been in and out of hospital for much of the autumn, but was now much better, and was giving a lot of thought to possibly creating a farm shop. His idea was very sensible, there was nothing at the time between Scruton Lane end and Hawes that catered for visitors and with land beside the main road into Wensleydale at Patrick Brompton it could have been possible, but after a meeting or two with the local council and the Highways department it seemed they would put every obstacle in our way in granting planning permission, and so we had to abandon the idea, though I think it could have worked, but they said to be a farm shop we had to produce it all ourselves on the farm etc. – how many farm shops have you been into where that would ever have been the case??

Early December saw the annual Black and White Sale at Carlisle, which was rather hampered by some bad weather, frost and snow, we had to go the long way round by Kirby Stephen, as the A66 was blocked. We had the young heifer from Spottie in the sale who had fortunately gone the day before and we were highly delighted with the trade when she made 3,100gns to a young Bob Lawrence.

Back home in the snow and then the next day down to Betws-y-Coed for the North Wales Club Annual Dinner. Only a small club and it seemed strange to attend a dinner on a Sunday night but it was probably the most enjoyable one we attended in the whole year. The next morning everywhere had a covering of snow and a very sharp frost giving the small town an almost "Christmas Card" look. The roads were very icy to start with and driving had to be careful as we headed home for Marnie to be able to go to work in the afternoon. The following day was very icy, down to -11°C and we had a lot of things frozen up, and then that night it was to the Yorkshire Milk Records dinner at the Millstones on the A59.

Two days later and it was off again, this time over to Belfast for the Royal Ulster Winter Fair, staying at the Ramada Hotel Belfast the night before the show. A good show of cattle although not huge numbers, but overall and a well organised show in the King's Hall (the show has now moved out of the city centre which makes it logistically much better for exhibitors and spectators alike. Champion was a Cousteau daughter up from the south, ahead of a Goldwyn Sara. Back to the airport for our delayed early evening flight home, supper at Fratelli's in Ponteland and back home to tidy up and get ready for the next day.

Mid-December and a long day – down to Scotsbridge House to interview the seven candidates for the Presidents medal with co-judges David Dunlop and John Torrance who had to deputise for Mike Miller as one of his daughters, Katie, was one of the candidates. We finished up with a final three of Neil Eastham, Neil Roberts and Craig Brough, with the winner to be announced later, and also presented the Littlestar award for more Junior members to Frances Griffiths of the Yorkshire Club.

There was a pause, as you would expect, for two or three weeks around Christmas and apart from the usual work of that time of year, there was also the family visits and visitors, including Emma and the twins coming to stay for a short week over New Year. We also went to see the "King's Speech" – a marvellous film, at York and supper at Sweet Basil on the way home.

By mid-January it was back on to the club roundabout and there was then a very hectic fortnight. Began with a 400 miles plus drive down to Newquay for the Cornish Club Dinner dance. Back up home on the Saturday before leaving again on the Sunday to drive up to Glasgow for the annual Semex Conference. The first time I had attended and so enjoyed it, that I have continued attending for the next ten years or so. Expertly chaired by Philip Halhead of Norbreck Genetics, the best chairman over the next ten years, it featured among other speakers, Alex Bach, Peter Kendall, Mark Logan from Clandeboye in Northern Ireland, Sheri Regan from Regancrest in Iowa, and David Wright from the Berryholme herd.

A couple of days later we had three heifers over at the monthly sale at Carlisle, I went later to take Mr J with me for a ride out and a potter about for a change of scenery, which he hadn't had for quite a while. Trade was rather up and down and bad to follow, with our three averaging 1400gns.

Friday of that week and off again, this time down to Hawkstone Park for the Shropshire Club Dinner – the largest of all the club dinners we attended with over two hundred there, and some very good beef to carve at each table, followed by a quick ten minute speech. No rest and the next day it was up the Western side to Blackpool for the Lancashire Club Dinner at the DeVere Heron's Reach hotel. We called for an hour en-route to see niece Samantha at Lytham St. Annes. Home on the Sunday and then on the Monday after farm Board Meeting plus Wensleydale Property Companies it was back down to Shropshire for the British Cattle Breeder's Conference at Telford. The first day was the beef day and there was a Holstein UK Board Meeting before the Annual Dinner which was preceded by the presentation of the President's Medal to Craig Brough from Cumbria. The judging of the Presidents Medal had made me realise just how many talented young people we have within the breed and agriculture generally. Friday again and over to Carlisle for the Border Counties Club Dinner which was well attended and enjoyable evening among many breeders we know well.

Just when he was getting better and able to get about with a stick when he was at home, Mr J had a stroke and a bad fall and was rushed into hospital. The day after I was fortunate enough to go with Dick and George down to Cardiff for the rugby international. A slow rail journey on four different trains though that was nothing compared to the slow journey back on the Saturday. The Stadium with roof closed is magnificent and when the Welsh start singing it is sheer magic. A good, fast, exciting game which England should have won more easily than the 26-19 score line suggests. That had been the first Friday night game in the Six Nations. As soon as I got back to Northallerton Marnie said I had to go and see Mr J in hospital, which we duly did, and it was sad to see him neither talking or anything else, though he gradually improved from there on.

A quiet couple of weeks as far as Holstein business was concerned, and then near the end of February, it was down to Norfolk for their club dinner where we stayed with Ken and Rebecca Proctor at Airfield. What a slow run it is across to Norfolk once you leave the A1 at Newark – you think you are never going to get there.

Into early March and after a mad rush down to the Royal Showground for an emergency Board Meeting which wasn't really necessary, it was back up at night for own local Holstein Club's AGM, after which I spoke both about our own herd and as Society President. Two days later and it was another long journey down to Narberth in South Wales for their Club Dinner. As we had to be in Cornwall on the Monday, it wasn't worth coming home, so we had a leisurely drive down to stay at Falmouth for two nights. On the Sunday we went to the Lost Gardens of Heligan where we walked a long distance but found them very interesting, particularly the fruit and veg garden.

As we had time on the Monday morning we decided to go to Lands End to say we had been – but the car park was some way off and you had to pay to go the last bit – which we refused to do – it is surely a part of our National Heritage. A bit like going to Cathedrals that need a payment to go in – I won't do it – I'll gladly leave a donation after looking round but I won't pay to go in.

The reason for going to Cornwall was to represent the Society at Ella Laity's funeral. Rodger had been on the Holstein Board with me earlier and we had become friends and also got to know Ella well – she was a lovely lady. Rodger was doing a second term on the Board at the time and it was only right to support he and Philip at that sad time.

Unfortunately, we had to rush away and left there at 3 o'clock, drove 393 miles back to be at the Yorkshire Club AGM for 9 o'clock to speak as the Club's President as I finished my two years in that role.

Off again after fothering next morning, and back down to Tewkesbury, which we had come past the afternoon before, but it couldn't be avoided. That was the AGM of the British Friesian Breeders Club, did a short speech, and I was amazed to discover that I was the first President for many years to have gone to their meeting – shocking, and I am glad that I set a precedent and I know quite a few of my successors in the role have followed suit.

A week or so then with normal work, did all the jobs one day when Stuart had a day's holiday to go up to his girlfriend's (now his wife) Graduation Ball. We then had three cattle over at Carlisle at a Border Counties Sale where we had champion with Dalesend Pansy 206 who sold for 2100gns with others at 1450 and 1500. I took Bill with me and we drove from there down to Somerset for me to speak to their Club at night. Bill was enjoying his trip, even when he spilled his coffee in the front of the car as we set off again after a comfort break. He couldn't get over the fact that once we got down there no one ever asked if we had eaten or wanted to, and it was only after the meeting he managed to persuade the pub landlord to make us a few chips so that we had something to eat, along with Bill's daughter Geraldine, who had driven across about an hour to see her father. It was up in good time again the next morning to drive back from Ilchester to East Harlsey for Phillip Corner's funeral (just a young man sadly lost in a motorcycle accident in the fields at home). Home for an hour or so and then up to speak at a Northumberland Holstein Club meeting. That was a last-minute job to stand in for Dairy Farmer columnist Roger Evans who had given backword.

The day after it was a quick trip down into Cheshire for the Western Club Show and back home by about 1 o'clock. The next day Marnie went to Ripon to do a Farmers Market for Sarah, who was doing the catering for the YFC Northern Area Field Day and I had to go to Bookers at Darlington for her to get more soft drinks etc.

A quiet week or two from Holstein duties and apart from farm work we managed to fit in a night away at Simonstone Hall, which Adam had won as a raffle prize and couldn't use. The hotel later became well known when television motor man Jeremy Clarkson punched the producer because he couldn't get a meal late at night.

April Fools Day and we went over to stay with John and Ruth Edge at Wimboldsley, ahead of the Western Club Dinner at Chester Racecourse. The following week we were classifying with Alastair Bell and had a good day with 8 new EX cows and 18 new VG's including seven VG-2yr-olds. Quite an early spring and good weather at this time, epitomised by swallows arriving on 8th April and hot and sunny.

On the Saturday we went across to Bishop Burton college for their 50th Anniversary stock judging/showing etc and was in exalted company alongside Sir Henry Plumb, ex-NFU President who judged the sheep handling and the overall championship. It was fascinating to see the difference among the students and how interested or keen they were in the project. Some hadn't a clue whether the heifer was in calf or not, or its date of birth. One young lady I asked what the heifer was sired by, said how was she supposed to know, asked me how I knew it was by Shottle – I told her it was written on the ear tag!! Straight from there, back home to change our clothes and pack a bag en route to Dumfries, calling at the Sandford Arms on the A66 for our supper, and quite late by we got to the Travelodge, ready for the next day at the HYB weekend rally hosted by the Scottish Club at Barony College. There were about 250 young members there altogether and that day they were doing the "Field to Foto" competition and their enthusiasm was a joy to behold, with both the A & B team competitions being won by Northern Ireland.

A couple of days at home, milking one day, then down to Rickmansworth for a Board Meeting – mostly on the new breeding science – genomics – we have come a long way in eight years since then! Overnight at the Two Brewers at Chipperfield and meeting continued until lunchtime. Back home and the next day I milked so Richard and Stuart could go on the Bishopton Vets trip up to Colin Dents (Bridgend) and Scarisbeck Farms. It seemed only fair to let them away for that when they had been so much at home while I have been touring the country. It was a very good, early spring and we got much of the maize sown by mid-April – which helped with the early maturity at the other end of the season, of which more later.

Towards the end of April had Board Meetings of the farm and property companies, ate lunch as we drove over to Carlisle for the Highoaks dispersal sale. The Wilson family had had a Triple Threat bull from us some years earlier, and we had known Edward for a long time – there was a really good solid trade.

The first day of May I did my usual spell on the farming stand at the Wensleydale Food and Farming Festival and then we went down to see Mr J for his 80th birthday, taking with us his special birthday present. Sometime earlier, as I think I have already mentioned old Dalesend Jessie 45 had been photographed up at Beamish Museum as at the time she was the oldest living recorded pedigree Holstein. That picture was used on the cover of the Holstein Journal issue that focussed on longevity. We got an extra copy and took it up to the picture framers at Leyburn who displayed it properly in a 3-D kind of way and Mr J was delighted with it and was even more delighted a few days later when he came home after thirteen weeks in hospital. After that it was a regular occurrence to go up to Hill Top East just to visit him and pass a little time – Mrs J said you could see him prime himself up when he heard my footsteps across the floor of Hill Top East.

A few days later it was off again to Harper Adams for their Dairy Technology day which was very poorly attended and wasn't very inspiring but at least Holstein UK had a presence there, but as far as I know the idea of it becoming an annual event never came to fruition.

After delivering a young bull somewhere in the back of Huddersfield one afternoon, it was off the next evening over to Belfast again to stay at the Malone Lodge Hotel in readiness for the Balmoral Spring Show the next day – a poor show of cattle by numbers – only about 20, but a very good championship line up. Back home that night and then away early the next morning to drive up to Ayr for Ayr Show – again not a very large turnout, but two tremendous cows at the head of the line – Parkend Jacob Betsy was Champion from Brian Weatherup, with Logan Mr Sam Hope from Messrs Yates in Reserve – and it could have gone either way. Then a long cross-country drive via Glasgow and Edinburgh motorways to call at Adam's, and we went out for tea with them before coming back home – a lot of driving in the day.

Being an early spring, we had first cut silage in the clamp by the 16th May, before the next day, after Marnie came home from school driving down to stay just outside Oxford ready for the following day. Robert Cooper's Noremead herd had won the Holstein UK Premier Herd Competition the previous year and so were hosting the annual open day, and Robert invited me to open it, which remembering visiting there some 40+ years ago whilst at college, I was very pleased to do. The farm as ever was immaculate, a huge attendance, though the mini-sale was a little disappointing – Robert was clear at the time, but the whole area was very bad with TB, and so barely an animal sold northwards, which was quite understandable.

From there we drove down to Exeter where we booked into the Gipsy Hill Hotel (all these hotels had fortunately been arranged for us by Heather at Scotsbridge House, rather than having to do it ourselves). The next day was a day off as it wasn't worth going back home. We visited Lydford Gorge, a National Trust Property and had a most enjoyable four hour walk through the woods and back up through the gorge before driving back across Dartmoor. The purpose of the visit was Devon County Show the next day where they start judging very early at 8.30. Not a massive turnout, though the best they have had for some years, but many of the local herds are tied up in that part of the world by TB restrictions. We had a good look round the show and watched intently as a gentleman demonstrated the rolling of a Cuban cigar, then the long, 320 mile drive back home as it was time to visit the first of the local Northern Shows at Otley the next day, and then on the Sunday over to near Preston for a Lancashire Club judging which was held at the Eastham's with a massive turnout from a very large club. With Neil Eastham our vet from the Bishopton vet group, there was an added connection.

There was a lot going on back on the farm at this time, but that will all become apparent in the next chapter, and much of the following week was spent at home before on the Friday evening travelling over to the Crown Hotel at Weatheral near Carlisle, the base for the next couple of days as Holstein UK hosted the European Judges Conference. On the Saturday the actual judges were put through their paces at Borderway Mart where they judged seven classes of six animals and gave reasons on some of them, and then a big dinner at night where I was speaking, and on the day after we travelled on coaches up to John Jamieson's at the Annan herd to show our foreign visitors a typical British herd. Just before that weekend, we had been up for the day at Northumberland County Show – we had some of our own cattle there and a decent day with Pansy 227 Reserve Champion Calf and Stuart Reserve Champion Handler. The day after all the Norwegians arrived for a few days, though I was away much of the time on Presidential duties.

It was off next to Staffordshire County Show, which again is in a TB area so numbers not great, though again some good cows at the top. From there straight down to Shepton Mallett to stay overnight at the Bannatynes Luxury Hotel – a very smart room with triple size jacuzzi bath etc – pity I was just on my own. Next day was the Bath and West Show, with rather better numbers than I imagined there might be, again being in a heavy TB area, well judged by John Jamieson of Firth, with both Champion and Reserve from Noremead, before Jeff Daw's own Jersey cow pipped them for the supreme title. A good look around the show, found the cheese show fascinating it is one of the largest in the country and started off with 38 judges as they worked all the way up to a Supreme Champion.

A weekend on at home and then it was away again, both work and presidential for the Society Genetic Elite Sale at Carlisle, which seemed a bit disorganised, but trade was very "hit and miss" to a top of 23,000gns for a Denmire Marie. We were reasonably happy with a Damion Amanda at 2400gns and MS Echo at 1800, they were just natural born yearlings – some people do expect silly amounts for such animals.

Two days later and it was off again, driving down to Cornwall in the afternoon ready for the Royal Cornwall Show the following two days. A very large, busy show but still have some of their own customs in operation, blue for first and red for second rosettes and they all wear white coats for showing. I remember watching one class which had one young man in proper showing whites, and as he came out of the ring, Roger Laity who was the head steward told him if he came back dressed like that for the next class he wouldn't let him in the ring – he must have borrowed a white coat from then on!! There was a good show of Holsteins with an outstanding champion from Ley's of Thuborough. Back to the show at Wadebridge the next morning to see the Holstein take Supreme. We met a lot of breeders around the show and got frozen – it was nearly mid-June and down in the South West, but it was bitterly cold – particularly when you were dressed up a bit for such events. We set off back home which took about six and a half hours, by which time Marnie had just about got thawed out.

Next day I officially became a pensioner, though not taking it, and we also got some very welcome rain, got caught up with a few things before on the Sunday going over to Coates' at Baildon for the Yorkshire HYB Linear Judging competition.

We photographed five cows the following day and then the day after took Mr Bill with me to drive up to Glasgow for the Scottish Clubs open day at Boclair, one of their major dates on the calendar with six classes to judge. A few jobs at home the next morning and then after Marnie came home early, we drove down to Peterborough to stay overnight at the Marriott Hotel ready for the East of England Show the next day. A decent show of cattle in a non-cow area, with Messrs Steeples from Cramar taking the Championship. As we walked round the show we stumbled across a tremendous display in the main ring. It was organised and done by the East Anglia Young Farmers and showed all the machinery used to produce a crop of corn – starting with tractor and plough and ended with the trailer load of bales going out of the ring. They had of course got everything as large as possible, but then finished lining them up across the arena in front of the grandstand. When the commentator finished by saying the machinery in front of them was worth £2.7 million, you could hear the gasp from the audience – the general public have no idea of the capital tied up in agriculture. I have suggested the idea to various show societies including the Great Yorkshire Show but no one seems to have taken up the idea, they would prefer to spend £1000's on main ring flying motor-cycles etc than something like that which could be done for much less, and could be adopted in this part of the world to a grassland scenario rather than arable.

Next day was North Yorkshire Show and so both jobs again, with some cattle there, had Champion Calf and Stuart was Champion handler, and Lucy Atkinson who was now very keen on showing and came regularly to practice, won her class. While we were at South Otterington for that show, Marnie was doing a cookery demonstration at Ripon.

A day at home catching up with paperwork and seeing to builders as they re-did our big foot bathing trough and re-did in front of the out of parlour feeders, before going off the next day to Cheshire County Show. A good show with about 50 cattle judged by Roland George, and some desperately slow judging by a South African who was judging the Brown Swiss, but then drew boo's in the judging of the interbreed, when he gave the Shorthorn Champion an insulting low score – it transpired later that he thought it was desperately short of condition for a Beef Shorthorn!! At the show it was interesting to talk to non-farming spectators who in many cases haven't a clue but appreciate you trying to inform them. One asked what a "heifer" was when the judge used the term, they didn't realise that an animal had to have a calf before it gave milk and had to keep doing so every year. He and his wife lived in the centre of Wigan so didn't know much about farming. Another show with a big cheese show, and again saw a lot of breeders, the North West Club have a marquee to entertain in.

The following night we went out for dinner with a group of Ex-Holstein UK staff at Solberge Hall. They meet for a couple of days every year in different parts of the country, and we had a very pleasant evening with Abbie Cotton, Dick Stapleton, Peter Spain among others. It just demonstrated the friendships made over many years and the camaraderie that exists after all these years.

An early start to the next morning and down to Lincolnshire County Show – the second day which is also a local show day and had some problems with the blatant injecting of a cow out in the middle of the sheds – do these people not realise it is only a photograph away from appearing in a red-top newspaper and harming the whole image of milk. I was in too much of a hurry to get away back home when I was "pinged" for speeding from a bridge over the A1 just as I set off back – the police notice followed a few days later, but I consider I was fortunate only to be caught the once in that year of hectic travel. Called at home to pick up cases and Marnie plus Stuart who was going to help at the Highland Show. We called in Carlisle for some supper and dropped Stuart off at the Show before finding our way to the Dalmahoy Golf and Country Club where we were to stay for two nights. Friday was show day for dairy cattle and there was a good turnout in the Holsteins judged by Eddie Griffiths and we had a good day with Dalesend Pansy 227 winning the maiden heifer class, a third and two fifths plus third with a pair and third in the group of three. Champion was the Rose from Butterfields of Ingleview and the Holsteins won the interbreed group. We attended the Scottish Club reception in late afternoon, and then on the next day watched the judging of the interbreed beef groups which is a fantastic display of all the different beef breeds and is quite a spectacle. Called to see Adam and Laura as we came home.

Sunday was a day of rest, or at least of catching up, we seem to practise, six days shalt thou labour and on the seventh catch up with everything you haven't got done on the other six. Off the next morning in good time to Waltham Abbey in Essex for a Holstein UK Board Meeting and then the next day to John Torrance's for a classification workshop and then picked Marnie up from Stevenage when she came down on the train after school and we drove to Chipping Sodbury to stay overnight before attending the RABDF Gold Cup Open Day at King Brothers. Then it was right back across country that afternoon and evening to stay at Norwich before attending the Royal Norfolk Show the following day. That was the second day of the show which featured mostly young stock, but in a non-dairying area, it was pleasing to see up to 14 calves and 17 handlers in some classes. Also had an interesting talk with a group of Latvian dairy farmers who were very intent on learning as much as they could about our agriculture in general and dairying in particular.

Next morning a few jobs and then off to Askham Bryan College at York where I was main guest and speaker at their graduation day, with over 900 people in a very large marquee. After speaking had to present all of the certificates to a massive number of students as it also included all the ones from day release centres as well.

The weekend was quieter at home, with my weekend on, though we did go to Thorpe Perrow arboretum in the evening for the Mowbray Friends group picnic and to see "A Midsummer Nights Dream". Sunday afternoon we used up a present of Marnie's with an afternoon tea at Swinton Castle, before I drove to Manchester airport ready for an early morning flight to Stockholm. The next four days in Sweden were for the European Holstein Conference, where there was a lot of talking, but also a lot of sitting and standing about as there always is at such events. The conference was based at the Marriott Hotel and was very well organised and good to have simultaneous translations on earphones as the various papers were given. On the second night we all went to the famous Grand Hotel for the gala dinner and entertainment. A superb, classical hotel and very good dinner, which it wanted to be as it supposedly cost £170 per head. The next morning was more talk including the AGM before we went to the DeLaval headquarters for a fascinating tour of their farm museum and new technology development labs. After that to a local farm to see typical Swedish entertainment, horseback jousting, horseback acrobats/jugglers, followed by a typical Swedish farm style dinner. Our flight home the next day wasn't until the afternoon, so vet Jon Mounsey and I went to the Vasa Museum to see the raised wreck from 50 years ago. They had built this new ship but got the calculations somewhat wrong and it sank before it got out of the harbour, but it was a very interesting visit.

Got caught up with things at home the next day before in late afternoon driving down to Carmarthen to stay at the Ivy Bush Royal ready for the HYB National Judging Competitions the next day which were hosted by "Gatrog" with a great show of cows. Had all the trophies to present. The farm had taken a little finding as we went, but a kindly garage man drew us a map of how to get there. Back home via Hereford and Worcester and the next day had two loads of cattle to take to the Great Yorkshire Show.

Whilst I was tied up Yorkshire Show week, Marnie was away with the Mowbray children for their activity week at Ullswater. Monday was a variety of jobs at home with Stuart away at the show, all day Tuesday at the show as Society President, so a lot of talking and hand shaking, and the Yorkshire Club did a President's reception in the afternoon. The second day of the show I was also in official capacity, receiving trophies on the Societies behalf in the interbreed classes. I was invited to the lunch in the President's pavilion that day. President that year was Sir Ken Morrison of the supermarket chain – a grand man I had met a couple of times previously with Mr J. The buffet lunch that day was in honour of the chief visitors of the day, Prince Charles and the Duchess of Cornwall. We were given much briefing ahead of the show, had to be there long before they arrived to go through security and were apportioned into groups of three or four for them to circulate round. When they did arrive, they just took absolutely no notice of what had been arranged and just came to speak to whoever they felt like doing. Prince Charles had a word about Holstein's which he doesn't like as they are too dairy, and then asked about milk prices etc., and when I said they could be better, said he would see what he could 'do'. There was no immediate jump in prices, so I guess nobody listened to him.

Saturday took us over to Carlisle racecourse for Cumberland County Show, on a horrible wet day, everywhere was very muddy and puddly – not a lot of cows but a good champion in Hodgson's Mr Sam daughter.

After a quiet Sunday and catching up on office work on the Monday morning we were off again – down to Builth Wells ready for the Royal Welsh Show the next day. We stayed in a smashing B&B a few miles away from the showground. Never having been there before we did as we were told and got there very early the next morning as traffic would be horrendous, but no such thing and we drove straight in and were pleased to have some of the best weather of the summer, it was warm and for the most part sunny. The show is staged in a very attractive natural bowl setting and had a massive attendance – I don't think a lot of farming work will get done that week in Wales. Another area of the country, which is suffering badly with TB, but a decent show of cattle number wise and a quite outstanding Champion who was 'right on the money'. What was even more pleasing was that the Champion Castlehyfryd Spirte Rosina was third or fourth generation down from a Stardust Rosina we had sold as a calf at the "Genetics for Millennium" sale at Beeston some years earlier. She went on to be All Britain that year, and we were all very proud that arguably the two best cows of those previous years had originated from "Dalesend". The judging rings at the Royal Welsh are much better used than at many shows, and once the judging is over, they are used for all sorts of things including the Young Farmer's inter county rugby finals. Second day of the show saw the Holsteins win all the interbreed competitions except the pairs. A drive home always seems to take a long time from Central Wales to get across to the M5 and onto faster roads.

Morning at home catching up on things and then down to Derbyshire to judge their Young Stock Herds Competition, staying with Andrew Dutton overnight. Judged four entries in the afternoon and five the next day, finding my winners at Holdcroft's and Reserve at Marshall's. Back home in early evening and then straight up to Leyburn for our own North Eastern Club annual barbecue and competitions at Metcalfe Farms.

The weekend and a couple of days early in the week at home catching up with all kinds of things and a couple of Board Meetings , before picking things up again with a trip to Nantwich Show, which we greatly enjoyed and watched as John Edge took the championship for his Wimboldsley herd then back home for a quieter week as we got into more normal farming as we started harvest.

Down to South Wales for the Judges Conference with Sarah, Alan Goldie and picking Rebecca Jarvis and Eddie Griffiths up on the way and we stayed at Newport overnight. To Carmarthen for the actual judging day and a race to be back home for an especially important meeting that night, of which more later. Saturday of that week took us over into Lancashire for Garstang Show – a good one day show and with no Royal Lancashire show for many years, it is one of their main shows.

Early the following week it was down to North Wales, overnight ready for Anglesey Show the next day where there was a good turnout of cattle without being anything really exciting before getting back home and early to bed before a 4am start the next morning to drive to Newcastle and then fly to Belfast. It was the only flight of the day and it was strange to arrive at our hotel at 9am in the morning and have breakfast before we slept there. Wilbert Rankin picked me up and we visited a couple of farms while his wife took Marnie to the Ulster Folk Museum, before we met up at the Causeway Classic Sale at Moira where trade was very mixed and then it was another early morning to catch the flight back home, a few hours work and then at night we drove over to Manchester airport for another early flight , this time to Douglas, Isle of Man. I found it rather disappointing and rather rundown in general, remembering what a smart, vibrant place it had been when we stayed there for a North Eastern Club trip about thirty years previously. The taxi driver who took us to the show near Peel explained that many young people had left for the mainland, and the powers that be had chased the money people for a couple of weeks residency a year, and the holiday makers from industrial South Lancashire now went to Ibiza, Costa Del Sol and such like, so that the businesses were struggling to keep going and it only really got busy at the time of the annual TT races. On arriving at the show, just about the first person we saw was Ian Scott from Palphramands the electricians in Bedale. He had connections with the island and came across regularly with his motorbike and to visit relatives. Youngstock on the first afternoon and then a good meal at Allesandro's in Douglas at night. We were back the next day for the main cattle show which was fairly well supported, a good look around and talk with members before getting the last flight out at 8.10pm, which was then delayed for another 45 minutes, so it was pretty late by we got back home.

Whilst harvesting was going on after the weekend, we left on the Monday afternoon to drive down to Pembrokeshire arriving at Wolfcastle about 7.15 ready for the County show next morning, to see the Welsh Show champion sweep all before it again in some very miserable weather and then back home again. A day at home and then over to Cumbria for a national HYB training day at Ellengrove, a good instructive day but very poorly supported. At home they were getting ready for hosting the Masham YFC (of which Stuart was a member) interclub "It's a knockout" which was rather spoilt by a very wet evening. Down to Ashbourne show on the Saturday, another county which did not have much of a county show and we saw a lot of breeders. Disappointing news at night when we got back to learn that Andy's father had collapsed and died very suddenly earlier in the day. Andy Stonehouse farmed the Norton herd with his parents at Pickhill.

The following week was rather quieter from a presidential viewpoint and I went to a farm safety meeting one morning at Leyburn. At that time, the Health and Safety Executive ran such meetings and if you attended them you did not get an on-farm visit. Interesting to note that earlier this year, that kind of option was withdrawn as the number of occupational injuries and deaths on farm if anything has increased and certainly have not been reduced. The only trip that week was over into Cheshire for the last of the HYB training at Stcyhe. It was our own local show at Wensleydale that Saturday and we had a couple of cows there, plus Stuart won the YFC class with his calf and he was Champion handler in the HYB classes with Lucy also winning her class.

We left after doing part of the milking on the Sunday morning to drive down to Surrey for the Edenbridge Show which Tim Gue as the local board member had told me was a much better supported show than the County Show and we were amazed at the number of cattle, particularly the calves and handlers that were present in another non dairying area, that also attracted a massive non farming audience over the Bank Holiday weekend. One of the main officials at the show was Bob Felton, who some twenty or so years earlier had been the odd job man and show get ready man for Herdwise. We were there in time for lunch and then I judged the calf classes as the judge was Mark Nutsford who was due to judge the National Calf Show later in the autumn and so was prevented from judging the calves, though he was still able to do the handlers and the senior cattle the next day. Overnight at the Marriott hotel at the adjoining Lingfield Park racecourse. We set off back home soon after lunch and it was amazing on a day like that just how much traffic was pouring back into London round the M25 ready for back to work the following day.

We went to Tim Stonehouse's funeral, such a pity for a young man of only 58, and the following day it was an early start and down to Buckinghamshire County Show where a nice young cow from Roger Steeples of Cramar was Champion and yet again a decent turnout for a non-dairy area. One got the impression over the show season that those who were left dairying in such areas made more of an effort to keep their shows going than was perhaps made in the heavier cow areas.

In early September it was down to the NEC for the Dairy Event which had both moved there and had a change of time from mid to late September, which wasn't very popular with either the farming fraternity nor the commercial firms, but it was still at that time an important event, though it wasn't many more years before it ceased to exist and more recently was superseded by the Society's UK Dairy Day. Much of the day was spent around the ring as I had quite a lot of presentations to perform, but kept out of all the arguments about "sealing" which was eventually resolved, though I think I would have called some of their "bluff" and let them walk away home instead of showing. There was no such problem in the youngstock competition where Stuart was judged to be the events National Showmanship Champion- a great reward for a lot of effort he had put in over the years. Champion was again the outstanding Rosina from Castlehyfryd. Next day was over to the final County show of the year at Westmorland based at Crooklands near Kendal. A very foresighted and old show society who had bought their own farm and hence showground so they could develop as they wished. Always very well supported and by all accounts nearly always wet, which it was that day – Marnie was glad she hadn't gone with me with having already been away for 2 ½ days in the first week of term, and Mr Tearle the headmaster had been very good in allowing her time off to support me at many events – seeing it as a bit of reflected glory for the school. Fortunately, nearly every car was parked down over on the hillside, so that unless you missed the gate as you slid downhill, you got onto the road ok to get out.

Sunday was the North East All Breeds Dairy Calf Show at Thirsk, where I did the commentary but we also had a good few calves entered, with Pansy 227 finishing up as Reserve Champion North East Calf and Stuart being North Eastern handling champion, both to go forward to the National a few weeks later, where Stuart was 5th in a very large strong class.

A successful flush of MM Spottie by Spike from Lambert, Leonard and May the day before going over to Carlisle to judge the club sale. A nice show of cattle with the Champion and Reserve both making 2600gns though the top was 3400gns for a heifer I considered to be narrow but with a particularly good udder and had tremendous pedigree. Later in the week we were at Stokesley Show where Pansy 227 was Champion calf and Stuart Champion Handler and that was followed on the Monday by the very last show in the North at Nidderdale, and my final show as Society President.

That was really my last job as President and after a week of jobs at home it was over to Preston for the Celebration and AGM when Jimmy Hull of Fortland took over. Sunday night was a coach tour of the Blackpool Illuminations, Monday morning a board meeting while the rest of the delegates went to Dewlay cheese factory, to feature in later years when helping Sarah with the Jersey Society World Conference and their judging field day, as both lunches featured Dewlay cheese, where the hosts the Pye family of Bayview Jerseys sent their milk. In the afternoon we visited Jimmy's at the Fortland herd and competed in a 6 out of 30 judging competition, followed by a ride onto their "wild moss" which was an area of SSI and was quite astonishing to feel the ground moving as you walked on it, not only that but you could also see it moving. The following day was lunch at Abbeystead hosted by Mr Tom Drinkall who welcomed everybody into the village hall personally and then we visited their Pennine herd – a really hard farm- no wonder the cattle do so well when they go to kinder surroundings. Another trailer ride up onto the top of the hill with fantastic views back across Morecambe Bay and the Irish Sea.

My last duty as President was to chair the AGM as well as making the Presidents report, in which I obviously thanked the society for the enormous honour of the position and all the people who had assisted over the year, but most particularly Mr and Mrs Ropner for allowing me the time to do it and all the staff at Dalesend who had so efficiently carried on with things all the times I was away.

Marnie had accompanied me on many of our trips, as ever a terrific navigator, and over that year we drove 23,000 miles and I think I said had somewhere in the order of 170 cups of Costa Coffee and saw about 3000 Stobart lorries.

All in all, a fantastic year and something we will never forget.

Chapter 23 – The End of an Era

Over the year of my Presidency of Holstein UK, and particularly the second half of that and very much so in the last couple of months, there had been a lot going on at home business wise, which I have kept separate from the previous chapter so the two don't get blurred together.

As a business it was becoming obvious that there were likely to be changes in the not too distant future on a number of fronts. Mr J was not in the best of health, I was at retirement age, and none of the next generation had the love or desire to farm as Mr J had, even though they liked the land and the freedom to walk over it with their friends at weekends or holidays. From the New Year of 2011 onwards I spent a lot of time, as did the Board Meetings discussing various scenarios as we moved forward.

We were very fortunate as a business that we had steered it into a position where it had no borrowed money and while not massive was in a positive cash balance position, and so financial pressure as such had little weight in our deliberations, other than how some cash could be returned to shareholders, bearing in mind that no dividends had been paid over the years, all the benefit had accrued in capital appreciation. Also, it had to be born in mind that other than the Chairman, no one else including myself had introduced any capital, the shareholdings had been gifted to them some years previously when J.G. Ropner & Co became Dalesend Farms Ltd at the time of the sale of Herdwise Ltd back in the mid 1990's.

I spent a lot of time investigating and then in more detail with Greg Ricketts from Andersons on the possibility of some kind of share-farming operation. The thinking was that it would be more on the lines of the New Zealand model where the share farmer would gradually acquire an increasing amount of the capital value of the business over several years, thus releasing capital to be distributed on a more regular basis to the shareholders. It was also a philanthropic idea of being able to give a young person an opportunity to get started in farming without a massive financial input or bank borrowing, an almost impossible task for young people today without large family backing. It was also a way for the 'Dalesend' herd, Mr J and my main interest to remain and be developed as a unit, and finally it would if required, allow me to go into semi-retirement and look after the business for the company, without all the day to day management of it. We had a presentation to a Board Meeting on all the possibilities and I was expecting at the next one in late July for agreement to be reached to pursue that avenue, when I was summoned to a meeting ahead of the Board Meeting to be informed that the next generation had decided that with its strong financial wealth, they wished to dispose of most of the asset and pursue other ventures. The final decision was left in abeyance for a few days for everyone's deliberation before being confirmed on the 2nd August.

It was then a question of making arrangements for the disposal of the business. We appointed George F White as the selling agents (they already looked after the light industrial estate at Dalesend for the Wensleydale Property Company) with Nigel Foster as the main man from the Bedale office. It was decided that initially we would try and sell the business as a going concern which had tax benefits and would also keep the herd intact and without the opportunity ever being advertised we had about half a dozen interested parties to look round, and after a few weeks the business was sold to Andrew Page to form Page Farm Enterprises. He, or at least his vans will be well known to many people who will have seen them all over the country delivering spare parts to garages, and also if you drove down the M1, the big new central distribution depot they had recently established on the new Industrial Estate in Derbyshire. By the very fact that the business was sold so quickly without ever being advertised tells you that it was sold at a very good premium price. We were also fortunate that this that time was arguably at the very top of the market for farmland prices. It soon became very clear that Mr Page did not want to take over the herd or continue dairy farming, so there was going to be a sale to organise.

Quite obviously as soon as the decision to sell had been taken there were going to be people coming to the farm, and it was only right that the staff be told as soon as possible and be re-assured that their jobs were secure until after the event and that they would be properly looked after and compensated for their loss of employment. Calling them into the office, informing them and explaining to them was one of the most difficult jobs of the whole episode, in their differing roles Richard, Stuart and Chris had all given tremendous service and were going to have to deal with a lot of disruption over the next six months. There were also a lot of phone calls to deal with over those few weeks as word spread that the farms were being sold, from local, and not so local businesses and people with whom we had worked with over the years. One or two bits of machinery that were on order needed to be cancelled, the main one being of a larger scale – the creation of a slurry lagoon with pumping equipment etc in the corner of the 20 acre, all of which was organised with Storth Engineering. Over the next few weeks there were a lot of legalities and paperwork to see to in completion of all the negotiations, discussion over the pieces of land which were being retained where it adjoined the three family homes. The sale of Fox Park farmhouse was completed to the sitting tenants who had been there for some time – Terry and Belinda (Mike Keeble's daughter) Williams of the Yorkshire Provender Soup Company and Yorkshire Party Company. The ongoing sowing of autumn crops was still to see to, and apart from some maize which we made early into silage to get into the cows, the rest of the maize was to sell, through Whites, as a standing crop, all of which was bought by David Webster and son from Well.

The main event that was to plan for and organise was of course the dispersal of the herd, and the day immediately after I completed my year as Society President we had Tom Brooksbank from Norton and Brooksbank and Glyn Lucas from Harrison and Hetherington here to see the cows and set up a date, as we had decided to use them jointly for the sale. Norton and Brooksbank had done all our previous sales and H&H had been our sales arena on a regular basis over recent years. I agreed with them on that walk round that the cows were looking rather on the lean side, hence the early cutting of some maize to get it into their diet. Remember we had from that day 28th September to sale day as arranged for 22nd November to work in, but the maize silage certainly did the trick and the auctioneers were astounded at the turnaround in the cow's condition in that eight week period.

We decided to have the sale at home and all on one day, though it would make for a very long day. With everything else that was going on I, nor the regular staff had much extra time to get the cattle ready, and so Sarah, who already saw to the showing and sale preparation and did a lot of that kind of work for other herds, was put in charge of cattle preparation. Norman Iveson very quickly made us a four animal walking stall to fit on the front of the JCB, and we had virtually all of the cows and most of the in-calf heifers halter led in the ring – no mean feat with that kind of number in such a short time. Although we had our own roll-over crush it was too time consuming to go through all the cows, and so we had Norman Walker in for the day to tidy up their feet, he and Stuart worked like demons in a very long day and did 145 cows – granted a lot just wanted a 'rub round', but it was still logistically a massive achievement. On a lighter note, it was something that had been planned and booked before all the sale of the farm had been known, Marnie and I that afternoon went over to Manchester to go to see Peter Kay – he lightened the mood for a while.

The second half of October was very busy with, besides the sale preparation, there were quite a lot of things that had previously been organised such as hosting an Asda/Arla Dairy Link meeting, the National Calf Show weekend, Sarah over in Holland for a day looking at cattle with Phil Alcock from Bishopton and James Simpson to replace the ones James had lost with an outbreak of botulism, which had such a devastating effect on his herd, but the stoicism he showed in overcoming it was to be admired. The Yorkshire Club Dinner at Walshford did us some good with the results of the herds competition when Dalesend Silky Rena and her daughter Lyster Rena stood 1st and 2nd cow in milk and not surprisingly, the Best Pair.

In the preparations for the sale, we also did a TB test in early October so that people could buy with confidence, though there was no real problem as we were in a four year parish and there had never been any problems. It no doubt did help come sale time that we were in such a good area on the TB scene, and also that we were only one clear blood test away from being CHECS accredited as Johnes free.

Stuart was away for a week in early November at the Royal Winter Fair trip to Canada which again had been long previously booked – he wanted to cancel but I wouldn't let him, we showed at our last show as a herd, over in Carlisle at Northern Expo, where Dalesend Drake Rena won one of the heifer classes. The sale catalogue was to be proofread, which was quite a long job with 320 in it.

During this very busy time, Marnie and I were scouring the local area for a new home, as we learnt that Mr Page wanted possession of Newton Grange by 28th February. We decided, or Marnie would say I decided that we would prefer a bungalow and thinking ahead to later years that was nearer to some population and if possible on a bus route as ultimately planned to run only one car. We looked at bungalows in

Northallerton, Morton-on-Swale, Firby Road in Bedale, Leeming, Leeming Bar, couldn't find anything available in Masham, and eventually we finished up at Harkness Close where we now have lived for almost eight years.

So, to the actual sale. A very busy weekend after some busy weeks – more people about helping to get ready for the sale day, which was a Tuesday. Sarah had organised a lot of people to help, particularly through the HYB members of both the Yorkshire and North Eastern Clubs, who both the day before and the main day did a fantastic job of washing, bedding and moving cattle about. As is "sods law" the starter motor went on the JCB, but Gareth Teasdale did a fantastic job in having it going again by 9am. The day before I was tied up much of the day talking and showing various visitors around, and then having got everybody away for a few hours rest at night, Marnie and I milked in three batches through the night, to get milk on them ready for the morning.

The washing gang started again at two in the morning and had everything done cow wise by 8.30am and Peter Corner's big collecting pen/race which was moveable and could be variously shaped was a great help through the preparation and sale days. Sale day opened up very foggy and there was an almost eerie silence about the place despite all that was going on, particularly with all the floodlights on that E&P Electrics had rigged up for us, but after that it got out into a very good, bright, sunny day with barely a breath of wind. Bearing in mind it was the 22nd November we were very fortunate with the weather – I'm just glad it was a much better autumn than we are having as I write this in 2019. And finally, we were at "Go" – 10 o'clock was start time, and what a crowd which was still growing. We reckoned there were about 1000 people present and cattle sold to about 100 different buyers from 26 different counties, and the best report I can give of the sale is to include the report which appeared on the Holstein (UK) website a few days later and the very satisfying average of £1850 per life sold over the 320 animals and what was particularly pleasing was that there was only one lot missing from the whole catalogue and that was my own fault. Dalesend Marigold 159 was a second calver who had lost her udder but giving a lot of milk and I thought she would sell at a certain price, but then she went very badly lame a couple of days before the event, so I had to get rid of her pretty quickly. Once the sale was ended at 5.30pm, there was absolute "mayhem" for a couple of hours as people were getting loaded up and away, and the next day there were wagon loads of cattle going all over, and a start on the tidying up.

23-11-20 – DALESEND HERD BOWS OUT IN GREAT STYLE

As the 300 head catalogue proclaimed this sale was truly "The end of an era" as Messrs Ropner's famous Dalesend herd was dispersed on farm on Tuesday this week. A massive crowd jammed into the sale arena with many more craning their necks from outside to see the fun. Over 100 buyers were recorded spanning 26 different counties from all over the UK. The Dalesend herd has a long and distinguished history spanning 60 years and following the retirement from farming of Jonathan Ropner and the sale of Dalesend Farm, the entire herd was put up for auction. Interest had been at fever pitch since the catalogue was published and a great result followed with 300 head averaging £1,854 per life.

There were 27 animals that made 3,000 guineas or more, but we waited till late in the sale to see the top price of 6,200gns. A fabulous red calf by Fradon Jet Red, bred from the same family as Simon Davies' exciting show cow of the same name was snapped up by Albert Innes-Smith from Ponteland for his Movistar herd. 4 telephone bidders provided a flurry of bidding, but as always there was only one winner!

A large load will travel to Wales as several discerning Welsh breeders bid keenly – sometimes against themselves! Among these was Peter Jones of the heavy milking Parcgwyn herd in Monmouthshire, who purchased 7 fine cattle, including the top priced cow Dalesend Talent echo EX-91 for 4,600gns. This lovely cow was adjudged by many as the best cow in the sale and was the only animal catalogued with a genomic test. Her GTPI was 1,824 but her 91 points and 50 litres a day will have been major factors. Her Mr Sam calf at foot made 2,100 to D.H Ryder of the Rypark herd near Otley.

Messrs A.L Dean & Son were in determined form and purchased the superb dam and daughter combo from the Spottie family. Dundee Spottie, the EX-91 show cow made 3,700gns and her daughter by Mr Minister, also successfully shown made 4,500gns – the second highest priced cow.

Young stock were a flying trade with 52 heifer calves averaging £1,268 and selling to a top of 2,800 guineas for a Talent daughter from the famous Maude family. Tony Hack of the Santamaria herd in West Wales was the successful telephone bidder and her dam travels to North Wales to join Messrs Jones' Puerto herd at 3,000gns.

An impressive group of 35 in-calf heifers averaged over £2,000 with a top price in the section of 3,200gns. This was for another Rosina, named Rosanna by Comestar Outside. She was carrying an embryo by Palermo out of Cogent Manat Scant EX-90 and was secured by Metcalfe Farms from Leyburn for their Washfold herd.

Maiden heifers continued to sell consistently well as the sun set with Dalesend Drake Rena selling for 4,000 guineas to join Peter Miles and family's Littlebridge herd near Northallerton, with the top price of 6,200gns referred to above, coming 10 lots later.

Tribute was made to Farms Manager Bernard Liddle, the immediate past President of Holstein UK, who with his family and expert team at Newton Grange had put a large dispersal sale together in great style in just 6 weeks. Their hard work looks to have been repaid in the best possible way. We wish all the team at Dalesend and the Ropner family every good fortune for the future.

AVERAGES

152	Cows & Calved Heifers	avg. £2,566.42	= £390,096.50	= 371,520 gns
35	Served Heifers	avg. £2,082.00	= £ 72,870.00	= 69,400 gns
62	Maiden Heifers	avg. £1,518.09	= £ 94,122.00	= 89,640 gns
249	Lots (incl 54 'A' lots @£1,245)	avg. £2,237.30	= £557,080.00	= 530,560

TOP 10 PRICES

LOT	NAME	BUYER	GNS
228	Dalesend Rosina Red PI	A.Innes-Smith (Movistar)	6,200
72	D. Talent Echo PI EX-91	T.G & D.AJones& Sons (Parcgwyn)	4,600
140	D. MM Spottie PI VG-852yr	A.L Dean & Son (Threshfield)	4,500
132	D. Emulate Gail VG-852yr	Showell Farms (Moordown)	4,200
145	D. Bolton Amanda PI	Harry Evans (Ceinwen)	4,200
158	D. MS Rosina PI	H Thompson	4,000
218	D. Drake Rena	J.L Miles & Sons (Littlebridge)	4,000
83	D. Silky Amanda 2 PI VG-86	D.C Hall (Airebank)	3,900
153	D. Marigold 177 VG-852yr	Harry Evans (Ceinwen)	3,900
32	D Dundee Spottie EX-91	A.L Dean & Son (Threshfield)	3,700

Auctioneers: NORTON & BROOKSBANK with HARRISON & HETHERINGTON

There wasn't a lot of time for anyone to sit or stand about and mope, as we still had the farm "dead stock" sale to get ready for in a fortnight, and bearing in mind this was going to be in December we wanted to get as much as possible of it under cover, so all the buildings and straw used for the sale had to be cleared out of the buildings, including a lot of the big bales of straw for some of the seating which we had borrowed from Martin Webster and Percival's had brought and took away. There were still a few cows to milk for a day or two and eventually down to a couple while they awaited test results to be able to go to Northern Ireland which we managed to get away just before the parlour was dismantled just a day or two before Christmas. Everything was to sort out, all the small tools etc were laid out down the cubicles and feed passageway, and what needed washing off, machinery wise was done and laid out in the young stock building.

Sale day was the 6th December and again we were very fortunate with the weather – a glorious sunny day after a shower of snow and a frost the night before. Again, a massive crowd for the sale run by Tom Oates of Whites who did fantastically well to keep things moving and keep his voice going in selling all 300 lots in just over 3¼ hours. As ever at a farm sale like that, prices were all over the place, some stupidly high and others disappointingly low, I often wonder if people ever check the price of something before, they go to such events. The best examples were a set of clippers I had to buy just before the sale when one set "blew-up" and we hadn't time to wait until they were mended – they made £40 more than we had paid Sam Turner's for them, and a cattle coaxer we had not long had, made about £70 and it had only cost about £50. The real big winners were the Heat time System at £3400, only slightly less than we had paid for it some two years plus previously and one man took all the collars at £60 each almost the new price and neither had any warranty on them, which as new at a similar price would have done. As ever there are always 'rogues' at such sales – early on someone bought the cattle coaxer and I told him to put it in his pocket straight away but being a genuine sort he said he would pay for it first – when he went back for it, it had gone – he didn't want his money back or anything – just accepted it was his own fault. We didn't have masses of machinery as we did a lot by contractors, but it was amazing how it added up with the JCB Loadall making £20,100 and the fittings for it coming to £3940. The one large tractor we ran made £16,900 compared to the £22,500 we had paid for it in 2008, and the old John Deere we had bought from Tony Welbourn of Ripon Farm Services in the late 1980's made almost three times what we had paid for it all those years before.

In the eight years since that sale I am amazed at how machinery prices have gone through the roof but as I have said to many farmers, it is only when you do actually sell up you realise just how much capital is tied up in the live and dead stock on a farm that has been accumulated over a long length of time – the proceeds from our two sales, plus the growing crops and semi- fixtures we had agreed values with Mr Page for them to stay in situ – came to not far short of £1 million. The general public just have no appreciation of the capital tied up in the production of their food!

There was a bit of tidying up and getting things away after that for the rest of the week, including the last cattle away to Northern Ireland just before a storm stopped the ferry sailing and the paperwork ran out of date. The paperwork involved in multiple copies was ridiculous, for a country which I always though was a part of us within the EU.

The night after the sale I went to the Yorkshire Grassland Society Central Group meeting, and it was rather ironic that we should win the main clamp silage for the first ever time. My car which had been on contract hire was at the end of its agreement and I had it to get all tidied up and ready to go back, and that good old "sod's law" kicked in again when I had a puncture the day before – the first one over the four year hire.

That week saw the end of work for the staff on the farm after varying lengths of time. Richard Lapthorne had been with us for over ten years from when he had taken over from Bill Faulds on his retirement and had seen the herd grow from 120 to 180 cows along with all the extensions to buildings during that time. He firstly went on to work for Bishopton Vet Group in setting up their foot trimming service before working for a couple of farming supply/chemical companies and now covers this area for Cogent Breeding. Stuart Clapham had matured from a boy still at school to a very useful full-time member mainly working with young stock and the show preparation side of the cattle over a seven-year period. He went to work from us with James Simpson at Gildersbeck, but the large herd (600) set up didn't suit him. He went on to work part-time with James Wilson on the beef side of his operation whilst also having some stock of his own with his father-in-law Gareth at Snape, but is now back working with dairy cows and living at Castiles at Dallowgill with the Nicholson family. He and Abi married after our sale and just showing how time flies, their eldest son Noah has already started school. I could scarcely believe it at the end of the week when Chris

Knox told me he had been coming part-time for nine years. He was local and flexible and a real good help, as I think in all honesty, we were to him. Latterly he had been a great help in wintering heifers for us up at East Farm, which was better for him than buying in cattle to fatten in the vagaries of the market and avoided us putting capital into more buildings. Chris carries on farming at home on a reduced scale and now helps his cousin Stephen at Mill Close with his farming alongside his Yorkshire Dales Meats business. The other person who had continued to help on an ad-hoc basis, was Mr Bill who over the years since his retirement had come to do some tractor-work, mainly slurry guzzling through the winter, and leading corn at harvest time.

After that there was just me left to tie up all the loose ends until my employment ended at the end of February, but there was a lot of odd jobs and things to do in that 10-12-week period. The bulk tank was to get out through a widened doorway and see to it getting built up again, the milking parlour was all taken out just a few days after the last milking cattle went to Ireland – it took 5 men from 8.30am in the morning till 10.30pm at night plus travelling either end from Carlisle, so it wasn't going to be a cheap parlour on top of the £3400 paid for it by it got re-fitted somewhere. Talking of the last milkers going, I suddenly realised next morning we had no milk for breakfast so had to buy some – didn't taste the same and from that bottle onwards we have almost exclusively used "Cravendale" which is an Arla product, double filtered and with almost unbelievable "use by" dates on it. A few weeks after when Keith Colley of BOCM-Pauls called for a coffee he said that nearly every ex-dairy farmer he knew used Cravendale as the nearest to farm milk they could reasonably buy.

We had a farm dinner at Akebar to say thank you to everyone connected with the farm and particularly all those who had helped with the sale – as my diary says – some were happy, odd ones miserable and some nostalgic. As part of the sale agreement, the "Mouseman" door and surrounds that were the office entrance was to remove and it went up to Hill Top East to become the door for the holiday cottage which was just being completed by Milos who could turn his hand to virtually any building job.

There was an awful lot of paperwork to sort out in the office and much of it to dispose of, mostly by burning which was a long job – it is amazing what had been accumulated over the years and had little current relevance though it was fascinating to read through some of it. What was to keep was to pack up and went up to Hill Top, including the big stone plinth and the cut out model of Dalesend Cascade that had stood on the front lawn, there were a lot of spare parts that we had carried for the cubicle auto-scrapers and we had a ride over to Storth at Carnforth with them, and a credit for almost £1100. Within the sale agreement most of the tyres that were around the farm for sheeting down the silage had to be disposed of by us, and Chris and Alex Wilkes came to help me on several days to load them up into skips from Shepherds of Thirsk who were easily the most reasonable of an expensive disposal which cost about £1500 plus our labour, but it certainly paid to have Alex stacking them in the container rather than just throwing them in at random – even if it did mean each one was over the weight limit and incurred extra charges.

299

Within the office papers as I was clearing I found the original plans for the office extension dated 1963, no one had been able to remember exactly when it had been done, though I knew it was pre-autumn 1964 when I had first arrived at Newton Grange. There were also a lot of papers concerning Patrick Brompton Buying Group of which we had been members since its inception and of which I had been secretary for a long time. They were all bundled up and went to Martin Webster as the Chairman. Latterly the Buying Group had only met once or twice a year and was more of a social meeting, as the business side of both the buyer and the supplier had changed markedly over the years. They decided that the buying group should be wound up and the final meeting was a dinner on 8th October 2012 at the Friar's Head at Akebar when Marnie and I were the guests in recognition of hosting the meetings and doing the very onerous paperwork over so many years.

Whilst all this tidying up and finalisation was going on, we were also organising an event to finalise the farming business and it all culminated in an "End of An Era" Hog Roast in Crakehall Village Hall on 21st January. Robert White of Morton-on-Swale did the hog roast, he had the dubious connection of having been the slaughter man when all the young stock were slaughtered in the Foot and Mouth epidemic of 2001, Marnie and Sarah did all the salads and sweets and Mrs J the flower arrangements. We had found a lot of photographs of the farm and staff over many years and made a display on the show boards which made fascinating viewing for a lot of people we invited as guests many of the previous staff from years previously, together with suppliers etc. who had looked after us for many years, our neighbouring farmers, and friends and associates from the North Eastern and Yorkshire Holstein Clubs. We had about 130 people in all and a memorable day was enjoyed by all, even if it was tinged with sadness.

Amidst all that was going on and being completed, we had also found a bungalow which we liked and filled most of our criteria. All the paper work was to complete on that and the solicitors said I must be the oldest "first time buyer" when I told them there was a special offer on for such people at the time which exempted them from stamp duty. All done and in very short time we got things packed up and moved things gradually until the main moving day when Sarah and Adam were a great help with the heavier furniture and on 17th February 2012 we slept for the first time in our new home – remember I had lived there nearly 48 years and Marnie for 40, so it was something of a wrench and truly...

"THE END OF AN ERA"

Chapter 24 – A Change of Lifestyle

In the last couple of months before moving, we had found a bungalow, packed up and moved for the first time and hopefully, only time in our lives. People used to ask, "how will you manage in a little bungalow after all those years in a farmhouse?" and "how will you manage without the cows and farming?". The answer to both in our case was "mindset" – accept it is happening and move on – the changes are just window dressing and life carries on. Some of our furniture was too large and we had to sell it and buy some new pieces. We still have farming contact through Sarah and because I was still looking after the land the family retained adjoining the three homes – about 140 acres in total, and on the dairy farming side through my continued membership of the Leyburn Dairy Discussion Group, the Grassland Society, both local Holstein Clubs and other such meetings, but it meant that we could attend or otherwise as we so wished rather than having to go as elected or otherwise member. I had on moving given up being the treasurer for St Patricks PCC when we moved out of the area, though we remained on its Electoral Roll and still go to church there a few times a year.

Marnie did so much decorating before we moved in and worked her way round the house over the next couple of years a room at a time, until it was as we wanted it. We put fitted wardrobes in our bedroom, I sanded down the kitchen table and the bed back to its original finish and jobs like that. The strangest thing was in the sitting room – we brought our wall lights with us to put up in place of what was there. When the electrician came to fit them, he discovered none of them were wired up and had only been put there for decoration!!

I was over into Lancashire for a couple of days to judge their Winter Herds Competition. Did 10 herds in the day on a very tight schedule that the long-serving Lancashire Club Secretary Sheila Robinson had planned and when David Tomlinson of Bilsrow who was stewarding came to pick me up, he had come in his Land Rover and suggested we put wellies on to start with as we wouldn't have time to keep taking them on and off. Less to see on the second day though a lot more mileage to visit them. Marnie and I went towards the end of March for one of their meetings to deliver the results – I remember as we went over the tops I have rarely driven into such bright sun at a low angle that made seeing very difficult, but it seems churlish to complain of good weather.

Marnie was still working at Mowbray at this time and so I had a lot of daytime to fill in, though I wasn't short of things to do. I did quite a lot of the veal deliveries for Sarah, going as far north as Fenwick's in the centre of Newcastle and south to Castle Howard Farm Shop. Varied week to week, the longest day I had, including going up to Cockfield to collect the meat from the butchers was 310 miles. There was work to do in our back garden, and I constructed two raised beds and got some soil delivered by a couple of neighbouring farmers to fill them up, so that I was ready for putting in vegetables that first spring. At the bottom along the hedge I filled up with a lot of gravel to get the levels right and then sand before laying the stone/concrete slabs to make it the same rather than the silly bit of lawn there was that you could neither get at to cut or anything else. I also constructed a quadrant shaped shrubbery in one corner, and enlarged and tidied up a rose garden down the side – bearing in mind we lived in Harkness, which had originally been the home of the famous rose breeders of years previously, the best known variety of which was "Ena Harkness".

The family decided to farm the retained land, and asked me to look after it for them, the main task that spring was the Single Farm Payment application. I had in the past always done that myself but decided because of the big change with the sale and that some fields had been split and needed new numbers, it was better to get it done professionally, and got this done with Whites. At one of the spring Board Meetings, the lunch evolved into a presentation from the Ropner family for all our efforts over the years in the form of a "Mouseman" book case and a painting by local artist Walter Parker of Newton Grange with the flags flying and Dalesend Lettice 23 my favourite cow of all the time there stood in front of it. Both are great reminders of the wonderful times we had.

A day or two after that I went to a vet meeting at Thirsk where I was avoided by quite a few people and others wouldn't look me in the eye. I had heard the odd whisper for a week or two and that night overheard one person telling another that I was the manager who had overseen Dalesend Farms Ltd going 'belly-up'. At the end of the meeting I asked the chairman if I might say a few words and explained to the meeting as we had no borrowings before we even started selling up money was not a problem, and that a Voluntary Liquidation was the way that a Limited Company could distribute its assets to its shareholders, and that even one like that had to be published in local and national newspapers. Amazingly the end of the meeting was all bonhomie and smiling faces and people were talking to me again. Strange how quickly people can get the wrong impression and just as soon go back to normal again!!

As we were packing up and moving there were quite a few things of both mine and Marnie's that were no longer relative or we wanted to keep such as stamp albums, some brasses etc and we saw advertised a valuation day at Ripon Spa Hotel, so off I toddled and hung about for a while, only to be told there was nothing of any real value and the very small amount he offered I took as an insult and brought them all home again.

On a non-farming working front, there was a lot going on that summer – it was the Queen's Diamond Jubilee and we watched some of the activities on the television and well remember in particular that awful cold, wet day with the flotilla down the Thames a marvellous sight but rather spoilt in the rain. We were also, that year hosting the Olympic Games, and shortly before the event we had the torch with all the circus in tow as it came through Bedale which was absolutely packed, but it was one of those things you will probably only ever witness once in you lifetime. We did see the torch again a few days later purely by accident when we went to The Dun Cow at Sedgefield for lunch on the day of our Ruby Wedding. We thought it was very busy in the town, particularly as we drove down the main street, virtually the last car before it was closed, but then got a good view over the crowds from the dining room window.

A month later we went down to London for the concert in Hyde Park for the opening of the Olympic Games – a great night, the actual ceremony highlights live on a massive screen – who can or will forget Her Majesty supposedly dropping into the arena with James Bond. Mollie was over from New Zealand and staying with us – we managed to get tickets for New Zealand v's Brazil football up at St James' Park – our only live participation in any of the actual Olympics. The day after the Opening Night of the Olympics, we walked across Hyde Park to the Royal Albert Hall and booked in for a conducted tour – when the time came we were the only two people, so had a private tour which was absolutely fascinating, both in how it had been constructed, particularly the dome fitting and also the scale of what was underground which you never see or are aware of when something is being televised. We watched a final rehearsal by the orchestra of the new Wallace and Gromit symphony which was to make its debut the following night.

We got a new reclining chair for the living room to replace the last of the cintique chairs we had bought when we got married. I took it to the tip and as I carried it across to a skip a young lady asked if I was going to throw it out – the answer was obviously yes and she asked if she could have it as it was better than anything they had in a flat she was moving into with her boyfriend, so I was quite happy to put it into her car and hope she enjoyed it.

Went on the North Eastern Club trip up to Scotland to visit Annan and Errolston herds, went down to Bristol for the Holstein UK Elite Sale and then over into West Wales for the Holstein UK Open Day for the Premier Herd winners Tregibby and a reconciliation with Dalesend Storm Maude who had done such a great job for them and helped promote our prefix. I then acted as Master Judge for the Yorkshire Club's 6 from 30 at Chris Hardcastle's Saltergate herd. Bill went with me down to Dorchester for the RABDF Gold Cup Open Day on a horrible, pouring wet day, then shortly after to just the same sort of a day at the Great Yorkshire Show – it was so wet that the next two days were called off and the show abandoned – the cattle championships were held on the second day on one of the horse arenas.

Late summer took me on a few judging assignments, down to judge the East Midlands Herd Competition, which I had to split in half, though all in the same week, as I had Driffield Show to judge in mid-week where Messrs Southwell from Huntholme took Champion and Reserve. Back down into East Midlands and saw some outstanding cattle at "Corringham" and some genuine cows at "Kilton" which I had never visited before, now dispersed – such a pity the following generations didn't want to continue dairying.

Early August saw me operating on home ground as I judged the Yorkshire County Milk Recording Herds Competition. Something I hadn't been able to do previously as it was our home county and we were regular competitors, but it meant I went to herds I knew of but had never visited, and saw a lot of good cows particularly over in the Skipton area at Moorhouse's "Aireburn", Booths "Feizor" and one I hadn't seen before and was very impressive at Throup's "Dalesbrad" herd.

David and Jane Lofthouse's (cousins) Golden Wedding Party at Haxby, York, got the Olympics finished and took a cooker up to Adam's at Lauder – stopping in Jedburgh Woollen Mill for a coffee we ran into Mr and Mrs Hugh Robertson of "Airies" who had farmed near Kelso before their son emigrated to Canada and started farming over there. Staying with Adam and Laura for the weekend, we went into Edinburgh and visited the Royal Yacht Britannia – absolutely fascinating, it is difficult to imagine without seeing it, just how much they could fit into such a small space and how luxurious it was for the time it was built.

Later in August I judged Wensleydale Show – another one I couldn't have done until now as it was local, and we showed there usually. It had been very wet for a day or two and it was a wellington and raincoat job, not the smartest turnout to judge in, but you have to be practical. Made a third calver from Pratt's Champion and Best Udder. In looking round the handicrafts tent ran into Alan Gregg of Home Farm fame, whom we hadn't seen for a long time – still as daft as ever and flower growing mad.

We were off the next day over to Lytham St. Anne's for Ian and Samantha's (Mary's daughter) Silver Wedding lunch. We couldn't find the golf club for the reception – neither could anybody else – the postcode was wrong on the invitation.

We were busy then helping Sarah get ready for and then move to the bungalow of Alastair Wilkin's at Danby Wiske. After being told there was no big hurry to vacate the bungalow at Newton Grange, it was suddenly needed and so like us, didn't have a long time to get organised. We had our old friend Bill down from Dundee for a few days – still driving down on his own well into his eighties and gave us a few days break from decorating John Wilkin of "Altern" fame bungalow. We had only been running one car since my company contract hire car had gone back the previous December, and Marnie's fairly old VW Polo was in need of changing. Neither of us are really into cars other than to get you from A to B and back again, but we had spent some time that summer looking at various alternatives – being less than impressed by a couple of garages, notably Audi at Harrogate who seemed to think we weren't serious because we were in an old Polo. We eventually narrowed it down to VW Golf or BMW 1 Series with little between them on price. I was determined to have a new car – the only new car I had ever owned in my own right – though had had plenty of company cars. So far, the car (BMW) has done us very well for 7½ years and 125,000 miles with remarkable fuel efficiency as a diesel at about 57 miles to the gallon over that whole time.

Completed base for and then concreted an area for Sarah's shed to go on. Stuart helped me to do that, then he went to the Dairy Event with me, and then a few days later helped to re-erect the shed, before I had another day of judging over at Hodder Valley Show – a smashing small village show which rotates around three villages in the area, real friendly people and a good show of calves and handlers. Champion and Reserve were both from Holgate's "Aliann" herd – a third calf cow and the milk heifer being shown for the first time and went on to be nominated for All-Britain. The interbreed and the pairs and groups I judged jointly with Tom Savage of "Shellen" Jerseys who hadn't much in his own classes, but we had very little argument about any of our placings. The day after was the N.E. All Breeds Calf Show at Thirsk – a tremendous show – handlers judged by Paul Harrison of "Chishillways" and Cameron Baty of "Tynevalley" the calves while I was doing the commentary, and very pleasing to see two class winners being Dalesend Pansy's.

Down to "The Belfrey" in Staffordshire – not to play golf but for the Holstein UK Convention for Tom Cope of Huddlesford becoming President. We visited the National Arboretum which was quite a moving visit and you had to admire what had been created from an old, worked out quarry and also made one realise that apart from the losses of the two Great Wars, the number of members of our forces who had given their lives in many conflicts since then. We visited Mr Robotham's outstanding "Deansgate" herd of British Friesians, cattle showcase of local cattle at Huddlesford, the following day to "Boughey" distribution centre and then to "Picston" to round off the visits.

The end of September brought some very heavy rain – as I write this in November 2019 with large areas around Doncaster badly flooded, it is as well to remember we have had it before. I hadn't at this stage got the rain gauge up and running, but I can tell you it was very wet. The Swale was over and impassable at Morton-on-Swale, Crakehall Beck was over, and the road was impassable there up to Leyburn, and the A1 was closed from Dishforth to Scotch Corner as it was flooded in places. The rain had stopped by the end of the week when I drove down to Cirencester, picking John Foss up on the way, for a college reunion. One or two facts we were given that weekend – quite astonishing was that 73% of UK land was either owned, farmed or managed by ex-RAC students. The other one showed how times have changed in that that year 53% of the students were women, compared to when we were there forty-five years earlier there were none. The day after that we drove down to Norfolk for Ken and Rebecca Proctor's party at "Airfield".

Sarah had just produced the first ever journal for the Montbeliarde Breed Society, but she had just gone over to Jersey to prepare animals for their autumn show, so we got the job of delivering them to their Open Day just north of Birmingham. It was an interesting day among a different sort of animal and also because they were having a workshop with some of the Holstein UK Classifiers, as they were about to start classifications and they were setting the standards for that. We came away quite impressed by what Montbeliardes could offer in terms of wearability, durability and a more valuable bull calf and carcase, and they certainly could easily have a part to play in cross-bred herds of grazing/low cost herds.

October was a quieter month apart from a trip down to Stoneleigh for the All Breeds

Calf Show, the Yorkshire Club Dinner at Walshford, which felt rather strange when we weren't competing, and then the East Midlands Club Annual Dinner and Herds Competition results at Sysonby Knoll Hotel.

The most important thing by a long way that happened in October was that we finally became grand parents for the first time when Ruby Liddle was born up in Scotland, to where we went a few days later to see her for the first time – and what a smashing girl she is now growing up to be!

Mid-November took me up to Edinburgh with Dick and George to see South Africa beat Scotland 21-10 and then it was a drive back up there just a couple of days later for AgriScot and call at Adam's to see the new family again on the way home.

Marnie was retiring from Mowbray at the end of the Christmas term and so there was an odd thing to thank her for all the effort she had made on all those children's behalf. Just a week before they broke up, she purposely was late one morning, just so she could say she had been – wicked!! With more time on her hands she found time to restore the small wooden box that we had had for many years and on the inside found that it had been lined with newspaper one of which carried the date of 1865 – we later went to Durham and Darlington to look through the Northern Echo and Darlington and Stockton Times to see if we could find the actual edition but couldn't. We then went down to Haydock for the Jersey Cattle Society Conference as The Farm Organisation reporter and photographer, which was on marketing. A fascinating paper by the Scottish Salmon Producers Organisation on their procedures, followed by some less interesting ones on various aspects and points about having a dedicated producer/marketing set up with a unique selling point.

Beginning of January saw the Yorkshire Milk Records Dinner at Millstones – I had judged the Black and Whites earlier in the summer, but was asked to propose the toast and then Marnie presented all the trophies – which is a very long affair but you have to admire the array of them beforehand when they are all on display – particularly the very old Shorthorn ones, most of which are solid silver. The change of night for the dinner to the Friday didn't work as numbers were down by about 30 and it also clashed with Ripley Show Dinner.

The 14th February was a very sad day with the death of Mr J, who had not only been my boss and mentor for all those years but had also become a great friend. A truly great man in my book, the most honest man I have ever met. There was obviously great sadness, but also a sense of relief – it had been most upsetting for everyone in those last few months to see someone losing his dignity in a downward descent. Mr J's funeral was held ten days later at the church he had so strongly supported for most of his life, followed by a reception at Dalesend. I went for a cousin of Mr J's, the Rev. Sir Timmy Forbes-Adams to Escrick as at 90 he didn't drive long distances. We came back here so he could get changed and have a drink before he helped officiate at the funeral, before we took him back home again – and I repeated the journey later in May when he also assisted at the Memorial Service in Ripon Cathedral.

Eulogy to Mr J, Mr Jonathan, Governor, Chairman

June 1964 saw me arrive at Newton Grange to be greeted by an imposing gentleman in multi-coloured shorts, flip-flops and very little else. To use that much over-used expression – it was a "life-changing" moment for me, and, I hope Mr Jonathan – we had 49 years of mostly ups, some downs, witnessed massive agricultural change and much fun along the way.

Mr Jonathan, Mr J, Governor, Chairman are all names by which he was addressed by those working alongside him – always that note of respect, which he always returned with the loyalty and trust he showed for his staff.

Wanting more than just farming, he formed Herdwise, described in the early days by a competitor as "a piddling little company from a second rate breeder". 24 years later that competitor had gone and when selling it as the largest private A.I. company in the country – Mr J's only concern was that his loyal staff, many of whom are here today, should have their jobs guaranteed.

I remember leading hay in the Shed Field when the Fergie 20 fired and Mr J ran to and fro from the water trough with upturned cowboy hat to put it out.

Cattle and embryos were brought from Canada to develop the herd, Dalesend Cascade was a leading bull of his generation, Dalesend Storm Maude is a living legend – the only cow ever to be five times All Britain after Championships at the Royal and Royal Welsh Shows, and Dalesend was twice National Premier Breeder.

We had many debates and discussion over the years, but only really fell out once – and that was over the colour of cows!! Talking of colour – thirty years ago a red calf was considered bad breeding and had to be moved very quickly. Recently we had a very well bred red calf, which by then was fashionable. If the cows were in the front field when Mr J came to the office he wanted to get rid of her, when we sold a daughter at a high price he immediately enquired in true entrepreneurial fashion – could we get some more of them!

The lowest point was April 2001 when 163 young stock were slaughtered as a contiguous Foot and Mouth cull, but his indomitable spirit which he has demonstrated in so many ways over so many years carried us forward to rebuild.

The Championship at the Great Yorkshire Show, of which he later became President, together with Presidencies of both the North Eastern and the Yorkshire Holstein Breeders Clubs were highlights amongst his farming achievements.

He was not only my mentor, but at times my tormentor – particularly the week after his fishing on the Tweed in early November – the ideas which came tumbling out were "challenging" to say the least.

The respect in which he was held in all walks of life, for his honesty and integrity was second to none (he sometimes had to be protected from himself, because he thought everyone was as straight as he was).

Many years ago as we travelled, he told me someone as we passed them was the most Christian man he had ever met, I thought then, and I'm even more convinced now that – as we say in Yorkshire "it takes one to know one".

(JB Liddle 18.05.2013)

After the "End of an Era" farming chapter, this was truly the end of another Era – but will return to Mr J at the end of the book with a short chapter dedicated to him.

Chapter 25 – Life's One Long Holiday

While we were both working, it was always difficult to plan far enough ahead to take many long holidays to go overseas, with the exception of going to Florida, Denmark and New Zealand. It is 'sod's law' as farmers that if you tried to fit it in when you thought there was a window of opportunity it was either a late or an early season that meant you needed to be at home. Whilst Sarah and Adam were young we didn't believe in them missing school, and bearing in mind there are ten years between them, we had been working round school holidays for twenty plus years, and then blow me if Marnie wasn't by then working as a Higher Teaching Assistant at Mowbray so it still had to be school holidays. We resolved that once retired and whilst funds allowed, we would do as much travelling as possible, which led some people to say we were always on holiday. So far, we have been able to follow that resolve, and starting in the spring of 2013 we have had some great trips. It always amused me over the years when Mr J and family were going away, if I wished him a good holiday, he always said it wasn't a 'holiday', it was an 'experience'. We have taken over that mantle now, and in truth, while some of our trips have been holidays, many of them have also been experiences.

The places that you remember from school days in geography or history lessons which conjure up magical thoughts of yesteryear, are on many peoples wish lists, and Marrakesh and Casablanca were the first two as part of our visit to Morocco in early March. To visit somewhere such as that, you have to be part of a tour because of the language in particular, and whilst we had a good tour, we were the only people on it with any rural outlook at all, and the remainder seemed to have little interest in the countryside around them as we travelled, added to which our guide was more interested in telling us the history of some Berber of the 14th century instead of telling us some interesting feature as we passed. It must also be somewhat true that farmers are more inquisitive and ask more questions as most of the group asked nothing. The best example was when we were watching them colouring the hides in small concrete square baths when the men paddle them under the liquid. Marnie asked a question which the specialist guide answered and the man next to her said he was glad she had asked because he wanted to know. Fortunately, I wasn't near him at the time, or I would have told him he should have asked it himself.

Marrakesh had a lot of unfinished hotels, and they had been unfinished for some time – as a previously French colony, the majority of visitors were from France but some terrorism and bombings in the 1990's had dropped the tourist trade by about 90% and so building had just stopped. We visited Casablanca, and on the way saw some very much subsistence farming on very poor land, with men stood watching their sheep or goats on bare land before they took them into a pen next to the house, if you could call it that, at night, or women weeding in crops by hand. As we began to drop down to Casablanca the land was much better and obviously some large companies involved in farming crops on a professional size and style. You can only marvel at all the building work that had been done so many centuries ago, and all the decoration that went with it.

We visited Menkes and marvelled at all the storks as they built their nests in trees, on chimneys, Sky dishes, TV aerials or anything else, and the amazing thing was that when they returned the following year they just built a bit more on top of the same structure, so that some of the nests were several feet high. On then to Fez and there was a lot of police and army presence, we had seen many coach loads as we travelled, and it transpired the King of Morocco was on tour and due in Fez that afternoon. We had a free afternoon and suddenly a great limousine swept past with a gentleman waving out of the car windows – we don't know to this day whether it was the real King or just a 'stooge'. He is supposedly now a "man of the people" and so doesn't live in any of the Palaces which adorn nearly every major city, only to be shown later in one of the cities the very luxurious gated estate where he lived and also had his own private race track. We had a guided tour of the Medina in Fez, went through a 1200 year old Souk and saw freshly slaughtered camel heads and all sorts of meat on display with flies and any sort of insect also inspecting them.

A very long 535km journey took us through the Middle Atlas Mountains, calling at the ski resort of Ifrane which had no snow and very little in the way of visitors – wrong time of year. The other side of the mountains the people were much darker skinned having originally moved northwards from Senegal. We stayed in Erfoud and the next day went out into the Sahara Desert, and Marnie and I were determined to go out into it on a camel ride. Most of the other tour members just wanted to go back to the hotel, but we did shame one or two into being rather more adventurous. The camel is most uncomfortable to ride on, and whilst not too bad to get on to, it is quite "hairy" to get down from as they go down very quickly in a double movement. Fortunately, we had a guide leading us up onto the dunes, supposedly to see the red sunset, which never materialised but in waiting for a couple of hours, you appreciate just how much that sand is moving – and how it gets in everywhere. Even when we got back home there was still enough came out of our shoes to be able to fill a little glass bottle with it as a memento.

Down through the Todra Gorges and the Valley of a 1000 Kasbahs to Ouarzazate, out into the desert to see the film studios and sets, where a lot of "westerns" have been filmed over the years, before returning to Marrakesh via the High Atlas Mountains where there was now even some snow. Our last day and Marnie wanted a pair of their slippers with the curled up toes but the man didn't have the right size but knew someone else in another Souk on the other side of town who did – so he took her by the hand and they went what seemed like miles and for ages before they came back with the slippers and a side kick from the other vendor who was to take the money back.

That was the end of Morocco – all kinds of stages of modernisation, generally very poor people and a country with little wealth – you couldn't get the Moroccan "dirham" until you got there, and had to change it back before you left – in that way they were getting foreign currency into the country, but it was a good start to our touring.

We have also been big believers that you should experience major events if you can – whilst many of them can be better seen on television, you don't sense the atmosphere the same, and so not long after Morocco it was off, nearer to home to go to Cheltenham for some of the Gold Cup week. We had a great couple of days, the only problem being the weather – it was very cold but dry, but the second day was horrible – cold and very wet, though that didn't seem to stop people's enthusiasm. The place is immaculately turned out for the Festival and people are mostly well dressed and behaved until later in the afternoon when a few have had too much to drink and get a little boisterous. A very long walk from the coach park and once in the main area, it is just like being at a show with all kinds of things being sold down the sales avenue – clothing, suitcases, jewellery etc.

The amount of money being spent with the bookies was also unbelievable to witness, particularly among the army of Irish who came over for their weeks holiday – you see them pulling great wads of notes out of their back pockets and of course to hear them talk they have all won on every race, and that can't be so. On top of that the racing is spectacular and on the Thursday the outsiders and the bookies had a field day and apparently over the nine races a £10 accumulator bet would have won you over £2 million. Gold Cup day was horrible weather-wise, but a great experience and we came away having won £15 over the two days between us.

I was asked to act as the sale manager for the Holstein UK Genetic Elite Sale which was to be held at Beeston with Wright Manley at the end of June, so a fair amount of time was spent in the spring making contact with breeders all over the country trying to get entries, and then travelling around the country to look at possible entries for the sale, a couple of times we stayed away over night when looking at animals down in the south or in Wales, the hardest bit was getting people to commit as there was great uncertainty over the likely markets as we were back in a period of falling milk prices. We finished up with a decent catalogue and some good animals, but the most difficult thing was telling one exhibitor with the deepest pedigree in the catalogue with 14 Excellents behind it that the animal had shocking legs and it wouldn't be allowed through the ring. The top price of the day was 10,000gns and the overall average was a very respectable £3200 or so, though trade was always "sticky". We called at Brian Moorhouse's 'Aireburn' herd for a N.E. Club visit on the way home after putting a bit of time in walking round a carp fishing lake that was doing a lot of business with competitions etc. I had no idea people camped overnight with the fishing line in all night and a rope or other means to wake them if they got a bite. Mind you, I never had any interest in fishing since my experience with Gavin Wrigley referred to much earlier when I was at boarding school.

In early April Adam and Laura got engaged and on the same day we went to Stuart and Abi's wedding at Snape Chapel and then the reception at the Pavilions at

Harrogate Showground, then a few days later over to Cheshire for the Western Club Evening Show where the Whittaker's of "Knowlesmere" had a field day with Champion and Reserve and Heifer Champion and Reserve.

A day or two later we had to go to Skelton for Cousin Ken Hood's funeral. Ken was the only nephew on Mother's side of the family, and he and Janet only had two daughters, so rather sadly that was the end of the Hood family name.

Early in May we went to Headingly for one of the Rugby Championship play off matches which saw the Falcons go back up into the Premiership. Our friend Gavin watching up at Kingston Park came down for a sandwich and went with us to the match, but sadly he died a year or so ago.

A trip then to Norway, for Elisabeth and Tore's wedding which was a very joyous occasion though tinged with sadness with neither her mother nor father able to witness it. A Norwegian wedding reception lasts a long time with songs specially written and sung by the leading participants in among all the broken up eating of the meal, people stood upon chairs kissing and people running round the room to kiss the bride or groom while the other half was out of the room. Dancing and then cakes and sweets gone midnight. We had some holiday whilst over there and took the eight-hour train journey across to Oslo – the first time we had been there.

We did a lot of walking round Oslo and were very impressed by the Royal Palace gardens and park which had some wonderful sculptures with the column of intertwined human bodies as its centrepiece. A lot of regeneration going on down at the Quayside, the main one being the new Opera House, built in white marble – and you could walk all over the flat roof of it which gave some fantastic views across the city and out towards the sea. Train from Oslo back to Myrdal to go on the train down to Flam – it is regarded as one of a handful of the special railway journeys in the world and so it is quite spectacular – dropping 800 metres down to sea level in less than 20km which took about 50 minutes before catching the high-speed ferry across to Balestrand a little village on the fjord, a fantastic hotel (The Kviknes Hotel) which specialised in exceptional Norwegian cold buffet tables with all the fish in which they excel. It had an idyllic little wooden church – in the summer visiting clergy come for short spells from England and live at the hotel – lucky them, and on the Saturday we witnessed a wedding there when most of the people were in Norwegian national dress. Ferry back from our break to Bergen where we had a quick look round the fish market which was busy for a Sunday afternoon and into some of the old warehouses on the quayside which has now been designated and being preserved as a World Heritage site. We stayed overnight with niece Christin before the 4½ journey back to Stavanger and so back home after a very good break. Norway is a very expensive country to visit, the locals don't really appreciate that, as they have such a high standard of living.

The early summer was busy with a lot of jobs about home like having to put wire up to stop a rabbit eating the pinks, some painting and varnish of garden seats by Marnie, and some rather more local outings than Norway. The N.E. Club day trip was down into Derbyshire to Sterndale and Overseal, two true breeding herds. Sterndale went on later that year to be named Holstein UK Premier Herd and we had a great trip down there again a year later for the Open Day and Select Sale.

Bill went with me to the dispersal of the very long established "Creskeld" herd near Otley – one of the oldest herds within the Herd book, but like our herd – good things come to an end. Evening at Thornborough Hall at Leyburn for a reception for helpers at the Food and Farming Festival, followed by a Leukaemia Charity Ball at Hackforth and then the Wensleydale Show Society summer lunch at Carlisle's at Finghall was a busy social weekend. A trip down to the newly dated Dairy Event in July demonstrated the futility of moving it to a time which didn't suit many farmers and prevented cattle which may go to Royal Norfolk or Great Yorkshire Show being exhibited.

The following week was the Great Yorkshire Show and we were there for three days of very hot weather in complete contrast to the previous year, which was washed out after day one. On the first day it was more about helping Sarah do the catering in the Yorkshire Holstein Club pavilion – Marnie in the kitchen and me running about changing money and going to Bookers to get extra water, juice etc to cope with the extra demand. The second day was more of the same, but we did get all spruced up to go to the President's lounge to be presented with a long service medal for 45 years with the same farm – another great honour, followed by a special tea along with the other recipients and their sponsors/employers. Back again on the third day where Marnie helped again during the morning while I was Master Judging the YFC Junior Dairy Cattle Judging and then reasons in the afternoon, which at that level are mostly quite outstanding.

The week after that down to Anglesey to judge the North Wales Holstein Club Herds Competition. Saw a lot of good cattle, quite a few from the Dalesend dispersal which it was great to see had done such a good job for their new owners and in most cases had given them all heifer calves to continue the lines of breeding. The most memorable bit of the whole trip was on the second day when my steward failed to turn up, and after some frantic phone calls it transpired that whoever it was had either forgotten or got his dates mixed up as he was virtually at the summit of Snowdon when he was contacted. It's the kind of mistake any of us can make, but no doubt the locals will keep reminding him over the coming years.

A trip to 'Feizor' for the Holstein UK Open Day, as the 2012 winner of the Premier Herd – a mass of people among an impressive herd of cows superbly managed. A ride out one Saturday afternoon to explore 'Swainby' not the one near Stokesley, the almost non-existent village off the side of the old A1, down a very basic road which passes an odd farm and house and comes out in Pickhill. Can't say we knew of its existence before and won't be in a hurry to go again, though it did satisfy our curiosity and quite a few people tried to tell us it didn't exist and we were mistaking it with the one next to Hutton Rudby!

Up to judge Appleby Show as we got into the late summer Northern show circuit, and as the interbreed judge had to decide between a Jersey and a Belgian Blue – not an easy thing to do. A week later we went up to Wensleydale Show at Leyburn which was a good day after some very heavy overnight rain. The day after it was across to Bishop Burton where the Yorkshire Holstein Club HYB were hosting the national weekend. It was the 'Field to Foto' competition that day, and I was judging the washing section along with Rebecca Jarvis, and there were odd moments of hilarity among the ever eager and enthusiastic youngsters.

Marnie was helping Sarah do a wedding reception at Studley – when we arrived they had just discovered they had been supplied with less plates than ordered, so I was dispatched to sister Mary's to borrow about 20 dinner plates. The day after I was doing the commentary at the All Breeds Calf Show at Thirsk and Sarah was away judging the same event at the South of Scotland Club. Mary and Eric had their Golden Wedding tea at Ripon Spa Hotel – met up with all the cousins and associates and then up to Lauder the day after.

At that time we had a few uncomfortable weeks, the first we knew of it was when Trading Standards Officers got in touch to enquire if we had got the necessary permission to run a business from our house which was the first we knew of such a thing – and it was unlikely to be the sort of a business I/we would be involved with – roofing, guttering, fascia panels and the like. Someone was circulating the area with promotional material advertising the service using our address and we even got one through our own letterbox. After that we began to get several calls from people around the area who had got some work done by these cowboys and there were problems with the work. We informed them we had no connection, odd ones took a bit of convincing, but we told them to contact Trading Standards and forwarded all the material to them, and it went quiet after a while and we have never heard anything of it since.

Down to Aberystwyth in some very wet weather for the Holstein UK Annual Convention in the area of Jimmy Wilson who was the incoming President and we visited their small but outstanding 'Tregibby' herd, and also visited the very large but equally impressive 'Brynhyfryd' herd. On the long journey down in the pouring rain I was sat besides Edward Perkins on the bus – a local estate agent but marvellously read on all the local history and agriculture which I found absolutely fascinating – he was also doing some of the commentary which I know some didn't appreciate, but I could have taken more.

Back home to judge Stokesley Show on the Saturday and then on the Monday to judge the Dairy Championship at Nidderdale. It was for me personally quite remarkable that in such a time I should judge the two shows most associated with me as a child, Stokesley close to where I was born, and Pateley Bridge near where I lived from 3 to 17. It was a surprise to many people at Nidderdale that as a Holstein Breeder I made a Dairy Shorthorn Champion which wasn't difficult with an outstanding young cow from the Collins family.

Mid-October we were down to Betwsy-Coed for the North Wales Club Dinner and award giving from the Herds Competition. Whilst down there we decided we were going to go to the top of Snowdon (no, not to see if the missing steward was still there!). It wasn't a very nice day, we weren't climbing but going up on the train, by the time we got halfway up it was thick fog and you couldn't see a thing. By we got to the top it was blowing a gale but there were still a massive number of people there. We went to climb the last little bit to the summit, but it was so windy it was nearly blowing Marnie away and I daren't try and help her as it might have taken both of us. From there we drove straight up to Lauder to look after Ruby as Laura was away for a 'hen party' and Adam was working.

I had bought some Royal Mail shares in early October when it was privatised but was only allocated 227 in the ballot. You could sell them at no cost for a few weeks and did so two weeks later to take a £300 profit on the £750 I had spent – good business if you could do it on a regular basis.

We had a walk round Thorpe Perrow Arboretum in early November, when the colours were fantastic, but for us spoilt that the trees and species were not named – they had a number on them and you were expected to buy a booklet for £3.50 to identify them, which on top of the £10 entry fee seemed a bit excessive, particularly as the RHS associate membership entry didn't apply during November. A week later up to Eyemouth for the day for Jimmy Hodges "Lemington" dispersal – we only went for the first day of the two day sale – Jimmy sold the farm as well and moved into Scotland and now has pedigree Hereford cattle – we delivered a promotional banner to him last year, which Sarah had got made, as we went up to Adams.

The end of November saw us off on holiday again, this time to Madeira and we had a great time on this warm, sunny island at that time of year, with some very pleasant people and not too crowded. Just a four-hour flight with no-time difference is much better than some of the long trips we have made. Funchal is a lovely town with many restaurants on the street sides and a host of wonderfully decorated walls and doorways as you walk about the streets. One night we were out to eat at a restaurant while Portugal were playing a qualifying match for the 2014 World Cup and whilst we were eating, Ronaldo, who originated from Madeira scored a hat trick. We stayed at the Porto Santa Maria hotel – a super hotel, right beside the main harbour and we could watch the big cruise liners come and go and the passengers scurrying back like ants to reboard before it sailed again – not our idea of holiday, though many do. We went up on the cable car and then came down on one of the street toboggans – fortunately there was someone to control it for us – they go a fair speed and it is a bit hairy when you meet a car coming the other way. Quite a few people who have been say they wouldn't dare, but it is quite safe, and you have to do these things. We took a one day trip over to the mountains and onto the plateau, having visited Camara de Lobos and stopped above the 580 metres high cliffs at Cabo Girao, the second highest in the world. To Porto Moniz and on another trip went to the highest point on the Island at 1810 metres, visited a wicker work factory, called at a trout hatchery and on to Santana where they have the small traditional triangular thatched cottages. A long climb up the hills of Funchal took us to the Botanical Gardens, pictures of which are often used on promotional literature for Madeira. Sadly, the Orchid Garden and much of that hillside were severely damaged by a devastating fire a couple of years later though I believe the Botanic Gardens were saved. We are not really into going on "lay about" holidays, because we like to see all around us in whatever country we visit, but we would go back again to Madeira on holiday as it was so pleasant and relaxing.

We were over to Carlisle for the Black and White sale with some good prices but nothing special, had a day out to walk round Harlow Carr as the RHS continue to develop it, up to see Adam and family with Ruby now walking, called at the newly opened BP garage and shop in Aiskew where John Gills garage had been, and this was just a month or so after a new small Tesco had opened in Bedale, so their trade must be coming from somewhere. Herbert Allison's funeral was just before Christmas – he was one of the local areas real characters, and he with his sons John and Tony had done a lot of the building work both farming and house wise for us over many earlier years. It was great to have Adam, Laura and Ruby down for Christmas which meant it was the first time we had all the family for Christmas in our new home after almost two years, and that was the end of another year.

A trip up to the Semex Conference and then to the N.E. Club dinner, with cattle and embryos from our dispersal sale taking three trophies in the Herds Competition. Down on the train to London and a few days with Emma who took us to the new exhibition about the "Cheapside" jewels which were discovered about a century ago, had a look round Liberty's store which had recently featured in a series on the television. Whilst we were at Kings Cross waiting for our train got a phone call from Laura to say Adam was in hospital. They were out on a drive when a massive rabbit warren collapsed underneath him, and he had broken both an ankle and leg. Up in the hills an ambulance couldn't get to him, so they had to use the air ambulance, but it couldn't get to him as it was between two hills, so had to use a Sea King and winch him up to fly him to Border's General Hospital where they have to close local roads for such a big one to land, and Adam said because of it being such an unusual event there were people taking photos as it did so. I said I hoped that he gave them a 'regal' wave from the stretcher. The bigger problem almost was his dog Penny who wouldn't leave him, wouldn't go with any of the other keepers after the airlift and they had to get Laura to go – and she eventually got her coaxed back home, where she just sulked until he came back home a couple of days later and wouldn't leave his legs once he was sat in a chair and just gazed lovingly at him. It was remarkable how quickly he mended and got back to work after the pins were removed. Fortunately, the accident happened just a day or two before the end of the shooting season and he was back at work quite a bit before the start of the rearing season at the end of April.

Mid-February and off we went again this time to New Zealand, principally to see Mollie and Len but also for a further look around South Island which was the only half we went to this time. Arriving in Christchurch after about 25 hours of actual flying time, we were a bit gentle but had travelled well. Stayed at Hotel 115 one of the first ones to re-open after the 2011 earthquake and ate at a close by Japanese restaurant which had only been open for five days and served some fantastic Tempura prawns. Over the recent years we have eaten there again more than once, and they are still every bit as good. We got a tram ticket for the city even though the whole system is not yet open, but the carriages have been beautifully restored. The Botanic Garden at Christchurch is well worth a visit and we were amused to see a rather elderly couple, both on their mobility scooters looking at a rose garden – it might be us one day in the far-off future. We looked at the Cathedral, still derelict, visited container city where many of the shops from the badly hit shopping area had been very imaginative in creating little double-storey streets and cut doors and display windows in them to carry on trading. Very novel – unfortunately now they have mostly gone back to the rebuilt mall, and many of the containers that remain are fast food places. We got a bite of lunch at the Cheese Shop run by a man from Barnsley and one of the first to re-open, and he did have some proper Hawes Wensleydale which he put into a teacake (freshly baked) for our lunch. We looked at the newly erected "Cardboard Cathedral" but couldn't go in as they were preparing for a fund-raising dinner that night.

Leaving Christchurch on the four-hour Trans-Alpine train over to Greymouth. Through the very fertile Canterbury Plains and the marvellous scenery up in the mountains and over the massive river beds which were mostly empty- they must be a fantastic sight when full of flood water in their spring melt, but this was our 'August' time. We then drove on in the hired car to stop overnight at Motueka which had a lovely little rose garden, and then we drove on the next day over the hills taking in the fantastic views over Golden Bay from the Takaka Hills – it was about 10 miles up and down each side which made Sutton Bank seem very tame and when we got out for a walk to take in the views we were nearly deafened by the crickets. We drove as far as we could along Farewell Spit but refused to pay to go up the final 4 miles on a guided tour. As we drove back we watched a cormorant catch a young salmon and have quite a battle to get it swallowed down and it wasn't until we started to move again we realised we were blocking the bridge and there was a car stood waiting at the other end. When we got there I apologised and the man wasn't very happy, but we explained what we had been watching and his wife told him to be quiet, just because he was never aware of things going on around him.

We stayed at Murchison overnight, then drove onto Mangatua, had a bite of lunch in Reefton, then through a heavy forest to Springs junction (the clocks weren't changing and them locking the doors again this time) and so to Hanmer Springs for an overnight stay (That was where the previous time there were no vacancies and we slept in the car and saw the Southern Lights). From Hanmer Springs via Culverden, Waipatu, Oxford, Sheffield and Mt. Hutt to Methven, Mayfield to Temuka, Timaru and Pleasant Point getting to Mollies about 4.30, and then we went out to eat as it was her birthday.

A ride out to Geraldine and then up to Tripp's Orari Gorge and to the Acland's Church which had suffered some damage to the stained glass with the earthquake.

The next day we looked round Timaru's Botanic Gardens and saw a plant which only flowers about every 30 years but was then actually in flower. A ride the following day up on "the saddle" where there are fantastic views all round, and the following day up to Waitaki to look at the hydro- electric scheme and lower down where they were constructing massive storage reservoirs for irrigation which the farmers in the area have to subscribe to and construct their own holding dam on farm. It was becoming apparent that there was a lot of foreign investment principally Chinese, going into many of the farming businesses.

Then we were off again, headed via Ashburton, over Arthurs Pass and stayed overnight at Hokitika, the centre of New Zealand's jade industry, after having visited the glow worm caves the evening before. We called at Franz Josef and then on to stay at Fox Glacier motel and walked up the Fox Glacier. A long drive via Haast Junction, Makarora, Lake Wanaka, through Queenstown, now totally overrun with tourists and on to Te Anau. Next morning we took the long drive down to Milford Sound, stopping at the Mirror Lakes and The Chasm which we found of more interest than Milford Sound – if you weren't going on a fjord cruise there was nothing and we have seen plenty of fjords over the years in Norway. We never found a fuel station there and were very close to running out, but then we saw a little sign and had to go 8km inland to something of a commune where the fuel was half as much again from an old hand primed pump – but it got us back to a proper fill up. We called at the Rakuta Wetlands where much work is being done in an environmental scheme to return it to its original state. We had lunch at Mrs Clarke's café at Riverton – a very famous old institution still going in the same building since 1891- you couldn't miss it, painted bright turquoise. Through Mossburn and Lumsden to Gore for a couple of nights.

The next morning Marnie treated me to an early birthday present – a flight in a Tiger Moth – I got all done up in the "Biggles" outfit, flying jacket, helmet and goggles. There was not a lot of room in the double cockpit, which was completely open and cold enough in mid-summer and we were at no great height, but it was a marvellous experience. We looked around the old aeroplanes and helicopters being restored. We called at Winton, but couldn't find Peter Waring (for the none pedigree people Peter farms the Winton herd near Bishop Burton). On to Invercargill, which is very industrial with massive piles of timber waiting to be shipped and to Bluff Point- its port and southerly tip of South Island. We called at an old lignite mine which had been transformed into a landscaped garden over the previous ten years. We drove around the Caitlins area and to Slope Point – the most southern point on the mainland, looked out over Porpoise Bay, with seals playing on the rocks and some Blue Penguins, visited Niagara Falls – a send up, it is just a stone in a small river, and an American we met there couldn't grasp the irony of it. We walked to McLean Falls which were worth the long walk and Marnie had a run in with another American who wanted his photograph taken saluting the Falls – and wanted it taking about four times before he was satisfied he and the Falls were in exactly the right position. Overnight at Balclutha, to Milton and Roxburgh where a bullock ran out into the road and stopped in front of us as

Marnie drove out of town. Through Alexandra to Lauder, not where Adam lives but of course many of these names tell you that it was originally settled by Scotsmen. We had a look at Mitchells cottage, that the two brothers had built when they emigrated from the Shetland Isles in 1876 – they were stonemasons, but what a courageous trip to make at that time, all that distance, and one of them had a wife and children, to start a new life on the other side of the world. The Botanic Gardens in Dunedin were very large and well maintained and very well visited by both locals and visitors alike.

On the coast road up from Dunedin we looked at the well known Moeraki Boulders on the beach there – since the first time we visited it had now developed a shop, café, souvenirs, plus a charge to go directly down to the beach, we didn't, drove a short distance to a community car park and walked back along the beach to them.

The last three or four days back at Mollies and we looked at various local sights when out for rides or a coffee, before driving back to Christchurch, got the car booked back in and then ready for the long flight back home which got off to a bad start with the flight delayed for 1½ hours. Stopped in Sydney, Bangkok and Dubai and by the clock soon back to Manchester – 17 hours by the clock from leaving Christchurch compared to the 41 hours by the clock going out to New Zealand.

By now into March and we had various bits to catch up on, including Marnie going on a course to Betty's Cookery School in Harrogate to learn about chocolate making and to make some – it was very good.

At the beginning of April Sarah fulfilled her lifelong wish to farm dairy cows herself and started a contract farming operation up at Carkin Farm on the A66. We spent a lot of time up there for about 18 months and Sarah put a terrific amount of work in and did a good job under very difficult circumstances and a falling milk price. I am going to write very little about this episode on the grounds that my comments might get me into trouble, but things didn't work out. Fortunately, she had kept her other business ticking over at a lower level and was able to resurrect and further develop The Farm Organisation from 2015 onwards.

All this moving about took a lot of time, with Sarah moving from Danby Wiske up to Carkin and more or less the same time Adam got promoted again and moved from No.1 into Longcroft House, a big old Scottish farmhouse with big rooms, thick walls, but very cold for much of the year.

We went to the RABDF youngstock walk at Coxwold as Marnie was helping Sarah J to do the coffee and lunch there. By now Sarah was also taking a Stage 4 Management class one day a week at Thirsk Centre for Askham Bryan, but occasionally couldn't do them and the day after the RABDF event she was down at Noremead for a Holstein Judging School, so I took the class for her, part of which was a visiting speaker Kevin Guy about tenancies, succession etc.

In early May I took Marnie for her birthday outing to somewhere we have never been before, the Isle of Wight. A long drive down to Southampton to get the 1 hour ferry crossing, once there we had to reassess our bearings as there was a road closed and we had to go a long way round to get to the other side of Cowes via Newport. We travelled about the Island and were rather disappointed as we thought parts of it were rather run down and the farming didn't look particularly on top of its job. At Ryde we drove along the pier, where most unusually there is a railway station. We also found the Crab and Lobster at Bembridge where we had a tremendous fish supper, and by that I don't mean fish and chips. For us the jewel in the crown of the Isle of Wight is Osborne House the family home of Queen Victoria. It was a fascinating house and we could have spent much longer there but had to get back for me to score at the N.E. Club judging at Neil Bellerby's that night, at which I was fortunate to win the £20 sweepstake with the only correct card.

We had our friends Malcolm and Eunice for a meal one night when they were having a short break up the dale, then the following day had a trip out to Grewelthorpe and the Himalayan Garden. For anyone from further away or locals who have never been, it is well worth a visit – at that time of year, with its own micro climate it houses a fantastic show of Rhododendrons, Azaleas of all sizes and colours, and since then, when we re-visited about four years later, they have even further improved it, and also created something of a sculpture trail through it. You need to check opening times, as it is not open all year round.

Down into North Wales to deliver things for Sarah and then stayed at Shrewsbury overnight before the RABDF Gold Cup Open Day at the Higgins Family of Wilderley Hall, a very well run family unit, with some genuine cows with a set up where things had been adapted rather than had money thrown at them – just a real good, genuine farm.

Our garden at home was by now beginning to look really well. We had put in some lupins, as one of my favourite flowers, which we had not been able to grow at Newton Grange and in the spring of this year I was particularly proud of a pink one which had forty four flower heads on it.

North East Club trip was down to Aintree and Rossett herds of Richard Pilkington and Andrew Jones – we had two good visits. I remember having lunch at Rossett and saying to Jenny Jones how early her sweet peas were to be in full flower and she said it was a complete fluke really, they had never got them taken out the previous autumn and surprisingly had overwintered outside with no ill effects – quite unusual. That night when we got home Bill and I went to Roger Hildreths at York for a Yorkshire Club 6 from 30 competition. I was equal second – won £3, less £2 entry for the two of us leaving £1 profit, at least better than a loss!!

In among all the farming of the time, we helped Sarah to move some calving cows and all three of us got stuck in a deep puddle hole in a triple gateway and some of us lost wellies in getting out of it. As it happened the cows almost took pity on us in our predicament and behaved themselves.

Down to the Cadbury House Hotel in Somerset for the Holstein Convention where we had some great visits. Marnie went to the Forde Abbey House and Gardens and

I went to the superbly run and great set-up of the 'Bettiscombe' herd of the Bugler family. It was no surprise when they won the RABDF Gold Cup about three years later, though unfortunately we were unable to go to the open day. We all visited the site of the Glastonbury Festival and had a conducted tour about three weeks before the event when everything was beginning to take shape, helper students and others looked in a parallel world as they decorated oil drums for the rubbish bins and we had a talk about the whole thing by farmer Michael Eavis – six miles of perimeter fencing cost £1.3 million per year to erect and dismantle, and the whole event at that time cost £32 million to stage. Back at the hotel after dinner that night we were entertained by "The Wurzels" who originated from that part of the world and many will remember their famous and chart-topping hit "I've got a combine harvester". Some of the originals were still involved with the group, and it was great fun. The next morning we had a ride through Cheddar Gorge and then a tour down into the caves with the spectacular flows of Calcium, colours and 3D reflections, before going on to the "Moorshard" herd of Randolph Miller, the incoming President for lunch, a 6 from 30 competition and on to Sedgemoor Auction Centre for a cattle parade ahead of the Genetic Elite Sale the next day.

As we got towards the end of June, excitement was beginning to build ahead of the opening day of the Tour de France which was in our area. When we headed down to Bill Nadin's for the Premier Herd Open Day, we went down through South Yorkshire, Brighouse and Holmfirth being the two prime examples, and they were already well decorated in readiness for the cyclists. We were inspired by that preparation and the next day had a ride around the course up at this end, and it was fascinating to see the decorating effort put in, particularly the smaller villages up in Swaledale and Wensleydale. The following weekend was the actual event and there is no doubt that the massive effort put in by all the local groups earned its reward with the visiting public from all over the world and the publicity generated by all the television coverage of the magnificent Yorkshire countryside. The welcome given to all the cyclists and viewing public was acknowledged to be the best start to "The Tour" ever. Visitor wise we had all the Norwegian family over for the event and Emma, Jake and Daisy up from London, and Adam, Laura and Ruby down from Scotland – we went to Coverbridge to watch them go round the sharp bend and over the bridge – the following team cars had more bother than the cyclists, who were past and gone in a flash, but at least we were there to savour the atmosphere. The following day we had a family gathering at home, the first time all the next generation of half-cousins had been together when they are spread so diversely.

Just a one day visit to the Great Yorkshire Show, not massive numbers of milkers but two very good ones from the Yates brothers down from Scotland with "Meikelfirth" taking the Championship and "Logan" in reserve.

A week later and over to Whitby for Richard Thompson's "Grinkle" dispersal sale, where there was a decent trade, before we went into Whitby and had our tea at the famous "Magpie" café – noted the world over for its fish and chips.

We had a trip down to Derbyshire for a party for Bill Higson's 70th Birthday. Bill was one of the gang of four who were friends while at Cirencester. Everyone was in good order, though looking a little older than that first meeting some 49 years previously.

Early August saw Sarah and I at Billy Atkinson's funeral up Wensleydale where he had farmed at Gammersgill for many years – a true Dales farmer, but always a kind word and he had bought a good cow or two from us over the years. The connections with the family, particularly Sarah, grew over the years, with grandson Thomas being very keen on the pedigree side and Sarah training and tutoring him in calf showing and he has done very well in HYB Competitions over the last few years.

A visit to the Premiership Rugby Sevens at Mowden Park – a superb stadium originally built for Darlington Football Club by the supposed "rascal" businessman George Reynolds, but now the home of the rugby club. The event had been moved there because the new 4G pitch at Kingston Park wasn't complete. Some exciting games as Newcastle Falcons qualified for the finals beating Sale, Leicester and London Welsh. The most memorable thing though, was just as the match ended, the heavens opened, and boy, did it rain, not far off an inch in less than an hour.

It was the 100th Wensleydale Show, and I was honoured to judge the Dairy Championships at such an event. The Miles family from "Littlebridge" were Champion with a Jersey from the Collins family in Reserve, and in the handling classes Rachel Goldie stood at the top with Lucy Atkinson in Reserve. This was followed a day later by going up to Lauder, Ruby and Laura coming back with us to stay for a few days before we took them back up to Galashiels before going to a pre-season friendly at Hawick.

An exploratory ride took us into the area between Pateley Bridge and Harrogate around Thruscross, and we managed to find Humberstone Bank Farm where I had lived for a short while (see the early chapter of the book). We had a talk with Mrs Heseltine now well into her seventies, and she remembered us being there when Father worked for them, some 65 years previously.

Down to Shropshire for the first UK Dairy Day at Telford – I didn't realise just how big a place and how important it was now as a business centre – the International Centre is a marvellous venue for such events. I had a long talk with another of the Cirencester gang – Dave Hampson, before watching the Holstein classes being won by the Tomlinson's with a super mature cow from their Bilsrow herd.

The following day was the Scottish Independence referendum which voted 55-45% to remain part of the Union, though they are still rumbling on with it and the SNP are demanding another one as part of their demands should they have to prop up a minority Labour government after the Christmas 2019 election. We were up in Scotland a day or two afterwards, and when out for tea at Cafraemill ran into Willie Tait, the Semex geneticist, who was walking a section of the South of Scotland Way with his wife. Whilst up there Adam and I spent some time with Mrs Sharpe trying to find her dog which was lost on the hill. Ruby by now was talking well for just on two years old and told us that sheep 'poo' was "degusting", when we nearly walked in some. We brought home the new bird table Adam had made for us, and since has given us many happy hours watching the birds behaviour as they feed, apart from the starlings as they are a nuisance when they descend en-masse, though we do enjoy them when they have a murmuration which we quite often see to the south of us as night falls in the autumn and winter.

I judged Supreme Dairy Champion at Nidderdale Show and made Andrew Jennings Champion with his local champion as I much preferred it to the Holstein Champion which had beaten it earlier, with a Jersey in Reserve. In early October I saw one of the most spectacular natural animal sights I have ever witnessed. I was up at Hill Top East for a Board Meeting, and as I left, I was aware of a great noise over towards Masham. On moving around to decide what it was I finally saw that it was 100's of Canada geese which had settled and were feeding on Howard Dyson's Masham road land – I called to tell Howard and they disappeared, never to be seen again. As we went through October, we were doing a lot of jobs helping both Sarah and Adam with things both inside and outside, and all the time gathering things up and preparing for our next big adventure or should I say experience.

In early November we set off with Bay Farm Tours for South America. We had known Neil McSporran since he and his father ran the Herdwise trips to the Canadian Winter Fair, and after our Morocco experience wanted to go with like-minded people and also get some feel for their agriculture as well as the tourist attractions, and we were very well looked after by Bernadette Tomlinson, who with her husband Peter had run the "Bilsrowan" herd over in Lancashire, we had decided on doing the full trip rather than just the first two thirds and we were glad we did so, a couple of the people who didn't said how much they were regretting it.

Flew into Rio-de Janeiro and as usual came past some very poor areas from the airport into the city. The first thing in the city was the mass of electric cables just hanging from anywhere in the streets – you couldn't imagine health and safety allowing that over here, and you.would think they would regularly have power blackouts, but apparently not. While there we visited Christ the Redeemer, Sugar Loaf Mountain, at night strolled along Copacabana beach, went to a Samba show and visited a flea market. Our visit to the Iguazu Falls, one of the new metropolitan Seven Wonders of the World, the sheer size and scope of them took your breath away. We saw them with normal water flow, which is unbelievable, 1.6 billion litres per second, when in flood can be up to 40. We saw them from all sorts of angles, some fantastic butterflies about and we saw an armadillo under one of the boardwalks. Visited a beef and arable estate managed by a lady vet and her husband who was Portuguese, and the interpreter had not got properly prepared to translate agricultural words, but farmers are fairly resourceful and we got by on yields, fertiliser usage, sprays and the like. The arable side totalled about 1200 hectares on a two-year rotation of soya and maize. We visited the Itaipu dam, the second largest hydro-electric site in the world, on the border and jointly run by Brazil and Paraguay which we visited across the dam to turn round at the other side, so we can also claim to have been to Paraguay – if only just!! We also viewed the site for the next Olympic games – very little had been done and we were told nothing much would happen until about a year before the event, when all the backhanders and such like would start moving and all would be done on time and ready – and it was.

Into Argentina and had a look at their side of Iguazu Falls – there are 275 falls in total making up the whole, situated within the national forest of sub-tropical trees. A tour of Buenos Aires including the square where Eva Peron used to speak, also visiting her mausoleum in the massive cemetery, went to a Tango show at night, usually eating at various steak places where they often come round and carve it at your table from large joints on a skewer. Generally we found their steak a little tough, mostly because they like it very fresh and only hang it for two days, and from what we could gather after our visit to the Liniers livestock market, they will be fairly stressed by they are slaughtered, which doesn't help tenderness. Liniers market had a quiet day the day we visited with only about 5000 there that day, when they can peak at 15,000, moved around by up to 35 mounted gauchos. We visited an 8500 head beef lot and also a 770-cow dairy herd. Whilst travelling in that area we were fascinated to see the most unusual of bird's nests just built on top of electric poles or in some cases on the top of a fence post. Flight for two hours further south to Trelew where the first Welsh settlers landed in the late 19th Century – a very bare and barren land, they must have wondered why on earth they came all that distance for such a poor area, and of course there was no way back. Stayed at Puerto Madryn (strangely enough when judging the North Wales Herds Competition, I visited the 'Puerto Madryn' herd, who had also bought a few animals at our dispersal – what a small world). We went whale watching in the Gulf of Nuevo and saw some of the Southern Right whales who came there to raise their young before leaving again in December. We saw many of them basking in the warm water, and you need to be up close to appreciate just how big they are when they come up out of the water. We went to a little estancia, one of the largest in Patagonia – only 24,000 hectares with 8000 sheep, mostly Merinos from which they shear about 5kgs at about £3 per kg – a better paying wool price than we have over here.

We visited one of the many Welsh chapels in the area, hosted by some descendants of the original settlers. The four Welsh members of our group together with our hosts sang round the organ played by Betty – three or four hymns in Welsh which was quite moving. We looked around a small fruit farm where the cherries were just about ready for picking and we had to sample them to see if they were!! A long drive the next day across the Patagonian plateau – a bare expanse of nothingness for several hours – our guide pointed out the estancia which belonged to the Benetton family – it was only 220,000 hectares and we barely saw a sheep – mind, the land was so poor they would need a lot per head! As we got further west the snow-capped Andes came into view, stayed overnight at Esquel, before visiting an experimental farm, who's main crop was peonies. It had developed into a commercial enterprise over several hectares. It took a dozen or so ladies who were cutting the blooms about a week to fill a large chilled container. It was then driven 10 hours to Buenos Airies before being flown to Holland and no doubt some of them come back into Bedale in one of those large flower lorries – fascinating to see, but what about the air miles? Adjoining the peonies, they were experimenting with New Zealand polled Dorset Horns via embryo transplant to improve growth rates and weight.

We stayed overnight at Bariloche on the shores of Lake Nahuel Huapi which is more of a Tyrolean style town and after a free day, another bus journey to the ferry across Lake Nahuel Huapi to Puerto Blest, across Lake Laguna Frias, known as the Cold Water Lake which took us into Chile and the customs on the other side. Unfortunately, we were first in the queue and they went through our suitcases like a toothcomb, by they got to the end of the group they barely opened the suitcases as it was Sunday lunchtime. More hairy bus journeys on rough country tracks and across Lake Todos Los Santos (Lake of All Saints or Emerald Lake).

Great bowls of fantastic fresh picked cherries for breakfast on the banks of Llanquihue Lake, visited the Angelmo fishing village where we watched a girl very expertly filleting salmon – you wouldn't want to get too close to the knife the speed it was working at. Whereas the Welsh settled in Argentina, the German's came round Cape Horn and settled in Chile. Still a big German influence and our local guide pushed everything German at us – including the food which was too heavy and spiced sausages and such. We visited a large dairy herd run on the New Zealand system, in fact it was more New Zealand style than much if it now is in the home country, Fronterra have more than 29% of the Chilean market. Next stop was a beef farm with pedigree Herefords and Angus, then on to Osorno for overnight. Into the grain area and the home of the Mapuche Indians the next day en-route to Villarrica, from where we decided to take a flight up and over the volcano nearby. No one else was interested in doing so, then eventually Gordon decided he would also like to go so off we went in a Cessna 180 that was about 60 years old and it took us a long time to get circled like working up a mountain pass in a car to get above the volcano and we made four passes over the top, though with the snow it was making it steamy and you couldn't see down into the crater. Whilst up there we looked over several extinct volcanoes that were tree fringed and a skyline that had a big fringe of monkey-puzzle trees, the Cessna was a bit shaky on both take-off and landing!!

Visit next day to a very well run arable farm, growing wheat and oil seed rape, much of it for seed, before going on to a llama and alpaca farm before we flew from the very new Temuco airport in the middle of nowhere to Santiago. Next morning to a typical Chilean dairy farm where the cows lived in earthen, muddy paddocks with some of the ricketiest fencing you could find (I think our cows would soon have demolished them), but they were being milked three times a day and averaging 38kgs/day. The amusing thing was that in all that second rate set up they were busy fitting rubber matting in the parlour and collecting yard to help the cows' feet!! A short journey to call at a vegetable farm and processing facility. It was being packed for a supermarket chain, a very basic one, and there was an ancient man with a fearsome looking chopping board and blade cutting up pumpkins which were then wrapped by hand by women just using "cling film" from a roll – not very mechanised! We drove on to Valparaiso where we had lunch looking out onto the Pacific Ocean. Our last visit was out to another experimental farm where they were doing much fruit work, but specialising on walnuts and had done most of the international work on reducing tree size to make management much more practical, work also on irrigation and tree spacing. We then visited the Santa Ruth winery, one of the oldest in Chile, a guided tour of the vines and all the storage and preparation area, before a super picnic out in the grounds in glorious sunshine.

The final night of the tour was in a revolving restaurant, sixteen floors up, with fantastic views over Santiago to the hills as the sun was setting. A flight home to Paris and then on to Manchester to get the train back to bring a fantastic, superbly organised tour to an end, with so many memorable moments.

Back to normality, I had tried to grow some winter potatoes, but already the frost had got them, so I dug them up in mid-December and the whole lot were barely enough for a meal – shan't bother again. A bad day was compounded when the Christmas presents for New Zealand wouldn't be accepted at the Post Office as they contained some perfume, and got caught without remembering to put a parking disc on the dash board in Bedale and had to pay a fine.

Just the week before Christmas Marnie wasn't very complementary, telling me I stank – which wasn't really surprising as a strong wind had blown a big door shut at Carkin, when I was helping Sarah as she was away lecturing at Thirsk, knocking me over into the slurry and covering me in it, fortunately it washed off and I had a change of clothes with me – what foresight!!

Into 2015 and a quiet start before I spoke at Masham Discussion Group and showed slides about agriculture around the world to the title "There's more to life than milking cows", a talk which I repeated as a last minute stand in three months later at Boroughbridge for the Grassland Society. The Semex Conference which was its 25th, and some good speakers, plus one or two professional committee men who droned on too long. Sandy Strang was as good as ever at the Burns Supper, but sadly he is no longer with us with his irreverent and not politically correct stories and jokes. A speaker from South Arabia told us about managing their 35000 herd of cows which they are planning to increase by another 15000 – importing forage from North Africa and sinking boreholes to great depths for irrigation – if it wasn't a way of spending all their oil money I don't suppose they would produce any of their own milk. We also had a visit and a short talk from Princess Anne.

Mid-January we were going to have chicken for Sunday lunch, and I went to get one out of the freezer which is in the garage. As I came back, I stepped onto some black ice and went flat on my back and the chicken flew across the stones and only the hedge prevented it ending up in the field. I managed to scramble on my knees to the French windows to alert Marnie to my plight and she helped me to lie down on the bed –

some pain killers gave some relief – I think the first time I have ever taken any in my life – another first at 68!! I am now very wary of stepping out onto anywhere icy.

Early February saw a good N.E. Club panel meeting with Sam Howarth, James Rogerson and Andrew Avison being quite controversial and giving us plenty to ask questions about.

Then it was off again to Norway for Emma's christening, Elisabeth and Tore's daughter. The vicars service at the christening was something of a first for us – he spoke from his I-pad which he held out in front of him all the time, and it was all about the finances of the church, nothing about the religious aspect or the welcoming of new children into the church.

That spring was all about getting ready for Adam and Laura's wedding, the ladies went up for Laura's hen party at Dryburgh in fancy dress outfits. Adam didn't bother with a stag party, that was in between getting the house ready for and Sarah moving to Hunton and trying to get lilies to open. Marnie was doing the flowers for the reception lunch tables and Laura wanted lilies and the lilies were got through Mrs J who had all the contacts through her flower arranging. You have to get them in good time to allow for them opening and they appeared very slow to do so. The last few days we had them in the dining room with the light on all night, moved them right in front of the radiator etc., set them up on a table right under the light but still they wouldn't come out. We got them all loaded up and taken to Scotland on the Friday and into a good warm room overnight at the hotel and by the Saturday morning they were beginning to move and by the reception in late afternoon they were magnificent – phew!! That was close. Adam and Laura's wedding was at Dryburgh Abbey Hotel conducted by a non-denominational Humanist which was something new, but very personal to them and a really good day with so many of their friends and relations to help celebrate. Then it was back home to more mundane matters.

Chapter 26 – Another Show Season and more Experiences

The 2015 show season started early with a visit over to the Western Club Show near Middlewich taking the banners with us. The Farm Organisation had been getting the Premier Breeder and Exhibitor banners made for Jane Arrell who was the show secretary for a few years, and Marnie made the pennants ready for professional embroidery and then we put the finishing touches to them. It took us a long time to get to the show as there had been an accident on the M1/M62 and we had to go all through the backstreets of Leeds to get past it, as had everyone else at the same time, but it is always quite interesting to travel through some of these industrial type areas you wouldn't visit out of choice.

A few days later we went up to Ponteland to meet Laura, Adam and Ruby for supper. They were staying overnight near the airport before flying to Tenerife the following morning and while we waited for them we saw that Sainsbury's which is on the ground floor under Fratelli's had some sweet pea plants on sale at what seemed a very reasonable price so got some – when we got them home there were about three times the number of plants there was supposed to be and they went on and developed into probably the best crop we have ever had for both colour and smell – and we had a very good meal at what has become our regular supper place on the way back from Adam and Laura's.

A visit to the 'Paradise' herd dispersal sale at York Auction Centre which isn't the most user friendly layout for dairy cattle sales, and then replanted three small bushes up at Fox Park which were growing to be too big for our garden, but will be ok there in the wood down the drive side. A trip up to Richmond was rather curtailed by half of it being fastened off ahead of a visit by The Queen the following day to present army colours – of which we were unaware, but a visit to The Station was well worth it and the purpose of our visit – a display of photographs taken at Thorpe Perrow all over the arboretum – very good.

Early May saw us off again, down into Somerset and to the RABDF Gold Cup Open Day, which had been won the previous year by Michael Eavis of Glastonbury Festival fame, so we were there on a not very nice, damp sort of day, but we can at least claim to have been on the main "Pyramid" stage, though it was only to have coffee!! Whilst we were down there, we had a couple of extra days, staying at Wookey Hole Hotel and visited Shepton Mallet, Wells and found a very nice village pub for a bar meal at Priddy. We weren't too impressed with what looked to us like the faded glory of Weston-Super-Mare, but found the Glastonbury Abbey fascinating – one of the earliest religious settlements in the country, with the original part dating back to about 60 AD, and the Abbotts kitchen which was still almost entire was unbelievable in trying to visualise how they had lived all those centuries ago before the Reformation.

A General Election soon followed which took us out of the Liberal/Conservative government with just a small Conservative majority – the beginning of the morass of stalemate we have been in politically for the last four and a half years, which could be resolved with the General Election next week – the first one in winter for about 80 years.

A trip over to Throup's 'Dalesbrad' herd for a Yorkshire Club judging night, where Sarah had prepared the animals during the day and made all the better on a nice evening and a good turnout of both cattle and people.

Ruby had given Marnie a pot wellington for her birthday about a month earlier with a plant in it, but a wind one night blew it over and broke it, not long before they were due down for a few days, so a hectic morning of phone calls located the last remaining one at Marks and Spencer in Middlesbrough, so off we went after lunch to save the situation. We have never liked the town, it always seems such a dull, grey place and the people seem to match it, but we got the wellington and out of the place as quickly as possible. Since then we have kept the wellington between two other plant pots to stop it falling over.

After going to Pateley Bridge for Cousin Hector Liddle's funeral – he was 82, and so half a generation older than me, (I remember going to his wedding in my school uniform the first year I started at Ripon). The day after was a more joyful occasion, with Sarah's 40th birthday party which she had organised to be held in Bedale Hall. A good night, with about 120 friends to help her celebrate, she had very ingeniously decorated each table with some of the things from her farmyard from all those years previously – a novel idea which was a talking point.

The day after it was up to Scotland as Adam was moving again, but only a couple of hundred yards. It was under rather sad circumstances – the farmer who owned the land and the houses which Eskdale used and shot over had been killed in a farm accident just after Adam had moved into the big house about a year earlier. His widow continued to run the farm with neighbour's help but regrettably could not quite manage and so needed to employ a good shepherd (sorry, they call them flock managers now) and needed the house for him, so Adam and family moved back to No. 3 having originally been in No. 1, but they soon got settled back in and are still there now, although due to move to a bigger house nearer to Lauder in the spring of 2020.

Another busy day followed, Sarah was away working in Jersey, so Marnie, Margaret Goldie and Marion Stonehouse did the catering for the British Friesian Club, summer open day at Sam Howarth and family near Pickering – well attended and a lot of farmers I knew to fill in the middle of the day while they saw to everybody's food and drink needs, just being useful at either end of the day fetching and carrying and going on errands for milk and such like.

A birthday ride out and treat for me was a ride up to Leyburn, where we had a look round the newly extended Tenant's Auction Rooms that had doubled in size, up the back roads of Wensleydale to Hawes, and up over Buttertubs and down through Muker into Reeth before going over The Stang to see the rhododendrons and finishing up at Fox Hall Inn for a delicious supper. It was outstanding for a few years at that time, has since been closed for quite a while, but has recently re-opened again, and though we haven't as yet been, it seems to be getting rave reviews.

A trip towards the end of June down into Wales, staying overnight at the Three Wells Hotel near Howey, close by Builth Wells, before moving on the next day to the "Feithy" herd for the Holstein UK Open Day at the previous year's winner of the Premier Herd – saw a lot of good people and good cows and then made our way back to stay at the Royal Oak in Welshpool, meandered back across Shropshire and over to Buxton after stopping at a small farm shop in the middle of nowhere – Marnie had a freshly picked asparagus sandwich for lunch. Via Glossop across the Derbyshire Peak District to Penistone and home.

A N.E. Club evening trip over the tops to Grassington and to Dean's – some good cows and fantastic views over the whole Craven district when up on the hills looking at heifers. Angus and his brother John had been very keen buyers at our dispersal, buying several of the top priced animals, among them Spottie who was still looking well as a relatively old cow by this time.

We didn't go to the Great Yorkshire Show on the first day, for the simple reason I was judging the Dairy Championships the next day, so didn't want to see any of the animals involved. It was a great honour and the pinnacle of my judging career, made even more so when I was told by Margaret Chapman who was the chief cattle steward and had invited me to do so, that I was the first Yorkshireman ever to be invited to do so in his native county. The dairy pairs went to a superbly matched pair of Shorthorns from the Collins' "Churchroyd" herd, the inter-breed heifer champion was the Holstein from "Littlebridge" with a Jersey reserve. The group of five went to the Holsteins with a group of Ayrshires in reserve. Interestingly nearly all the groups struggled to have a dry cow or in-calf heifer to match the rest of their compatriots in quality – I suppose that tells you something about modern day dairy cattle showing. The Supreme Individual Championship was probably the easiest class with a superb mature Holstein, Mikali Seaver Erle from David Wright, though he would have been hard pressed by his other home-bred senior cow which had stood reserve the day before. The final job was judging the Blythwood Pairs in the main ring during the cattle parade – a bit of nonsense really as I had judged them earlier but not tapped them out, and had to make a bit of a show of it for the people in the grandstand, but it was won by the two Holsteins ahead of the pair from "Churchroyd".

The two pots of lilies we have had growing for several years were fantastic this year, even better than they usually are, one pot had 76 blooms on it and the other one did even better with 87. With Ruby staying with us for a few days, we went that weekend down to Sam Turner's for their first ever "Fun Day".

We went to the Donaldson's "Barlees" dispersal sale at Stokesley in early August. Father Les had bought a Dalesend Bullet Pansy in our first ever draft sale, which went on to score EX, and the heifer calf it was carrying also went EX, and they developed into a very good family. They also bought an Echo bulling heifer at our dispersal sale

– it was by now scored EX and looked tremendous on the day and was one of the top priced lots at 2550gns with its calf making 1250gns.

Mid-August, I cut three roses for Val across the road so she could take them to the last ever service at Aiskew Chapel before it closed. Mother had been a regular there before her death, and both Mother and Father's funeral services were there, though we had never been regulars there.

Shortly after that the car was to go into Stratstone for a service and it's first MOT, so we went into Harrogate for the day. As we walked past one of the big stores, there was a man fixing big signs up in the window ahead of a sale, which read "Eclusions apply", when I asked him what an "Eclusion" was, he realised that he had got them all wrongly printed and it was meant to be "Exclusions apply". He had a good swear as he began to remove them all but did have the good grace to thank me for pointing it out before anyone much had seen it.

Wensleydale Show was rather better weather in 2015 and I was asked if I would do the commentary on the Dairy Cattle Judging as it went on, something they have not done before, and apart from keeping up to date with the placings among the various breeds, it was a great opportunity to also practice a bit of interaction with the non-farming general public- an increasingly important thing we must all do to keep them informed of how their food is produced and counter some of the myths which the vegetarian but more particularly vegan groups seem to be able to peddle on social media without any problem or control. It was good to see a very good sixth calf Shorthorn from Alex Wilkes go on to take the Dairy Championship. Another commentary job a week or two later at the North East All Breeds Calf Show at Thirsk. UK Dairy Day followed with another tremendous show of cattle. The reserve champion cow from the Great Yorkshire Show I referred to earlier triumphed for David Wright of Berryholme. Then the last show of the season as I judged the Dairy Championships at Nidderdale Show with Andrew Jennings Champion and a Shorthorn from Collins' in Reserve.

Excitement followed a couple of days later when Harriet Liddle was born all good and healthy, so a few days later it was off up to Lauder to see the latest addition to the family. I thought I had better have a haircut before going to see my newest grandchild, so went to Bedale for it, forgetting to put my parking disc in. I was actually in the barber's chair, halfway through having it cut when the traffic warden came into view with my car right in front of the window. Although I shot out of the chair straight away, he wouldn't be deterred and insisted on issuing a ticket, so I went back and finished the haircut!!

By now it was college reunion time, so down to Cirencester, picking up John Foss and to Marple near Stockport to travel down with David Hampson. A moderate beef dinner at night, for which we later all received a rebate and the following day we went to the University Innovation Centre but couldn't see that they were doing anything very radically new, we had been having tele-handling, chain saw courses and the likes for many years at our local Agricultural centres such as Bedale – hardly very innovative!

Whilst we were up in Scotland after Harriet's birth, we went off for parts of the day, one such visit was to look round the gardens at Monteviot House about four miles out of Jedburgh. There was no entry gate and you were asked, as we did, to leave the £5 entry fee in a box, though I am sure many didn't bother. A very well laid out and maintained gardens set in beautiful surroundings beside the River Teviot and an interesting arboretum. As we were looking around we met a gentlemen who appeared to be the owner and had a pleasant chat – to discover later he was the Marquis of Lothian – had earlier been better known as Michael Ancram, a former Minister for Northern Ireland.

The rugby World Cup was being staged in England that autumn and as season ticket holders at Newcastle Falcons we had the chance to buy tickets ahead of the general public and were fortunate enough to get them for two games at St. James' Park. One was the Friday evening and the other the following afternoon and we thought it sensible to stay up there. Discovering that virtually everywhere was already booked up and that prices had about tripled we decided to travel up for both games as the best and cheapest option. We watched the All Blacks finally overwhelm Tonga 47-9 after being the better team in the first half and if it had been anybody but the All Blacks they would have conceded a penalty try after collapsing several scrums in succession on their own line. The following day saw Scotland scrape past Samoa 36-33 when definitely the better team lost, Scotland just playing to win kickable penalties. From England's point of view the tournament was a disaster on home ground, failing to make the knock-out stages.

At this time we were helping Sarah get ready for and move from Hunton to Rose Cottage at Little Fencote – things go round in circles – this is the village where Marnie's Mother and Father had started their married life when they farmed there before going back to Clapham Lodge. There was quite a lot of tidying up to do at Rose Cottage but with its couple of acres in two paddocks and a couple of small buildings, it means Sarah can keep a couple of calves there, once she got it properly fenced and the rubbish that had been dumped in one or two places tidied up and levelled out to be re-seeded, and eventually made a straight drive in off the road, after long delays with the local council.

After booking with Bay Farm Tours to visit China the following year, we were off on our adventures again, going to Istanbul and then to Cyprus. The city is another of those names your imagination had conjured with from childhood, particularly its earlier name of Constantinople. It wasn't until we were travelling from the airport to the hotel that I realised just how large a city Istanbul is – nearly 15 million population and so much history and truly the gateway between Europe and Asia. The Dolmabahce Palace, a grand Ottoman building with everything symmetrical, including the artefacts within it was massively impressive as were the views from the Asian side back over the Bosphrous and the Sea of Marmara. The fascinating sights and smells within a spice market, much cleaner that they had been in Morocco and the tasting of proper Turkish Delight in its homeland were new experiences. We found a favourite coffeeshop which we used exclusively and got onto good terms with the owner as we enjoyed their baklava at every opportunity. The Topkapi Palace had a lot of jewels and fantastic ceilings, we visited the Grand Bazaar which had 21 gates into it, before visiting the Blue Mosque and on to the Hagia Sophia which is now a museum. A very busy and thriving city which has had a lot of violent troubles since we were there – we just hope our little coffee house man is alright.

As we travelled back to the airport, we saw all the large ships queuing up to go through the Bosphorus to deliver everything through the Black Sea and into Russia. In Northern Cyprus we stayed in Kyrenia, another very old and interesting city, though much smaller. It was also very strange to be in a country, divided in half politically, with us in the northern Turkish half and the south under Greek control, which meant it was part of the EU and the northern part wasn't though we did see various work which had been funded by them. It happened to be Remembrance weekend when we were there and there were a lot of ex-servicemen over for the services – they apparently come every year to remember their past and those lost in the conflicts there in the 1950's. As we visited and explored Kyrenia Castle we saw a large black snake laid out basking in the sun – we were told it was harmless, but I wouldn't have wanted to risk it. We then took a trip over to Famagusta via the mountains where all the quarries and cement factories were based, visited the St. Barnabas Monastery which had been there for 1000's of years, visited the giant amphitheatre and gymnasium at Salamis, the "Othello" Tower in Famagusta, St. Nicholas Cathedral which had been taken over by the Muslim religion, though they had not been able to change it either internally or externally. We saw part of what they call the "ghost city", a large part of all empty houses, streets etc which were owned by Greek Cypriots but had been vacated in the separation of the country in the late 1950's and had stood empty ever since. A boat trip on the African Queen out into the Mediterranean for a few hours was very relaxing, even if the sea was a little "choppy", before a visit to Karni, just along the coast. It had been developed along English lines and most of the streets and paths had English names, we heard a Scottish voice and an ex sergeant-major welcomed us into his home and showed us round his holiday home and explained the local village pubs offered fish and chips on a Friday night and a carvery for Sunday lunch – truly home from home!! As you walked about in the towns you were aware of the water and feeding stations for all the homeless cats and dogs which were roaming around – the feed hoppers were smaller versions of self-feed bunkers we see on farms at home. We weren't too impressed with Cyprus and wished in hindsight that we had had seven days in Istanbul and four in Cyprus rather than the other way round.

Back home to more mundane matters to find HSBC bank in Bedale had closed while we were away, and, following on from Nat West closing a year earlier, it only leaves Barclays open four days a week. Added to that B&Q the DIY suppliers closed in Northallerton as well, the nearest one now being Darlington.

The Black and White sale over at Carlisle that autumn was an average sort of a sale, which reflected the poor price being paid for milk, some decent cattle at average prices, but what was particularly memorable about that day was the weather – I have never seen it rain so heavily for so long, by night time parts of the city were already flooded and the road home was just to say passable in places. It wasn't until the next day when we saw all the devastation caused by the rain on the television – somewhere in the nearby Lake District had had 14 inches in 24 hours – that's what you call rain!! The damage to local infrastructure – roads, bridges etc was colossal but as far as I know, thankfully there was no loss of life.

Went over to Grewelthorpe to a farm sale where Sarah was interested in a skid-steer loader if it only made about £1200 but couldn't touch it and it made £6200, so we had rather underestimated its worth.

Just before Christmas we had a very enjoyable evening at Betty's in Harrogate for one of their Christmas concerts whilst we had a three-course dinner. A ten-lady ensemble entertained us with 26 carols and songs throughout the meal and afterwards and were very good, we admired all the festive lights in Harrogate as we drove through it both ways.

Into 2016 and up to the Semex Conference in Glasgow, bored by a typical bureaucrat Sophie Helaine from the European Commission, then greatly improved by John McDougall speaking about the practicalities of working in China, men from Muller and Glanbia were good, before the star of the day was Prof. Hughes of Imperial College, typical professor type, all over the place with arms waving whilst he talked about worldwide food usage. Various other meetings and outings in the early part of the year, though nothing of particular note. In early March the Leyburn Dairy Discussion Group had its away day to look round the year-old set up at Newton Rigg College – a nice set up and they look to be doing a good job now that it is back under the control of Askham Bryan rather than Cumbria University which had no real interest in farming. Another trip over to Cumbria took us to Dairy Expo at Carlisle with a lot of stands to look round and then watched the Laird's of Blythbridge take the Championship ahead of Sterndale.

A good day out to Harlow Carr as spring awoke. Interestingly enough when we spoke to one of the gardeners who was cutting the lawns with a small lawn mower he said they cut all the grass like that the first time over as doing it with a ride-on does not set it off properly for the season.

A nice fine day at the end of March took us on a ride out up into the hills and over to Askrigg and Bainbridge, Hawes and over to Sedbergh and we had a look up Cotterdale for the first time ever, to Nateby and back over the tops to coffee at Thwaite and then called to see Mrs Whitehead at Muker and on to Thrintoft for supper at the New Inn.

Our next trip out was a rather longer one – via Manchester to meet up with Bay Farm Tours and via Amsterdam to take the 10-hour flight to Shanghai and the start of our Chinese adventure. We expected their hours of daylight to be similar to ours in mid-May, but it was dark by 8pm at night and not light until about 6am in the morning. One of the largest cities in the world – 24 million population, traffic chaos everywhere, but all seemed very prosperous. From the Bund we looked on the old British Centre of the 1840's on one side and the much newer skyscrapers in the financial centre on the opposite riverbank. We were immediately struck by how clean it was – none of the pollution we were led to expect, and that applied throughout the whole of our trip. Quite a lot of open park land within the city and the roadsides and the centre of the dual carriageways were very attractively flowered. Visited the Jade Buddha Temple before going to the new Shanghai Tower, the tallest building in the world, though soon afterwards Dubai put a bit more on one of theirs to reclaim the title, although it wasn't due to officially open for another couple of months. We went up to the 126th floor on a lift moving at 18 metres per second, though no sensation of moving, let alone speed. The views over the city were staggering and we observed two and three storey buildings being demolished and replaced with six and seven storeys. The Chinese Acrobat show at night was tremendous, very cleverly choreographed, the highlight being the eight motor-bikes going round inside a giant sphere – they had a job to get them all into it never mind going round two different ways without ever colliding.

A two-hour flight to Yachong, called at a typical Chinese supermarket which was quite illuminating – quite a lot of British products in Chinese wrappers before joining the cruise ship to enjoy a four-day cruise up the Yangtze. With only about 200 passengers on a ship which could take 440, and we had some tremendous meals in the upper restaurant and some great trips off the boat at various points of interest, listened to an interesting lecture on Chinese acupuncture, watched an amazing artist painting the inside of small bottles – unbelievable concentration and skill and we eventually bought one as a memento of our trip. We went to visit the Three Gorges Dam Project – the largest in the world which is for hydro-electric and has lifted the river level by 75 metres. Took us about four hours for the cruiser to go through the five locks to get us up to the new level to continue the journey. They were still constructing a ship lift to make this much quicker – I would have liked to see it in action – it was apparently for the smaller ships – up to 3000 tonnes which would sail onto it with the smaller half hanging over the end and taken up like a giant Ferris wheel and placed on the higher level. Another trip off took us to see the "hanging coffins" up the Daning river, to a village at the end of the Shennong stream, up 147 steps to their new arts centre for a music and dance performance by the local Ba't people. Quite foggy by this time, but we managed to avoid hitting any of the many ships on the river, mostly commercial carrying all sorts, sand, gravel, giant loads of cars and vans, watched a green-tea making demonstration followed by a very good concert performed by many of the crew members. Visited the very old wooden structure of the Precious Sone Fortress, having to weave our way past all the stalls selling everything from second-hand books, pottery and snakes.

Our first stop after disembarking in Chongqing was to the zoo to see the pandas happily munching away on their bamboo. From there to the airport to fly to Tibet where you immediately felt the difference in altitude – everything and everybody moving more slowly, they say if you go there permanently it takes up to six months for your body to fully adjust. We didn't have that long and different people react in different ways. My main problem was sleeping – I had about four hours on the first night and that in total the remaining nights put together – worst affected was our tour guide who had to be flown back down to lower levels. The remarkable thing is that when we returned to mainland China, within half an hour, everyone is back to normal. As we travelled into Lhasa we had to stop at a check point and use the toilets which were absolutely disgusting and the whole area was very depressed and much less affluent than the remainder of the country and one got the impression the authorities were determined to keep it so, in that way they had control of the people. Visited the Jokhang Temple – Tibet's' holiest shrine, which was almost overrun with pilgrims, the overriding smell of yak oil which they used to keep the candles burning. Many of them walk round the pilgrim's way, and apparently the ones from a long way off may come for a week and walk round it about 10 times a day, every day, their holiday.

We visited a dairy farm – if you could call it that. Groups of animals (up to 5) tethered in pens, hand milked looked after by one man though belonging to many owners who came to milk them. They told us the cows were giving 25kg daily which I couldn't envisage, but when we got down to the nitty gritty that was what each pen was producing. Mind you – when you saw what they were eating that wasn't surprising – very old grass brought in for them. There were dung pats on the walls to dry out for winter fuel. Originally, we were to go to the much larger "state" dairy, but this was cancelled at short notice for no apparent reason.

The Potala Palace was another visit, three passport checks to get in and 388 steps to climb where there were only apparently two of the original rooms left, so we looked at the replicas in the ground level museum. A visit to a farm with a lot of poly tunnels growing chillies and watermelon and on to a large poultry farm with 200 cockerels and 800 hens which they kept for five years and were producing 200 eggs per day. We saw two herds of yaks wandering about as we travelled before going to a Tibetan supper and performance of singing, dancing and storytelling including a mock 'Yak' dance which could loosely be described as a "bull in a China shop".

A visit to Yumbu Lhakhang, the oldest known building in Tibet, the home of the Yarlung kings. To get to the Temple you could either climb a massive number of steps or go round the track by horseback – so I had my first and probably last horse ride. Fortunately there was a guide to lead the horse and they both knew the way fairly well, it was just as well as on the way back down the horse knew it was the end of the day and was finished when at the bottom – it was fairly hairy at times, with some very sharp drops from the roadsides with no fencing or anything.

A two-and-a-half-hour flight to Xian, a much smaller city than Shanghai, only eight million population, it had been the capital of China through thirteen dynasties. The main purpose of coming here, and one of the highlights of the trip was to see the

Terracotta Warriors – pictures or television programmes cannot do them justice and you have to be with them and see them to truly appreciate the size and scale of them – nearly everyone has a different expression on their face, and remember, they were done about 2000 years ago to guard one of the Emperor's tombs, before being destroyed and buried about 400 years ago. The farmer who discovered them when investigating a drainage problem got paid about ten shillings for it – not very much for the millions it now generates in tourism. They haven't as yet done anything with the Emperors tomb which is about a mile away and you get the feeling, they have a vested interest in not being in too much of a hurry to unearth it.

Another two-hour flight to Guilin which is more of a resort. You have no option but to spend hours in airports and flying because of the immense size of the country. More of a garden city, alongside the River Li. On a walk round the city we looked in a craft centre, and in particular a studio and bought a picture by a young man, who was that autumn coming to Manchester University to lecture for a year on Oriental art. We watched cormorants fishing on the river, and my scepticism told me that there was someone out of sight on the boat putting the fish in for them to catch – classic recycling as they had tapes round their necks to stop them swallowing the fish.

A visit the next day to a massive and very well-run fish farm, with several big lakes and reared from a few days old for 4 to 8 months until about 0.5kg to go to a wholesaler. He was selling 10 tonnes per week. This was followed by a visit to a vegetable farm growing cucumbers, tomatoes, loofah, sour melon – all outside rather than in greenhouses. A visit to an agricultural research unit, followed by going to a tea plantation followed by a tea ceremony. During a cruise on the River Li, we saw cattle, water buffalo and the odd sheep grazing in the water meadows, before going to a kumquat orchard and education centre. Kumquats are a big crop in the area, some 800 acres there producing about 40kg per tree, and the valley sides all around growing them, and they were working with Coca-Cola to develop them into a health drink. It must be quite a sight in late autumn as they cover the trees from October to January as the fruit must not get wet as it ripens – and there are 10,000 hectares altogether in that area.

Another flight of about two and a half hours back to Beijing with its population of about 20 million. Visited the Summer Palace and also to see the Marble Boat moored on the lake. First stop next morning was Tiananmen Square – an absolutely massive area – long queues and passport showing to visit the Forbidden City and the Palace Museum, with well over 10,000 rooms you would have got lost if you had lived there all your life – fortunately we had a guide. A rickshaw ride through the Hualong district was a new experience and we visited an 'old' courtyard, which I guess was set up for the tourists, followed by a cruise on Houhai Lake where there was a musician on each boat playing different traditional Chinese instruments. An evening at Peking opera which is rather different to our traditional perception of opera.

Next morning off to a large beef rearing farm and with its own slaughterhouse. They could house 4000 head all in individual yoke beds, but only 600 head in it. The cattle were taken to large weights and were tremendous looking animals, but apparently it cost them 26 yuan/kg (8.65 yuan to the pound, so about £3/kg) to rear them to that stage and they can buy beef in from Australia for half that. Mostly Simmental cross from the indigenous Chinese yellow cattle. It was rather refreshing to see that the Chinese were being treated as they have treated the rest of the world in recent years and were being undercut on price. They then took you to their very large restaurant where they marketed much of their expensively reared beef.

Finally, a drive up into the hills and we came to visit the Great Wall. A long climb, onto a bus, then a cable car, makes you wonder why they constructed it in such inhospitable country. It was a fantastic feeling to be on it, walk along it, marvel at its construction and the views of it far into the distance, and you can only imagine the numbers involved in moving all the materials and the construction of it over such a distance so many years ago, without any of the equipment we take for granted today. It is so very wide and high in places, there were couples having their wedding photos taken in various places on the wall. That wasn't the only place we saw them doing this – they took them, usually weeks in advance of the event – that would avoid everyone hanging around for hours as we do in this country, before the reception. That was the end of a long-remembered trip – not all leisure by any means, but for some parts, particularly Tibet, if you don't go soon it will have changed beyond all recognition.

Soon back into normal routine, a day after to Northallerton to get some shopping, but we also took back the spare ironing board Sarah had got for us. We returned it to Wilko's, who after some persuading gave us a replacement plus £5, but when we told Sarah, we discovered it had come from B & M, so they did very well to do anything for us.

The World Jersey Conference was being held in this country with visitors from all over, and Sarah was very involved with it at various stages. We had a long morning helping to put all the bits from the various sponsors into each "goodie bag" for the delegates. We helped her get ready for and then do the lunch catering at Pye's Bayview Jersey herd where they served some superb Garstang Blue and other cheeses provided by Dewlay Foods where their milk went. We collected Sarah from the airport from Jersey where she had a team getting ready for the tour going over there, but before that we went with her down to Will Patten's in Cheshire for the Jersey judging competition and helped do the scoring – 67 entries in the first class without one correct placing! Returned Sarah to Robin Hood airport, we always connect Robin Hood with Nottingham, not Doncaster, but it is only a small airport and easy to get to. They then did all the cattle for the show in Jersey which was rather larger than usual because of the visit and then had sourced and organised the select sale which they held on the Island with very good results.

Just after this we had the EU Referendum with an unexpected 52% vote to leave against 48% to remain. As I write this some three and half years later, we have had that length of time spent by politicians of all sides doing their best to thwart the wishes of the people and stop Brexit. Nothing else has been dealt with in the direction of many things within the political and economic areas, and latterly the uncertainty has been having something of a damaging effect on businesses and the economy. Finally, last week, the politicians got their "come-uppence" in the General Election when the general public overwhelmingly voted for a Conservative government to "get Brexit done" and move on to the wider agenda.

The Holstein UK Celebration was held this year over in Lancashire, based at the De Vere hotel on the edge of Blackpool. We started off with a trip over to Proctor's Farm near Slaidburn, owned by the Moore's family of store and football pools fame and Everton football club. They still have the famous pedigree Angus cattle at another farm, but here they have a very highly regarded Limousin herd based upon a bull they had purchased for 100,000gns about ten years previously who had really typed them, but it was getting to the point of needing a replacement as nearly all were descendants from him. They were also experimenting with hydroponic grass to feed them on in winter, and whilst interesting, it is as yet a long way from commercial realisation, reality and automation. Lunch that day was at the Stardale herd of Messrs Burrows where we looked round a great herd of 200 plus cows.

On the second day we went for a conducted tour round Old Trafford, home of Manchester United, and walked on the hallowed pitch. Returning to David Tomlinson and family's Bilsrow herd for lunch, had a good look round some good buildings, including a super calf rearing house, without being able to get too involved in the cows as they are permanently housed. Back for the AGM at night which saw David Tomlinson become Society President and then another great speech from Howard Petch who had spoken at my incoming Presidents Dinner some five years earlier. Howard had been a lecturer at nearby Myerscough college where David had been a student under him, before he went on to be Principal at Bishop Burton.

From Lancashire straight down to Sussex to stay at Horsham in readiness for judging the Dairy Championships at the South of England Show at Ardingly. Another non-dairying area in this day and age, but still a good turn out with 11 from all breeds turning out for the "Super cow" competition. In the All Breeds Championship I had little hesitation in tapping out Easthaugh Audrey 70 shown by Peter Prior, but jointly owned with her breeder Eddie Brigham. She had a good year that year and the next and was Reserve All Britain Senior Cow in 2016/17. Headed home via the Dartford Tunnel and then stayed overnight at Welwyn Garden City. It was very interesting to go round one of the early social town development projects, based on Shredded Wheat, with very open streets and roads with roses down the centres and large open green areas. What a contrast with current housing developments when it seems to be how many they can squeeze onto a given area. In total from leaving to go up to Adam's the previous Sunday morning to getting back home on the Saturday afternoon we had driven 1003 miles.

The North East Club trip that summer was over to Dalston to the Brough's "Carrock" herd, a very well-run farm operated by Stephen and his son Neil with help from Craig who at that time was a Land Agent with Harrison and Hetherington. Their three robots have now been in for about a year, are operating very well and they seem very pleased with the results – an increase in herd average of 1200 litres per cow. In the afternoon we went to Catterlen run by the Horsley family. Their "Woodcatt" herd is again about 250 cows and with two young sons just getting towards the end of their schooling we are likely to hear more of this herd in the future.

The day after we went down to Beeston to give James Alston some moral support as he dispersed his "Uphall" herd from Norfolk. His father and Mr J had been great friends for many years and Dalesend Cascade had been jointly owned by the two farms when marketed through Herdwise in the late 1970's.

Bill and I went down to the NEC for the Dairy Event – it was rather sparse of both stands and people, and sad to say it was the last one - the end of another Era, speeded up by the move to the NEC and the change of timing, now superseded by a high-tech event in February which seems to be well supported by the trade.

Mid-July one Sunday afternoon took us on the short trip up to Wynyard Hall to see the new rose garden which had been instigated by Sir John Hall. It had only been planted just over a year and the roses have grown and developed tremendously well in such a short time and the complementary planting of other species within the beds sets them off to great advantage. What really helps is the guide of the different varieties in their positions and we created our own "sniff" guide with our favourite being 'Gertrude Jekyll'.

During the school holidays Ruby came down to stay for a few days before Laura and Harriet came down to join her and we had a trip out to Newby Hall. First time I have ever been and now a very busy visitor attraction drawn by the doll's house exhibition – even I was fascinated by how small they could make those things – especially the set of dominoes on a little table, but you could still see every dot on them and the Giles Brandreth teddy bears were on display. A trip to Cleveland Show was the end of her holiday week – capped by Marnie buying raffle tickets at a face painting stand which she learned later had won her first prize – a doll's house which she then fitted out with curtains, carpets etc ready for later use by the girls.

Over to Carlisle for the Holstein Premier Herd Open Day at the Hodgson's "Wormanby" herd. It was amazing to see as we went through the back streets of Carlisle to get there, that a lot of the houses were still empty after the floods of nine months previously and there were vans of plumbers, joiners, plasterers and builders parked everywhere. Cows looked well despite being outside when they are normally housed, and not settling too well. Plenty of friends to talk with and look at Tag sale heifers.

Another short trip away, this time over to Southern Ireland, which was really our Christmas present from Sarah, or at least the reason for going was. A long drive across to Anglesey to get the ferry from Fishguard. From Dublin up to Navan to stay overnight before we had a drive around the northern part of Southern Ireland, which was the first time we had been in that area, thousands of acres of very few stock and poor land, but for the first time since I was a boy at Middlesmoor, peat cut and laid out to dry for the winter fuel. Dotted about in this very poor landscape, you kept coming across large, fancy, fairly newly built houses in the middle of nowhere, nearly all of which had an oldish cattle trailer stood somewhere in the grounds, no doubt how they got the planning permission for the new "farmhouse" because of the stock! After another night in Cavan we made our way to the Castle Leslie Estate at Glaslough.

We were staying in the lodge there and had a good walk round the estate which was also set up for horse riding enthusiasts, and we had a good look round the stables which can take up to 55 horses. Finally, we had our Christmas dinner in the Snaffles restaurant, a fine affair with six courses over about 2½ hours – absolutely superb food and service, but we needed another walk before going to bed. The next day was a long one with the drive back to the ferry and then from the ferry home in the dark in some pretty awful driving rain.

We are gluttons for punishment and only the next day it was off again, though nor so far this time. Only over to Bolton Abbey for the Katherine Jenkins concert. A long walk down into the park beside the River Wharfe and a long sit and wait on a beautiful sunny September evening, but by the end we wished we had taken more coats with us, as it wasn't very far off a frost on such a clear, moonlight night. A superb performance.

The day after and it was off to York for the All Breeds Calf Show to do the commentary, and the next day it was straight into putting the monthly inserts into the CIS diaries ready for delivery the next day down to Telford and UK Dairy Day.

When up to Hill Top East a few days later, Mrs J told me the amazing story of one of her hens. She believed the fox had been out and got one of her last remaining two or three, but that weekend Mrs Waddington from Burrill, brought her hen back. The previous day a van had delivered something to Hill Top and whilst he was doing so, the hen had jumped into the van. He shut the door and off to his next delivery at Burrill, where upon everyone was surprised (don't know whether it was him or the hen) when the hen appeared. It might have been better if he had re-delivered it rather than just telling Mrs Waddington where it had come from!

A few weeks later at Stokesley Show after Marnie and Ruby had gone for a walk round, I had a short walk and called at the Redmayne-Bentley stand to talk with my contact. Whilst waiting to see him I entered their competition to name the best five performing FTSE 100 since the EU referendum and fortunately I got four of them right which won me the prize of afternoon tea for two at Wynyard Hall – which was very nice when we had it.

Shortly after that we had a very interesting part day with David Petch. I had previously given two old photographs of farmsteads which we couldn't identify to

Martin to ask his father about, and he invited us over to show us round the Great Ayton neighbourhood, one was easily identified but the other is still a mystery. He took us to meet George Proud and his family who lived in a beautiful green valley in the middle of nowhere up on the hills above Kildale – almost like an oasis. He was about 90 and greeted me with "I remembers thou be'in born". He had lived there all his life and it was very well farmed even though his health was beginning to fail, but he couldn't help us much with the photographs. He gave up the tenancy of the farm about 18 months later, and I learnt only recently that he had not enjoyed a very long retirement before his death about a year ago. We had a cup of coffee and a cake at Little Ayton's Fletchers farm and shop before we left Mr Petch's.

Early November and it was off to New Zealand again to see Len and Mollie. The long haul is unavoidable, you just have to grin and bear it. We noticed immediately that it was quite a bit more expensive than previously, because of the fall in the value of our pound rather than a cost rise at their end. The first time we went 11 or 12 years previously the exchange rate was almost 3 NZ dollars to the pound, last time we were there it was about two, but now down to 1.65 to the pound.

Timaru had quite a large Indian population and we went to their Diwali Celebration of friendship and happiness with various performances by mostly children, with a curry and rice supper. A visit the next day to their Botanic Gardens to see the roses was disappointing as most weren't out, until we discovered round the back a species rose garden which had all the old five-leaved flowers with a lot of scent, from these very old roses, most of the modern roses have been developed – more petals, less scent!!

We headed for Lake Tekapo, where all the lupins were in full bloom and were a terrific sight; we didn't visit the church as we saw there were a couple of busloads of Chinese swarming about the place. While we were having a bite of lunch we watched a stock agent call for his late breakfast and while he got up to get some sauce a seagull swooped down and pinched a rasher of bacon but dropped it when he shouted at it. He ate it up as if nothing had happened. The drive from there to Twizel was very attractive, the roadsides covered in lupins and poppies in all colours and sizes and stayed overnight in Cromwell. The Heritage Centre there was very interesting looking in the old buildings of the village, before we continued on and had another look at Jesse Mitchell's old cottage from the 1860's. The staff at the coffee house in Balclutha told us the motels there were ok, though one was run by a JAFA – we looked mystified until she explained – "Just Another F**king Aucklander". Down into the Caitlins in some awful wet weather, but when it eventually faired up, we drove to Waipapa Point and walked to the light house and along the beach among the sleeping sea lions. Visited the Cathedral Caves set on a fabulous open beach, one of the 30 largest in the world, which had a double entry that the water had created with the tide over the centuries. A walk to the McLean falls and then via Clydevale to Route 90 and on to Lawrence. Marnie then took over the navigating onto some very rough unsealed roads but across endless farming land of all types. We seemed to travel for many miles, but it was only slow going with the odd place almost impassable. Finishing back at Lawrence the lady in the café told us we shouldn't have been on those sorts of roads in a hire car – which is quite correct but was none of her business.

Staying in Dunedin for a couple of nights we visited their superb Botanic Gardens, they are very well used by the locals and then we visited the South Otago Iris Show featuring some real beauties – particularly the almost black "Ghost Train" – we have since tried to get one but they aren't available in the UK. We visited the "steepest street in the world" and it would be an overstatement to say it was a disappointment – it was pathetic. Fairly short, yes it was steep but straight up and down. We drove to the top, turned round and back down again. Averages 1 in 3.3 and the steepest bit is 1 in 2.6. At least we can say we have done it.

Dunedin railway station was well worth a visit just to see the original tiled hallway and was very ornate. The upstairs holds the Sports Hall of Fame which was very well done as was the Settlers Museum more or less next door which showed very clearly the development of the area and you could relate to it much more easily as it had all happened in the last 150 years or so.

Another 60 or 70 kilometres on unsealed road was again very interesting, across fjords and wet and rutted tracks, eventually we were back to Ranfurly, before, the next day travelling up on Dead Horse Pinch to Palmerston. So, named after many men and horses were lost in the 1860's hauling gold mining supplies from Dunedin to Ranfurly. A ride up the side of Aviemore Lake and down the other side brought us back to Kurow to stay the night. Into Waimate, a rather run down town with a lot of empty and second-hand shops.

When in Timaru, Len had a couple of places to call, to collect two new hats, they were to stretch on his home made "hat stretcher". One of the shops was a big Sam Turner type of place, where I spied some I'Anson's Speedi-beet, all the way from Masham. We then set off again and up to Greymouth, then up towards Westport, and a good walk round the blow holes and such like at Pancake rocks – amazing how the sea erosion over the years had shaped them. It has been well laid out for people to walk round on platforms – just as well as they had 650,000 visitors last year. A drive further up the coast road and we had lunch looking out on the Southern Ocean. Booked the hire car back in at Greymouth and came the reverse way back over to Christchurch on the train, with much more water in the rivers than the previous time we went over. Whilst we were waiting for the train in Greymouth there were two tremendous showers of hailstones, not really what you expect at the end of November (our May).

The rose gardens were unbelievable in the Christchurch Botanic Gardens - we hit them right at the height of flowering. Whilst sitting admiring the roses we saw an unusual phenomenon within a clear, blue sky. Suddenly a large cloud just appeared from nowhere, followed by a couple of smaller ones. They didn't move and after a while just melted away again, and no we hadn't been drinking it was the middle of the day. We were aware something was happening in the city as we had struggled to find a motel or hotel, and discovered they were hosting the World Bowls Championship, a four-yearly event. The opening ceremony was to be at City Hall just up the road, and we sat and watched the members from about 70 countries parade past. They had to cross a main road just down from where we were, and amazingly as the parade approached it, two men put on their high-vis jackets and stopped the traffic and then just opened it again – you can't imagine that happening as simply as that in the UK. We walked to the Cardboard Cathedral, which was very interesting, though disappointingly nothing has yet been done with the actual one since the earthquake. We ate at night at the Japanese restaurant – same as last time and the tempura prawns were still as good.

Back home on the last day of November to a very frosty reception – it had been down to -5°C, lower than we had had all the previous winter. The next day to give my 100th pint of blood, having given all the others either at Cirencester or Bedale, they have now stopped coming to Bedale and quite a lot of other places, and I felt a bit deflated having to go to Northallerton which comes under Teesside rather than Leeds.

The annual trip to the Semex Conference in Glasgow was good if not exceptional and then a few days later on a good day we had a walk round the gardens at Harlow Carr. The highlight of that trip was the exhibition about the civilians who were held and became prisoners of war in Berlin during the Second World War. They established gardens and did a lot of gardening to keep themselves occupied and were supplied with seeds and guidance by the RHS. I was totally unaware this had happened, or the large numbers involved. On the way home we called at Morrison's in Ripon where we met Mr "Chippy" Chambers who had taught wood work at Ripon Grammar School fifty years of more ago and it was amazing he knew me and my name after all those hundreds of students over the years. I still have the unfinished table lamp I half made at school somewhere.

Early February took me on a final trip to rugby with Dick Brown before he retired in the April. Up to Edinburgh with he and George Leggott, had lunch at "Browns" after booking into the St. George Hotel before going to see Scotland beat Ireland 27-22 in not the best of matches. As we watched the televised England/France match in a pub later, I couldn't believe the nastiness in the effusive cheering of every French bit of success and the booing of England at every moment – England winning 19-16, totally unnecessary – we don't do that if the Scottish are playing.

A walk round the gardens at Kipling Hall on a lovely, sunny February afternoon to view the fantastic show of snowdrops which were at their very best. We were left in charge of everything for a week or two with Sarah going to Australia on holiday and Adam, Laura and the girls away in New Zealand.

Mid-March saw us away on our travels again, this time to Sri Lanka, again with Bay Farm Tours. Flying from Manchester via Dubai, still a long way to go. Another of those places you remember from childhood that you want to visit someday, though of course then it was still called Ceylon. An island country which had had its problems sometime before but had been settled for some years now and was also getting over the massive Tsunami of some seven years earlier. Sadly, they have had more terrorist trouble in 2019, though it seems to have gone quiet again. The capital Colombo is very much a city of two halves, the old colonial type area with a lot of history, and the newer more industrial type area. Our first hotel, the Galle Face Hotel right next to the Indian Ocean had been the colonial headquarters when we were in power there and had been beautifully re-furbished. A tour of the city showed us a lot of construction work going on, much of it hotels for the coming tourist boom, we were immediately struck by the fact that while there were massive numbers of poor people they all had a smile on their face. A visit to a Buddhist temple, cultural museum with an agricultural section was fascinating and on this Sunday afternoon we learnt that that is where nearly all the locals go at that time of the week.

Beginning our travels the next day, we were soon aware of how erratic much of their driving is, particularly the service buses which race to get in front of a competitor before the next stop, plus the tuk tuk's which seem to cut through the narrowest of gaps. A visit to a coconut experimental farm was fascinating as we saw the work going into developing heavy yielding, but lower trees, and watched them planting them on top of shells for fertiliser. We travelled on to Dambulla to stay at the Amaya Lake Hotel – we had a friendly little gecko in our bathroom for company.

As we travelled to Sigiriya – the Rock, we marvelled at the flowers and blossoms in the trees which were very showy and with many varieties. This is the big rock which became a small city on the top of it many centuries ago, but we didn't climb the 1200 steps to the top, saving ourselves for later in the day when we went off on an Elephant Safari which was fantastic, and we were lucky in that we were the last two loaded into a Land Rover so had our own personal guide. We travelled about 10km into the park and round the lake, seeing odd males on their own before coming across a group of about 30 cows and calves. We also saw water buffalo and the odd elephant bathing and a large variety of birds including, storks, herons, pelicans and eagles, plus a turtle.

A visit to CIC, a private research institute creating the seeds to sell on to the regions farmers, and watched them fertilising the onions – the women walked through them every day for 10 days touching all the heads in turn to help the fertilisation to produce the seed, we also saw them counting out the seeds into envelopes to go to the farmers. Whilst there we saw the biggest snail I have ever seen, it must have been about 2½ - 3 inches long and high. We watched them bringing in trailer loads of bananas and going through the washing, sorting and packaging process – this like everything else was still very heavily manual with plenty of labour and it seemed two people for every job. A visit to a milking water buffalo unit which wasn't doing very well as they couldn't get them to let their milk down to the machine and so had reverted back to hand milking, giving about five litres per day on average. We watched them combining rice with a six-foot cut combine on skids, having earlier watched a field on our travels where they were cutting it with scythes and threshing it by hand.

Here they put the rice out on large sheets to dry for four hours in the sun, turning it by walking through and tipping with feet, while the birds removed any insects. In the rice fields it only takes 2-3 weeks from stopping watering the paddy to being able to combine it. We saw them cultivating lotus flowers on a big lake to sell to people visiting the temples and watched some kapok being made and bagged up.

The next day we visited a wholesale fruit and veg market, with produce brought in by individual growers or local collectives to be bought by dealers and retailers to go all over the country. The minimum quantity was 20kgs but up as large as a wagon load. There were too many cucumbers about and a boy with eight bags would not accept 10 rupees (£5.50) per bag, so they would probably be wasted. Betel leaves were very expensive as they were used as a present for respected guests. Called for ten minutes to see the Golden Buddha and saw a massive bee's nest and then visited a wood carving centre and then to a spice garden.

On arriving at Nuwara Eliya we had to change to a smaller bus to be able to get up the hill – very twisty up to the hotel in a beautiful setting with fantastic views. A visit to a research station on vegetables and insect control, followed by a lecture on plant breeding – they seem to have a different definition of genetic modification than I have.

Next day a visit to the Temple of the Sacred Tooth, supposedly it had belonged to the Buddha, though we didn't see the actual tooth as there was a long queue. The botanical gardens were large with a magnificent display of unusual trees at all stages from blossom to fruit, a lot of honey bats hanging in the trees, then later in the day had a Sri Lankan dance performance which was very lively and colourful, and finished outside with some fire walking and eating.

A visit to the Taylor's Tea Plantation, they took us round and we did some tea plucking – the ladies pick about 35-40 kgs in an 8-hour day for about £1/hour. We toured the factory where it goes onto drying beds for five hours about 12 inches deep and turned every 20 minutes, during which it loses about 80% of its moisture. The bushes are picked about once a week in dry weather and more often in the monsoon season – they only want the young tender shoots/leaves. The plantation was 1250 acres and employed 1250 people, and we had a drink of tea made with a tea which costs 3000 rupees (about £16.50) per kilo – not PG Tips! We boarded a train at Peradeniya and then a four-hour ride to Nuwara Eliya through thousands of acres of tea plantations to arrive at the Grand Hotel – again one in colonial style.

A trip to Ambewela Farms through a market gardening area of mostly small, individually owned farms but selling collectively, potatoes, carrots, leeks and cabbages. They obviously have no problem with root fly in Sri Lanka! The large dairy farm was a long way from anywhere but on a public holiday could have over 10,000 visitors. It had originally been New Zealand owned, but not now, they have a large Ayrshire herd on a separate farm, though we visited the Holstein herd – 8 a side herringbone, milked three times a day, averaging 27 litres/cow and getting about 40p per litre. Staff were paid £4 per day and worked a six-day week with no holidays other than state holidays.

They made their own cheese and yoghurt for sale in the farm shop and also had meat rabbits and goats. We watched in amazement as they mixed their own tarmac for potholing the road. Three men with shovels and the lady in charge poured tar on as they mixed, she had plastic bags tied over her bare feet. Back at the hotel that day we enjoyed a walk round the garden – it has been and is the Champion Hotel Garden in Sri Lanka – some amazing topiary in a massive hedge.

A long journey through fantastic scenery, with veg fields and paddy fields, we watched 22 ladies busy plucking tea, and up to a height of 14,000 feet. Lunch at a restaurant built over-hanging a cliff edge with amazing wood sculptures, particularly a collection of horses. To our hotel set in the midst of a wildlife park, we watched crocodiles in the lake and monkeys and wild boar roamed in the grounds and if you were out after dark you had to have an escort as wild elephants crossed the grounds.

An early start the next day took us to Yala where we saw mongoose, lizards, elephants, water buffalo and deer, but none of the elusive leopards, which we were disappointed though not surprised by, even though Sri Lanka has the highest concentration of them in the world. We saw many different wild birds, including their national one, which looked to be like a bantam cock. That was all before breakfast back at the hotel before we headed across to Bentota where we visited a ministry farm of milking buffalo – 38 milking, 140 litres of milk with 19 staff – hardly economic by our standards. We had our very first rain that afternoon, just getting to the start of their monsoon season – what a show of thunder and lightning, they don't need fireworks. Ferry across the lake to the hotel, fortunately the storm had by then passed.

Visit to a rubber plantation and an old boy showed us how he cut the tree every day and it would run for about four hours before it began to set, if the price was good he sold straight away, if not he cast into rubber mats in a mould and it could then be melted down again when the price improved. In the afternoon we, along with fellow travellers Robert and Dianne from Gloucestershire, had a boat trip round the lake, up the river and almost out to the Indian Ocean. We had a very good guide with eagle eyes, and he showed us lizard, two chameleons, into the mangroves to find a crocodile and watched some crab fishermen.

The following day we visited the turtle rescue centre – they collect the eggs, to stop predators getting them, and after hatching keep them for three days before letting them go down the beach to the sea – in that way they know where to return to subsequently lay their eggs. In this way they have an 80% survival rate against 20% in the wild. We also saw some injured and disabled ones being nursed, and also a very rare albino turtle. A coach trip along the side of the Indian Ocean showed us some of the damage from the Tsunami, and then into Galle which had been the centre of the island when it was under Dutch and Portuguese control. Before dinner at night we had a long stroll along the beach and a paddle in the very warm Indian Ocean, as the sun set on Sri Lanka. We were leaving at night, and we were all about on the coach when there was a massive explosion which was caused by the air bag on the rear suspension blowing up. The two coachmen were very organised, had a spare and replaced it and we were on our way within three quarters of an hour – in the dark, only torchlight to work in – could you imagine that scenario happening in England.

Overnight flight to Dubai and into the Park Hyatt hotel, then a three hour conducted tour of the city – interesting but the place lacks character, a walk around the fabulous hotel grounds the next morning with views right across the cityscape, and watched the Japanese queuing up to have half hour flights on the seaplane over Dubai – at £375 a time – we didn't bother! That was the end of our stay in Dubai – very interesting but we wouldn't want to have stayed any longer – too hot, too over the top in many ways and a totally soulless place.

A busy few days soon after we came back when we had all eight Norwegians visit at the same time as we had Laura, Ruby and Harriet staying. They were staying at a cottage in Exelby, and it was great for all the half cousins to play together. On the Saturday Adam managed to come down for the day and we had a total of 17 for lunch before everyone went off to Sarah's for an Easter egg hunt. Very quiet the next day when Adam took his family back to Scotland and the Norwegians went home.

A busy week in early May, saw us helping Sarah by delivering various lunches for AHDB, Kite and Bishopton Vets while she was over in Lancashire getting the cattle ready for the Jersey Cattle Society judging school at Bayview, and then over there for the actual day to help with the lunch as well.

We went down to Chatsworth for the very first day of the first ever RHS Chatsworth Flower Show. We stayed overnight at Shrigley Hall Hotel – very old and an Ex-Salesians missionary college/monastery – a very good meal but a restrictive menu which we assumed was changed weekly until the waitress excitedly told us the staff had tried the new menu that day before it was introduced – twice a year! If you had been staying for a week you would have to repeat things before the week was out. The flower show was flooded with people considering it was a members only day and they seemed rather disorganised. It seemed a long wait for a coffee, when the supervisor came to see what the problem was, the waitress said no coffee was coming out of the machine, to be told "well it won't when there is no water in it!". A great day seeing all the innovation by some very clever people, fantastic displays in the flower tents and then we looked at some "Well Dressing" a peculiarly Derbyshire tradition which goes on through the summer in the villages. We got a much better meal on the way back to the hotel at a little pub in Whaley Bridge.

A quickly called General Election was expected to return an increased Tory majority to progress Brexit but we finished up with a hung Parliament with no overall majority – thus heralding two and a half years of treading water.

A change of scenery for the Yorkshire Holstein Club 6 out of 30 competition held at Oxton Farms at Tadcaster with their Oxton Organic Shorthorns – totally different and some good young cows followed by a hog roast supper. The North Eastern Club trip was only a week later and we headed up to Kelso to Mitchell's at Kennetsideheads where they milk over a 1000 cows – very good, well run unit averaging 11,800 litres, three times a day milking through a 60 point rotary. The farm for the afternoon visit pulled out the day before, and lunch was near there, 30 miles out of our way so we had it at the Collingwood Arms at Coldstream – we stayed there for a week about 40 years earlier, and still as good now as it was then. At short notice Alan Goldie arranged for us to visit the Baynes family at "Marleycote" near Slaley. A fantastic herd of Ayrshire and Shorthorn Cattle milked through robots and then looked at the milk processing business marketed under the Northumberland Pedigree Milk name.

Andrew Birkle's "Whinchat" herd was the venue for the Society Premier herd open day not far from Leicester. A tremendously consistent herd of cows, particularly the red ones which were like "peas in a pod". The next Society event was the Convention which this year was held in Northern Ireland as David Perry became President. The Galgorm Hotel and Spa was about 30 minutes' drive from Belfast and was a superb up-market place which specialised in weddings with its own chapel and could cater for up to three weddings in a day. The first visit was to Abercorn and the herd of Messrs Wallace – a good herd of cows by mostly natural service bulls, before going on to the "Simlahill" herd of the McCann family. Whilst I was there, Marnie went on the alternative tour to the nearby Clandeboye Estate to see the gardens, beehives etc. The next day saw us visit the Bushmills Irish Whiskey Distillery for a conducted tour which was very interesting and ended with product sampling, after which we visited the Giants' Causeway. The rocks there are an amazing sight and you wonder how some of them remain standing. Coming back, we were shown the fantastic Black Hedges roadway of trees used in the "Game of Thrones" series.

The lunch for the 100 pints of blood donors was held at Crathorne Hall. I felt a bit of a fraud having given 99 to the Leeds team and only the 100th to the Middlesbrough one. When we arrived, we were told they had a kitchen problem and it was to be afternoon tea instead, which at best could only be described as average.

Laura gathered the two Norwegian girls, Christin and Elisabeth up at Newcastle as she and Ruby came down. Leaving Ruby with us they all headed off to Rudding Park for the weekend for Emma's 50th birthday, Sarah going the next day to join them, and it seems a good weekend was enjoyed by all.

The English Heritage property at Broadsworth Hall near Doncaster was well worth the visit, a lot of work being done on it, with very extensive gardens and the house which was built in the 1860's.

A trip to Beamish Museum in early August was the first time we had visited for about twenty years, and it has certainly developed in those years in between and is now a major tourist attraction in the north east. It was heaving with people and took about 25 minutes to get in, and later about 45 minutes to get our fish and chips for lunch. Laura and the girls were staying with us and they, Ruby in particular really enjoyed it and they marvel at what life used to be like, so different from life today.

Sarah was doing Angus Dean's draft sale at Threshfield in early September, including the catalogues and one day while she was over there clipping we enveloped over 400 of them and took to post – they preferred to label them rather than put a stamp on – the Post office get a bigger commission that way and they rang when they had finished so I could go and pay for them – stamps cost £662.02 and I got a very sharp reply when I asked if there was any discount – not even the two pence.

In late September we got the pork pies and belly pork at Appleton's in Ripon to take up to Scotland, called at Adam's for an hour and then over the very newly opened Forth Road Bridge and to Dundee to stay overnight at the Premier Inn. The morning was spent in Dundee – a very expensive car park at £1.90 for 40 minutes, a lot of development going on by the riverside and a look round the new Discovery centre. We found Bill in good health and drove out along the coast for a while through some of the fishing villages. We then had a drive the next day south of Edinburgh to meet up with Rebecca (Rab) who was with daughter Katrina taking part in the horse vaulting championships, which is basically gymnastics on horseback. As we drove back by Stirling, we called at the Powis Farm Shop/Café which has grown a lot since the Logan's of Holstein fame of years ago had opened it. Unfortunately, John wasn't there to catch up, but it was very busy. Called at Adam's on the way home for Harriet's second birthday party before a slow run home held up by an army convoy over Carter Bar and to Otterburn.

A note in early October, tells me I started to write this book, so it has only taken me two and a quarter years so far, but it won't take me as long to finish it.

Another trip to Beamish without the grand children gave us more time to look at what interested us. We took Muv's old stairs hoover for them, but after a long search for the reception centre, they didn't want it, as they already had 12 of them – and there were we thinking it would by now be quite rare, so had to carry it around the rest of the day.

Then it was off again, this time for a holiday to Italy. We flew from Manchester to Naples on a very clear day, when we could see all the land below us, very interesting and then drove round the Bay of Naples to Sorrento and the Imperial Tramontano Hotel, just off the main square. It was Halloween and they obviously make a lot of it in Italy – all the shops were open with jars of sweets for all the children just to walk in and help themselves. Purely by chance, we realised it was the last performance by the three Tenors (not the famous ones) at 9.30pm, had supper and then to the museum for the performance to about 40 people. They were fantastic as were the acoustics in the very old but very small building before starting our customary cappuccino before bed in the bar with Pepe. A ride round the town on a road train for 35 minutes and that day, a Wednesday was a Bank Holiday as was the rest of the week for All Saint's Day. Much of Sorrento closes down at the end of October for the winter season, and it was strange to see a busy restaurant one day, and it all closed up and in some cases cleared completely the next, they didn't even go to the end of the week. Sorrento is noted for its marquetry and after looking in one or two of their workshops we visited the Marquetry Museum – privately run by a retired architect with three architect sons. He had bought the building as eight apartments and then restored much of it back to its original style, uncovering false ceilings to find the original frescoes, and a false wall to uncover four storeys of a secret stone circular staircase. He had travelled the world buying back furniture made in Sorrento – what a wonderful place. Later that day we had a look at a Limoncello factory – another speciality of the town which we enjoyed sampling.

The following day we sailed over to Capri, the very good skipper sailed us right round the island, which was the best bit, the Blue Grotto was closed because of high tide, but he said we didn't miss much and took us to see a better one not known by many, but it was green. The island and town itself was something of a come down – a glorified Blackpool and it was again noticeable that all the fancy fashion shops had already closed for the winter and some of them had or were clearing out all the clothes etc to take elsewhere for selling.

The day after we were much more impressed by our tour along the Amalfi coast, with its amazing coastline and scenery. Up over the Milky Mountains to Positano, saw all the artists busy along the sea front. On to Amalfi itself and a ride round the Bay of Amalfi to see the picturesque scenery from a different angle. Then to Ravello – famous for its Gelato which was as good as its reputation, along a long narrow passageway which had been originally built to protect the ladies from the invading forces. A coffee at the "Bettys" of Italy before the long twisty ride back.

In Italy all public places such as museums are free to enter on the first Sunday of the month, pity they don't do that here. We were unaware of that until we arrived at Pompeii. We took a train from Sorrento which cost £9.60 return for the two of us, stopping at eight stations in the 35-minute journey but stops right outside the entrance to the ruins. An immensely fascinating day as we walked round some of what had been uncovered, restored and preserved and what is still left to do, remembering that Vesuvius covered it in ash in 79AD, almost 2000 years ago. The murals, tiles and mosaics were to marvel at and that you could touch them or walk on them after all that time. An unbelievable experience and could have spent longer – to stand in the centre of the arena and imagine the chariot racing or the lions there all those years ago!

In early December we went to Harlow Carr to see it lit up at night for the first time, only to discover it was only open Thursday to Saturday nights and this was a Wednesday. Foolish us, we should have checked, but we were by no means the only ones who had done the same. We went a week later on a proper night and it was well worth the visit. We went to the Leeds Arena one night to see Alfie Boe and Michael Ball in concert, another trip that was well worth it, though the nearly one hour to get out of the car park afterwards wasn't so good!

Chapter 27 – The last two years

Not because there is anything special about them, but the story has to end somewhere, and the end of the decade, 2019 seems to be as good a place as any.

It was soon off to New Zealand again in January 2018. We flew with Singapore Airlines rather than Emirates because at the time of booking they were a lot cheaper. Slightly different times and the beauty of that route is that they have a hotel in the airport at Singapore which you can book by the hour. We had done so, and as it was our body clocks bedtime by we got there, straight to bed and a good night's sleep and were as fresh as daisies the next morning. A walk in the butterfly garden within the airport was another excellent idea to pass time and calm people down as they travel, and it was noticeable that everyone in there had a smile on their face.

Len and Mollie were in good fettle and we stayed there the first few days. The first job on day one was to go with Len into Timaru to get a new television as theirs had blown up the day before. Len explained to them that it had done so and although not complaining told them he had got it there, but wouldn't accept it when they had said they didn't and never had stocked that make or model, nor was it on their computer system. A ride out to Fairlie to the dam at Opuha and along the back roads to Washdyke.

After a few days we set off up the main coast road through Christchurch to Kaikoura, which was now open, even if only partially after the earthquake of a couple of years previously. Still some very rough parts to the road and we soon had a puncture, but a young Scotsman working on the roadworks changed the wheel for us – he said it was the sixth he had done in the week – obviously there were bits on the road and when we got a new tyre the next day it had a 2-3 inch piece of metal in it. We stayed at the Panorama Motel which was well named with a fantastic bay view. Also staying were a couple of real old eccentrics from North Island with a 1924 van. Rigged out with a bed in the back and the lady carried a plant or two with them for decoration, plus a spade shovel for the essentials when they were camping out. A pair of real characters.

We toured around Blenheim among the vineyards and by chance came across St. Clair vineyard. We had a very good bottle of theirs the previous weekend, so did some sampling, an English girl looked after us and sold us a bottle at more than it costs in a supermarket. That night in Blenheim we ate at the Bamboo Garden – the best prawns in the lightest batter ever – superb, and the bonus was when we got back home, someone had made a mistake on the visa payment and the supper only cost us 55 pence.

Picton is the ferry port for travelling between the islands, only a small, but attractive town. We then took the short cut but very slow road over the tops to Havelock – it took us nearly 1¾ hours to go the 25 kilometres. Stopped overlooking one of the bays with some terrific views and looking down on a massive wood yard where wood was being got ready for loading onto ships. On the way we also called at a very old, late 1800's wooden cottage which was being kept preserved by local volunteers. The next two nights we stayed in the Palazzo Motel in Nelson, the next day visiting the Miyazu Japanese Gardens, very novel but very peaceful. Down the road the Founder's Museum was much the same as Beamish or Hjerl Hede in Denmark. They had moved and rebuilt buildings from all over the area and laid it out as a small town, at $5 each for about three and half hours, it was hardly expensive.

We visited Queen's Park and then drove along the Tahunanui beach road and back to Nelson for a Big-Mac supper.

The next day we were heading for Greymouth, it was too wet to stop in Richmond, and as we travelled there were trees or branches down in the road, some being cleared by workmen. Coffee and a muffin in Murchison and on towards Westport to turn for Greymouth only to be stopped by council men with road closed signs, so into Westport. It had been hit by high tides and the northern end of the town was flooded so we couldn't go north either. We thought it best to get a motel found quickly ahead of everyone else who would be in the same boat. With the road still blocked the next morning, there was to be no Pancake Rocks this visit, and we had to retrace our tracks for most of 40 kilometres to Lewis Pass and to Hanmer Springs, then to Reefton and on to Amberley to find everywhere was fully booked for the weekend, with a wedding plus opera at one of the wineries being the cause, but eventually found a bed at Woodend.

We headed back via Oxford and Methven to Ashburton as we wanted to look round what we thought would be a very good botanic garden, but it was more of a parkland setting, and as we had our sandwiches watched some cricket matches going on – there were four or five different ones of different ages and abilities going on in different areas of the park – it was the town "domain" rather than Botanic Gardens. Going by Caroline Bay outside Timaru, but there was no sign of any penguins.

Len and Mollie took us to look at Taiko Village Hall where Len is the sort of caretaker – cutting the grass and making various bits of furniture for the bar, stools and cupboards.

Across to Richard Peckitt's, originally from Thirsk with the "ute" to pick Len up after he had taken his tractor for moving the combine header about. I had a ride with Richard on his combine with a 40ft header, chopping the straw and marvelled at all the information coming off the combine computer – the actual yield as it varied across the field, the fuel usage per tonne, the varying moisture as it came through. When he had earlier combined Len's paddock around the bungalow – it is just under 20 acres and the combine travelled 12.6km's to cut it. Amazing what you can now know as you do things.

Off again, south this time, called at Oamaru for lunch – had a sausage roll but won't have another one as they are very spicy and a funny texture. We hadn't realised it was Waitangi Day (Maori National Day) so everywhere nearly was closed, which was great as the next two visits were free entry because it was a public holiday. We called again at the Totara Estate from which the first lamb was frozen and shipped to England all those years ago. Just down the road was Clarke's Mill – full of all the old milling equipment which all runs, though not when the public are present – too many belts etc. and little in the way of guards. Because it was a public holiday, all the volunteers at both places were dressed in the period costume of their times – adding to the interest and atmosphere.

Took a detour to Waikouaiti via the coast with some fantastic views, then through Dunedin to Mosgiel to find a motel for the next couple of nights. A walk round Dunedin's Botanic Gardens the next morning before driving round the Otago peninsula. A beautiful scenic drive for miles along the water's edge, then turned inland for a 3km climb up twisty roads to arrive at Larnach House – the only castle in New Zealand. Right on the highest point with terrific views out over the ocean, it had been completely restored from a ruin, which had been done by the owner with no financial help. We took 4½ hours to look round the house and the tremendous gardens – still more to do, though they are well on with it. We then drove right to the point of the peninsula, but we were too early to see any penguins or albatross.

Down to Balclutha, booked into a motel and then on into the Caitlins and the scenic route down to Nugget Point, and then on to visit Jack's blowhole. A long walk to see them a long way inland for the incoming tide to find a way to relieve the pressure. It is 200m from the coast and 55m deep. The next day through Lawrence, a nice village with some of the local notables of the past depicted on wooden totem poles, one of which was the man who had started the local school and remained as a teacher for 48 years. After going to check on Mitchell's cottage again we went to Alexandria and Cromwell, through the Lindis Pass with some very bleak and unforgiving landscape and down to Kurow. As we travelled that day we saw something we had never seen before, even in New Zealand which is still more relaxed about such things than we are – two dead cows waiting for the knackerman at a drive end – but they had already been skinned, one assumes for the hides – being more valuable – a horrible sight.

Waimate had a farmer's market and we talked to one or two stall holders before the shops closed at noon on a Saturday and all day on a Sunday – good for them – pity we don't do it at home. A terrific bronze sculpture of a miner sat on a bench in the town centre. Down the Esk valley with some good and well farmed land. As we had a bite of lunch on a side road, we watched a helicopter putting fertiliser onto something over the hill – took about four and a half minutes for a round trip including about forty seconds to refill. We went to find them, they were putting 200kg per hectare onto a 20 hectare field of fodder beet which cost about 40-45 New Zealand dollars per hectare which they reckoned was cheaper than the damage they would otherwise do to the crop. What we also found from talking to the farmer, was that the two fields nearby which we didn't know what they were, were actually carrots for seed – which is about a two-year crop. Imagine how many carrots you could grow from about 40 hectares of seed.

Len and Mollie took us on the back roads to Campbell's Castle – no longer in use, a lovely small village which were originally houses for the estate staff, but now owned by the Chinese who seem to be doing nothing with it. Called at Riverdale for coffee, started by a farmer's wife who had developed It Into a high-end garden centre, restaurant and an Aladdin's cave of curios.

To get back to Christchurch we got the Inter City Gold bus in Timaru and it was a great ride in the top front of a double-decker to really see everything around you. We stayed in an old-style boutique hotel – The Grange, another visit to their Botanic Gardens. The next day spent in the city, re-roofing Marnie's little church but still nothing had been done with the Cathedral, then to check that the tempura prawns were still as good at our Japanese restaurant – they were!!

On the way home we were waiting for our change in Singapore and the man we were speaking to – his parents live in Northallerton, and we were also talking to a man from Bury, who was a judge of gun dogs – he knew Wilson Senior and had shot at Eskdale where Adam operates. What a small world!!

In mid-March Marnie had a fortnight of Jury service to do at Middlesbrough – she went on the train from Northallerton each day, sat about all the days, was never called and dismissed at the end of the first week, so she never got to sit on a case at all. I know we need a proper justice system, but there seems to be some scope for tightening up some of the time scales and people involved.

A trip to London in mid-April took us to stay with Emma before we went back to the Aldwych Theatre for our Christmas present from Sarah – Tina Turner the Musical was superb with a very good young lady playing the lead role – it had a very good run for a few months after that before it went to Broadway. The next morning, we walked about half a mile to Sutton House, the oldest house in Hackney which when built had been out in the countryside – very interesting. A trip to and a look round Alexander Palace in the afternoon – on top of a hill would have had superb views over London if it hadn't been so foggy.

We went down to Shrewsbury to view the Perfection Collection sale which was supposed to be ground breaking but it wasn't a lot different except that there was even more hype than usual and you would struggle to know sometimes who was buying and selling what. A massive cost had been put into the staging of the sale, but I don't think anybody would make a lot out of it. They are planning to stage another in spring of 2020, but I don't suppose we shall bother going. We had a bite of supper at the Gingerbread Man at Market Drayton.

On the last day of April, this branch of the Liddle family was assured for another generation when Laura had a little boy, and all was well. No, they didn't call him Sam (see the first line of the book) but he is called Freddy.

The Tour de Yorkshire Cycle race has become quite a feature of the early spring calendar and in 2018 the start one day was from Richmond and we watched it all on the television until the leaders got to Patrick Brompton when we walked round the corner to watch them go past us on the Northallerton road, with one solitary rider 2½ minutes ahead of the field. I counted 26 police motor bikes, 8 police cars and 6 ambulances with the race – I know some are necessary but that is total overkill and a terrific waste of valuable resources. The following day they came from South Yorkshire somewhere, over the top to Middleham, then via Masham and Kirkby Malzeard to Pateley Bridge, the gruesome climb up Greenhow to finish somewhere about Skipton. The scenery shown on the television is fantastic and is more interesting when you know the roads fairly well, but it does provide a great boost for the local economy and ultimately brings visitors to see our great county.

Newcastle Falcons had had a good 2017-18 season and to most people's surprise and I think even theirs, they finished the season fourth in the league which meant they qualified for the playoffs, though that was an away game against Exeter Chiefs. We wanted to continue our support and so travelled down there for the game staying at Worcester on the way there and back. The match itself was something of a disappointment, the Falcons never got or kept enough possession to have much impact and were well beaten 36-5. On the way back on the Sunday, we called at Ashby-de-la-Zouch to visit its castle as part of English Heritage, just a ruin and not a lot to see except an underground passage. We then visited, as we came north, Bolsover Castle, partly restored, much more interesting and from high up some great views over the Derbyshire landscape.

A few days later, Bill, Martin Webster and I had a good day up at I'Ansons at Masham. Martin was a big seller to them of peas and naked oats and Howard Jackson who had worked for us for about eight years from being 16 until he went to them and worked his way up to being a director and one of the main buyers had been pestering us to go for a long time. We had a fascinating few hours with him as he took us on a very informative private tour of the facilities. I had not realised just how big a business they now are, also producing own label products for other companies. Mostly fuelled by gas and Howard told us that their gas bill the previous year was just over £1 million – makes mine look small!! We then had a bite of lunch at the White Bear and a good talk. Sadly, that was the last time I had any talk with Howard, and it was with a real sadness we went to his funeral not much more than a year afterwards when life had all become too much for him, what a waste.

A happier time was at the end of May at Richard and Hannah Barker's wedding at Burneston on a glorious sunny day and then back to the reception in the fields at the back of their house.

The North Eastern Club day trip was up in Scotland, and we took Karen Hutchinson and Mr Bill with us. A good run up to Dumfries and to the Meiklefirth herd of David Yates at Haugh of Urr, which he runs with the great help of his two daughters, and his father David whom we have known for many years was on hand to save Bill walking and keep them all in order. Lunch in the village pub run by David's wife and third daughter before going across the valley to his brothers. Brian and son Michael run the Logan herd in a set of new and very smart buildings and we admired their potential show team for the summer. When we got back home, we went for supper on Karen's recommendation to the Shoulder of Mutton at Middleton Tyas – very good, never eaten there before but will do again should the need arise – there are so many good eating places around us, and with eating regularly on our trips to Scotland, we don't go out to eat around home as we used to.

Another unusual birthday present was enjoyed by Marnie when she went for a day's wirework, and she made a duck with chicken netting all crunched up. For a first-time effort it was very good, and "Oscar" now stands guard at the corner of the shrubbery.

The Holstein Convention was held over in East Yorkshire for Peter Waring coming in as President, based at the Castle Cave Hotel at South Cave. The first trip was to the large beef unit of Messrs Liversidge and Sons – rearing mostly dairy cross calves and some pure breds – interesting to see a different section of the industry – the ladies had gone on a conducted tour of York and we all joined up for lunch at the "Newbirks" herd of David and Claire Lawson at Arthington, close by the original home of the now dispersed "Creskeld" herd. A tremendous herd of cows which had won the Yorkshire Club competition the previous year. The evening's entertainment was a brass band ensemble who were very good. Second day was to the Winton herd of Peter and James Waring and families where they have also just begun to market fresh milk from a machine on farm. We should have seen the Atkinson Horses later, but due to the BBC altering the filming schedule for filming "Victoria" that was cancelled and we had a coach run across the Wolds and to the Wold Top Brewery – on farm and started by looking for a better price for their barley and now developed over 15 years into a fairly large concern.

The Holstein UK Premier Herd open day was up at Brewster's "Boclair" herd on the outskirts of Glasgow, a large turnout as it also included the Scottish Clubs Judging Competition. A good day in glorious sunshine, we got called away and drove over to the other side to look after the girls as Freddy had to go into hospital for a hernia operation – all went well and he was soon home.

The early summer of 2018 was very hot and dry with large parts of the country almost in drought. We had not suffered quite as badly here, as at the start of the long sunny spell we had about a week of hazy, east coast weather and so not exposed to as much sun. This was really brought home to us when we delivered some food for Sarah over to near Skipton for a Kite meeting and over the tops and down into that area, everywhere was brown and burnt off, much worse than around home. Fortunately, the weather broke with them before us, and in an area like that it was soon green again with all the heat in the ground. Farming wise it left everybody rather short of silage, though nature has a great way of balancing things out, and a very good open autumn and early winter meant stock were out longer, and though expensive, most got through without shortages of fodder.

An interesting evening in late summer took us up to Bishop Auckland to see the Kynren spectacle – a massive production involving about 1500, mostly local, participants. Very extravagantly choreographed with fantastic lighting effects. Well worth a visit, though there are questions as to whether it will be staged again, only so many nights a week in late summer – it has to be dark when it is performed to create the dramatic effect.

The Darlington and Stockton Times always feature a walk every week – we nearly always look at them, some are in areas we know and most of them are longer than we, or rather I , want to do, but one caught our attention and so we set off to do it and had a great day. Leaving the car in Arncliffe, the walk took us up Littondale along the riverbank and into the small village of Litton. A break at the pub in the village before the walk back by the road – about 4½ miles in total. A marvellous walk in peaceful surroundings and great scenery. Another good day out was to Scampston Hall walled garden, the other side of Malton. The garden has all been restored back to the layout it used to have centuries ago.

After another season of helping to assemble the CIS diaries it was time to deliver a carload to their offices at Telford when we went down for the UK Dairy Day. Saw a lot of old friends and acquaintances as we moved about, had a long talk with Dave Hampson on the For Farmers stand and also with Wynne Morris who had been their chief nutritionist adviser but has now left them to be Chief Executive of Crystalix. Champion on the day was a super second calver Davlea Bradnick Alicia, followed in Reserve by the second in its class Riverdane Ashlyns Gold from Evening Holsteins.

At Stokesley Show in late September I did the commentary on the cattle classes for the first time and also in the main ring at the time of the trophy presentations. John Seymour, who had done the job for many years is due to be President next year and so was showing me the ropes this year as he won't be able to do it next year, and I think wanted to give it up anyway. All went well although, sadly John didn't get much of a retirement as he passed away in the Autumn of 2020.

An interesting stop on the way up to Dundee to look round Belsay Hall and Gardens. We usually stop at Belsay for coffee as we go to Adam's and never have the time to go to the hall but made time this day. It is a big plain house with very little inside, but interesting in that it is all built from stone quarried in the grounds which was subsequently converted into a walk through garden with some unusual plants, a particularly previously unseen one was the American Pokeweed. The following day when up visiting Bill Gayford we went to the newly opened Victoria and Albert art centre – the first one outside London, very busy, very modern and open, there was an absorbing "history of design" exhibition. As we came home the following day, and the timing was right for the tide, we went across to Holy Island and had a drive round Lindisfarne.

We had a very enjoyable evening at Harrogate International Centre to see James Martin cooking and talking. He was very good, very entertaining with a completely laid-back manner and not at all full of himself as some of these 'celebrities' are.

The 2019 Semex Conference was another good couple of days with some very good papers from NFU President Minette Batters, DEFRA Minister George Eustice, Sue McCloskey from Fair Oaks in America, Ash Amirahmadi from Arla and Tom Levitt a food magazine editor. All very interesting.

A Sunday afternoon outing took us up to Tennant's at Leyburn where they had a Darlington and Stockton Times photo exhibition from the Dales over the years – very good, and while we were there we were stood outside and watched the special steam train – the recently built Tornado come past which was linked in with the fly past tour of the Tornado aircraft as they were being removed from service.

Our final trip for this book began towards the end of February with a tour to Australia with Bay Farm Tours. Manchester to Dubai and on to Melbourne, it's the hanging about in airports and the security checks which make it so long – they must have thought Marnie was hiding something in her clothes as she kept getting stopped for explosive checks! A guided tour of the city was interesting including the garden's where Captain Cook's cottage had been rebuilt after moving from Great Ayton. Looking right across the city from the War Memorial there was a face on the end of a new large block of flats – very cleverly created by the verandahs.

On the Monday morning we had about 1½ hours coach ride out of the city to a beef farm, mostly Angus cattle and watched them use a moveable pen on the side of a 'ute' to catch a calf and tag it without too much trouble. We visited the old Gold Town with some very old, reconstructed buildings.

Next morning was a short 55-minute hop over to Tasmania and into its capital Hobart. Our first visit was to the courtroom, including the hanging chamber. The last person hung there was in 1946, Fred Thompson, but as far as we know no relation to Marnie and certainly not her Uncle Fred. The doomed person was allowed three visitors before hanging, the doctor to say he was fit to hang, the priest for prayers and the judge. The hangman's noose always had 13 coils round it to signify the 12 jurors plus the judge. After that we travelled out to their Botanic Gardens before visiting the small village of Richmond, which boasts the oldest bridge in Australia dated 1641. They tried to tell us it had never been touched since, but it looked to me as if it had been re-pointed in the last couple of years!! We then travelled up a very twisty, tight, and at times steep road to Mount Wellington – the highest point to look down over the city with fantastic views.

Next morning off to David Taylor's large sheep farm, plus quite a large arable acreage, including poppies and hemp, both for medical use. I always thought the poppy seed was the important bit, but it is the bits in the seed head and the top of the stalk which is valuable. The first time he had grown hemp – it has male and female plants, the male one grows more quickly before shedding its seed and then dying off and the female one is later harvested for medicinal marijuana and quinoa. Only a remarkable 110 days from sowing to harvesting.

On then to Launceston at the northern end of the Island before the next day visiting the Armidale Stud where they paraded three stallions and told us a bit about the business. Interestingly the eldest offspring by the middle aged stallion Alpine Eagle was going over the next day to race at Melbourne for the first time. He did and won so got an automatic wild card entry into the new big multi-million-pound race two weeks later – and went on and won that as well. We then went to a dairy farm where the man was just as unpleasant as everyone else had been pleasant. Totally anti-British and had a snipe at every opportunity. Having said that, he was obviously very successful, milking 4500 cows on five units, with a super central young stock unit. They made cheese and ice-cream which had both apparently been started by his sister, though he never acknowledged the fact.

Next day we visited the largest lavender farm in the southern hemisphere, but they had not laid on a specialist guide which was rather disappointing when they knew we were a group of agriculturists. On to Barnbougle for lunch on a double golf course totally created among the sand dunes and overlooking the sea. A new experience when we got back to the hotel – the lift stopped about 3-4 feet after setting off and when we notified them on the emergency button it was some company based elsewhere and it took them about forty minutes to get an engineer there, force a door half open and get us out – didn't bother us, though one or two got a bit wound up. What tickled me was that the barman from along the corridor who was the first to the lift door, when they eventually got it open and some steps to climb down on, he was helping everyone, still with his white tea towel neatly folded over his arm. The hotel itself had originally been a hospital and despite a very good transformation was still all corridors with doors off it everywhere.

Back to Melbourne overnight and then the next day to Holbrook to meet up with the farming families we were to stay with overnight. Dick and Jenny Turnbull had a 2500 acre farm and Dick took us on a ride round the holding – saw plenty of kangaroos which are a nuisance for the farmers as they burrow under the sheep netting on the fences rather than jumping over them, so they are all to go round before sheep can be put back in. It was very hot and very dry there, before we made our way to Arbury to look at the new Auction Mart. They had travelled the world to look at others before construction, in many ways like the Liniers one in Buenos Aires, just a lot more modern.

We then flew to Sydney and the following morning a tour of the city included a walk and a paddle on Bondi Beach, which was nowhere near as large as we imagined, then a fascinating tour of the Opera House. The opera Turandot was being performed that night I discovered, but no one else was interested and as we had already booked for a trip to the Blue Mountains early the next morning and the tickets were £160 each, we didn't go, one of the disappointments as you can't get much more iconic on the world stage than to see an opera at the Sydney Opera House.

As I write this now in early 2020, after the devastating fires of the last few weeks in Australia, we were fortunate to do a one day tour in the Blue Mountains before they were devastated as they will take several years to return to what they were. We went through a forest of gumtrees, we also saw the massive rock outcrops of the 3 Sisters and "Little Dave". Cable Car ride, walked for half an hour in the temperate rain forest and then in what was called the steepest passenger railway in the world, though it was really more of a lift than a railway. To Featherdale Wildlife Park, saw the koalas but they are very unsociable, nearly always asleep with their backs turned on you, saw some birds of all shapes, colours and sizes, the most noticeable was the very striking cassowary.

We didn't do the climb up and over the Sydney Harbour Bridge, but did walk to the end and got the elevator up onto It and walked over and back across it, it is about a kilometre long, walked through the "rocks" the oldest part of the city, before an early night as we were off early the next morning to fly to Cairns, which also had an hour's time difference. I had no idea it was such a centre of the sugar cane industry and we visited a large farm and contractor who explained its management and importance in the area with thousands of acres of it, and small, narrow, dedicated rail lines to the factories. The harvesting machine looked like a cross between a forager and a potato harvester and apparently cost about £350,000.

We visited a beef farm, pedigree Brangus which is a stabilised American breed at 62.5% Angus and 37.5% Brahman to cope with the heat and the flies. There we had a drink and some dumper cake – so called as in olden days it was cooked on the fire as it was going out. No trip to the area would be complete without going out to the Great Barrier Reef – it was certainly worth going to see it, but was a bit disappointing – I suppose you watch it on some of the nature programmes on the television where the lighting and colours are fantastic, but it is not quite replicated – though we did see some from the glass bottomed boat or the observation deck. It was interesting while in Cairns to watch as dusk fell thousands of the large fruit bats fly off across the bay. We enquired where and why they were going and the reaction from most people was "why do you want to know that", but we never got an explanation. The following day at the Aborigine Park we saw dancers, took part in spear and boomerang throwing, saw how to play a didgeridoo before a long ride up and over the forest canopy on a monorail to Kurunda and then a train journey back down to Freshwater through some superb scenery. We ate out that night and sampled both kangaroo and crocodile meat – but don't think we will bother again – both were rather tough and chewy.

A 2½ hour flight early next day took us to Ayers Rock and the "Sails in the Desert" hotel. We visited the actual rock, but rather like the Great Barrier Reef we had perhaps expected too much, and it is what it is – a great big red rock – though I acknowledge its great significance to the Aborigines. We didn't go onto it, and from that autumn it is not going to be allowed for anyone to climb on it, other than the native men. That night and the next morning we went to see the sunset and sunrise over Ayers Rock which didn't do a great deal for me – I have seen equally good or better sunsets from our own front garden. I thought we were in the wrong place to see them at their best, but they were the sites set up for such so I assume it was the best.

We then had a 500km drive from Ayers Rock to Alice Springs, calling at a big million-acre farm en-route. Murray Grey cattle plus a petrol station, restaurant, rooms to let, they said there was more money in diversity than farming. The two children attended school on the "school of the air". It was interesting to hear about the problems they have in the outback with the wild camels – a couple of years previously they and the government had shot almost 2000 in a fortnight around New Year. That long journey made you realise just how large and bare the outback is – vast areas of nothingness. We visited the Aborigine Desert Park, watched a tremendous display of birds of prey, were fascinated by some of the insects and snakes in the nocturnal house, and then visited Standby Chasm. Alice Springs itself felt a little bit more run down than some of the towns, but I suppose that was more its situation, and a lot of the native Aborigines wandering the streets – they felt a bit intimidating as they always seemed to be in twos or threes as if they were hunting in a pack.

A visit to the Telegraph Museum where the first overland telegraph lines were operated. Alice Springs was named after the wife of Charles Todd, but sadly she was never there. We then went to the "School of the Air" where the children are taught by air all over central Australia. Eleven teachers operate from 8.30am to 3.30pm with the children having two hours of actual teaching time with the rest home study with a tutor. Currently they have 105 pupils.

Whilst travelling we had seen one or two of their giant road trains carrying all sorts of things, they are quite alarming with the "swagger" they have when travelling at full speed. We had a fascinating visit to Tanami Road Train depot and a long talk with the boss – the first time they had ever had a tour visit. A full train costs about £1¼ million, 160 cattle per train it takes about one kilometre to stop properly when loaded. The drivers last about ten years, pay is about £150,000 a year, and by then they have made enough to do something else, or have become alcoholics.

A two-and-a-half-hour flight to Adelaide was on a clear, sunny day meaning we could see the land below us all the way. Thousands of acres of absolutely nothing other than salt beds, Lake Eyre was virtually dry, they have had no real rain around there for nearly seven years.

Adelaide was a coach tour of the city with a very good guide, much the nicest place we have been in, very wide avenues with a lot of trees and parks. It was the last weekend of their "Fringe" so was very busy. That was the end of the tour and the group left that evening to go back for a spell in Dubai, so we bid them farewell before we stayed for another night before leaving the next morning. It seemed a bit silly when we were so close not to go to New Zealand to see Len and Mollie. Unfortunately there is no direct flight Adelaide to Christchurch so had to go to Auckland and then down to Christchurch which took a big lump of the day and we didn't get there until about 11.30pm, without as much problem as we thought there might be – it was just the day after the terrorist attack with the mass shooting in a Mosque. Len and Mollie picked us up the next morning and we went back with them to Rolling Ridges Road.

A couple of days later whilst visiting Timaru's Botanic Gardens, we were admiring the very colourful display of dahlias in one of the borders which also had quite a few Monarch butterflies on them. As we did so, a friendly cat wandered past us and in among the dahlias before suddenly jumping up about four foot and caught a butterfly which meant it wasn't so friendly, nor was it the first time it had done so by the skill it displayed.

As we toured again, Lake Tekapo was almost overrun by Chinese and Japanese, but like everywhere else in the world, they are building like mad. Another first that night when the only bed we could find in Wanaka was a caravan – and I'm not built for caravan living. Travelling alongside the Tasman Sea the following day up past Franz

Josef and Fox Glacier country to stay for a couple of nights at Hokitika. Just outside the town the shanty town Is a fantastic living museum including a train ride into the jungle where they had cleared timber many years ago, some very old buildings had been brought here and re-constructed. A visit up to Pancake Rocks and then back down to Kumara and Marnie spotted on the map a place called "Londonderry Rock" and being from there originally wanted to visit. A rock it certainly was, apparently it weighed about 400 tonnes and much of it was in the ground – had a walk round it and there was nothing else of any significance.

Peel church which we had visited previously and had been badly damaged by the earthquake has now been restored which was so good to see in such a tranquil setting. The church is within the grounds of the estate originally owned by the Acland family, and the churchyard is occupied by mostly their family, staff from the estate and friends who wanted it to be their final resting place, which included the well-known author Ngaio Marsh.

After a couple of weeks getting back to normal routine after our long trip, we had a night out to Harrogate to see Alfie Boe in concert. He was very good, and the support act was an interesting story. Hattie Briggs was busking at one of the London stations as Alfie headed home one evening. He heard her singing but hadn't time to talk other than to get her contact details. He rang her once home and offered her the chance to be the support act on his tour, and she didn't let him down.

A totally random paragraph but in the midst of quiet weeks at home, we watched a fascinating programme on the television one night, which was about the earth viewed from space. The one fact which really struck home was that in a year, 27 million tonnes of sand is blown from the Sahara across and onto the Amazonian rain forest. Having been on the Sahara and witnessed how it moves, I can believe it, but not that amount or that distance. Our universe never ceases to amaze!!

The Tour de Yorkshire was in the area again, and Bedale was the finish one day for both the men's and women's races. It brought a lot of people into the area for a few days, though it was almost impossible to get into the town on that day. Unfortunately, the weather didn't help, and the heavens opened when the cyclists were about at Carthorpe on their way to the finish. Again, you see the racing and the local countryside much better on the television, particularly the shots and sequences from the helicopter. The following day the race came via Kilnsey, over the tops to Middleham and back by Masham to Pateley Bridge.

Through this quiet spring spell, Adam and family were here a couple of nights and a bit later Laura brought the children down for a few days, by then Adam was back very busy as the rearing season was underway again. Great to have them though never enough. We go up about every three weeks for the day, though I haven't written it in here other than if something out of the ordinary happens. Again, once a year I take a big bunch of lilac up to Hudswell to visit Dennis Courtney, a former partner in KPMG, whom I referred to all those years ago when I was a new manager and told him it was a funny way to go on buying two new tractors when you were losing money. We have remained friends ever since and keep in regular contact. The lilac was originally some he took for his late wife who's favourite it was, and the annual ritual has continued for about the last 25 or 30 years, sadly Dennis passed away in April 2020.

Over the months and years we have done a lot of jobs to help Sarah with her business, Marnie more than me as catering has often been involved, either as an extra pair of hands or doing the job if Sarah was busy with something else. One which really stands out was at the end of May. The two Sarah's had both set off for Jersey after doing the catering most of the week for Bishopton Vets at Bank's at Coxwold where they were training a group of Russians who were the equivalent of the field officers which most of our milk buyers employ, and they were the second largest dairy group in Russia, part owned by Pepsi Cola. They had earlier in the week asked for lamb, had had lamb sandwiches one day and on this one had lamb-burgers amongst other things. Apparently, they very rarely get lamb at home and were all very grateful for the efforts made to give them it. That seemed to us like a potential export opportunity. The following week, Marnie was again helping Sarah at Northern Sheep over near Settle, when they were doing hot beef and pork rolls for l'Ansons. I went along as the logistics man, and during the day enquired on one or two stands to be explained that some exports had begun a few years previously but had soon fizzled out as the backhanders required (usual trade format in Russia) became too large to become economic.

Down to London for another birthday present to the Theatre Royal on Haymarket to see "Only Fools and Horses - the musical" which was very well choreographed to stay true to the original situation comedy but with odd twists to keep it different. Riding through London on the top deck of a bus after midnight is quite a revelation to country people – the place is almost more alive than it is during the day. The next day Emma took us to Shoreditch and the "Sky Garden" which has apparently been there about five years. Up on the 36th floor for lunch with amazing views right over London as we had lunch even though it was a bit murky.

One Saturday I was going with Sarah to a farm sale as there was a cattle crush in it which was of interest to her. What made it of interest to me was that it was Alan Firth's dispersal sale at Middlesmoor. Alan, who had succeeded my Father as tenant of Ivy House Farm, had sadly died and only had daughters, so no one to follow him. Off we went by Masham to go over the tops to Lofthouse. There was a sign just out of Masham saying the road was being re-surfaced, but as all the other traffic was carrying on and it was a Saturday morning, we assumed it to be open. We got right on to the tops, almost onto Lofthouse Moor when we came upon the road gang. Although in Sarah's truck we could easily have got up the roadside, they wouldn't let us past – health and safety issue you know, although it annoyed me that they let a group of cyclists through, though they had to dismount and walk past. So, we turned round and by the time we got back to almost Masham to go a different way it was going to be too late, so we came home. Interestingly, as I write this in early 2020, the wheel goes round, and next week, with Sarah away elsewhere, Marnie and I are going to do a lunch for her up at Middlesmoor Village Hall.

The RABDF Gold Cup Open Day was a local trip for us this year, which made quite a change. Metcalfe Farms up at Leyburn had won in 2018 and it was a glorious, sunny day and a massive crowd of approaching 2000 people to witness this large diverse business alongside the 1200 or so cows they manage. A lot of people we knew from all over the country, so a lot of talking to be done.

Then up to Scotland to stay at Dunbar overnight. I had always assumed that town to be a fairly dull, industrial sort of a place, but we were pleasantly surprised by its rugged coastline round the bay and wide-open main street. After staying overnight with Jayne and Chris and a very good meal at The Rocks, we went the next day up to Dundee for Bill (Jayne's father) Gayford's ninetieth birthday party at the Rufflets Hotel just outside St. Andrews, where a good lunch was had by everyone. As we travelled up to Dundee we called at a farm shop for a coffee, I decided to have an ice-cream instead and ordered two scoops of rum and raisin and we were amused when they brough it in two separate dishes – obviously thinking it was for two different people. We came back by and stayed overnight at Lauder to spend the Sunday with Adam and family.

A fascinating evening followed the next week with a North Eastern Club meeting visit to the Genus bull stud at Whenby Lodge. It was interesting to see many of the layoff bulls members had used, the majority of them all genomic ones. As a breeder I found it rather sobering that so many of these bulls are now actually bred 'in house' by their top genomic bulls out of females they own or control, many of which have never as yet had a calf. Multiply up this control by the other American studs and Semex doing the same in Canada, and the breeder has almost lost control of the breeding.

Next stop was Llanelli for the Holstein UK Convention to welcome in Brian Thomas as President for the next year. We had known Brian for many years and his Gelliddu herd. He had been one of the main joint owners of Collycroft Aladdin whom Herdwise had marketed some 25 years previously, and he and I had sat together on the Holstein Board at the turn of the Millennium, Brian majoring on Show and Sale while I looked after Finance. Then only a few years ago, we were on the same Bay Farm Tours trip to South America. Just as we were leaving that morning to go to South Wales, sister Mary dropped a bit of a bombshell by telling us that they were selling up in Ripon and moving over to Lytham St Annes to an apartment where they will be a lot nearer Samantha and her children, grand-children and great grand-children.

First visit was to the Prairie herd of the Davies family – an amazing story. He has been on or owned about 25 farms in this country, Canada and America and still only mid-forties. A lot of them he had bought cheaply, done up, modernised and sold them on, with the help of his wife and family. Now a fantastic set up housing about 800 cows, immaculately maintained both cows and buildings. They have been there about ten years and he is getting itchy feet again as he needs another challenge and is fancying South America this time. A horse racing stud farm in the afternoon was a good visit with just a young man doing his job very well.

Next morning to Cross Hands to visit Castell Howell Foods. The owner was a contemporary of Brians, farming on a small family farm when milk quotas arrived, and he diversified into food deliveries. In 30 years, it has become Wales' largest food distributor with a £140m/year turnover employing over 800 staff. Still family owned and run, including its own butchery and bakery units, it takes in loads of many products and splits them up into individual deliveries to shops, hotels, farm shops etc – with about 1800 customers all over Wales and the South West. Back to Brian's for lunch and a look round some of his cows which were out in a field, though normally housed all the time. After the AGM we had a very good dinner followed by the Carmarthen Male Voice Choir – you wouldn't expect anything else in South Wales, and a couple of good individual solos.

As we travelled home, we called in Abergavenny for a bite of lunch, but as we got there were staggered by the roadworks making a dual carriageway through the hills – must have cost or is costing a fortune. Whilst in the town we were pointed to the high-end Ladies Clothing and Wedding Shop owned and run by Marion Williams who had run Semen World for her father before it was sold, and it was they who had given Sarah her first job after leaving university.

Mid-July was an interesting evening when for once it was clear and we saw the partial eclipse of the moon. It was so clear, and we could just watch it from the comfort of our chairs in the living room.

The North Eastern Club summer evening was this year hosted by the Crozier family up in Durham, when they put on a fantastic display of 30 cows in full milk, fastened in yokes for the six from 30 and it was very difficult, any permutation would have been difficult to argue against, but we did win two of the other competitions - identifying the cheeses and the town anagrams.

We had an eventful evening soon afterwards. We had been looking for a while for a play shed to give Ruby, Harriet and Freddy. Sarah had located one at Marske and we went to collect it in her trailer one Friday evening. Calling to get some bales of straw out of the field at Martin Petch's on the way we got caught in a heavy shower there, but it was nothing compared to what we endured later. It was fine by we found the house in the back streets of Marske. The playhouse was in the back garden with only a very narrow passageway, so it was to take to pieces though the man suggested getting it up and over the roof of the garage, but that was a non-starter. The play house had only been recently put up by the man to make a superior kennel for his dog, but the dog had taken one look at it and refused to even go in for a look – hence the sale. He had made a really good job of fitting it up and re-fitting it but had put screws and nails in every conceivable place. We had just nicely started on the demolition of it when the heavens opened, we had one spell with Sarah, Marnie and I all inside undoing what we could in there. It became obvious that the rain wasn't going to stop so we had no alternative but to get on, and by we got it loaded up we were all like drowned rats. By now it was well past teatime, so we called at a very busy fish and chip shop in Redcar to get our supper, and going on the number of people queuing and staff in the place, everybody else though they were good as well. We eventually took it up to Scotland, but that's another story. This was about the start of the very wet spell that seemed to last pretty well from July to December – one of the wettest autumns I have ever recorded – large acreages of winter corn, more so further down country, have never been sown.

It was only a few days later that there was a cloud burst up above Leyburn and Wensleydale suffered so badly with floods with roads and bridges destroyed and Leyburn and Reeth both badly flooded.

We had never visited a food festival before, so later that weekend we went to the much-hyped one at Saltburn, thinking there would be a lot of demonstrations and promotional stalls, but it was really just a food selling opportunity which was absolutely heaving with people but still an interesting trip.

Laura and the children were down for a few days during the summer holidays and they went to Newby Hall for the day while I went with Sarah down to Barnowl Jerseys of the Reader family for the Jersey Open Day and AGM – made a change to look round a different breed. We went back to Newby Hall a week or two later when you could see things much more easily without children and also had a guided tour of the house – it has been very well restored and maintained and has some magnificent design work by Robert Adam and furniture by Thomas Chippendale.

We took Bill Gayford over for a ride on the Embsay, Bolton Abbey steam train, which was very busy, but none of us were too impressed by either the quality of the train or the scenery on the eight-mile journey. We called for lunch at Keelham Farm Shop on the auction mart roundabout at Skipton and were much more impressed with it.

A year soon seems to have passed and its back to UK Dairy Day and CIS diaries to make up and then deliver. We went this time by Derby and onto the A5, calling at the Bradford Arms at Aston Wheaton to return Malcolm Watson his autobiography which he had left me when he had visited some weeks previously with an American friend. The only reason for such a one-off place to meet was that they were holding a college reunion lunch, which seemed to be lasting quite well as it was by then gone 3 o'clock. The show the next day was again a great event with good cows and the championship going to Robert Butterfield with Newbirks Jazz 1584. We stayed that night at the Roman Way Hotel at Cannock -don't think we'll bother going there again. Nearby is the English Heritage maintained Boscobel House – never heard of it, though it has an important place in English history. It is where Charles II hid in the oak tree to avoid capture by Oliver Cromwell's troops, the guide had Marnie down in the priest hole under the floor boards and the house was well hidden, even now among woodland, so must have been difficult to find all those years ago – one tree among so many. Across country then into Cheshire and the RHS partner garden at Tatton Park and a long walk round the very large arboretum and gardens – the walled veg garden a bit untidy but the rest was immaculate and the Italian garden stunning when looked down upon.

A ride out on one of the better days of the autumn took us up over Sutton Bank to Malton, which like everywhere else, has houses being built all around it, had our picnic lunch at Sledmere and then toured around the Wolds. We stopped at York on the way back and watched the new Downton Abbey film – very well made and good, harmless entertainment before calling at Sweet Basil for a very good Thai supper.

The UCI World Cycling Championships were being held in the area towards the end of September. They were based in Harrogate, but various events were around the region. Northallerton was the starting point one day for the World Time Trial and we walked round the corner to watch them come past our road end. A time trial is a bit like watching paint dry as they come past individually at intervals, so it was soon back to watch it on the television. It amazes me that they can cycle from Northallerton, Bedale, Masham and via Grantley, Ripley and a couple of circuits around Harrogate to finish in such a quick time. They were lucky that day as the weather was not too bad, but the rest of the week they had torrential rain and on the last day of the week had to abandon part of the course up around Reeth as they were again flooded.

Another wet day was doing some lunch for Sarah while she was away working in Jersey. The Jerry Green Dog's Sanctuary at Catton have various charity days and we were doing hot beef, pork or sausage rolls, but it hardly ceased raining all morning after a very wet spell, and hardly anyone turned up, about 30 instead of the expected 100, and most of those were staff or volunteer helpers.

I wasn't doing a lot of jobs at this time as the Rugby World Cup was in progress from Japan, and all the matches were at odd times through the day. There were some interesting and exciting games such as Japan beating Ireland in the opening game. England were superb in beating New Zealand in the semi-final, but never got into the game against South Africa in the final. In among these games we were away for a few days to Norway to stay at Elisabeth and Tore's and Christin came down from Bergen for a couple of them. A visit to Stavanger and the Oil Museum gave a great insight into that industry which is so important within their economy. Interestingly, the environmentalists over there are suggesting they should abandon it – how can they when something like 75% of their GDP is in the oil industry, and the do-gooders have not suggested any alternatives. Remember Norway, because of its oil industry is one of the richest countries in the world with one of the highest standards of living. The next day Tore and Christoffer took me to see an ice-hockey match at the stadium in Stavanger – they are having a very good season in the Norwegian league, winning this one 4-0. It is very fast and furious but gets a bit monotonous, but also with a lot of stops and starts. It took nearly 2¼ hours to play three 20-minute periods. I wasn't too impressed as we set off back when a car shot out in front of us to get in the queue, but when Tore said he owned the team and had built the stadium, I though he was maybe entitled to jump the queue.

I went over to Barton near Preston for Jim Burrow from "Stardale" funeral. He was ninety nine but it is many years since I remember he and his wife staying with us after he had judged the herds competition and them bringing an Easter egg for Sarah when she was only little, and we had remained in touch all the time, his son Robert and I were on the Holstein Board together and we had bought a Vaakje cow from them many years previously. Met a lot of people I knew so quite a lot of talking, one farmer in particular said they had already had 12 inches of rain so far in October and it was only the 18th, we think we have been wet!

Back to the saga of the play shed. We took it up to Lauder towards the end of October and got it almost finished before the rain came, apart from a couple of bits of wood on the roof edges. With the trailer on the back of Sarah's truck we set off back in good time and all went well until nicely out of Otterburn towards Belsay when we suddenly lost all power halfway up a hill and on a bend and couldn't go again – felt as if the clutch had gone, and so it proved. We got hold of the support team from Sarah's contract hire company and after an hour and a half a breakdown truck eventually arrived. It was a fairly hairy place to be stopped and there seemed to be a lot more traffic than we usually saw on that stretch of road. The mechanic got the trailer loosed off, the vehicle winched up onto the breakdown lorry and the trailer onto the back to get us onto a layby where he rigged up the lights etc onto the trailer and brought us back home. Another first like being stuck in the lift six months earlier – riding home in the back of a breakdown truck, but we were glad to be home and safe, even if we had to give up our Fratelli supper in Ponteland and make do with a Macdonald's at Leeming Bar about midnight.

Over to Carlisle for the first part of Tony Brough's "Tallent" dispersal – he was joint owner with John Pickford of the dam of the great Picston Shottle. As we went, we had to divert off the A66 to get past Penrith which on a lovely sunny morning was a super ride through the grounds of Lowther Castle. We were lucky up as far north as this weather-wise - there had been torrential rain and widespread floods in South Yorkshire, Notts and Lincs. We seem to have been very lucky over the years in missing them in this part of the world, and as I write this in early February 2020, we have had another very wet weekend of nearly 1½ inches, but nothing compared to the floods over in Appleby and also the Yorkshire Dales.

I was in Bedale one day and as I came back past the charity shop I glanced at the books on the table outside and there I spied what we had been searching for, for quite a long time. We have an AA Book of the Countryside which we will have had for about forty years, but much of it is still relevant and it has been out of print for many years. Ruby is very interested in natural history and is always asking questions about such things as shells or birds and we thought it would be ideal for her to do her own reading about things when she gets the book. It was in great condition and still had the outside dust cover on it so had been very little used.

Another mornings 'job' was down at the Agriculture Centre at Thirsk Auction Mart. Alex Welch from Askham Bryan who had been in charge of Stuart when he did his apprenticeship with us about 10 or 12 years ago, rung to ask for my help. They have newly revamped the apprenticeship scheme which now concludes with an oral exam with an outside examiner and wanted me to act as an outsider with some of the students to give them some experience. It wasn't a big job and I saw three interesting young men who want to make their future in livestock farming, though I think quite a bit of the new scheme is way off the mark in sensible, practical usage.

The Christmas Fayre at Tennants in Leyburn was something of a revelation to us, never having been to one before, you could hardly move in the place. We had planned to go the previous day, but things had cropped up to stop us, though we had planned it as we thought the Friday would be quieter. We met somebody there who said it was a good job we hadn't as it was even busier than the Saturday with several coach parties from all over the place. At night we went up to the testimonial dinner at Kingston Park for David Robinson. 'Robbo' had been a prominent member of the Gosforth team that won the cup at Twickenham in the early seventies before the game went professional. We knew him through his "Kellywell" herd over near Cockermouth and he had also been on the Holstein Board at the same time as me at the turn of the millennium. It was a very interesting evening as we were on a table with among others Semore Kurdi the owner of Newcastle Falcons and Dean Richards the Director of Rugby, so there was plenty to talk about!!

I won't dwell on the General Election just before Christmas, just let's say after 3½ years of wasted time and stalemate it looks like Brexit will finally come to pass.

We, and by that I mean most of us, don't realise how lucky we are both in health and everything else until you know of someone like Doddie Weir, who's charity for Motor Neurone disease which he has and has as yet no known cure, was the reason for the rugby match at Kingston Park near the end of the year. To be played annually between Melrose and Falcons XV which were the two clubs he played for as a long serving Scottish International, and it was so moving to see a relatively young man struggling to talk and walk onto the pitch there, or when he accepted the Helen Rollason Award at the BBC Sports Personality of the Year Awards two weeks earlier. He is raising terrific amounts for his Foundation for research into the condition. Adam used to see him quite regularly as he brought some if his dogs to "pick up" at Eskdale when they were shooting.

That brings us to the end of 2019 and the end of this narrative part of the book, all that remains is a short chapter on two very important men who feature through much of the book. So, after seventy-three years of ups and downs of personal and agricultural history and experiences, it is time to get back to normal, though there will still be a lot of editing and such like to get this to print. We won't stop travelling, we're off to New Zealand shortly and have Japan pencilled in for spring 2021!

Chapter 28 – Two Important Men

Throughout this book, for most of the farming part of it, two men have been a recurring theme or presence in it, and I felt it only right to give them a small chapter on their own to finish off with Jonathon Ropner and Bill Faulds.

My first meeting with the 'Guvnor', Mr J, Mr Jonathon or whatever else he was known as, was about fifty five years ago, when as a very nervous and untravelled youth, as most of us were back in the mid 1960's, I turned up at Newton Grange in best suit for an interview to come to Dalesend as a student for the a year before going to college, to be greeted by, as I have said before a man in shorts, and Hawaiian shirt, flip flops and very little else. I wondered what I had let myself in for, little did I know it was going to be an association that would last some 48 years, and though he is sadly no longer with us, but with Mrs J and the rest of the family, continues to this day. I very quickly learnt what a busy man he was, with so many different interests both in business and other things, but also that he always had time for people and was as happy, if not happier with ordinary ones than the upper reaches of society. He had that great ability to see the best bits in people, sometimes to his own disadvantage, as he thought everyone was as honest and genuine as he was, and at times he had to be protected from that. He had a particular affinity with where he had had his agricultural education in the day of Principal Bobby Boutflour and the Farm Manager Ken Russell, two of the great and early dairy thinkers and pioneers of that era, and he would tell me stories of Mr Boutflour, who was a little man, punching a much larger student who was more interested in the good life than learning and knocking him to the floor. That kind of action today would have landed him in great trouble, but back then all it did was dent the pride of a student and he was no more trouble. Together those two men developed the famous "Steadings" herd from bought cows from the local mart into a 2000 gallon herd, when the national average would be about 800 gallons.

In those days Mr J's main interest was in the farm and he did a lot on the farm, particularly at hay time or harvest when he would handle nearly every bale, as in those days it was before there were even flat eight bale lifters. I remember him in the Shed Field leading straw one day when the Fergi 20 pulling the trailer took fire and he ran backwards and forwards to the water trough to get water in his "cowboy" hat to put it out. He usually liked to fork or throw up the bales – by his own admission he wasn't much of a stacker, the odd loads he did stack often did well to get back to the yard, even if driven very steadily.

His great love was always the cows and having spent some time over at the famous "Pabst" Farms in America, he was always an advocate of the Holstein, and had great patience in converting me to their advantages. He had always also wanted to start his own bull stud and soon after I became his manager he got me talked into doing the budgets for him and supporting his development of that great wish even though the figures didn't really stack up and it was a very difficult path in the early days of Herdwise but what started off as a very small and, lets be honest, second rate start was developed over some 24 years until sold as a going concern as the largest independent AI Company in the country, and his only wish at that time was that all the sales staff should be transferred to the purchaser to protect their jobs after the great service they had given him.

Many of the little stories and anecdotes about Mr J are within the early pages and I don't want to repeat them, one of the things which really made Herdwise was the arrival of the Holstein as the breed of the future as the British Friesian had become too small and neat and lost much of its natural milking ability, and he was a great friend of Jim Alston of "Uphall" with whom he purchased among others Dalesend Cascade or Hyways Star by his Canadian name. He became one of the giants of his time and within Herdwise was quickly followed by Dalesend Performer among others, and as in many farm situations where the first cross gained a lot of hybrid vigour.

At that time his only office was the farm office and he had a part-time secretary who did the farm paperwork but also looked after all his other business and personal paperwork. If I was working in the office at the same time, I would marvel and almost stop to listen to him dictating letters, not at the content of them, but just the perfect speed and balance with which he delivered them – a rare talent he had developed over many years – just as well as he loved writing and receiving letters. Witness the letters I recount him writing to a purchaser of some cows who had got some "luck money" out of him, when I had told him it was included in the price as he had begged them.

As time went on and his other business interests developed he eventually converted the old stables at Bedale Hall into what became known as Amen House and became the headquarters of Dalepak Foods and he moved his office down there, so we lost some of that close, regular contact. I well remember going to the bank with Mr J to renew the farms borrowing arrangements, and as we came away he asked the Manager if he had got an answer on the other matter, to be told, yes he had an answer but that was no. That's alright he said, "I'll just walk across the road and see Mr Barclay", and that was how they became bankers to what was to become Dalepak Foods. How must Nat West have regretted that decision as it developed into the leader in the frozen meat "steak" market and went on to be a listed PLC. He didn't just do it once but repeated it again a few years later with ice-cream. When milk quotas came in, the feasibility study the farm did told us there was so little milk used it wasn't worth us doing, but being involved in the food industry, he pursued the idea by purchasing Cardosi Bros. from Redcar and leading it to a public listing in a relatively few years. What became Richmond Foods Ltd has since changed hands several times and the family no longer have any involvement and it is now privately owned by investment companies and I believe has just been taken over by another American Private Investment Company which also makes Haagen Dazs ice-cream among others. The massive factory on the industrial estate at Leeming Bar is now the largest in Europe. He was the first person to help develop the whole industrial estate down there into its place today as a mostly food-based site, which is still in ongoing development and expansion.

Apart from being very involved with the development of Herdwise over a lot of years, I was also involved with Mr J in the establishment and ongoing development of Wensleydale Property Company which was involved in the ownership of commercial properties mostly in local towns in addition, latterly of the Dalesend Business Park which they took over from the farm on advice from our financial advisers. That was to me an interesting and totally different scene which opened my eyes to a totally different business. When I knew the details of what some tenants were paying in rents plus rates and other expenses I often wondered how they ever made any money, or it explained why many of the retailers had obviously massive mark-ups on these products, which at the end of the day we as ordinary consumers pay. For instance, one of our tenants was a sandwich bar, not very large but was paying about £15,000 per year in rent before any other costs – that was £50 per day before he even put the key in the lock, or paid any rates. That's all very well on a nice sunny day in midsummer, but won't add up very fast on a cold, squally raining day in mid-February, and he still had to pay for staff plus fillings for a sandwich at £2 or £3 which doesn't add up very fast. The Business Park at Dalesend is a different matter, what had been our young stock unit prior to Foot and Mouth in 2001 is now 29 units of various sizes and generating a gross rental of towards £90,000 per annum. It is interesting now to read of the voluntary arrangements some of these businesses enter to fend off full liquidation, when they get massive rent reductions from the landlords to carry on. Some of these large property companies have spent millions in acquiring them and cannot for long continue on 40% rents, added to which the other solvent businesses next door then want a reduction. At the moment the giant Intu which owns several shopping centres, including the Metro Centre and Eldon Square in Newcastle are looking for new funding to continue their business. Like many businesses, once the bricks start to fall apart it can take a lot of shoring up.

Mr J still continued, almost up to the end to want to start another business and develop it, he kept saying, I would just like to do it one more time. As always, his very fertile mind came up with all kinds of ideas, some very wild and way out, others at least worth considering, but that third great success after Dalepak and Richmond eluded him.

Ultimately the last few years of Mr J's life were rather difficult for a person who up to that point had always been so active. His lasting legacy in the locality, which he was instrumental in starting and getting established was Dalescare in Bedale. It was developed as a meeting place for people of a certain age to get some interaction, have a meal, and at one time they had a hair dresser on a regular basis and ran all kinds of activities for people in the area. After some funding from the Alzheimers Society was withdrawn it was closed for a while, though it has now re-opened two days a week and I believe being well used. As a tribute to Mr J and in recognition of the work the centre does, 25% of the receipts of this book, should there be any, will be donated to Dalescare, which for some administrative reason has now to be called Dalescentre.

Sadly Mr J passed away on 14th February 2013, his funeral ten days later was followed in May with a memorial service in his name at Ripon Cathedral, attended by many whose lives he had touched in all kinds of ways over so many years. The ultimate accolade for to me a Great Man. As I said in my eulogy he once told me as we passed a certain man's home, he was the most Christian man he knew, and I thought then, as I still think now, it takes one to know one.

Mr Bill – Bill Faulds is the other recurring personality throughout the book, strangely enough we were just reminiscing about "Let the Bugger die" last night at a North Eastern club meeting, both he and I remember it as if it was only yesterday, for all it is 34 years ago.

Many people over the years have asked how he got the name, and in fact when he was to become President of the North Eastern club about five years ago, quite a few asked me what his surname was as they didn't know as he had become known to everyone over the years as Mr Bill. That came about when Sarah was very little, more than 40 years ago. Back then people still showed respect for their elders and when she went out to help him clean up after milking, she couldn't call him Mr Faulds, nor could she just call him Bill, so we settled on Mr Bill and it just stuck and still does to this day. As time went on even Mr J, called him Mr Bill.

Bill and I first met in the mid-sixties, when he came to take over as the herdsman at Newton Grange, which he stayed as until his retirement in 2001. He lived first of all at the bungalow in the farmyard, but as his family grew, he moved down into the farmhouse at Fox Park, and he and Lys remained there until moving to Crakehall on retiring. Before coming to Dalesend he had been assistant herdsman to David Aykroyd at Nun Monkton with their "Tinklers" herd, but prior to that most of his work had been lorry driving, for a time for one of the very early ready-mix concrete firms Yorkshire Henebece, from which he still wore sometimes their purple trousers for which he got severely "ribbed" each time he told us about them. Prior to that he had been a long distance lorry driver and would often regale us and still does with some of the histories and exploits, and for years he would tell you if you were travelling where a lorry was from by its number plate and had some funny pronunciations such as "Muccalm of Brookfield" which was W.H. Malcolm the large transport firm and if you met a Hayton Coulthard lorry he always told you that was the racing driver David Coulthard's father's company.

We had many great bits of fun over the years, many of those anecdotes are recorded as they occurred in earlier sections of the book, odd ones were serious and in some cases Bill took too seriously what was said as a joke, which caused an explosion for a while but soon settled down when he realised or it was explained to him. After he had retired, Bill used to come back and do some tractor work for us, particularly when Malcolm had died so suddenly, mostly either slurry guzzling, or leading corn in harvest time. One particular time he had handed me in a big bill of hours and as always liked cash if possible. I paid him one afternoon as he finished slurrying and he borrowed something from the workshop to do a job at home that night. When he came back the next morning to wash off the machinery, he said he had brought the thing back as it was no good, so I asked if he had brought the money back as well. Massive eruption followed, he was going to do the washing off, that was him finished for good and he was never going to come to the place again. Needless to say, he simmered down as he cleaned off the tractor and we carried on as if nothing had happened.

When he was still milking, I could tell as I went in to see him if he was in a bad mood, and sometimes just shut the door again and left him to it. One other morning which caused an explosion until he saw the funny side was when I told him he was ten seconds late coming to milk. How the 'F'ing' do you know that and are you down to keeping that keen an eye on me?? I told him I was usually just putting my pants on when the engine started up and that morning, I had got my shirt on as well, so I knew he was late!

Bill retired in 2001 the year of Foot and Mouth and although the young stock were lost in the April and he retired in the August, it didn't greatly affect him in his last few months of work, it meant he wasn't involved in the rebuilding of the herd or the movement of the young stock unit up to the new building at Newton Grange.

After his retirement Bill and Lys moved from Fox Park to live in a bungalow in Crakehall and have lived there happily now for eighteen years. Even whilst he was working Bill's leisure interests of shooting and fishing took up quite a lot of his time – he took a lot of odd day's holiday through shooting season to go off somewhere or other. After retirement he seemed to be busy at least three or four days a week right through the season either beating, loading or shooting all over the place – I think all his hosts enjoyed having him as a guest as he kept everyone amused. Fishing wise through summer he would be off a couple of days a week at least with various friends such as Nick Buck up to the rivers of Scotland or down to Hampshire and everywhere in between. He was obviously quite good because he sometimes would bring us a salmon he had caught, though I used to pull his leg by asking him which supermarket he had called at to buy it on the way home – the reply was usually unprintable.

In recent years as Bill, like all of us, has got older, his old legs aren't what they used to be and he can no longer scramble down river banks and stand in the water for hours, nor can he do a lot of walking on rough ground when shooting, but he still enjoys his days out and many of the shoots now lay on an ATV or such for him to get about. He also in his retirement did quite a lot of odd job gardening for various people, notably John Shephard at the Bay Horse in Crakehall and he looked after the grounds and gardens at Kirkbridge Mill on the back road to Langthorne. He even in the early days of his retirement went to do some golf-caddying for Terry Jobling, but I don't think that was quite his scene, and as far as I know never tried to play the game.

Bill still goes to most of the North Eastern Holstein Club events, as much for the company as to see the actual herds or listen to the speakers. We usually go together, whichever of us is going past the other is usually the chauffeur and we have our usual healthy banter throughout the evening which keeps us and everyone else amused.

Within all this apparent humour and fun, there has also been great sadness in Bill and Lys's lives. They lost Robert many years ago after a motorcycle accident and then only last year their youngest daughter Geraldine finally lost her long fight with cancer. Most of us would struggle with the loss of one child, but to lose two out of the three ahead of your own demise must take some living with but they have earned all our admiration for the way they have faced up to those losses and just kept on going. We keep in touch on a very regular basis, when I ring Bill, he nearly always says I must be a mind reader as he was about to ring me, a likely tale. They have always shown a great interest in both Sarah and Adam's path through life and although he often sees Sarah, he doesn't often see Adam but always enquires after "the big fella" and often knows something or sees something before we do as they keep in touch on Facebook and on the rare occasion Adam is down here, he always go to see Mr Bill.

What men.... What stories!!!

Chapter 29 – THANK YOU

To everyone who makes an appearance in or has given me a story for this book a massive thank you. Without everyone else, there would be no story to tell, and the help and advice I have received over so many years from so many people has made this possible.

Most of all my great thanks must go to my own family without who's great support over so many years I couldn't have got the great memories which I have recalled.

To Marnie, Sarah and Adam who have all made my life story so much more fulfilling than it might otherwise have been, it has been a great adventure which hopefully has many more years to run and many more adventures to undertake along the way, along with Laura and the three grandchildren - Ruby, Harriet and Freddy.

It has been a wonderful life in the great British countryside, alongside many great farming people, a life I wouldn't have changed for the world.

"Every morning you are handed 24 golden hours.
They are one of the few things in the world that you get free of charge.
If you had all the money in the world, you couldn't buy an extra hour.
What will you do with this priceless treasure?
Remember, you must use it, as it is given only once, once wasted you cannot get it back!"

Billy Mills— Lessons of a Lakota:
A Young Man's Journey to Happiness and Self-Understanding

THANKYOU ALL

The end.

Dalescare to Dales centre - 1988 to the present day

The Dalecare charity was founded in 1988 by Jonathan Ropner following the success of two of his companies namely Dalepak Foods Plc and Herdwise Ltd. The purpose of the charity was to provide a walk in centre for the elderly of Bedale supplying a wide variety of care and support. Initially the plan was to establish the centre at Mowbry Grange in the south of Bedale but this did not come about and the Dalescare centre was created where the workshop of Bucktrout and Firth (signwriters) was formally situated central to Bedale. The contractors were Randall Orchard of Richmond and the architect was Sir William Grey. The centre was formally opened by Princess Alexandra of Kent on 4th June 1992 following its completion in the same year.

Dalescare was created to provide support in the community centred round the provision of a hearty meal where local folk could come together and socialise going some way toward trying to alleviate loneliness in the community which is a large and growing problem. The centre provided lunches for clients five days a week.

Initially the centre was funded by private donations combined with fundraising events and gradually local government increased their support for the centre using it as a way to provide help in the community. Following the economic downturn of 2008/9 and the austerity that followed, local government reduced their support and the centre now provides lunches on Tuesday's and Thursday's to approximately 60 customers a week. The centre is run by a board of trustees, two managers and volunteers and continues to provide an important service to the people of Bedale and its surrounding area.